D1320364

ELEMENTS OF CONTINUOUS MULTIVARIATE ANALYSIS

This book is in the
ADDISON-WESLEY SERIES
IN BEHAVIORAL SCIENCES: QUANTITATIVE METHODS

Consulting Editor

FREDERICK MOSTELLER

Elements of
CONTINUOUS MULTIVARIATE ANALYSIS

A. P. DEMPSTER

Department of Statistics, Harvard University

ADDISON-WESLEY PUBLISHING COMPANY

Reading, Massachusetts · Menlo Park, California · London · Don Mills, Ontario

PRINTED IN THE UNITED STATES OF AMERICA. PUBLISHED SIMULTANEOUSLY IN CANADA. LIBRARY OF CONGRESS CATALOG CARD NO. 68–57774.

To my teachers

PREFACE

Three short courses make up this volume. These are Parts 2, 3, and 4, following the introductory chapter which is Part 1. The first substantive part aims to present the essentials of vector space theory for statistical data analysts, at a fairly advanced level and with emphases on geometric understanding and on computing language and technique. The following part, which is central intellectually as well as structurally, describes and explains with the aid of numerical examples the basic methods of multivariate data analysis. The final part is more nearly in the tradition of contemporary mathematical statistics with its concentration on sampling distributions and their role in drawing inferences from sample to population. Through organization I have tried to reduce the subject to its elements, so that the data analyst may see clearly the various layers of mathematical development which are more often wrapped into a single neat package. Although the three courses are designed to be followed in order with frequent references back, I believe that the reader having some familiarity with the subject matter may derive benefit from dipping in at places of particular interest.

The publication of this book marks the completion of a decade at Harvard University, where much of the material was developed, but clearly the roots go much further back. I should like to acknowledge especially H. S. M. Coxeter and R. G. Stanton as undergraduate teachers at Toronto, J. W. Tukey and S. S. Wilks from graduate student days at Princeton, and my colleagues W. G. Cochran and F. Mosteller at Harvard. Many students in the Harvard Statistics Department have contributed over the years as tolerant and not-so-tolerant audiences and proofreaders. These include Robert Berk, John Chambers, Robert Elashoff, Will Fairley, Stephen Fienberg, Robert Miller, Martin Schatzoff, and Rhett Tsao. Among the many who carried out programming for numerical computations, special credit is due to Albert Beaton who devised most of the computing operators which are featured in my presentation, and to Rod Montgomery who carefully tended to the more complex analyses. Finally I should like to thank Mrs. Cleo Youtz for unfailing advice and help on routine matters both technical and administrative throughout my decade with the Harvard Statistics Department.

Research work in connection with this book was supported by the grant GS-341 from the National Science Foundation to Harvard University. The numerical computations were also aided by the National Science Foundation through their grant GP-2723 to the Harvard Computing Center, and by the Faculty-Aide Program administered under the Faculty of Arts and Sciences by the Student Employment Office of Harvard University. The final touches were added to this book while I was a Fellow of the John Simon Guggenheim Memorial Foundation.

Cambridge, Massachusetts Arthur P. Dempster
July, 1968

CONTENTS

PART 1

ORIENTATION

CHAPTER 1

INTRODUCTION

1.1 WHAT THE BOOK IS ABOUT

The purpose of this book is to describe certain methods of analysis of statistical data arising from multivariate samples. A basic aim of such data analysis is to reduce large arrays of numbers to provide meaningful and reasonably complete summaries of whatever information resides in sample aggregates. Another aim is to draw inferences from sample aggregates to larger population aggregates from which the samples are drawn; that is, to understand how certain information about a sample provides uncertain information about a population. Usually statistical analyses are part of a larger endeavor. For example, a scientist may wish to test some scientific theory or hypothesis about a set of populations, or a decision-maker may require the output of statistical data analyses as part of the input for a cost-benefit study. It is a characteristic feature of this book, however, that the technical aspects of these larger endeavors are not explicitly treated.

Part 2 (Chapters 2 through 6) reviews the mathematical theory of vector spaces, emphasizing geometric and computational aspects. Vector space theory is fundamental both for purposes of description and illumination in the two statistical parts of the book. Part 3 (Chapters 7 through 11) presents the basic methods of data reduction while Part 4 (Chapters 12 through 15) is devoted to random sampling theory and its implications. Numerical examples are inserted throughout Part 3 and the same examples are reconsidered in the light of sampling theory in Chapter 14.

Underlying the organization of Parts 3 and 4 is an attitude towards statistical data analysis. While most books on statistical theory start out with sampling theory and attempt to make methods of data analysis follow, the attitude in this book is that the methods of data analysis are carried out largely because of the intrinsic appeal of the sample quantities computed. Such, at least, were the historical origins of the methods described here. Moreover, when viewed as producing descriptive or summary statistics, the methods have value even when assumptions like randomness of samples and normality of populations are quite unwarranted. Mathematical statistics can provide justifications for the methods used, and the main approaches to such justifications are sketched in Chapter 15. Mathematical statistics also suggests modifications to those raw sample statistics which are especially misleading as estimates of their population analogues. Examples of such modifications are to be found in Chapter 14.

The next three sections of Chapter 1 relate to the third, second, and fourth parts of the book and are designed to convey in a rough way the dimensions of the subject matter. But the reader should recognize at the outset that the methods described are, while fundamental, a very restricted class. For one, variables are generally regarded here as producing numerical scores distributed along a line. It is tempting to apply the methods to classification variables taking the values 0 and 1 only, and some applications of this kind are discussed in Chapters 8 and 9. But more tailored methods and theories exist for analyzing data arising from crossclassifications. In addition, whole fields of data analysis methods which have grown up in particular disciplines are barely touched upon here. For example, there are several approaches to factor analysis and many variants of these methods mostly coming from attempts to structure sets of psychological variables. In this book, only one near relative—namely, principal component analysis—is discussed. Likewise, economists have created highly developed methods of solving sets of uncertain linear equations, whose only relatives in this book are multiple regression analyses. Engineers and psychologists talk a great deal about pattern analysis, which often turns out to be close to the multiple discriminant analysis of Chapter 10. But there are other techniques for clustering individuals which may be described as pattern analysis. Clearly there are much wider horizons to be considered. By studying a narrower class of proven methods in greater depth, this book aims to provide a framework to enable the reader to proceed more easily to these wider horizons.

1.2 INDIVIDUALS, VARIABLES, QUANTITIES, AND RELATED CONCEPTS

A *population* is the collection of all entities belonging to some recognizable and reasonably well-defined type or class, and a *sample* is a subset of a population. The choice of an interesting population is largely determined by the development of each individual scientific discipline. In this book, the entities which make up a given sample or its parent population will be called *individuals*. A sample individual is like a bird in hand, and it is not always clear what flock it came from nor how it was selected. Some sample surveys are designed with great care to be representative of a population under study, but samples of skulls such as those analyzed in Example 10.3 must be collected where they may be found and their representativeness is often a matter of hope. Thus, although the aim of an investigation is generally to study some populations, the data analyst's first emphasis must be on understanding the various angles from which to view a given sample. He may then be satisfied with a naive belief that what he learned from his sample will be roughly or at least possibly true of a population, or he may be willing to pay the price of assuming randomness of samples in order to have formal mathematical tools of statistical inference which provide precise probabilistic ways to think about the population.

The term *variable* will be reserved in this book for a quantitative real-valued attribute or characteristic which is possessed by every individual of a population. A variable is defined by some rule or procedure whereby its numerical *value* on any individual may be established. The rule should be reasonably precise and reasonably objective in the sense that different observers will generally feel that they agree on what is meant by a given variable determined over a specified population. A value of a variable may be directly observed, like the weight of an animal in grams or the response of a human subject to a questionnaire item on a five-point scale. Or a variable may be such that any value must be computed from directly observable variables, like a scale formed by weighting and summing the responses to several questionnaire items. In any particular study, a set of variables is usually dictated by the subject of investigation. The variables may be of the directly observable type or of the computed type. Usually there is no functional relation among them. A statistician may often suggest modifications of a given set of variables, replacing some by transforms or other computed variables. This is generally done for technical rather than fundamental reasons, however, and it is essentially assumed in this book that the set of variables entering an analysis is given.

The starting point of multivariate analysis is therefore a multivariate sample or several multivariate samples with given individuals and given variables. For each individual in each sample one has (ideally at least) all of the values of a specified set of variables.

The concept of variable needs to be distinguished from a related concept which will be called here *quantity*. Actually, there are four different technical terms which need to be distinguished and understood: namely, *variable*; *set of values of a variable*; *quantity*; and *value of a quantity*. The term *variable* connotes mathematically a function or mapping from the individuals of a population to a real line. The *set of values of the variable* is the set of real numbers associated with the individuals of the population by the variable. The term *quantity* as defined here also has the mathematical connotation of a function, but the real world context of a quantity differs sharply from that of a variable.

A simple and basic type of quantity will be defined first. Each pair consisting of an individual and a variable defines a real number which is the value of the variable on that individual . Such a pair defines a *quantity* whose associated real value is the *value of the quantity*. For example, the weight of a specific rat in grams is a quantity having a specific value. In its applied context a variable really does vary, for it takes different values over different individuals, while a quantity actually takes only one value. The set of actual values of the variable becomes the set of *possible* values of the quantity. The quantity itself should be viewed as a function which maps a generally hypothetical space of all possible states of the real world into the real line which includes the set of possible values of the quantity. Following a convention much used in probability theory, a single symbol, such as X, will be used ambiguously for a quantity or for the value of the quantity. One thinks of X as standing for the value of the quantity, and rigorously speaking a function notation should be used for the quantity itself, but in practice such double notation is awkward and unnecessary.

A function of a variable or of a set of variables defined over a common population is again a variable over that same population. On the other hand, a function of a set of quantities is a meaningful concept provided only that each quantity may be regarded as defined over a common set of possible states of a real world. It is natural therefore to extend the notion of a quantity to include any function (or, in some theories, any measurable function) defined over the set of possible states of the real world. As before, the range or set of possible values of such a quantity is the real line while its actual value is a single number. Such quantities are the daily bread of statistics. Indeed, a function of a set of sample quantities is another quantity which is often called a sample *statistic*.

1.3 THE ROLE OF VECTOR SPACE THEORY

There is a strong emphasis in this book on geometric thinking as a means of visualizing and thereby improving an understanding of methods of data analysis and their associated normal sampling theory. At the same time, when precise mathematical reasoning is required it will be carried out in terms of the theory of finite dimensional vector spaces. This theory may be regarded as a precise mathematical framework underlying the heuristic patterns of geometric thought.

Consider a multivariate sample defined by n individuals and p variables. If this sample is observed, it may be represented by a set of np real numbers, whose typical member $X_j^{(i)}$ is the value of the quantity defined by the ith individual and the jth variable for $i = 1, 2, \ldots, n$ and $j = 1, 2, \ldots, p$. These values are usually regarded in this book as forming a rectangular array or *data matrix* with n rows and p columns and with $X_j^{(i)}$ in the ith row and jth column. For each i, the row vector

$$[X_1^{(i)}, X_2^{(i)}, \ldots, X_p^{(i)}] \tag{1.3.1}$$

may be viewed as determining the coordinates of a point or a vector in a p-dimensional geometric space. This point carries the sample information about the ith individual, and the n points thus defined for $i = 1, 2, \ldots, n$ carry information equivalent to the data matrix. Any point in the p-dimensional space represents a potential sample individual and the space itself will be called the *individual-space* corresponding to the given p variables. On the other hand, for each j, the column vector

$$\begin{bmatrix} X_j^{(1)} \\ X_j^{(2)} \\ \cdot \\ \cdot \\ \cdot \\ X_j^{(n)} \end{bmatrix} \tag{1.3.2}$$

determines the coordinates of a point in an n-dimensional geometric space. The p points thus defined correspond to variables, and, like the n individuals in individual-space, these points also determine the whole data matrix. The n-dimensional space thus defined is special to the n sample individuals, but when $p \leq n$ it contains a p-dimensional subspace which is abstractly equivalent to a space called *variable-space* to be introduced shortly. Most methods of continuous multivariate analysis have simple descriptions in terms of either individual-space or variable-space, or both.

A restriction on this book is that almost all of the methods discussed are based on sample mean vectors and sample covariance matrices. Excepting some graphic techniques for plotting individuals, none of the information in each multivariate sample is retained except that contained in a special set of linear and quadratic statistics. Such a cutting operation should always be regarded with suspicion, even though mathematical statistics offers some good justifications in the case of random samples from multivariate normal populations. The attitude here is not meant to exclude more catholic approaches, but the range of methods in our restricted class is nontrivial and is unified by its close ties with vector space theory, and so these methods form a natural class for inclusion in a single volume.

The *sample mean vector* is defined to be

$$[\bar{X}_1, \bar{X}_2, \ldots, \bar{X}_p], \tag{1.3.3}$$

where

$$\bar{X}_j = \frac{1}{n} \sum_{i=1}^{n} X_j^{(i)} \tag{1.3.4}$$

for $j = 1, 2, \ldots, p$. The definition of this mean vector should be regarded as illustrating vector space operations; specifically, the mean vector is found by taking the vector sum of the n vectors (1.3.1) and multiplying by the scalar $1/n$. Similarly, the *sample covariance* between the jth and kth variables is defined to be

$$\frac{1}{n-1} \sum_{i=1}^{n} (X_j^{(i)} - \bar{X}_j)(X_k^{(i)} - \bar{X}_k) = \frac{1}{n-1} \left[\sum_{i=1}^{n} X_j^{(i)} X_k^{(i)} - n \bar{X}_j \bar{X}_k \right]. \tag{1.3.5}$$

When $j = k$, this is called the *sample variance* of variable j. The square matrix whose element in row j and column k is the covariance (1.3.5) is called the *sample covariance matrix* of the given sample. The diagonal elements of the covariance matrix are variances and the matrix is symmetric in the sense that the covariances (1.3.5) are unchanged by interchanges of j and k. In Chapter 3 the sample covariance matrix will be identified with the vector space concept of an inner product defined over variable-space and the inner product concept will in turn be visualized geometrically in terms of an associated ellipsoid.

With such a choice of basic statistics it becomes natural to consider not only the p given variables but also all linear combinations of them. This is natural because the means, variances, and covariances of the wider class of variables are determined by those of the original set. Suppose that $\alpha_1, \alpha_2, \ldots, \alpha_p$ denotes a given set of real numbers. Then

$$V = \alpha_1 V_1 + \alpha_2 V_2 + \cdots + \alpha_p V_p \tag{1.3.6}$$

defines a new variable over the same population. The rule for determining the value of V on a given individual asserts: first determine the values of each of $V_1, V_2, \ldots, V_p$ and then substitute these values for the variables in (1.3.6). For example, if a sample is defined as above by the values $X_j^{(i)}$ for $j = 1, 2, \ldots, p$ and $i = 1, 2, \ldots, n$, then the sample values of V in (1.3.6) are given by

$$X^{(i)} = \alpha_1 X_1^{(i)} + \alpha_2 X_2^{(i)} + \cdots + \alpha_p X_p^{(i)}, \tag{1.3.7}$$

for $i = 1, 2, \ldots, n$. The set of variables V thus defined when $\alpha_1, \alpha_2, \ldots, \alpha_p$ range over all sets of p real numbers will be called *variable-space* and will be formally identified in Chapter 2 with a p-dimensional vector space.

It is now natural to generalize (1.3.4) to define the sample mean of V, namely

$$\bar{X} = \frac{1}{n} \sum_{i=1}^{n} X^{(i)}. \tag{1.3.8}$$

It follows easily that

$$\bar{X} = \alpha_1 \bar{X}_1 + \alpha_2 \bar{X}_2 + \cdots + \alpha_p \bar{X}_p, \tag{1.3.9}$$

which shows, as mentioned above, that the sample means of the given p variables determine the sample means of the continuum of variables in variable-space. In a similar way, if $W = \beta_1 V_1 + \beta_2 V_2 + \cdots + \beta_p V_p$ is another variable with sample values $Y^{(1)}, Y^{(2)}, \ldots, Y^{(n)}$ and sample mean $\bar{Y}$, then (1.3.5) generalizes to

$$\frac{1}{n-1} \sum_{i=1}^{n} (X^{(i)} - \bar{X})(Y^{(i)} - \bar{Y}), \tag{1.3.10}$$

which will be called the *sample covariance* of V and W. The reader may easily show that if (1.3.5) is denoted by $\operatorname{cov}(V_j, V_k)$ and (1.3.10) is denoted by $\operatorname{cov}(V, W)$, then

$$\operatorname{cov}(V, W) = \sum_{j=1}^{p} \sum_{k=1}^{p} \alpha_j \beta_k \operatorname{cov}(V_j, W_k), \tag{1.3.11}$$

which shows how the sample covariance matrix determines the covariance between any pair of variables in variable-space.

Geometric or vector space reasoning avoiding unnecessary reference to particular sets of coordinate axes may often be carried out. Such reasoning, called *coordinate-free*, can simplify both mathematics and understanding by reducing matters to essentials. Concepts such as ellipsoids and linear projections which appear repeatedly may be visualized in a coordinate-free way.

Another important theme of vector space theory is *duality*. In Chapter 6 it will be seen that individual-space and variable-space stand in the formal mathematical relation of a pair of dual spaces. Any concept or chain of reasoning in terms of one space has a dual image in terms of the other, and one of these may sometimes appear simpler than the other. Alongside the mathematical concept of duality there is a corresponding pair of dual attitudes which may be assumed toward any variable. One common attitude to a variable is to regard it as an entity in itself; for example, one commonly feels that the concept of height, perhaps the concept of height of human beings in inches, is a very real thing closely tied to a world view which integrates many such concepts. On the other hand, a variable may be regarded as a device for producing a pattern of points on a line, these points being the values of the variable for a sample or population. More generally, a set of p variables may be viewed initially as entities in themselves, or they may be alternatively and dually regarded as a device for producing a pattern of points in a p-dimensional individual-space. It is part of the flavor of multivariate statistical analysis that it concentrates on the latter attitude by providing some ways of looking at linear and quadratic aspects of patterns in individual-space. This concentration is what makes statistics seem a dry subject, since it may obscure the more fascinating aspects of what variables mean, what motivated them, and how they relate to the world-picture of their associated scientific disciplines. Statistical data analysts must in practice try consciously to build better bridges between formal methods and their scientific contexts; the examples of Chapters 8 through 11 may help the reader in this direction, but they do not pretend to go very far.

1.4 THE ROLE OF SAMPLING THEORY

The final four chapters of this book are concerned with multivariate normal populations and with formal procedures for statistical inference which assume random samples from such normal populations. The mathematics of multivariate normal sampling theory is highly developed, and no attempt is made to review all that is known. Instead, a selection is made which appears to the author to provide those parts of the theory most relevant to data analysis. As always, stress is laid on geometric arguments to bring out the simplicity and elegance of the mathematics.

It is rarely possible to believe with certainty either that populations are normal or that samples are random. It is often possible to make data shed light on the failures of such assumptions or, less often, on the effect of these failures upon specific inferences. Such checking is not analyzed in a formal way in this book, but a few specific examples are given. Inevitably, one must make careful but informal judgments about how far any particular inference may be trusted.

Even accepting the assumptions of normality and randomness, the user of formal methods of statistical inference must decide between two sharply contrasting approaches. To see the nature of the cleavage, suppose that a statistic has been decided upon to define an interesting characteristic of a sample or a population. The question which immediately arises is of the magnitude of the *sampling error* of the statistic, defined to be the difference between the sample value and the population value. Such a magnitude may be judged in one of two ways which will be called *postdictive* and *predictive*, and which determine a basic difference among schools of statistical inference. According to the first approach the population is regarded as fixed but unknown, and the randomness of the sample determines a probability distribution for the sample statistic and thence for the sampling error of the statistic. These *sampling distributions* provide the key to inference from sample to population. According to the second approach, the population is regarded as unknown, but it is the sample in hand which is viewed as fixed. A probability distribution is sought which may be used to provide judgments which are appropriate *after the sample is given*, and which concern the uncertainties of knowledge of the population. Such distributions are often called *posterior distributions.* Now the sampling distribution of a sampling error is not at all the same concept as the posterior distribution of a sampling error. The latter uses probability in the standard forward-looking mode (called here *predictive*) which regards probability as a measure of the uncertainty of some uncertain outcome or value. The sampling distribution on the other hand may be regarded as having a predictive interpretation only *before* the sample is observed, for it specifically reflects the randomness induced by the random sampling hypothesis. The question therefore is: what meaning can be attached to a sampling distribution *after* a sample is known? The answer is: for each hypothesized population which determines a sampling distribution for a particular sampling error, one knows which point along the sampling distribution was realized in the observed sample. To make this answer useful for statistical inference, one must add a principle asserting that an observed point in the far tail renders a sampling distribution implausible, and thus also renders implausible the hypothesized population which produced the sampling distribution. This form of reasoning, called here *postdictive* inference, includes significance testing and confidence region methods. Note that the word "confidence" may be misleading here because the argument proceeds in a double negative way, failing to reject certain hypotheses instead of positively supporting them.

Predictive inferences are undoubtedly more desirable in principle than are postdictive inferences. But the two main schools of predictive inference, namely Bayesian inference and fiducial inference, are not yet available in a form applicable in a routine way to multivariate data. Most statisticians feel unable to specify the prior distributions required by the Bayesian approach, especially in the presence of the large number of parameters required to specify a normal population of even modest dimension. At the same time, the fiducial methods are somewhat ambiguous. Thus, while predictive inference is analyzed further in Chapter 15, the only applications of inference to data are those of Chapter 14 which rely on postdictive reasoning.

One of the standard terms of probability theory clashes with the basic terminology of this book. The offending terms are *random variable* and *variable*. Since the latter concept as defined in Section 1.2 is so basic to multivariate statistical analysis, the probabilist's term random variable will be altered here to *random quantity*. This use of the term quantity coincides with that introduced in Section 1.2. The adjective random signifies only that the quantity comes equipped with a probability measure or a family of probability measures. The value of a random quantity will be called a *random value* and denoted by a symbol like X. As already mentioned, X will be used in the familiar ambiguous way to denote either the quantity or its value.

1.5 RELATED WORKS: A VERY BRIEF SKETCH

Along with Harold Hotelling, R. A. Fisher, John Wishart, and M. S. Bartlett, one of the pioneers of multivariate statistical analysis among mathematical statisticians was S. S. Wilks. Wilks (1962) remains an excellent source for some of the basic work on multivariate normal sampling theory. A fuller exposition of a similar approach is given by Anderson (1958). Other distinguished theoretical statisticians have books which treat the subject, including Cramér (1946), Kendall (1957), Kendall and Stuart (1961, 1966), Rao (1952, 1965), and Roy (1957). The review paper by Bartlett (1947) is of historic importance and interest. Readers preferring mathematics of lower power may be helped by the books of Cooley and Lohnes (1962), Morrison (1967), or Seal (1964). Multiple regression analysis and related analysis of variance ideas are fundamental to multivariate analysis; a range of books on these topics is covered by the set Acton (1959), Deutsch (1965), Plackett (1960), Scheffé (1959), Draper and Smith (1966), and Williams (1959). Glimpses at a wide range of current work are to be found in Krishnaiah (1966). An extensive bibliography of statistical literature on multivariate statistical analysis will shortly be published by Anderson, Das Gupta, and Styan (1969). Other literature on multivariate analysis, especially original sources in research papers, will be cited throughout the text.

While the treatment of vector space theory in Chapters 2 to 6 is nearly self contained and adequate for the purposes of this volume, many readers will benefit from deeper coverage of different approaches. Excellent books for the abstract mathematical content are Birkhoff and MacLane (1965) and Halmos (1958). For matrix theory, see MacDuffee (1943), Gantmacher (1959), and Rao (1965). Good sources for geometric orientation are Coxeter (1961) and Sommerville (1958). Important computational theory is given by Householder (1964), Varga (1962), and Wilkinson (1963, 1965). Books at a more down-to-earth level include Aitken (1958), Dwyer (1951), Faddeeva (1959), Horst (1963), Ralston and Wilf (1960), and Searle (1966).

PART 2

MATHEMATICAL FOUNDATIONS

CHAPTER 2

BASIC THEORY OF VECTOR SPACES

2.1 ABSTRACT VECTOR SPACES DEFINED

Most areas of applied mathematics lean heavily on the theory of vector spaces over the field of real numbers. The abstract mathematical content common to these applications is sketched below and briefly illustrated by the relation of the theory to multivariate analysis. More complete sources of the theory are listed in Section 1.5, while more detailed applications abound in the later parts of this book.

A *p-dimensional vector space over the field of real numbers* is a mathematical construct which specializes in the case $p = 1$ to the set of all real numbers with their familiar operations of addition and multiplication. In general, the elements of the vector space are called *vectors* and should be regarded for the moment as abstract entities, although in applications they will be identified with or at least labelled for concepts with a real world basis. Vectors will often be denoted by capital letters such as U, V, W, . . . The theory requires that any two vectors may be added to give a third vector, i.e., given any pair of vectors U and V there exists a unique vector W which will be written in the familiar way as

$$W = U + V. \tag{2.1.1}$$

This operation may be called *vector addition* to distinguish it from the specialized concept of *addition of real numbers*, but the term *addition* will be used for either and the meaning will be clear from the context. The theory requires also that any real number and any vector may be multiplied to give another vector, i.e., given any real number x and any vector U, the product of x and U is uniquely defined to be a vector Z which will be denoted by

$$Z = xU. \tag{2.1.2}$$

Real numbers are sometimes called *scalars* in vector space theory. The operation of passing from U to Z may be called *scaling by the factor x* and the multiplication operation itself is often called *scalar multiplication.*

The operations of addition and multiplication are required to obey the following rules:

a) Vectors form an additive abelian group, i.e.,

There exists a *zero* vector $\emptyset$ such that

$$\emptyset + V = V + \emptyset = V$$

for all V.

There exists a *negative vector* $-V$ for every V such that

$$V + (-V) = \emptyset.$$

Vector addition is commutative, i.e., (2.1.3)

$$V + U = U + V$$

for all U and V.

Vector addition is associative, i.e.,

$$(V + U) + W = V + (U + W)$$

for all U, V, W.

b) Multiplication of vectors by real numbers obeys:

$$x(U + V) = xU + xV, \qquad (x + y)V = xV + yV,$$
$$(xy)V = x(yV), \qquad \text{and} \qquad 1V = V \tag{2.1.4}$$

for all real numbers x and y and all vectors U and V.

These basic axioms together with some simple deductions from them make up a set of working rules which are used almost automatically by anyone familiar with vector spaces. Some of the simple deductions, not derived here, are as follows:

$$\begin{aligned} OV &= \emptyset, && \text{for all } V, \\ x\emptyset &= \emptyset, && \text{for all } x, \text{ and} \\ (-1)V &= -V, && \text{for all } V. \end{aligned} \tag{2.1.5}$$

The notation $U - V$ abbreviates $U + (-V)$.

As indicated in Chapter 1, two applications of vector spaces will be used repeatedly in this book:

Example 2.1.1. Suppose that $V_1, V_2, \ldots, V_p$ represent p different observable or measurable variables. Here V_1 might be a symbol representing the concept of the height of a human being in inches, V_2 might similarly represent arm length in inches, etc. Then, as explained in Section 1.3, the notation

$$\sum_{t=1}^{p} \alpha_t V_t$$

is to be understood to represent a variable for which a value may be computed in the obvious way once $V_1, V_2, \ldots, V_p$ are assigned observed values. It is clear that the elements $\sum_1^p \alpha_t V_t$ can be regarded as the elements of a vector space satisfying the axioms. That is, sums are defined by

$$\left(\sum_{t=1}^{p} \alpha_t V_t\right) + \left(\sum_{t=1}^{p} \beta_t V_t\right) = \sum_{t=1}^{p} (\alpha_t + \beta_t) V_t, \tag{2.1.6}$$

and multiplication by a real number is defined by

$$x\left(\sum_{t=1}^{p} \alpha_t V_t\right) = \sum_{t=1}^{p} (x\alpha_t) V_t. \tag{2.1.7}$$

Also, $\sum_1^p \alpha_t V_t$ is defined to be the vector $\emptyset$ when $\alpha_1 = \alpha_2 = \cdots = \alpha_p = 0$ and $\sum_1^p (-\beta_t) V_t$ is defined to be the negative vector of $\sum_1^p \beta_t V_t$. The reader may further check through the axioms. The space whose typical member is $\sum_1^p \alpha_t V_t$ will be referred to as *variable-space* throughout the book.

Variable-space suffers from the disadvantage that it does not allow changes of location of a variable although it does allow changes of scale. For example, if V represents a temperature variable in degrees Centigrade, then the same variable measured in degrees Fahrenheit, namely "$32 + 1.8V$," is not in the space of variables under consideration. This difficulty may be circumvented by a device of adding an artificial variable V_0 whose observed value is always unity, and replacing the space of variables $\sum_1^p \alpha_t V_t$ by the *augmented variable-space* $\sum_0^p \alpha_t V_t$. Then the variable loosely referred to above as "$32 + 1.8V$" can be written precisely as $32V_0 + 1.8V$ in the augmented space of variables. For the most part, it will not be necessary to bring in the artificial variable V_0 and attention may be focused on the original variable-space defined above.

Example 2.1.2. Suppose that the p-tuple of real numbers

$$[x_1, x_2, \ldots, x_p]$$

represents a set of measurements on the p variables $V_1, V_2, \ldots, V_p$. Again the reader may check that all such p-tuples form a vector space under the operations:

i) the sum of $[x_1, x_2, \ldots, x_p]$ and $[y_1, y_2, \ldots, y_p]$ is defined to be

$$[x_1 + y_1, x_2 + y_2, \ldots, x_p + y_p],$$

ii) the product of x and $[x_1, x_2, \ldots, x_p]$ is defined to be $[xx_1, xx_2, \ldots, xx_p]$.

Each point of this space may be thought of as a set of possible measurements on an individual, and the space will be referred to as *individual-space* throughout the book. In Chapter 6 the concept of *duality* which relates variable-space and individual-space will be discussed.

Again, it would be possible to consider an *augmented individual-space* consisting of $(p + 1)$-tuples

$$[x_0, x_1, x_2, \ldots, x_p],$$

where $x_1, x_2, \ldots, x_p$ are as above and x_0 denotes an observed value of the artificial variable V_0. However, in the application of this mathematical structure x_0 is always unity, and so it is clear that nothing essential can be gained by adding x_0 to the p-tuple $[x_1, x_2, \ldots, x_p]$.

2.2 SUBSPACES, HYPERPLANES, LINEAR DEPENDENCE, BASIS VECTORS, AND DIMENSION

Any subset of the set of vectors in a vector space is a *subspace* if it forms a vector space under the operations defined for the whole space. Clearly any linear combination of the vectors of a subspace also lies in the same subspace, where a *linear combination* of $U_1, U_2, \ldots, U_r$ means any vector of the form $\sum_1^r a_i U_i$ where $a_1, a_2, \ldots, a_r$ are any real numbers. Conversely, the set of all linear combinations of any subset $U_1, U_2, \ldots, U_r$ constitutes a subspace. This is called the *subspace spanned* by $U_1, U_2, \ldots, U_r$. The simplest examples of subspaces are the whole space and the subspace consisting only of $\emptyset$. The simplest nontrivial example of a subspace is the set of vectors αU for any given vector U as α ranges over all real numbers.

Given two subspaces $\mathscr{U}$ and $\mathscr{V}$ one may consider their intersection $\mathscr{U} \cap \mathscr{V}$ and union $\mathscr{U} \cup \mathscr{V}$. It may be checked that $\mathscr{U} \cap \mathscr{V}$ is itself a subspace but that $\mathscr{U} \cup \mathscr{V}$ cannot be a subspace unless $\mathscr{U}$ and $\mathscr{V}$ are identical. The elements of different subspaces $\mathscr{U}$ and $\mathscr{V}$ span a subspace which may be called the *direct sum* of $\mathscr{U}$ and $\mathscr{V}$ and written $\mathscr{U} \oplus \mathscr{V}$. Subspaces $\mathscr{U}$ and $\mathscr{V}$ are called *complementary* subspaces when their intersection is as small as possible, i.e., consists only of $\emptyset$, while their direct sum is the whole space.

Consider any subspace $\mathscr{U}$ of a vector space $\mathscr{E}$. For a given vector V the subset of $\mathscr{E}$ consisting of all vectors $V + U$ where U is in $\mathscr{U}$ will be called a *coset* of $\mathscr{U}$ and will be written $V + \mathscr{U}$. If W belongs to the coset $V + \mathscr{U}$, then the cosets $V + \mathscr{U}$ and $W + \mathscr{U}$ are identical, i.e., there are as many different ways of expressing the coset as there are vectors in the coset. Any vector V in $\mathscr{E}$ belongs to the coset $V + \mathscr{U}$ and to no other coset of $\mathscr{U}$; in other words, the cosets of $\mathscr{U}$ determine a partition of $\mathscr{E}$ into mutually exclusive subsets. Suppose that $\mathscr{V}$ is a subspace of $\mathscr{E}$ complementary to $\mathscr{U}$. Any such $\mathscr{V}$ defines a one-to-one correspondence between the vectors of $\mathscr{V}$ and the cosets of $\mathscr{U}$, defined by making V in $\mathscr{V}$ correspond to $V + \mathscr{U}$ in the class of cosets. If desired, this correspondence could be used to define vector space operations over the class of cosets, and it could be checked that these operations do not depend on the particular choice of $\mathscr{V}$ complementary to the given $\mathscr{U}$, i.e., there is a natural way to regard the cosets of $\mathscr{U}$ as forming a vector space. The group-theoretic term coset will be replaced later in this chapter by the more familiar geometric term *hyperplane*.

Vectors $U_1, U_2, \ldots, U_r$ are said to be *linearly independent* if the relation

$$c_1 U_1 + c_2 U_2 + \cdots + c_r U_r = \emptyset \tag{2.2.1}$$

implies that $c_1 = c_2 = \cdots = c_r = 0$. Otherwise they are *linearly dependent*, and at least one of them can be expressed as a linear combination of the rest. A *basis* of a vector space is a linearly independent set of vectors which spans the whole space. Any vector has a unique expression as a linear combination of the vectors of a given basis. A basis always exists but is never unique; in fact, any linearly independent set of vectors can be incorporated into a basis. Each basis of a given vector space has the same number of elements. If this number is finite it is called the *dimension* of the space, but otherwise the space is called *infinite-dimensional. There will be no discussion of infinite-dimensional vector spaces in this book.* At the other extreme, a vector space consisting only of $\emptyset$ is defined to have dimension 0. If $\mathscr{U}$ and $\mathscr{V}$ are subspaces, it can be shown that

$$d(\mathscr{U}) + d(\mathscr{V}) = d(\mathscr{U} \cap \mathscr{V}) + d(\mathscr{U} \oplus \mathscr{V}), \tag{2.2.2}$$

where $d(\ldots)$ denotes the dimension of a subspace. Thus, if $\mathscr{U}$ and $\mathscr{V}$ are complementary subspaces of a p-dimensional vector space,

$$d(\mathscr{U}) + d(\mathscr{V}) = p. \tag{2.2.3}$$

It may be shown that a set of r vectors is a linearly dependent set if and only if the subspace spanned by the set has dimension less than r.

It is clear that variable-space and individual-space in Examples 2.1.1 and 2.1.2 are both p-dimensional vector spaces. In Example 2.1.1, the vectors $V_1, V_2, \ldots, V_p$ constitute a basis, and $\alpha_1, \alpha_2, \ldots, \alpha_p$ represent the *coordinates* of $V = \sum_1^p \alpha_t V_t$ relative to this basis. In Example 2.1.2 the p-tuples

$$\begin{array}{c}(1, 0, \ldots, 0)\\(0, 1, \ldots, 0)\\\cdot\\\cdot\\\cdot\\(0, 0, \ldots, 1)\end{array} \tag{2.2.4}$$

form a basis. On the other hand, it is clear that the augmented variable-space and the corresponding augmented individual-space are both $(p + 1)$-dimensional vector spaces.

2.3 LINEAR TRANSFORMATIONS

A mapping

$$V \rightarrow v \tag{2.3.1}$$

from the elements V of a vector space $\mathscr{E}$ to the elements v of a vector space $\mathscr{F}$ will be called a *linear transformation of $\mathscr{E}$ into $\mathscr{F}$* provided that

$$\alpha_1 V_1 + \alpha_2 V_2 \rightarrow \alpha_1 v_1 + \alpha_2 v_2, \tag{2.3.2}$$

for any real numbers α_1 and α_2, and any V_1 and V_2 in $\mathscr{E}$, where $V_1 \to v_1$ and $V_2 \to v_2$ under the mapping.

If $\emptyset$ denotes the zero vector in $\mathscr{E}$ and $ø$ denotes the zero vector in $\mathscr{F}$, then clearly $\emptyset$ maps into $ø$ under *any* linear transformation from $\mathscr{E}$ to $\mathscr{F}$. More generally, if $\mathscr{U}$ denotes the set of vectors in $\mathscr{E}$ which are carried into $ø$ in $\mathscr{F}$, then it is easily checked that $\mathscr{U}$ must be a subspace of $\mathscr{E}$. $\mathscr{U}$ will, of course, be the subspace of dimension zero if only $\emptyset$ in $\mathscr{E}$ maps into $ø$ in $\mathscr{F}$. A basic property of $\mathscr{U}$ is that if V in $\mathscr{E}$ maps into v in $\mathscr{F}$, then the whole coset $V + \mathscr{U}$ maps into v and conversely the coset $V + \mathscr{U}$ consists of all the vectors of $\mathscr{E}$ which map into v in $\mathscr{F}$. The range of the transformation, i.e., the set of vectors of $\mathscr{F}$ reached by mapping all V in $\mathscr{E}$ into $\mathscr{F}$, need not include all of $\mathscr{F}$ but must be a subspace $\mathscr{V}$ of $\mathscr{F}$. Thus, in general, a linear transformation is a many-one transformation from $\mathscr{E}$ to a subspace of $\mathscr{F}$. It becomes a one-one relationship between $\mathscr{E}$ and $\mathscr{F}$ if and only if $\mathscr{U}$ consists of $\emptyset$ and $\mathscr{V}$ consists of $\mathscr{F}$, and in this case there is a unique inverse mapping which is also a linear transformation. Such a one-one relationship may be called an *isomorphism*.

Suppose that $\mathscr{E}$, $\mathscr{U}$, $\mathscr{F}$, and $\mathscr{V}$ defined above have dimensions p, r, q, and s, respectively, where, since $\mathscr{U}$ is contained in $\mathscr{E}$ and $\mathscr{V}$ is contained in $\mathscr{F}$,

$$0 \leq r \leq p \quad \text{and} \quad 0 \leq s \leq q. \tag{2.3.3}$$

In particular, s is often called the *rank of the linear transformation* and obeys $s \leq p$ as well as $s \leq q$. This may be seen by noting that the transforms $v_1, v_2, \ldots, v_p$ in $\mathscr{F}$ of a set of basis vectors $V_1, V_2, \ldots, V_p$ in $\mathscr{E}$ must span $\mathscr{V}$, and no subspace of dimension s can be spanned by fewer than s vectors. Thus, the rank s of a linear transformation from a p-dimensional vector space $\mathscr{E}$ to a q-dimensional vector space $\mathscr{F}$ obeys

$$0 \leq s \leq \min(p, q). \tag{2.3.4}$$

An additional important relation is that

$$r + s = p. \tag{2.3.5}$$

To see this, consider a basis $V_1, V_2, \ldots, V_p$ of $\mathscr{E}$ such that $V_1, V_2, \ldots, V_r$ span $\mathscr{U}$. Then it may be checked that the transforms $v_1, v_2, \ldots, v_p$ of $V_1, V_2, \ldots, V_p$ satisfy the requirements that $v_1 = v_2 = \cdots = v_r = ø$ and that $v_{r+1}, v_{r+2}, \ldots, v_p$ are linearly independent, the latter set therefore forming a basis of $\mathscr{V}$ with $s = p - r$ basis vectors.

Any given linear transformation may be completely specified by only the transforms $v_1, v_2, \ldots, v_p$ of an arbitrary basis $V_1, V_2, \ldots, V_p$ of $\mathscr{E}$. Conversely, an arbitrary linear transformation may be constructed by picking an arbitrary set of elements $v_1, v_2, \ldots, v_p$ in $\mathscr{F}$ and asserting that they are the transforms of a basis $V_1, V_2, \ldots, V_p$ of $\mathscr{E}$. By such constructions, it may be checked that any r and s satisfying the inequalities (2.3.3) and (2.3.4) are possible. In particular, if $p = q$ and one chooses a basis $v_1, v_2, \ldots, v_p$ of $\mathscr{F}$ to be the transforms of a basis $V_1, V_2, \ldots, V_p$ of $\mathscr{E}$, then $r = 0$ and $s = p$. Since this clearly defines an isomorphism between $\mathscr{E}$ and $\mathscr{F}$, it follows that an isomorphism may be defined between any pair of p-dimensional vector spaces, actually in infinitely many ways. Also, such an isomorphism has rank p, which is the largest rank allowed by (2.3.4).

It is sometimes useful to define vector space operations on linear transformations from $\mathscr{E}$ to $\mathscr{F}$. Thus, if A and B denote linear transformations from $\mathscr{E}$ to $\mathscr{F}$ carrying V in $\mathscr{E}$ into v_{A} and v_{B} in $\mathscr{F}$, then $\alpha\mathsf{A} + \beta\mathsf{B}$ may be defined as the mapping which carries V into $\alpha v_{\mathsf{A}} + \beta v_{\mathsf{B}}$ in $\mathscr{F}$.

A product notation for linear transformations is also useful. If C denotes a linear transformation from $\mathscr{E}$ to $\mathscr{F}$ and D denotes a linear transformation from $\mathscr{F}$ to $\mathscr{G}$, then CD will denote the transformation from $\mathscr{E}$ to $\mathscr{G}$ defined by first applying C to $\mathscr{E}$ and then applying D to $\mathscr{F}$. It is easily checked that CD is a linear transformation.

An important special case of the foregoing theory concerns linear transformations of $\mathscr{E}$ into itself, i.e., where the roles of $\mathscr{E}$ and $\mathscr{F}$ are both played by $\mathscr{E}$. Some additional concepts arise here. For example, one is led to consider the identity transformation I which carries each V in $\mathscr{E}$ into itself.

Clearly I satisfies

$$\mathsf{AI} = \mathsf{IA} = \mathsf{I} \tag{2.3.6}$$

for any A from $\mathscr{E}$ into itself.

A linear transformation A from $\mathscr{E}$ into itself which satisfies

$$\mathsf{AA} = \mathsf{A} \tag{2.3.7}$$

is often called an *idempotent transformation*, or, in geometrically more natural terms, a *projection*. Suppose that $\mathscr{U}$ and $\mathscr{V}$ denote, as before, the subset which maps into $\emptyset$ and the range space of A. It is easily shown that if A is idempotent, then $\mathscr{U}$ and $\mathscr{V}$ must be complementary and thence that every vector in $\mathscr{V}$ is left unchanged by A. Any vector W in $\mathscr{E}$ has a unique expression as

$$W = V + U \tag{2.3.8}$$

with V in $\mathscr{V}$ and U in $\mathscr{U}$, where A carries $V \to V$ and $U \to \emptyset$ and thence

$$W \to V. \tag{2.3.9}$$

Thus A is a projection in the sense that it removes the $\mathscr{U}$-component of W while leaving the $\mathscr{V}$-component unchanged. To construct an idempotent transformation of rank s, one need only specify a pair of complementary subspaces $\mathscr{U}$ and $\mathscr{V}$ of dimensions $p - s$ and s and use (2.3.9). Note that the identity I is a special projection—in fact the only projection with maximum rank p.

2.4 AFFINE GEOMETRY: VECTOR SPACE AS GEOMETRIC SPACE

It is often more natural to shed the formal abstract language of Sections 2.1, 2.2, and 2.3 and discuss vector spaces in geometric language. According to this language, vectors are called *points*, and, in particular, the zero vector $\emptyset$ is called the *origin*. A subspace $\mathscr{U}$ of dimension r is called a *hyperplane of dimension r through the origin*, and the cosets $V + \mathscr{U}$ are the r-dimensional *hyperplanes parallel* to $\mathscr{U}$. A *line* and a *plane* are hyperplanes of dimensions one and two respectively.

A line is uniquely determined by any two points on it. Specifically, the line through U_1 and U_2 may be written $U_1 + \mathscr{U}$ where $\mathscr{U}$ is the subspace spanned by $U_1 - U_2$. Alternatively, the points of this line may be written $\alpha_1 U_1 + \alpha_2 U_2$ where $\alpha_1 + \alpha_2 = 1$. The subset of these points satisfying $\alpha_1 \geq 0$ and $\alpha_2 \geq 0$ define the *line segment* $U_1 U_2$ joining U_1 and U_2.

More generally, the smallest hyperplane containing a given set of points $U_1, U_2, \ldots, U_r$ is $U_1 + \mathscr{U}$ where $\mathscr{U}$ is the subspace spanned by the differences among the U_i. This hyperplane may also be characterized as the set of points

$$\sum_{i=1}^{r} \alpha_i U_i, \tag{2.4.1}$$

where

$$\sum_{i=1}^{r} \alpha_i = 1. \tag{2.4.2}$$

This hyperplane has dimension $r - 1$ if and only if no U_i lies in the smallest hyperplane containing the remaining U_j. In this case the set of points (2.4.1) obeying (2.4.2) and

$$\alpha_i \geq 0 \qquad \text{for} \qquad i = 1, 2, \ldots, r \tag{2.4.3}$$

defines the $(r - 1)$-dimensional *simplex* with *vertices* $U_1, U_2, \ldots, U_r$. A one-dimensional simplex is a line segment, a two-dimensional simplex a triangle, and a three-dimensional simplex a tetrahedron.

A different generalization of the one-dimensional concept of a line segment is that of a *parallelotope*, which specializes to a parallelogram in two dimensions and to a parallelepiped in three dimensions. For any linearly independent points $W_1, W_2, \ldots, W_r$ of $\mathscr{E}$ and any point U of $\mathscr{E}$, the set of points

$$D + \sum_{i=1}^{r} \beta_i W_i \tag{2.4.4}$$

such that

$$0 \leq \beta_i \leq 1 \qquad \text{for} \qquad i = 1, 2, \ldots, r \tag{2.4.5}$$

define the points of *an r-dimensional parallelotope*. The 2^r points such that each β_i is zero or unity are called the vertices of the parallelotope. The set of points such that $\beta_i = 0$ for a single specified i define an $(r - 1)$-dimensional parallelotope, as do those points such that $\beta_i = 1$. These subparallelotopes may be called the ith pair of parallel faces. A point on at least one face of a parallelotope lies on the surface of the parallelotope while the remaining points are interior points.

The point (2.4.4) such that

$$\beta_i = \tfrac{1}{2} \qquad \text{for} \qquad i = 1, 2, \ldots, r \tag{2.4.6}$$

defines the *center* of the parallelotope.

A basis $V_1, V_2, \ldots, V_p$ determines a *coordinate system* in the familiar sense of analytic geometry. The line segments $\emptyset V_1, \emptyset V_2, \ldots, \emptyset V_p$ are the *coordinate axes* and the point $V = \sum_1^p \alpha_i V_i$ is said to have *coordinates* $\alpha_1, \alpha_2, \ldots, \alpha_p$.

The kind of geometry which can be carried on using only the operations allowed by vector space theory is called *affine geometry*. Affine geometry is characterized by the presence of concepts of parallelity of lines, planes, and hyperplanes, but the absence of concepts of length, angle, and perpendicularity. Note, however, that the ratio of the lengths of parallel line segments is an affine concept. Suppose that UV and U_1V_1 are parallel line segments and that $W = V - U$ and $W_1 = V_1 - U_1$. Then W and W_1 must lie in the same line through the origin, i.e., in the same subspace of dimension one, and hence $W_1 = \alpha W$ for some α. This α is the ratio of the length of the line segment U_1V_1 to that of UV.

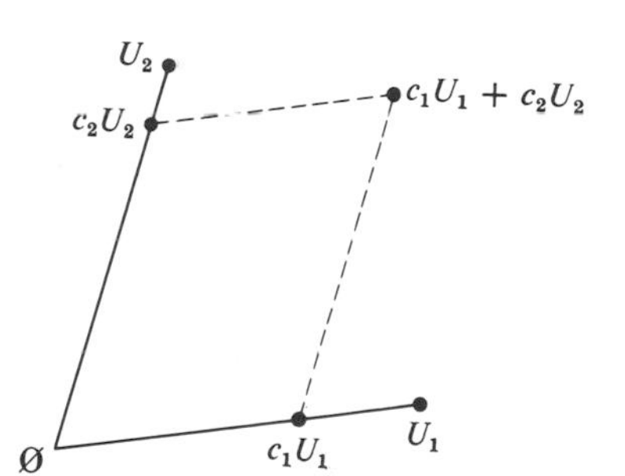

Fig. 2.4.1. Construction of the vector $c_1U_1 + c_2U_2$.

The reader may object that although geometric language has been introduced, nothing has been done to tie this language to his intuitive understanding of two- and three-dimensional geometric space. Consider therefore an "ordinary" geometric plane, or space of two dimensions, which may be thought of as a flat piece of paper extending to infinity in all directions. Suppose that a two dimensional vector space with basis vectors U_1 and U_2 is to be represented geometrically in this plane. The first step in the representation is to choose a point in the plane to be called the origin. Then any two line segments from the origin may be taken to represent the axes determined by $\emptyset U_1$ and $\emptyset U_2$. With these choices the correspondence between the vectors of the space and the points of the plane is defined. In order to construct the point corresponding to the vector $c_1U_1 + c_2U_2$, as illustrated in Fig. 2.4.1, one needs only the notions of (i) multiplying a line segment by a real number and (ii) moving a line segment parallel to itself. Note that (i) and (ii) are the geometric versions of the fundamental operations (2.1.1) and (2.1.2) on abstract vectors. This discussion could be repeated in three dimensions and embellished by explicitly tying together the intuitive notion of a family of parallel lines or planes with the abstract notion of a subspace and its cosets. Note that, in thinking this way about vector spaces, care should be taken not to introduce concepts alien to affine geometry. It is impossible to draw geometric diagrams without some intuitive notions of length, angle, and perpendicularity, but if the space is regarded as affine these notions must not be used.

In four or more dimensions it is not possible to make concrete geometric representations of a vector space as illustrated in Fig. 2.4.1. However, it is possible and useful to develop a geometric intuition in p-dimensional space through trying to reason by analogy with two and three dimensional spaces, resorting when necessary to the rigorous abstract language of vector space theory.

In considering an affine plane or, in general, an affine p-dimensional space, it is not required to think of the origin as geometrically different from any other point. However, in order to regard affine geometric space as a vector space, a specific origin must be chosen, and as stated in Exercise 2.1.4 different vector operations result when different points are chosen as the origin. Thus, the concepts of an affine geometric space and a vector space are not identical, but the concepts of an affine geometric space with a specified origin and a vector space may be identified. Strictly speaking, *geometric affine properties* are those which continue to hold when defined in terms of a vector space arising from different choices of the origin $\emptyset$.

When thinking in geometric terms with various possible choices for origin, it is convenient to widen the notion of a linear transformation of $\mathscr{E}$ into itself to include transformations which shift the origin as well as other points. Thus, if $\emptyset$ is any point in an affine space $\mathscr{E}$ and the set $V_1, V_2, \ldots, V_p$ together with the origin $\emptyset$ forms a basis of the resulting vector space, then a mapping of $\mathscr{E}$ into itself which carries

$$\sum_{t=1}^{p} \alpha_t V_t = \emptyset + \sum_{t=1}^{p} \alpha_t (V_t - \emptyset) \qquad \text{into} \qquad \emptyset^* + \sum_{t=1}^{p} \alpha_t (V_t^* - \emptyset^*)$$

for some set of $p + 1$ points $\emptyset^*, V_1^*, \ldots, V_p^*$ will be called a *wide sense linear transformation.* Note that the wide sense linear transformation carries an origin $\emptyset$ into another point $\emptyset^*$ whereas the narrow sense definition always requires $\emptyset$ to be invariant.

The simplest type of wide sense linear transformation is a *translation* $V \to V + \emptyset^*$. In geometric terms, this translation simply shifts each point along a line parallel to $\emptyset\emptyset^*$ by an amount equal to the length of $\emptyset\emptyset^*$. It may be easily checked that the general transformation of the previous paragraph may be regarded as the net result of first carrying out the narrow sense linear transformation carrying $\emptyset$ into itself and V_i into $V_i^* - \emptyset^*$, for $i = 1, 2, \ldots, p$, and then carrying out the translation $V \to V + \emptyset^*$. In this sense, translations are the only new operations needed to define wide sense linear transformations from narrow sense linear transformations.

As suggested in Section 2.3, idempotent transformations have a natural geometric interpretation as projections. To define such a projection one needs a pair of hyperplanes $\mathscr{U}$ and $\mathscr{V}$ of dimensions r and s where $r + s = p$ and such that $\mathscr{U}$ and $\mathscr{V}$ intersect only in the origin. The operation of removing the component of W along $\mathscr{U}$ may also be regarded as the operation of replacing W by the intersection of the hyperplane $W + \mathscr{U}$ with the hyperplane $\mathscr{V}$. Thus the projection is often described as projection *along the family of hyperplanes parallel to* $\mathscr{U}$ *into the hyperplane* $\mathscr{V}$. The definition extends easily into a wide sense linear transformation with $\mathscr{V}$ replaced by a hyperplane $V + \mathscr{V}$ parallel to $\mathscr{V}$ but not through the origin, i.e., the transformation carries W into the intersection of $W + \mathscr{U}$ and $V + \mathscr{V}$.

2.5 MATRICES AND COORDINATE SYSTEMS: ANALYTIC VECTOR SPACE THEORY

Matrix algebra can be introduced without reference to vector space theory and has applications not related to vector space theory. Here, however, matrices are introduced primarily as mathematical and computational tools for describing and relating vectors. The elements of matrix theory are so widely known and available that they are only lightly treated here. In general, an *$r \times s$ matrix* is an array of r rows and s columns of real numbers and will be denoted by a bold-face letter. Typical notation would be

$$\mathbf{M} = \begin{bmatrix} m_{11} & m_{12} & \cdots & m_{1s} \\ m_{21} & m_{22} & \cdots & m_{2s} \\ \cdot & \cdot & & \cdot \\ \cdot & \cdot & & \cdot \\ \cdot & \cdot & & \cdot \\ m_{r1} & m_{r2} & \cdots & m_{rs} \end{bmatrix}, \tag{2.5.1}$$

where m_{ij} is often called the *element in position* (i, j). Occasionally the elements may be taken to be abstract vectors. If $r = 1$, a matrix may be called a *row vector* and if $s = 1$, a *column vector*. The matrix formed by interchanging the rows and columns of $\mathbf{M}$ is called the *transpose* of $\mathbf{M}$ and is denoted by $\mathbf{M}'$. When a matrix $\mathbf{M}$ is *square*, i.e., when $r = s$, one may ask whether $\mathbf{M}$ is *symmetric*, i.e., whether $\mathbf{M} = \mathbf{M}'$. The (i, j) elements of a matrix with $i = j$ will be called the *diagonal* or *main diagonal* elements and those with $i \neq j$ will be called the *off-diagonal* elements. The sum of the diagonal elements will be called the *trace* of the matrix and denoted by $\text{tr}\,\mathbf{M}$. The concepts of diagonal and trace are especially relevant to square symmetric matrices.

Matrices whose elements are all zero or all unity will be denoted by $\mathbf{0}$ and $\mathbf{1}$, respectively. The dimensions of any specific $\mathbf{0}$ or $\mathbf{1}$ must be defined in each case or be clear from the context. Similarly, a square matrix of specific dimension whose diagonal elements are all unity and whose off-diagonal elements are all zero will be denoted by **I** and called an *identity matrix*.

Given an $r_1 \times s_1$ matrix $\mathbf{M}_1$ and an $r_2 \times s_2$ matrix $\mathbf{M}_2$ with $s_1 = r_2$, the product $\mathbf{M} = \mathbf{M}_1\mathbf{M}_2$ is defined to be the $r_1 \times s_2$ matrix whose (i, j) element is given by

$$m_{ij} = \sum_{t=1}^{s_1} m_{1it} m_{2tj}, \tag{2.5.2}$$

where m_{ij}, m_{1ij} and m_{2ij} denote the (i, j) elements of $\mathbf{M}$, $\mathbf{M}_1$, and $\mathbf{M}_2$, respectively. Two matrices of the same dimension may be added to give a third matrix of the same dimension, $\mathbf{N} = \mathbf{N}_1 + \mathbf{N}_2$ being defined by $n_{ij} = n_{1ij} + n_{2ij}$, where n_{ij}, n_{1ij}, and n_{2ij} denote the (i, j) elements of $\mathbf{N}$, $\mathbf{N}_1$, and $\mathbf{N}_2$, respectively. The product $x\mathbf{M}$ of a real number x and an $r \times s$ matrix $\mathbf{M}$ is defined to be an $r \times s$ matrix whose (i, j) element is xm_{ij} where m_{ij} is the (i, j) element of $\mathbf{M}$.

The first use of matrices is to represent the coordinates of individual vectors in a vector space relative to a given coordinate system (i.e., basis). Suppose that a vector space $\mathscr{E}$ has a basis $V_1, V_2, \ldots, V_p$. Then any vector $\sum_1^p \alpha_t V_t$ can be written $\boldsymbol{\alpha}\mathbf{V}$, where

$$\boldsymbol{\alpha} = [\alpha_1, \alpha_2, \ldots, \alpha_p] \quad \text{and} \quad \mathbf{V} = \begin{bmatrix} V_1 \\ V_2 \\ \cdot \\ \cdot \\ \cdot \\ V_p \end{bmatrix}. \tag{2.5.3}$$

It should be stressed that in this notation the elements of $\boldsymbol{\alpha}$ are real numbers but *the elements of* **V** *are abstract vectors*. It is easily checked that the operations defined for vectors and those defined for matrices agree in the sense that if $U_1 = \boldsymbol{\mu}_1\mathbf{V}$ and $U_2 = \boldsymbol{\mu}_2\mathbf{V}$, then $c_1U_1 + c_2U_2 = (c_1\boldsymbol{\mu}_1 + c_2\boldsymbol{\mu}_2)\mathbf{V}$. Thus one can dispense with the basis column vector **V** and simply identify the vectors of $\mathscr{E}$ with the p-tuples $\boldsymbol{\alpha}$ in the obvious way. This gives a matrix representation of the space $\mathscr{E}$.

This matrix representation is different for different choices of a basis in $\mathscr{E}$. A second use of matrices is to relate the representations corresponding to different bases. Suppose that the column vectors **U** and **V** represent different bases $U_1, U_2, \ldots, U_p$ and $V_1, V_2, \ldots, V_p$. Then any V_i has a unique expression as a linear combination of $U_1, U_2, \ldots, U_p$, i.e.,

$$V_i = \sum_{j=1}^{p} a_{ij} U_j, \; i = 1, 2, \ldots, p, \tag{2.5.4}$$

which may be written $\mathbf{V} = \mathbf{AU}$ in matrix notation where **A** has the (i, j) element

a_{ij}. Any V in $\mathscr{E}$ may be written $\sum_1^p \alpha_t V_t$ or $\sum_1^p \beta_t U_t$ where $\boldsymbol{\alpha}$ and $\boldsymbol{\beta}$ are the coordinates relative to $\mathbf{V}$ and $\mathbf{U}$. Thus $\boldsymbol{\alpha}\mathbf{V} = \boldsymbol{\beta}\mathbf{U}$, or $\boldsymbol{\alpha}\mathbf{A}\mathbf{U} = \boldsymbol{\beta}\mathbf{U}$, so that

$$\boldsymbol{\beta} = \boldsymbol{\alpha}\mathbf{A}. \tag{2.5.5}$$

Of course, one could equally well have expressed $\mathbf{U}$ in terms of $\mathbf{V}$ as $\mathbf{U} = \mathbf{B}\mathbf{V}$ and have expressed

$$\boldsymbol{\alpha} = \boldsymbol{\beta}\mathbf{B}. \tag{2.5.6}$$

Note that $\mathbf{U} = \mathbf{B}\mathbf{V} = \mathbf{B}\mathbf{A}\mathbf{U}$ and $\mathbf{V} = \mathbf{A}\mathbf{U} = \mathbf{A}\mathbf{B}\mathbf{V}$ so that

$$\mathbf{B}\mathbf{A} = \mathbf{A}\mathbf{B} = \mathbf{I} \tag{2.5.7}$$

where $\mathbf{I}$ is an identity matrix. In (2.5.7) the result relating matrix multiplication and successive coordinate changes has been used implicitly. The general result, which may be easily checked, states that if the bases $\mathbf{U}$ and $\mathbf{V}$ are related by $\mathbf{U} = \mathbf{B}\mathbf{V}$ and the bases $\mathbf{V}$ and $\mathbf{W}$ are related by $\mathbf{V} = \mathbf{C}\mathbf{W}$, then the bases $\mathbf{U}$ and $\mathbf{W}$ are related by $\mathbf{U} = \mathbf{D}\mathbf{W}$, where

$$\mathbf{D} = \mathbf{B}\mathbf{C}. \tag{2.5.8}$$

A more general use of matrices is to represent linear transformations. Suppose that A is a linear transformation from $\mathscr{E}$ to $\mathscr{F}$ where $\mathscr{E}$ has the $p \times 1$ basis $\mathbf{V}$ and $\mathscr{F}$ has the $q \times 1$ basis $\mathbf{U}$. Then $\mathbf{V} \to \mathbf{A}\mathbf{U}$ for some $p \times q$ matrix $\mathbf{A}$. Conversely, any $p \times q$ matrix $\mathbf{A}$ determines a linear transformation $\boldsymbol{\alpha}\mathbf{V} \to \boldsymbol{\alpha}\mathbf{A}\mathbf{U}$ from $\mathscr{E}$ to $\mathscr{F}$ in terms of the bases $\mathbf{V}$ and $\mathbf{U}$. A further linear transformation B from $\mathscr{F}$ to $\mathscr{G}$ defines and is defined by an associated matrix $\mathbf{B}$ relative to bases $\mathbf{U}$ and $\mathbf{W}$ of $\mathscr{F}$ and $\mathscr{G}$, respectively. The product transformation AB from $\mathscr{E}$ to $\mathscr{G}$ is easily seen to be represented by the matrix product $\mathbf{A}\mathbf{B}$ relative to the bases $\mathbf{V}$ and $\mathbf{W}$, for $\mathbf{V} \to \mathbf{A}\mathbf{U}$ under A and $\mathbf{U} \to \mathbf{B}\mathbf{W}$ under B so that $\mathbf{V} \to \mathbf{A}\mathbf{U} \to \mathbf{A}\mathbf{B}\mathbf{W}$ under A followed by B.

The *rank* of any matrix $\mathbf{A}$ may be defined to be the rank of a linear transformation A which it represents. A $p \times p$ matrix $\mathbf{A}$ of rank p defines an isomorphism A between $\mathscr{E}$ and $\mathscr{F}$ which has a unique inverse B, in turn represented by the *inverse matrix* $\mathbf{B}$. Since $\mathsf{AB} = \mathsf{BA} = \mathsf{I}$, the inverse matrix $\mathbf{B}$ of $\mathbf{A}$ satisfies (2.5.7). A $p \times p$ matrix of rank p is called *nonsingular* or *of full rank*, whereas it is *singular* or *of less than full rank* if it has rank less than p. Every nonsingular matrix $\mathbf{A}$ has a unique inverse $\mathbf{B}$ satisfying (2.5.7), but no singular matrix has such an inverse.

Any $p \times p$ matrix $\mathbf{A}$ defines a transformation $\mathbf{V} \to \mathbf{A}\mathbf{V}$ of $\mathscr{E}$ into itself. $\mathbf{A}$ is said to be *idempotent* if the transformation $\mathbf{V} \to \mathbf{A}\mathbf{V}$ is idempotent, i.e., if

$$\mathbf{A}\mathbf{A} = \mathbf{A}. \tag{2.5.9}$$

Mathematical theory can often be derived either by using purely vectorial or geometric reasoning, or by using analytic manipulations with matrices. The former reasoning often makes use of no basis and may then be called *coordinate-free*. The latter always must express vectors in terms of particular coordinate systems and may be called *coordinate-dependent.* Simplifications in analytic arguments often result from the special choice of a basis or coordinate system.

2.6 PSEUDOINVERSION

From time to time it is useful to be equipped technically to handle matrices of less than full rank. These arise in various ways which can usually be related to linear transformations of less than full rank, and in geometric terms the situation is often easy to understand. In particular, consider the following generalization of the concept of inverse of a linear transformation.

Suppose that A denotes a linear transformation from a p-dimensional vector space $\mathscr{E}$ to a q-dimensional vector space $\mathscr{F}$. Suppose that $\mathscr{U}$, $\mathscr{V}$, r, and s are defined as in Section 2.3 where s is the rank of A. Suppose that $\mathscr{U}^*$ is any $(p - r)$-dimensional subspace of $\mathscr{E}$ complementary to $\mathscr{U}$ and $\mathscr{V}^*$ is any $(q - s)$-dimensional subspace of $\mathscr{F}$ complementary to $\mathscr{V}$. Define $\mathsf{I}(\mathscr{U}, \mathscr{U}^*)$ to be the projection of $\mathscr{E}$ into $\mathscr{U}^*$ along hyperplanes parallel to $\mathscr{U}$ and define $\mathsf{I}(\mathscr{V}^*, \mathscr{V})$ to be the projection of $\mathscr{F}$ into $\mathscr{V}$ along hyperplanes parallel to $\mathscr{V}^*$. Note that these projections both have rank s. Now the points U^* of $\mathscr{U}^*$ are in one-one correspondence with hyperplanes $U^* + \mathscr{U}$, and these hyperplanes are in one-one correspondence under A with the points of $\mathscr{V}$. In other words, A defines a one-one linear transformation from $\mathscr{U}^*$ to $\mathscr{V}$; call this A_1 and call its inverse B_1. Finally, define the linear transformation

$$\mathsf{B} = \mathsf{I}(\mathscr{V}^*, \mathscr{V})\mathsf{B}_1 \tag{2.6.1}$$

from $\mathscr{F}$ to $\mathscr{E}$ to be a *pseudoinverse* of A.

It is clear that given A there is a different pseudoinverse B for each different pair of chosen $\mathscr{U}^*$ and $\mathscr{V}^*$. Three basic and obvious properties of such a pseudoinverse are

i) B has the same rank s as A,

ii) $$\mathsf{AB} = \mathsf{I}(\mathscr{U}, \mathscr{U}^*), \tag{2.6.2}$$

iii) $$\mathsf{BA} = \mathsf{I}(\mathscr{V}^*, \mathscr{V}). \tag{2.6.3}$$

These properties say that B comes as close to being an inverse as is possible when A has rank s in the sense that a projection of rank s is as close to the identity as can be managed with a transformation of rank s. The particular definition is motivated by the following theorem.

> ***Theorem 2.6.1.*** *Suppose that* A *is a given rank s linear transformation from* $\mathscr{E}$ *to* $\mathscr{F}$. *Suppose that* B *has rank s and* AB *and* BA *are both projections of rank s. Then* B *is a pseudoinverse of* A *as defined above.*

To prove this, define $\mathscr{V}^*$ to be the subspace of $\mathscr{F}$ which maps under B into $\emptyset$ in $\mathscr{E}$, and define $\mathscr{U}^*$ to be the range space of B in $\mathscr{E}$. The objective is to prove that B has the structure (2.6.1) with the $\mathscr{V}^*$ and $\mathscr{U}^*$ as defined. Since B has rank s, $\mathscr{V}^*$ and $\mathscr{U}$ have dimensions $q - s$ and $s = p - r$. Also, AB carries any hyperplane parallel to $\mathscr{U}$ into a single point in the range space $\mathscr{U}^*$, and since AB is a projection of rank s it must be $\mathsf{I}(\mathscr{U}, \mathscr{U}^*)$. This proves, incidentally, that $\mathscr{U}$ and $\mathscr{U}^*$ must be complementary. Defining A_1 and B_1 as above, it follows that B is defined by B_1 over $\mathscr{V}$ and it remains only to show that $\mathscr{V}$ and $\mathscr{V}^*$ are complementary. If, to the contrary, the intersection of $\mathscr{V}$ and $\mathscr{V}^*$ were to contain more than the origin, then a larger subspace of $\mathscr{V}$ than simply the origin would map under B into the origin in $\mathscr{E}$. From this, $\mathscr{V}$ could not be in one-one correspondence with $\mathscr{U}^*$, yielding a contradiction which completes the proof.

In matrix terms, the analogue of A is a $p \times q$ matrix $\mathbf{A}$ of rank s. A *pseudoinverse of* $\mathbf{A}$ is naturally defined to be any $q \times p$ matrix $\mathbf{B}$ of rank s such that $\mathbf{AB}$ and $\mathbf{BA}$ are both idempotent of rank s. Clearly, $\mathbf{B}$ is a pseudoinverse of $\mathbf{A}$ if and only if B is a pseudoinverse of A where A and B are defined relative to bases $\mathbf{U}$ and $\mathbf{W}$ of $\mathscr{E}$ and $\mathscr{F}$ by

$$\mathbf{U} \to \mathbf{AW} \qquad \text{and} \qquad \mathbf{W} \to \mathbf{BU}. \tag{2.6.4}$$

The structure of $\mathbf{A}$ and its pseudoinverse $\mathbf{B}$ may be explored as follows. Consider a basis $\mathbf{U}^*$ of $\mathscr{E}$ such that the last $p - s$ elements $\mathbf{U}_2^*$ map into the origin under $\mathbf{U} \to \mathbf{AW}$, i.e., $\mathbf{U}_2^*$ spans the subspace $\mathscr{U}$ defined for the transformation A. Then the first s elements $\mathbf{U}_1^*$ span a complementary subspace $\mathscr{U}^*$. Similarly, suppose that $\mathbf{W}^*$ is a basis of $\mathscr{F}$ whose first s elements $\mathbf{W}_1^*$ span the range space $\mathscr{V}$ of A and whose last $q - s$ elements $\mathbf{W}_2^*$ span a complementary subspace $\mathscr{V}^*$. Since $\mathbf{U}^*$ and $\mathbf{W}^*$ determine $\mathscr{U}^*$ and $\mathscr{V}^*$, they determine a particular pseudoinverse B and its corresponding $\mathbf{B}$. Now A may be described as carrying

$$\mathbf{U}_1^* \to \mathbf{C}_{11}\mathbf{W}_1^* \qquad \text{and} \qquad \mathbf{U}_2^* \to \emptyset, \tag{2.6.5}$$

where $\mathbf{C}_{11}$ is an $s \times s$ nonsingular matrix and $\emptyset$ is the origin in $\mathscr{F}$. The corresponding pseudoinverse B carries

$$\mathbf{W}_1^* \to \mathbf{D}_{11}\mathbf{U}_1^* \qquad \text{and} \qquad \mathbf{W}_2^* \to \emptyset, \tag{2.6.6}$$

where $\mathbf{D}_{11} = \mathbf{C}_{11}^{-1}$ and $\emptyset$ is the origin in $\mathscr{E}$.

Now (2.6.5) and (2.6.6) may be written

$$\mathbf{U}^* \to \mathbf{C}_{11}^{+}\mathbf{W}^* \tag{2.6.7}$$

and

$$\mathbf{W}^* \to \mathbf{D}_{11}^{+}\mathbf{U}^* \tag{2.6.8}$$

where $\mathbf{C}_{11}^{+}$ is a $p \times q$ matrix with $\mathbf{C}_{11}$ in the first s rows and columns and zero elsewhere, and $\mathbf{D}_{11}^{+}$ is a $q \times p$ matrix with $\mathbf{D}_{11}$ in the first s rows and columns and zero elsewhere. Also there exist nonsingular matrices $\mathbf{G}$ and $\mathbf{H}$ such that

$$\mathbf{U}^* = \mathbf{GU} \qquad \text{and} \qquad \mathbf{W}^* = \mathbf{HW}. \tag{2.6.9}$$

From (2.6.7), (2.6.8), and (2.6.9), it follows that

$$\mathbf{A} = \mathbf{G}^{-1}\mathbf{C}_{11}^{+}\mathbf{H} \tag{2.6.10}$$

and

$$\mathbf{B} = \mathbf{H}^{-1}\mathbf{D}_{11}^{+}\mathbf{G}. \tag{2.6.11}$$

These formulas provide the following prescription for finding a pseudoinverse $\mathbf{B}$ for a given matrix $\mathbf{A}$. *First find* $\mathbf{G}$ *and* $\mathbf{H}^{-1}$ *such that* $\mathbf{GAH}^{-1}$ *has the form of* $\mathbf{C}_{11}^{+}$. *Then find* $\mathbf{D}_{11} = \mathbf{C}_{11}^{-1}$ *and use* (2.6.11) *to find* $\mathbf{B}$.

Finally, consider the special case where $s = \min(p, q)$. First suppose that $p < q$ while A has rank p. Then $\mathsf{AB} = \mathsf{I}$ since AB is a rank p projection of $\mathscr{E}$ into itself. Similarly, any pseudoinverse $\mathbf{B}$ of a $p \times q$ rank p matrix $\mathbf{A}$ satisfies $\mathbf{AB} = \mathbf{I}$. The situation with $q < p$ is similar. When $p = q$, B is simply the inverse of A, i.e., $\mathbf{B} = \mathbf{A}^{-1}$.

2.7 EXERCISES

2.1.1 Derive the relationships (2.1.5) from the given axioms.

2.1.2 From the axioms (2.1.3) and (2.1.4) prove the theorem that $xV = \emptyset$ for $x \neq 0$ implies $V = \emptyset$. Conversely, show that this theorem together with (2.1.3) and (2.1.4), excluding $1V = V$ from (2.1.4), is sufficient to imply that $1V = V$ for all V.

2.1.3 Show that variable-space and individual-space as defined in Examples 2.1.1 and 2.1.2 do in fact satisfy the axioms of vector space theory. What are the zero elements of these two spaces? How does one define the negative of a vector in these two spaces?

2.1.4 Suppose that $[a_1, a_2, \ldots, a_p]$ is a particular point in the vector space of p-tuples of real numbers $[x_1, x_2, \ldots, x_p]$. Show that this same space of p-tuples can be regarded as a vector space in a different way, where

i) the zero vector is taken to be $[a_1, a_2, \ldots, a_p]$,
ii) the sum of $[x_1, x_2, \ldots, x_p]$ and $[y_1, y_2, \ldots, y_p]$ is defined to be $[x_1 + y_1 - a_1, x_2 + y_2 - a_2, \ldots, x_p + y_p - a_p]$, and
iii) the product $\alpha[x_1, x_2, \ldots, x_p]$ is defined to be $[\alpha x_1 - (\alpha - 1)a_1, \alpha x_2 - (\alpha - 1)a_2, \ldots, \alpha x_p - (\alpha - 1)a_p]$.

What is the negative of $(x_1, x_2, \ldots, x_p)$ in this vector space?

2.2.1 Prove the unproved statements in the first two paragraphs of Section 2.2.

2.2.2 Show that any set of vectors including the zero vector is a linearly dependent set.

2.2.3 Show that vectors $V_1, V_2, \ldots, V_s$, all different from $\emptyset$, are linearly dependent if and only if some one of them may be expressed as a linear combination of the rest. Under what circumstances can $V_1, V_2, \ldots, V_s$ be linearly dependent while V_1 is not expressible as a linear combination of the rest?

2.2.4 Show that the cosets $V + \mathscr{V}$ and $W + \mathscr{V}$, where $\mathscr{V}$ is a subspace of a vector space $\mathscr{E}$, are identical if and only if $V - W$ belongs to $\mathscr{V}$.

2.3.1 Show that the single condition (2.3.2) is equivalent to the pair of conditions that

$$\alpha V \to \alpha v$$

for all real α and any V in $\mathscr{E}$, where $V \to v$, and that

$$V + U \to v + u$$

for any V and U in $\mathscr{E}$, where $V \to v$ and $U \to u$.

2.3.2 Show that the mapping $V \to V^* = -V$, for all V in a p-dimensional vector space $\mathscr{E}$, defines a linear transformation of rank p of $\mathscr{E}$ into itself.

2.3.3 Show that any linear transformation of a p-dimensional vector space $\mathscr{E}$ into itself has rank p if and only if it is an isomorphism.

2.3.4 Give an example of a specific linear transformation of rank 2 of the vector space spanned by the basis V_1, V_2, V_3, V_4 into itself. Specify $\mathscr{U}$ and $\mathscr{V}$ in the example.

2.3.5 Show that the set of points left invariant by a linear transformation of $\mathscr{E}$ into itself is a subspace $\mathscr{W}$ of $\mathscr{E}$. Show further that the dimension of $\mathscr{W}$ is less than or equal to the rank of the linear transformation, with equality only if the transformation is a projection.

2.3.6 Suppose that A is a linear transformation from $\mathscr{E}$ to $\mathscr{F}$, and that B is a linear transformation from $\mathscr{F}$ to $\mathscr{G}$. Show that the rank of AB is no greater than the smaller of the ranks of A and B.

2.3.7 Show that the vector space of linear transformations from $\mathscr{E}$ of dimension p to $\mathscr{F}$ of dimension q has dimension pq.

2.3.8 Suppose that $\mathscr{U}$ and $\mathscr{V}$ are complementary subspaces of the vector space $\mathscr{E}$. Suppose that I represents the identity mapping of $\mathscr{E}$ into itself, $\mathsf{I}(\mathscr{U}, \mathscr{V})$ represents the projection along $\mathscr{U}$ into $\mathscr{V}$, and $\mathsf{I}(\mathscr{V}, \mathscr{U})$ represents the projection along $\mathscr{V}$ into $\mathscr{U}$. Show that

$$\mathsf{I} - \mathsf{I}(\mathscr{U}, \mathscr{V}) = \mathsf{I}(\mathscr{V}, \mathscr{U}),$$

i.e., that the difference of I and a projection is another complementary projection. What is the transformation $\mathsf{I}(\mathscr{U}, \mathscr{V})\mathsf{I}(\mathscr{V}, \mathscr{U})$?

2.4.1 Interpret geometrically the following statements:

i) $\mathscr{U}$ and $\mathscr{V}$ are complementary subspaces of a three-dimensional vector space $\mathscr{E}$,

ii) $\mathscr{U}$ and $\mathscr{V}$ are subspaces of a three-dimensional vector space $\mathscr{E}$ such that $\mathscr{U}$ and $V + \mathscr{V}$ have no common point,

iii) U_1, U_2, U_3, and U_4 span a subspace of dimension 2 of a p-dimensional space $\mathscr{E}$, and

iv) U_1, U_2, U_3, and U_4 are linearly dependent in a p-dimensional space $\mathscr{E}$.

2.4.2 Give a definition of the statement that an r-dimensional hyperplane is parallel to an s-dimensional hyperplane in p-dimensional affine space.

2.4.3 Strictly speaking, a geometric property should not be called affine unless it is proved to hold regardless of the choice of an origin. Examples of such properties are (a) the parallelity or nonparallelity of two hyperplanes and (b) the ratios of lengths of parallel line segment ratios. Can you prove that (a) and (b) are affine properties?

2.4.4 Suppose that $U_1, U_2, \ldots, U_r$ are any r points in p-dimensional affine space. How would you define the center of gravity of these r points? Is this an affine concept?

2.4.5 Define in a natural way the set of 2^{r-s} parallel s-dimensional faces of a given r-dimensional parallelotope, including the vertices when $s = 0$ and the ordinary faces when $s = r - 1$. What is the condition that a face of dimension t be contained in a face of dimension s for $t < s$? Show that a face of dimension s is the intersection of all faces of dimension $r - 1$ which contain it.

2.4.6 Suppose that $\mathscr{U}$ and $\mathscr{V}$ are hyperplanes through the origin of dimensions r and s, respectively, in p-dimensional affine space $\mathscr{E}$. What is the possible range of values of $\dim(\mathscr{U} \cap \mathscr{V})$? What is the condition on r and s such that $\mathscr{U} \cap \mathscr{V}$ must have dimension greater than zero?

2.4.7 Suppose that $U + \mathscr{U}$ and $V + \mathscr{V}$ are arbitrary hyperplanes of dimensions r and s, respectively, in p-dimensional affine space $\mathscr{E}$. Show that if $r + s \leq p$, then the hyperplanes do not necessarily have a common point, but that, if $r + s > p$, then the hyperplanes intersect in a hyperplane of dimension $\geq r + s - p$. (*Note. The results of Exercises* 2.4.6 *and* 2.4.7 *should be checked against three-dimensional geometric intuition.*)

2.4.8 Show that any parallelotope is invariant under the wide sense linear transformation of reflection in its center. What other wide sense linear transformations carry a parallelotope into itself?

2.5.1 Show that the matrix product $\mathbf{A}_1\mathbf{A}_2$ is not generally the same as $\mathbf{A}_2\mathbf{A}_1$ even when both products are defined and have the same dimensions.

2.5.2 Show that matrix multiplication is associative, i.e., that $(\mathbf{A}_1\mathbf{A}_2)\mathbf{A}_3 = \mathbf{A}_1(\mathbf{A}_2\mathbf{A}_3)$ provided that these products are all defined. Show how this property is used in deriving (2.5.5) and (2.5.8).

2.5.3 Show that any $m \times n$ matrix $\mathbf{A}$ has rank $r \leq \min(m, n)$.

2.5.4 Suppose that $\mathbf{M}$ is a $p \times q$ matrix of rank r and $\mathbf{N}$ is a $q \times q$ matrix of maximal rank q. Show that $\mathbf{MN}$ is, like $\mathbf{M}$, a $p \times q$ matrix of rank r.

2.5.5 If $\mathbf{A}_1$ and $\mathbf{A}_2$ are matrices of dimensions $p \times q$ and $q \times s$ and of ranks r_1 and r_2, respectively, what is known about the rank of $\mathbf{A}_1\mathbf{A}_2$?

2.5.6 Show that an $m \times n$ matrix $\mathbf{A}$ has rank $n - r$ if and only if there exist at most r linearly independent $n \times 1$ row vectors $\gamma_1, \gamma_2, \ldots, \gamma_r$ such that

$$\mathbf{A}\gamma_i = \mathbf{0} \qquad \text{for} \qquad i = 1, 2, \ldots, r.$$

2.5.7 Give a coordinate-free statement of the following result. The three equations

$$\begin{aligned} a_{11}x_1 + a_{12}x_2 + a_{13}x_3 &= 0, \\ a_{21}x_1 + a_{22}x_2 + a_{23}x_3 &= 0, \text{ and} \\ a_{31}x_1 + a_{32}x_2 + a_{33}x_3 &= 0 \end{aligned}$$

have a set of roots not all zero if and only if the matrix $\mathbf{A}$ of coefficients has rank less than 3. What is the nature of the set of all solutions if $\mathbf{A}$ has rank 2? Or if $\mathbf{A}$ has rank 1?

2.5.8 Under what conditions does the set of equations

$$\mathbf{AX} = \mathbf{B}$$

have a unique solution for **X**, given that **A** and **B** have dimensions $n \times p$ and $p \times r$, respectively?

2.5.9 Show that the analytic form of a wide sense linear transformation of $\mathscr{E}$ into itself relative to a basis **V** is

$$\boldsymbol{\alpha} \rightarrow \boldsymbol{\alpha}^* = \mathbf{B} + \boldsymbol{\alpha}\mathbf{A}.$$

2.5.10 Show that the rank of the sum of two $m \times n$ matrices is less than or equal to the sum of their ranks.

2.5.11 Show that, if $\mathbf{PQ}$, $\mathbf{P}^{-1}$, and $\mathbf{Q}^{-1}$ exist, then $(\mathbf{PQ})^{-1}$ exists and equals $\mathbf{Q}^{-1}\mathbf{P}^{-1}$.

2.6.1 Show that, if B is a pseudoinverse of A, then A is a pseudoinverse of B. What subspaces play the roles of $\mathscr{U}$, $\mathscr{U}^*$, $\mathscr{V}$, and $\mathscr{V}^*$ when A is regarded as a pseudoinverse of B?

2.6.2 Express the result of Exercise 2.6.1 in matrix terms.

2.6.3 Suppose that **A** is a $p \times q$ matrix of rank q where $p \geq q$. Suppose that a $p \times 1$ vector $\boldsymbol{\alpha}$ is given and is known to have arisen as

$$\boldsymbol{\alpha} = \mathbf{A}\boldsymbol{\beta}$$

for some $q \times 1$ vector $\boldsymbol{\beta}$. Show that $\boldsymbol{\beta}$ may be reconstructed from

$$\boldsymbol{\beta} = \mathbf{B}\boldsymbol{\alpha},$$

where **B** is any pseudoinverse of **A**.

2.6.4 Suppose that **B** is a pseudoinverse of **A**. Show that $\mathbf{B}'$ is a pseudoinverse of $\mathbf{A}'$.

2.6.5 Suppose that **A** is a $p \times q$ matrix with a $q \times p$ pseudoinverse matrix **B**. Suppose that **C** and **D** are nonsingular matrices of dimensions $p \times p$ and $q \times q$, respectively. Show that $\mathbf{D}^{-1}\mathbf{B}\mathbf{C}^{-1}$ is a pseudoinverse of $\mathbf{CAD}$.

CHAPTER 3

EUCLIDEAN VECTOR SPACES

3.1 ABSTRACT EUCLIDEAN VECTOR SPACES

Consider any p-dimensional vector space $\mathscr{E}$. It is proposed to enrich the structure of this space by giving it an *inner product*. An inner product is defined by a rule which assigns a real number (U, V) to each pair U and V of vectors in $\mathscr{E}$, i.e., an inner product is a function or mapping from the product space $\mathscr{E} \times \mathscr{E}$ to the real line. The term *inner product* will be used ambiguously either for the function or as an abbreviation for the *value* (U, V) *of the inner product* for given U and V.

The inner product must obey three simple rules:

i) *symmetry*, i.e.,

$$(U, V) = (V, U) \quad \text{for all } U \text{ and } V, \tag{3.1.1}$$

ii) *bilinearity*, i.e.,

$$(\mu_1 U_1 + \mu_2 U_2, V) = \mu_1(U_1, V) + \mu_2(U_2, V) \tag{3.1.2}$$

for all real numbers μ_1 and μ_2 and all vectors U_1, U_2, and V,

iii) *positiveness*, i.e.,

$$(U, U) > 0 \text{ for all } U \text{ different from } \emptyset. \tag{3.1.3}$$

The term bilinearity in (ii) is justified by the companion relation to (3.1.2) which follows from the application of (3.1.1) to each term in (3.1.2).

Some simple deductions from the axioms are

$$(\emptyset, V) = (V, \emptyset) = (\emptyset, \emptyset) = 0 \text{ for all } V, \text{ and} \tag{3.1.4}$$

$$\left(\sum_{i=1}^{r} \alpha_i U_i, \sum_{j=1}^{s} \beta_j V_j\right) = \sum_{i=1}^{r} \sum_{j=1}^{s} \alpha_i \beta_j (U_i, V_j), \tag{3.1.5}$$

for any real numbers $\alpha_1, \alpha_2, \ldots, \alpha_r, \beta_1, \ldots, \beta_s$ and vectors $U_1, \ldots, U_r, V_1, \ldots, V_s$. In particular,

$$\left(\sum_{i=1}^{p} \alpha_i V_i, \sum_{i=1}^{p} \beta_i V_i\right) = \sum_{i=1}^{p} \sum_{j=1}^{p} \alpha_i \beta_j (V_i, V_j), \tag{3.1.6}$$

where $V_1, \ldots, V_p$ denote any basis and $\sum_1^p \alpha_i V_i$ and $\sum_1^p \beta_i V_i$ are any two vectors in $\mathscr{E}$. Formula (3.1.6) implies that the inner product on $\mathscr{E}$ is defined by specifying it for all pairs of elements of any basis. In fact, if **Q** is the $p \times p$ matrix whose (i, j) element is (V_i, V_j), then the inner product of $\boldsymbol{\alpha}\mathbf{V}$ and $\boldsymbol{\beta}\mathbf{V}$ is given by

$$(\boldsymbol{\alpha}\mathbf{V}, \boldsymbol{\beta}\mathbf{V}) = \boldsymbol{\alpha}\mathbf{Q}\boldsymbol{\beta}', \tag{3.1.7}$$

a simple elegant formula. Such a matrix **Q** will be called the *inner product matrix* relative to the basis **V**.

To show that the definition of an inner product is not empty, i.e., that an inner product exists, simply set

$$(\boldsymbol{\alpha}\mathbf{V}, \boldsymbol{\beta}\mathbf{V}) = \boldsymbol{\alpha}\boldsymbol{\beta}'. \tag{3.1.8}$$

This is equivalent to choosing **Q** in (3.1.7) to be **I**. It is easily checked that the quantities defined by (3.1.8) satisfy the axiomatic requirements for an inner product. Using different bases in place of **V**, one can define an inner product in different ways on the same space $\mathscr{E}$. Conversely, it will be seen in Chapter 4 that any inner product can be characterized as in (3.1.8) for some basis, in fact for an infinite family of bases.

A vector space with an inner product defined on it will be called a *Euclidean vector space*. In Euclidean vector space terms, the square root of the inner product (V, V) is called the *norm* of V, and a pair of vectors U and V is said to be *orthogonal* if $(U, V) = 0$. A set of vectors such that every pair of vectors in the set is orthogonal will be called a *(mutually) orthogonal* set, and, if the set constitutes a basis of $\mathscr{E}$, it will be called simply an *orthogonal basis*. A set of vectors is called *orthonormal* if it is orthogonal and each vector has unit norm. For example, **V** is an orthonormal set according to the inner product defined by (3.1.8). If an orthonormal set **V** constitutes a basis it is called an *orthonormal basis*. Two subspaces $\mathscr{U}$ and $\mathscr{V}$ are said to be *orthogonal* if $(U, V) = 0$ for every U in $\mathscr{U}$ and V in $\mathscr{V}$.

Example 3.1.1. Consider the variable-space of Example 2.1.1 where each variable or linear combination of variables is a point. Unfamiliar as it may be for a statistician to think of such variables as points, still it is very familiar to think of an inner product on this vector space. Simply substitute the familiar terms covariance and variance for the less familiar terms inner product and norm squared, i.e.,

$$(U, V) = \operatorname{cov}(U, V) \quad \text{and} \quad (U, U) = \operatorname{cov}(U, U) = \operatorname{var}(U). \tag{3.1.9}$$

It can be easily checked that the sample covariance function introduced in (1.3.5) satisfies the requirement for an inner product provided that a variable $\sum_1^p \alpha_t V_t$ has zero variance only if $\alpha_1 = \alpha_2 = \cdots = \alpha_p = 0$. In fact, the covariance matrix whose (i, j) element is $\operatorname{cov}(V_i, V_j)$ plays the role of **Q** above and gives the standard form of the definition of an inner product in terms of its values for a set of basis elements. The converse result that any inner product function is a possible covariance function is easy to prove. Thus the notions of covariance and inner product are abstractly identical.

Example 3.1.2. At this point, one might suspect that variances and covariances could be used to define a natural inner product for the individual-space of Example 2.1.2. This is true, but not trivial, and a discussion of this matter is postponed to Chapter 6.

3.2 EUCLIDEAN GEOMETRIC SPACE

Euclidean geometry bears the same relation to affine geometry as Euclidean vector spaces bear to ordinary vector spaces. The geometric terminology introduced in Section 2.4 remains valid, and additional terminology becomes possible when affine space is enriched to Euclidean space. For example, the norm of V may now be called the *distance* from $\emptyset$ to V or the *length* of the line segment $\emptyset V$. More generally, the distance from U to V or the length of the line segment UV is given by the norm of $U - V$, i.e.,

$$\sqrt{(U - V, U - V)}. \tag{3.2.1}$$

Similarly, the line segments UV and U_1V_1, or the lines determined by them, are said to make *angle* θ with one another, where

$$\cos\theta = \frac{(U - V, U_1 - V_1)}{(U - V, U - V)^{1/2}(U_1 - V_1, U_1 - V_1)^{1/2}}. \tag{3.2.2}$$

The line segments UV and U_1V_1 or the lines determined by them are said to be *perpendicular* if $\cos\theta = 0$, i.e., if

$$(U - V, U_1 - V_1) = 0. \tag{3.2.3}$$

Two hyperplanes $V + \mathscr{V}$ and $U + \mathscr{U}$ are said to be *perpendicular* if the subspaces $\mathscr{U}$ and $\mathscr{V}$ are orthogonal.

To check that these definitions of geometric terms agree with what one intuitively regards as ordinary Euclidean geometry in $p = 2$ dimensions, consider a Euclidean plane with an orthonormal basis W_1, W_2 corresponding to a pair of perpendicular line segments $\emptyset W_1$, $\emptyset W_2$ of unit length, which define perpendicular coordinate axes, as in Fig. 3.2.1. Given the coordinates of the end points of any pair of line segments UV and U_1V_1, the standard formulas of elementary analytic geometry for the length of UV, the cosine of the angle between UV and U_1V_1, and the perpendicularity of UV and U_1V_1 are seen to agree with (3.2.1), (3.2.2), and (3.2.3), respectively, when the inner product is defined as in (3.1.8) using the basis W_1, W_2. Similar checking could be done with three-dimensional Euclidean geometry. In the case of p dimensions, for $p > 3$ geometric intuition must be backed up by abstract theory.

The statistical importance of the present section is that the variable-space of Example 2.1.1, together with a definition of covariance between each pair of variables, may be regarded as an ordinary Euclidean p-dimensional geometric space with its associated well-known concepts and propositions. For example, variances may be regarded as squared lengths, zero covariance means perpendicular, and the *correlation coefficient*

$$\rho_{ij} = \text{cov}(V_i, V_j)/[\text{var}(V_i)\,\text{var}(V_j)]^{1/2} \tag{3.2.4}$$

between V_i and V_j is the cosine of the angle between $\emptyset V_i$ and $\emptyset V_j$.

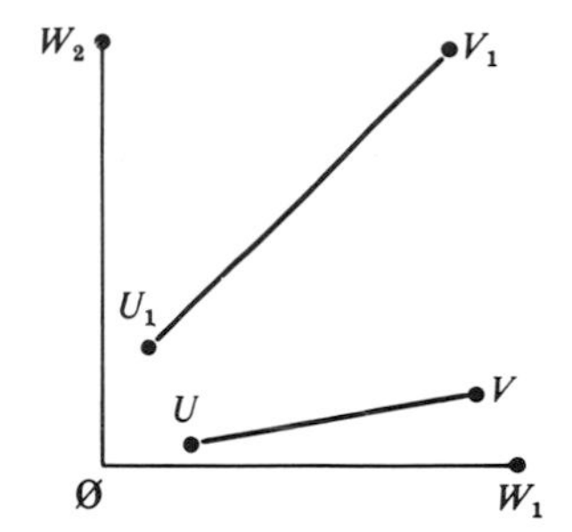

Fig. 3.2.1. The Euclidean plane with orthonormal coordinate axes $\emptyset W_1$ and $\emptyset W_2$ and arbitrary line segments UV and U_1V_1.

The concept of inner product is geometrically equivalent to the concept of an ellipsoid centered at the origin. In the present development an *ellipsoid centered at the origin* is defined to be the "solid figure" consisting of points V such that $(V, V) \leq 1$ according to some inner product. The points V such that $(V, V) = 1$ are said to be on the *surface* of the ellipsoid while the remaining points of the ellipsoid are interior points. Two different inner products cannot give rise to the same ellipsoid. To see this, note that the set of norms determined by an inner product uniquely define the whole inner product function, for

$$(U, V) = \tfrac{1}{4}[(U + V, U + V) - (U - V, U - V)]. \tag{3.2.5}$$

Consequently, if two inner products are different, there must exist a vector W with different norms under the two inner products. The vector αW for suitably chosen α has unit norm under one inner product and norm greater than unity under the other inner product, i.e., αW belongs to one ellipsoid but not to the other, and so the ellipsoids are different. The notation π will often be used either for an inner product or for its associated ellipsoid.

In terms of Euclidean geometry, the set of points at unit distance from the origin defines the unit sphere centered at the origin. However, even if an inner product is fixed in a space it is possible to consider a further range of inner products and the corresponding range of ellipsoids of which the unit sphere is just one. This idea is illustrated in the case $p = 2$ where a sphere is just a circle and an ellipsoid is an ellipse. Figure 3.2.2 is intended to be an affine plane where, because of an inability to draw such spaces without an implied Euclidean inner product, vectors W_1 and W_2 appear to be orthonormal. If an inner product is defined by taking W_1, W_2 as an orthonormal basis, then the set of points at unit distance from $\emptyset$ simply traces the unit circle. However, suppose that an arbitrary pair of vectors Z_1, Z_2 is chosen to be orthonormal for a *different* definition of inner product on the *same* space. Then it may be checked that the set of points at unit distance from the origin defines an ellipse as drawn. This ellipse has the property that the tangent line at Z_1 is parallel to $\emptyset Z_2$ and the tangent line at Z_2 is parallel to $\emptyset Z_1$, and no other ellipse has this property. These tangency properties will be derived in the p-dimensional case shortly. Note that the tangency properties appear obviously true in the case of the inner

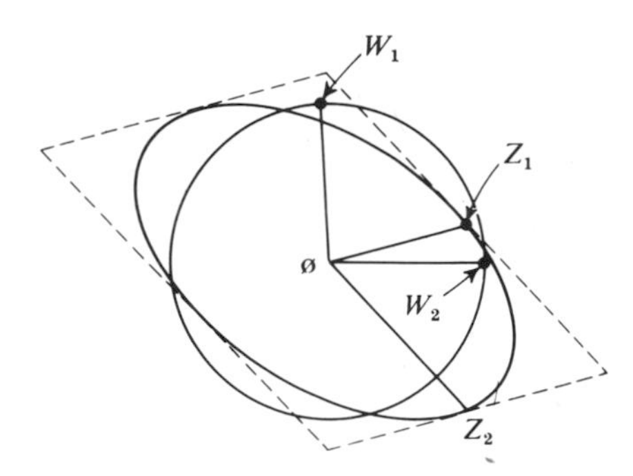

Fig. 3.2.2. Inner product ellipses associated with orthonormal bases W_1, W_2 and Z_1, Z_2. The latter is shown as conjugately contained in an associated parallelogram.

product represented by the unit circle, and, since any two bases are equivalent from an affine point of view, one might expect these properties to hold for any basis in a reasonable mathematical theory.

Any line through the center of an ellipsoid intersects the ellipsoid in a line segment which will be called an *axis* of the ellipsoid. The center divides such an axis into two *semi-axes* of equal length. In discussing a p-dimensional ellipsoid the word *conjugate* is often used in the same way that the word orthogonal is used in vector space language. Thus if two lines through $\emptyset$ are orthogonal under an inner product, they determine *conjugate axes* of the associated ellipsoid. The line segments $\emptyset W_1, \emptyset W_2, \ldots, \emptyset W_p$ defined by an orthonormal basis $\mathbf{W}$ are *a set of conjugate semi-axes* of the ellipsoid.

Suppose that $\mathscr{V}_0$ is the $(p - 1)$-dimensional subspace of $\mathscr{E}$ orthogonal to some unit vector V_0 according to a given inner product. Then $V_0 + \mathscr{V}_0$ is defined to be the tangent hyperplane at V_0 to the ellipsoid of the inner product. This definition makes sense because (i) V_0 lies on both the hyperplane and the surface of the ellipsoid and (ii) every other point $V_0 + V$ lying on $V_0 + \mathscr{V}_0$ has

$$\begin{aligned}(V_0 + V, V_0 + V) &= (V_0, V_0) + 2(V_0, V) + (V, V)\\ &= (V_0, V_0) + (V, V)\\ &> (V_0, V_0),\end{aligned}$$

and so is outside of the ellipsoid. Now suppose that W_1 and W_2 are any pair of orthonormal vectors. Then the tangent hyperplanes $W_1 + \mathscr{W}_1$ and $W_2 + \mathscr{W}_2$ clearly have the property that W_1 lies in $\mathscr{W}_2$ and W_2 lies in $\mathscr{W}_1$. More generally, if $W_1, W_2, \ldots, W_p$ constitute an orthonormal basis with tangent planes $W_i + \mathscr{W}_i$, then each W_i lies in $\mathscr{W}_j$ for $i \neq j$. In fact, $\mathscr{W}_j$ may be characterized as the subspace spanned by the W_i for $i \neq j$.

It is also natural to say that the ellipsoid is *conjugately contained* in the parallelotope with faces $\pm W_i + \mathscr{W}_i$, for the ellipsoid is tangent to each face of the parallelotope, and these tangent faces have the property of being conjugate to their points of contact. It is clear that only one ellipsoid can be conjugately inscribed in a given parallelotope, but it will be seen that many parallelotopes have this property relative to a given ellipsoid, i.e., a specified orthonormal basis determines an inner product, but a given inner product has many orthonormal bases.

In thinking of the ellipsoid of an inner product, it is instructive to note that the size of the ellipsoid varies inversely with the size of the inner product. To be more precise, changing the inner product from (U, V) to $\lambda(U, V)$ has the effect of multiplying the length of each axis by the factor $\lambda^{-1/2}$.

The foregoing discussion has defined only ellipsoids with center at $\emptyset$. To define an ellipsoid having an arbitrary center $\emptyset^*$, simply translate an ellipsoid with center $\emptyset$, i.e., if V ranges over a given ellipsoid with center $\emptyset$, then $\emptyset^* + V$ ranges over the translated ellipsoid with center $\emptyset^*$.

3.3 ORTHOGONAL LINEAR TRANSFORMATIONS AND ORTHOGONAL PROJECTIONS

An *orthogonal linear transformation* of a Euclidean space $\mathscr{E}$ into itself may be defined as a linear transformation $V \to V^*$ (narrow sense) which leaves the norm unchanged, i.e.,

$$(V, V) = (V^*, V^*) \tag{3.3.1}$$

for all V in $\mathscr{E}$. It is left to the reader to show that not only is the norm preserved, but every inner product is preserved, i.e.,

$$(V, W) = (V^*, W^*) \tag{3.3.2}$$

for every V and W in $\mathscr{E}$. Consequently, any configuration of lengths and angles determined by a set of vectors $U, V, W, \ldots$ is mirrored precisely by the set of transformed vectors $U^*, V^*, W^*, \ldots$ It is obvious that *every orthogonal linear transformation of the p-dimensional Euclidean space $\mathscr{E}$ into itself has rank p*, for if the rank were $r < p$, then a subspace $\mathscr{U}$ including vectors having nonzero norm would transform into the origin which has zero norm.

It is easily checked that any translation of a Euclidean space $\mathscr{E}$ leaves all lengths and angles invariant. Thus a translation followed by a narrow sense orthogonal linear transformation may naturally be called a *wide sense orthogonal linear transformation* because it leaves invariant all configurations of lengths and angles concerning a set of points. If Euclidean space is regarded as physical space, then such a wide sense orthogonal linear transformation may be regarded as a rigid motion in the space, perhaps followed by reflections. An analytic approach to characterizing the class of all orthogonal linear transformations involves orthogonal matrices which are taken up in Section 3.4, and methods of constructing such matrices are presented in Chapter 4.

An *orthogonal projection* is a special type of linear projection where the family of parallel hyperplanes along which the projected points move is orthogonal to the hyperplane into which points are projected. The definition of an orthogonal projection requires that one have a pair of subspaces $\mathcal{U}$ and $\mathcal{V}$ which are both orthogonal and complementary. It will be proved in Section 4.1 that the set of vectors orthogonal to any subspace $\mathcal{U}$ defines a subspace $\mathcal{V}$ which is complementary to $\mathcal{U}$, and, since no other subspace can be both orthogonal and complementary to $\mathcal{U}$, the subspace $\mathcal{V}$ may be called *the orthogonal complement of* $\mathcal{U}$. If $\mathcal{V}$ is the orthogonal complement of $\mathcal{U}$, then $\mathcal{U}$ is the orthogonal complement of $\mathcal{V}$. If $\mathbf{W}$ is an orthonormal basis, then $W_1, W_2, \ldots, W_r$ and $W_{r+1}, W_{r+2}, \ldots, W_p$ span a pair of orthogonal complements. With this theory in hand, it is clear that the concept of *orthogonal projection into the hyperplane* $V + \mathcal{V}$ is uniquely determined by $V + \mathcal{V}$, for $\mathcal{V}$ determines the orthogonal complement $\mathcal{U}$ along which the projection takes place.

A different characterization of an orthogonal projection is the following. The orthogonal projection W^* of any point W into $V + \mathcal{V}$ is that point in $V + \mathcal{V}$ at minimum distance from W, i.e., that point W^* such that

$$(W - W^*, W - W^*) < (W - V^*, W - V^*) \tag{3.3.3}$$

for any V^* in $V + \mathcal{V}$ different from W^*. To prove this, note that the line segment WW^* lies in the hyperplane $W + \mathcal{U}$ where $\mathcal{U}$ is the orthogonal complement of $\mathcal{V}$, and hence WW^* is perpendicular to any line segment in $\mathcal{V}$. Thus,

$$(W - W^*, V^* - W^*) = 0, \tag{3.3.4}$$

so that

$$\begin{aligned}(W - V^*, W - V^*) &= ([W - W^*] - [V^* - W^*], [W - W^*] - [V^* - W^*]) \\ &= (W - W^*, W - W^*) - 2(W - W^*, V^* - W^*) + (V^* - W^*, V^* - W^*) \\ &= (W - W^*, W - W^*) + (V^* - W^*, V^* - W^*) \\ &> (W - W^*, W - W^*), \end{aligned} \tag{3.3.5}$$

whenever V^* is different from W^*, as required.

A third characterization of an orthogonal projection is as follows: if W^* in $V + \mathcal{V}$ has the property that WW^* is perpendicular to every line segment VV^* in $V + \mathcal{V}$, then W^* is the orthogonal projection of W into $V + \mathcal{V}$. The proofs of this theorem and its converse are left to the reader.

When $V + \mathscr{V}$ is simply $\mathscr{V}$, i.e., a hyperplane through the origin, the orthogonal projection W^* of W into $\mathscr{V}$ is often called the *component of* W *along* $\mathscr{V}$ and $W - W^*$ is called the *component of* W *orthogonal to* $\mathscr{V}$. Note that $W = W^* + [W - W^*]$ is the sum of these two components.

The reader should consider the intuitive meaning of the operation of orthogonal projection in ordinary Euclidean space of two and three dimensions.

3.4 POSITIVE DEFINITE SYMMETRIC MATRICES AND ORTHOGONAL MATRICES

A $p \times p$ matrix $\mathbf{Q}$ is said to be *positive definite* if $\boldsymbol{\alpha}\mathbf{Q}\boldsymbol{\alpha}' > 0$ for every $1 \times p$ vector $\boldsymbol{\alpha} \neq \mathbf{0}$. Given a Euclidean space $\mathscr{E}$ and a basis $\mathbf{V}$, the inner product matrix $\mathbf{Q}$ defined in Section 3.1 is clearly positive definite and symmetric. Conversely, any positive definite symmetric matrix may be used to define an inner product over a vector space $\mathscr{E}$ in terms of a basis $\mathbf{V}$ via (3.1.7). Thus the concept of positive definite symmetric matrix is the natural analytic coordinate-dependent counterpart of the concept of inner product. When the inner product is a covariance, the inner product matrix relative to $\mathbf{V}$ will be called the *covariance matrix* of $\mathbf{V}$. Thus the class of all possible covariance matrices is identical with the class of all positive definite symmetric matrices. Similarly, in geometric terms the class of all ellipsoids centered at the origin is in one-one correspondence with the class of all positive definite symmetric matrices. For given any basis $\mathbf{V}$, the ellipsoid of the inner product with matrix $\mathbf{Q}$ consists of points $\boldsymbol{\alpha}\mathbf{V}$ such that

$$\boldsymbol{\alpha}\mathbf{Q}\boldsymbol{\alpha}' \leq 1. \tag{3.4.1}$$

Since covariance inner products based on sample data must in general be represented in terms of a covariance matrix $\mathbf{Q}$, computations with such matrices are basic for multivariate analyses. Chapters 4 and 5 are largely concerned with operations on positive definite symmetric matrices.

A basic lemma which will be used over and over again, beginning in the next paragraph, is that *if* $\mathbf{Q}$ *and* $\mathbf{Q}^*$ *denote inner product matrices of* $\mathscr{E}$ *relative to a pair of bases* $\mathbf{V}$ *and* $\mathbf{V}^*$, *where* $\mathbf{V}^* = \mathbf{AV}$, *then*

$$\mathbf{Q}^* = \mathbf{AQA}'. \tag{3.4.2}$$

The proof is left to the reader.

A $p \times p$ matrix $\mathbf{G}$ is said to be *orthogonal* if

$$\mathbf{GG}' = \mathbf{I}. \tag{3.4.3}$$

Equivalent definitions are obviously

$$\mathbf{G}' = \mathbf{G}^{-1} \tag{3.4.4}$$

or

$$\mathbf{G}'\mathbf{G} = \mathbf{I}. \tag{3.4.5}$$

Clearly $\mathbf{G}$ is orthogonal if and only if $\mathbf{G}'$ is orthogonal. Orthogonal matrices arise in relating two orthonormal bases and in expressing an orthogonal linear transformation in terms of an orthonormal basis. Thus, if $\mathbf{U}$ is an orthonormal basis, then from (3.4.2) $\mathbf{U}^* = \mathbf{G}\mathbf{U}$ is an orthonormal basis if and only if $\mathbf{G}$ is an orthogonal matrix. Note that the rows of $\mathbf{G}$ express $\mathbf{U}^*$ in terms of $\mathbf{U}$ while the columns of $\mathbf{G}$ express $\mathbf{U} = \mathbf{G}'\mathbf{U}^*$ in terms of $\mathbf{U}^*$. In a similar vein, it is clear that the linear transformation $\boldsymbol{\alpha}\mathbf{U} \to \boldsymbol{\alpha}\mathbf{G}\mathbf{U}$ where $\mathbf{U}$ is an orthonormal basis of $\mathscr{E}$ is an orthogonal linear transformation if and only if $\mathbf{G}$ is an orthogonal matrix.

The simplest orthogonal matrix is no doubt $\mathbf{I}$. Perhaps the simplest non-trivial class of orthogonal matrices is defined by

$$\mathbf{G} = \mathbf{I} - 2\boldsymbol{\gamma}'\boldsymbol{\gamma}, \tag{3.4.6}$$

where $\boldsymbol{\gamma}$ is any $1 \times p$ vector satisfying $\boldsymbol{\gamma}\boldsymbol{\gamma}' = 1$. These matrices may be called *elementary orthogonal matrices* and are playing an increasingly important role in modern computational practice under the name *Householder transformations*. (See Exercise 4.3.3 and Section 5.4. See also Householder (1964), Wilkinson (1965), and papers referred to by these authors.) Regarded as a linear transformation in Euclidean space, $\mathbf{G}$ in (3.4.6) expresses the simple geometric notion of reflection. To see this, suppose that $\mathbf{U}$ is an orthonormal basis of $\mathscr{E}$. Then $\boldsymbol{\gamma}\mathbf{U}$ defines a unit vector and any $V = \boldsymbol{\alpha}\mathbf{U}$ may be decomposed into a component $(\boldsymbol{\alpha}\boldsymbol{\gamma}')\boldsymbol{\gamma}\mathbf{U}$ along $\boldsymbol{\alpha}\mathbf{U}$ and a component $V - (\boldsymbol{\alpha}\boldsymbol{\gamma}')\boldsymbol{\gamma}\mathbf{U}$ in the subspace orthogonal to $\boldsymbol{\gamma}\mathbf{U}$. The linear transformation of reflection in the subspace orthogonal to $\boldsymbol{\gamma}\mathbf{U}$ is defined by changing the sign of the component orthogonal to the subspace while leaving the component in the subspace unchanged. Thus $V = \boldsymbol{\alpha}\mathbf{U} = (\boldsymbol{\alpha}\boldsymbol{\gamma}')\boldsymbol{\gamma}\mathbf{U} + [\boldsymbol{\alpha} - (\boldsymbol{\alpha}\boldsymbol{\gamma}')\boldsymbol{\gamma}]\mathbf{U} \to -(\boldsymbol{\alpha}\boldsymbol{\gamma}')\boldsymbol{\gamma}\mathbf{U} + [\boldsymbol{\alpha} - (\boldsymbol{\alpha}\boldsymbol{\gamma}')\boldsymbol{\gamma}]\mathbf{U} = \boldsymbol{\alpha}[\mathbf{I} - 2\boldsymbol{\gamma}'\boldsymbol{\gamma}]\mathbf{U}$ in agreement with (3.4.6).

As a first illustration of the use of elementary orthogonal matrices, consider the problem of finding an orthogonal matrix with a given first row. Any $1 \times p$ matrix $\mathbf{g}$ satisfying $\mathbf{g}\mathbf{g}' = 1$ is a candidate for the first row of an orthogonal matrix. In terms of an orthonormal basis $\mathbf{U}$ of a space $\mathscr{E}$, what is needed is an orthogonal linear transformation $\mathbf{U} \to \mathbf{G}\mathbf{U}$ carrying $U_1 \to \mathbf{g}\mathbf{U}$. This is easily accomplished by reflection in the subspace which bisects the angle between the vectors U_1 and $\mathbf{g}\mathbf{U}$. Thus $\boldsymbol{\gamma}\mathbf{U}$ lies along $U_1 - \mathbf{g}\mathbf{U}$ or

$$\boldsymbol{\gamma} = \lambda(1 - g_1, -g_2, -g_3, \ldots, -g_p), \tag{3.4.7}$$

where

$$\lambda = \pm[2(1 - g_1)]^{-1/2} \tag{3.4.8}$$

and $\mathbf{G}$ is defined by (3.4.6).

The reader should check directly that $\mathbf{G}$ defined by (3.4.6) is orthogonal and that, if (3.4.7) is used, the first row of $\mathbf{G}$ is $\mathbf{g}$.

3.5 DETERMINANTS AND VOLUMES

The concept of determinant plays an incidental role in the theory of this book, usually in the context of describing a volume. A number called the *determinant of* **A** and denoted by det **A** may be associated with every square matrix **A**. If **A** is a $p \times p$ matrix with (i, j) element a_{ij}, its determinant may be defined by the formula

$$\det \mathbf{A} = \sum \pm a_{1j(1)} a_{2j(2)} \dots a_{pj(p)}, \tag{3.5.1}$$

where summation is over the $p!$ permutations $j(1), j(2), \dots, j(p)$ of the integers $1, 2, \dots, p$ and the signs + and − are used depending on whether an even or odd number of interchanges of pairs is required to modify the permutation $1, 2, \dots, p$ into $j(1), j(2), \dots, j(p)$.

A few of the basic properties of determinants will be given without proof. If **A** is a triangular matrix, i.e., either $a_{ij} = 0$ for all $i > j$ or $a_{ij} = 0$ for all $i < j$, then det **A** is given by the product of the diagonal elements, i.e.,

$$\det \mathbf{A} = \prod_{i=1}^{p} a_{ii}. \tag{3.5.2}$$

If **A** and **B** are both $p \times p$ matrices, then

$$\det \mathbf{AB} = \det \mathbf{A} \times \det \mathbf{B}. \tag{3.5.3}$$

For any nonsingular matrix **A**

$$\det \mathbf{A}^{-1} = 1/\det \mathbf{A}, \tag{3.5.4}$$

while **A** is nonsingular if and only if det $\mathbf{A} \neq 0$. For any orthogonal matrix **G**,

$$\det \mathbf{G} = \pm 1. \tag{3.5.5}$$

The concept of r-dimensional volume in p-dimensional Euclidean space generalizes the concept of length, which is volume in the case $r = 1$. Two parallel line segments have a ratio of lengths which is affinely determined, and they have actual lengths in Euclidean space whose ratio coincides with the affinely determined ratio of lengths. Similarly, it is possible to develop a theory of r-dimensional volumes whereby regions of parallel r-dimensional hyperplanes have affinely determined ratios of r-dimensional volumes and have consistent actual volumes when the space is regarded as Euclidean. To derive this theory would be to go too far afield into areas of measure and integration, so only a few facts will be given with some heuristic justification.

A set of r linearly independent points $W_1, W_2, \dots, W_r$ determines the r-dimensional parallelotope consisting of the points $\sum_1^r c_i W_i$ where $0 \leq c_i \leq 1$ for $i = 1, 2, \dots, r$. Suppose that $U_1, U_2, \dots, U_r$ is an orthonormal set spanning the same subspace as $W_1, W_2, \dots, W_r$ and that $\mathbf{W} = [W_1, W_2, \dots, W_r]' = \mathbf{DU} = \mathbf{D}[U_1, U_2, \dots, U_r]'$ for some $r \times r$ matrix **D**. Then it can be shown (cf. Sommerville, 1958) that the volume of the parallelotope is given by $|\det \mathbf{D}|$. Thus the square of the volume is given by det **Q** where $\mathbf{Q} = \mathbf{DD}'$ is the inner product matrix of $W_1, W_2, \dots, W_r$. The role of this formula as a generalization of the familiar "area = base × height" rule for a parallelogram will be pointed out in Section 4.1.

An r-dimensional unit sphere consists of the set of points $\sum_1^r \alpha_i U_i$ such that

$$\sum_{i=1}^{r} \alpha_i^2 \leq 1 \tag{3.5.6}$$

where $U_1, U_2, \ldots, U_r$ is an orthonormal set. By ordinary multiple integration the volume of the region (3.5.6) is shown in many calculus books to be

$$K_r = \frac{\pi^{r/2}}{\Gamma(r/2 + 1)}, \tag{3.5.7}$$

where $\Gamma(\ldots)$ denotes the gamma function given by $\Gamma(m + 1) = m!$ and $\sqrt{\pi}(1/2)(3/2)\ldots([2m - 1]/2)$ for $m = 0, 1, 2, \ldots$ The integration for a general ellipsoid is not essentially more difficult and may be facilitated by a special choice of $U_1, U_2, \ldots, U_r$ which are orthonormal not only for the given inner product of the Euclidean space $\mathscr{E}$ but are also orthogonal for the inner product defined by the general ellipsoid. This amounts to locating the principal axes of the ellipsoid, as discussed in Section 5.2.

A more heuristic argument will be used to derive an expression for the volume of a general r-dimensional ellipsoid. Such an ellipsoid may be specified by a set of conjugate axes $\varnothing W_1, \varnothing W_2, \ldots, \varnothing W_r$ where $W_1, W_2, \ldots, W_r$ are any set of linearly independent vectors. This ellipsoid is conjugately contained in the parallelotope of points $\sum_1^r c_i W_i$ where $-1 \leq c_i \leq 1$ for $i = 1, 2, \ldots, r$. This parallelotope is twice as long in every dimension as the parallelotope considered above and so has volume $2^r[\det \mathbf{Q}]^{1/2}$ where $\mathbf{Q}$ is the inner product matrix of $W_1, W_2, \ldots, W_r$. At the same time, the ratio of the volume of the ellipsoid to the volume of the parallelotope is known to be $K_r/2^r$, since the ratio is affinely invariant and therefore the same as in the special case where W_1, $W_2, \ldots, W_r$ form an orthonormal set. Thus the volume of the ellipsoid is

$$K_r[\det \mathbf{Q}]^{1/2}, \tag{3.5.8}$$

where K_r is defined in (3.5.7).

It may be helpful in interpreting (3.5.8) to express the ellipsoid in terms of an orthonormal set $\mathbf{U}$. The point $\boldsymbol{\alpha}\mathbf{U} = \boldsymbol{\beta}\mathbf{W}$ lies in the ellipsoid if $\boldsymbol{\beta}\boldsymbol{\beta}' \leq 1$. But $\mathbf{W} = \mathbf{D}\mathbf{U}$ where $\mathbf{D}\mathbf{D}' = \mathbf{Q}$ so that the desired definition of the ellipsoid in $\mathbf{U}$ coordinates is

$$\boldsymbol{\alpha}\mathbf{Q}^{-1}\boldsymbol{\alpha}' \leq 1. \tag{3.5.9}$$

3.6 SEMI-DEFINITE INNER PRODUCTS

The class of inner products over a vector space $\mathscr{E}$ may be widened by relaxing the axiom (3.1.3) to

$$(U, U) \geq 0 \qquad \text{for all } U \text{ in } \mathscr{E}. \tag{3.6.1}$$

The additional inner products permitted by this relaxation will be called *semi-definite* while the labels *proper* or *definite* will be used to distinguish the original class. The term *wide sense inner product* will be used to cover both types. The general theory of semi-definite inner products is easily derived once the theory of proper inner products is known.

A wide sense inner product is semi-definite if and only if there exists a $U \neq \emptyset$ in $\mathscr{E}$ such that $(U, U) = 0$. From (3.1.1) and (3.1.2) it follows that the set of vectors such that $(U, U) = 0$ forms a subspace $\mathscr{U}$ of $\mathscr{E}$. A wide sense inner product is semi-definite if and only if its associated $\mathscr{U}$ has dimension greater than zero. Defining the *rank* of an inner product to be $p - \dim(\mathscr{U})$, it follows that a proper inner product has rank p while a semi-definite inner product has rank f, satisfying $0 \leq f \leq p - 1$.

Any vector U in $\mathscr{U}$ has the following properties:

$$(U, V) = 0 \qquad \text{for all } V \text{ in } \mathscr{E}, \tag{3.6.2}$$

and

$$(V + U, V + U) = (V, V) \qquad \text{for all } V \text{ in } \mathscr{E}. \tag{3.6.3}$$

Conversely, if (3.6.3) holds for a given U, then U is in $\mathscr{U}$. Thus, $\mathscr{U}$ may be characterized as that subspace whose elements do not affect the norm when added to any vector.

Suppose that $\mathscr{V}$ is any f-dimensional subspace complementary to $\mathscr{U}$. Clearly, if the inner product is considered only over $\mathscr{V}$, it is no longer semi-definite (although still of rank f). Furthermore, to specify a semi-definite inner product completely, one need only specify it on any $\mathscr{V}$ complementary to $\mathscr{U}$. For, if W_1 and W_2 are any vectors in $\mathscr{E}$ and $W_1 = V_1 + U_1$ and $W_2 = V_2 + U_2$ where V_1 and V_2 are in $\mathscr{V}$ and U_1 and U_2 are in $\mathscr{U}$, then from (3.6.2)

$$(W_1, W_2) = (V_1, V_2). \tag{3.6.4}$$

Thus the structure of semi-definite inner products as well as their means of construction has been made clear.

In geometric terms, a semi-definite inner product may be thought of in relation to the operation of projection along the family of $(p - f)$-dimensional hyperplanes parallel to $\mathscr{U}$ into the f-dimensional hyperplane $\mathscr{V}$. All those points which project into the same point in $\mathscr{V}$ are indistinguishable in relation to the semi-definite inner product, i.e., lie at distance zero from one another. The ellipsoid of a semi-definite inner product is an ellipsoidal cylinder based on the f-dimensional ellipsoid in the subspace $\mathscr{V}$ and including all of the hyperplanes $V + \mathscr{U}$ where $(V, V) = 1$.

A $p \times p$ symmetric matrix $\mathbf{Q}$ will be called *positive semi-definite symmetric* provided that

$$\boldsymbol{\alpha}\mathbf{Q}\boldsymbol{\alpha}' \geq 0 \tag{3.6.5}$$

for any $1 \times p$ vector $\boldsymbol{\alpha}$ with equality holding in (3.6.5) for some $\boldsymbol{\alpha} \neq \mathbf{0}$. If such a $\mathbf{Q}$ is used to define an inner product over a vector space $\mathscr{E}$ relative to a basis $\mathbf{V}$ of $\mathscr{E}$, then the resulting inner product is semi-definite, and conversely any inner product matrix for a semi-definite inner product is a positive semi-definite symmetric matrix. It will now be shown that a semi-definite inner product and its inner product matrix relative to any basis must have the same rank. Suppose that a rank f inner product has the inner product matrix $\mathbf{Q}$ relative to a basis $\mathbf{V}$ of $\mathscr{E}$. Suppose that as above $\mathscr{U}$ is the $(p - f)$-dimensional subspace of vectors with zero norm and that $\mathscr{V}$ is any f-dimensional subspace complementary to $\mathscr{U}$. By the process of Chapter 4 there may be found an orthonormal basis $\mathbf{U}_1$ of $\mathscr{V}$. This basis $\mathbf{U}_1$ of $\mathscr{V}$ together with any basis $\mathbf{U}_2$ of $\mathscr{U}$ determines a basis

$$\mathbf{U} = \begin{bmatrix} \mathbf{U}_1 \\ \mathbf{U}_2 \end{bmatrix} \tag{3.6.6}$$

of $\mathscr{E}$ whose inner product matrix $\mathbf{I}_f$ is a $p \times p$ matrix whose first f diagonal elements are unity and whose remaining elements are all zero. If $\mathbf{V} = \mathbf{DU}$, then

$$\mathbf{Q} = \mathbf{D}\mathbf{I}_f\mathbf{D}', \tag{3.6.7}$$

which, since $\mathbf{D}$ has rank p, clearly has rank f.

Incidentally, from (2.6.10) and (2.6.11) a pseudoinverse $\dot{\mathbf{Q}}$ of $\mathbf{Q}$ is given by

$$\dot{\mathbf{Q}} = \mathbf{C}'\mathbf{I}_f\mathbf{C}, \tag{3.6.8}$$

where $\mathbf{C} = \mathbf{D}^{-1}$. Note further that if $\mathbf{D}_1$ denotes the $p \times f$ matrix consisting of the first f columns of $\mathbf{D}$ and $\mathbf{C}_1$ is an $f \times p$ matrix consisting of the first f rows of $\mathbf{C}$, then (3.6.7) and (3.6.8) may be written

$$\mathbf{Q} = \mathbf{D}_1\mathbf{D}_1' \tag{3.6.9}$$

and

$$\dot{\mathbf{Q}} = \mathbf{C}_1'\mathbf{C}_1, \tag{3.6.10}$$

where $\mathbf{C}_1$ is a pseudoinverse of $\mathbf{D}_1$.

As an illustration of the concept of a wide sense inner product, consider a linear transformation A from a vector space $\mathscr{E}$ to a vector space $\mathscr{E}^*$. Curiously enough, A provides a very simple mechanism for carrying an inner product in the reverse direction from $\mathscr{E}^*$ to $\mathscr{E}$. For if π^* is a wide sense inner product defined over $\mathscr{E}^*$ with $(U^*, V^*)^*$ denoting the corresponding value for U^* and V^* in $\mathscr{E}^*$, then

$$(U, V) = (\mathsf{A}U, \mathsf{A}V)^* \tag{3.6.11}$$

for each U and V in $\mathscr{E}$ defines a wide sense inner product over π. The subspace $\mathscr{U}$ of $\mathscr{E}$ consisting of vectors with zero norm according to π may be characterized as that set of vectors in $\mathscr{E}$ which map under A into the subspace U^* of $\mathscr{E}^*$ whose vectors have zero norm according to π^*. In particular, if π^* is a proper inner product, then $\mathscr{U}$ is determined by A alone to be the subspace of $\mathscr{E}$ which maps into the origin in $\mathscr{E}^*$.

3.7 EXERCISES

3.1.1 Derive the formulas (3.1.4), (3.1.5), and (3.1.6).

3.1.2 Check that the inner product defined by (3.1.8) satisfies the axioms.

3.1.3 Show that the covariance function over variable-space defined in Section 1.3 satisfies the axioms for an inner product function.

3.1.4 Suppose that $U_1, U_2, \ldots, U_r$ are mutually orthogonal. Show that $\sum_1^r c_i U_i$ has norm $[\sum_1^r c_i^2 (U_i, U_i)]^{1/2}$ and that the pair $\sum_1^r c_i U_i$ and $\sum_1^r d_i U_i$ has inner product $\sum_1^r c_i d_i (U_i, U_i)$.

3.1.5 Construct a p-variate sample of size n which has the covariance matrix $\mathbf{I}$.

3.1.6 Show that the sum of two inner product functions is always an inner product function, but that the same is not always true of differences.

3.1.7 Show that any set of mutually orthogonal vectors, excluding $\emptyset$, is linearly independent.

3.1.8 Suppose that $\mathscr{U}$ is a subspace of a Euclidean space $\mathscr{E}$. Show that the set of all V orthogonal to every U in $\mathscr{U}$ forms a subspace $\mathscr{V}$ of $\mathscr{E}$. Show that $\emptyset$ is the only element common to both $\mathscr{U}$ and $\mathscr{V}$.

3.1.9 Suppose that $\mathscr{U}$ is a subspace of a Euclidean space $\mathscr{E}$. Show that if V in $\mathscr{E}$ can be written $V = V_1 + V_2$ with V_1 in $\mathscr{U}$ and V_2 orthogonal to $\mathscr{U}$, then this decomposition is unique.

3.2.1 Consider an arbitrary triangle in a two-dimensional vector space $\mathscr{E}$. Show that there is a unique inner product over $\mathscr{E}$ such that the triangle is equilateral with sides of unit length.

3.2.2 Derive the Pythagoras theorem in p-dimensional Euclidean space, i.e., show that the squared length of the hypotenuse of a right-angled triangle is equal to the sum of the squared lengths of the other two sides.

3.2.3 Suppose that $V_1, V_2, \ldots, V_p$ is a basis of an ordinary vector space, and suppose that A is a given point in this space. In Exercise 2.1.4 it was shown that the same set of elements may be regarded as a different vector space with origin A and basis $A + V_1$, $A + V_2, \ldots, A + V_p$. Either of these vector spaces may be made into Euclidean vector spaces by regarding the basis $V_1, V_2, \ldots, V_p$, in one case, or the basis $A + V_1$, $A + V_2, \ldots, A + V_p$, in the other case, as an orthonormal basis. Show that the concepts of length of a line segment and angle between two line segments are the same for these different Euclidean vector spaces, regardless of the choice of A. That is, these concepts may be regarded as belonging to Euclidean geometry proper, where no special origin is singled out.

3.2.4 Suppose that UV and U_1V_1 are parallel line segments in an affine space whose affine ratio of lengths is α. Show that this concept of length is consistent with the definition of length in Euclidean space, i.e., show that for any choice of an inner product over the affine space the ratio $(U - V, U - V)/(U_1 - V_1, U_1 - V_1)$ is α^2.

3.2.5 Give a definition of the angle between a line and a hyperplane of dimension r.

3.2.6 Show that the intersection of an ellipsoid with a hyperplane is either empty or is an ellipsoid in the hyperplane.

3.3.1 Show that the operation of orthogonal projection into a given hyperplane requires only the structure of Euclidean geometry, i.e., is independent of the choice of an origin.

3.3.2 Suppose that V is restricted to lie in a hyperplane $U + \mathscr{U}$ of a Euclidean space $\mathscr{E}$. How should V be chosen to minimize (V, V)?

3.4.1 Show that the sum of two positive definite symmetric matrices is itself positive definite symmetric.

3.4.2 Suppose that $\beta_1 V_1 + \beta_2 V_2 + \cdots + \beta_r V_r$ is the orthogonal projection of $\alpha_1 V_1 + \alpha_2 V_2 + \cdots + \alpha_p V_p$ into the subspace spanned by $V_1, V_2, \ldots, V_r$, where the inner product matrix is $\mathbf{Q}$ relative to $\mathbf{V}$. Write down a set of r linear equations which must be satisfied by $\beta_1, \beta_2, \ldots, \beta_r$.

3.4.3 Show that every $p \times p$ positive definite symmetric matrix has rank p.

3.4.4 Assuming that an orthonormal basis always exists, show that any positive definite symmetric matrix $\mathbf{Q}$ may be represented in the form

$$\mathbf{Q} = \mathbf{D}\mathbf{D}'$$

for some $p \times p$ matrix $\mathbf{D}$ of rank p. Deduce that any pair $\mathbf{Q}, \mathbf{Q}^*$ of positive definite symmetric matrices stand in the relation

$$\mathbf{Q}^* = \mathbf{A}\mathbf{Q}\mathbf{A}'$$

for some $p \times p$ matrix $\mathbf{A}$ of rank p.

3.4.5 Show that if $\mathbf{Q}$ and $\mathbf{A}$ are $p \times p$ rank p matrices where $\mathbf{Q}$ is positive definite symmetric, then $\mathbf{A}\mathbf{Q}\mathbf{A}'$ is positive definite symmetric. (In particular, $\mathbf{A}\mathbf{A}'$ is positive definite symmetric.)

3.4.6 Suppose that $\boldsymbol{\alpha}_0$ is a point on the surface of the ellipsoid defined by (3.4.1). Show that the set of points $\boldsymbol{\alpha}$ on the tangent plane to the ellipsoid at $\boldsymbol{\alpha}_0$ is characterized by the linear equation

$$\boldsymbol{\alpha}\mathbf{Q}\boldsymbol{\alpha}_0' = 1.$$

3.4.7 Suppose that $\mathbf{Q}$ is a positive definite symmetric matrix and $\mathbf{C}_1$ is any $p \times p$ matrix such that $\mathbf{C}_1\mathbf{Q}\mathbf{C}_1' = \mathbf{I}$. Show that $\mathbf{C}$ is a $p \times p$ matrix satisfying $\mathbf{C}\mathbf{Q}\mathbf{C}' = \mathbf{I}$ if and only if $\mathbf{C} = \mathbf{G}\mathbf{C}_1$ for some orthogonal matrix $\mathbf{G}$.

3.4.8 Suppose that $\mathbf{x}$ is a given $1 \times p$ vector and that $\mathbf{Q}$ is a given positive definite symmetric matrix. Show that $\boldsymbol{\alpha}\mathbf{Q}\boldsymbol{\alpha}'$ is minimized over choices of $\boldsymbol{\alpha}$ subject to $\boldsymbol{\alpha}\mathbf{x}' = 1$ by choosing

$$\boldsymbol{\alpha} = d^{-2}\mathbf{x}\mathbf{Q}^{-1},$$

where

$$d^2 = \mathbf{x}\mathbf{Q}^{-1}\mathbf{x}',$$

and that the resulting minimum is d^{-2}.

3.4.9 Suppose that $\mathbf{U}$ and $\mathbf{W}$ are orthonormal bases of Euclidean spaces $\mathscr{E}$ and $\mathscr{F}$, respectively. Suppose that a linear transformation A from $\mathscr{E}$ to $\mathscr{F}$ is defined by

$$\mathbf{U} \to \mathbf{A}\mathbf{W}$$

and suppose that a linear transformation A' from $\mathscr{F}$ to $\mathscr{E}$ is defined by

$$\mathbf{W} \to \mathbf{A}'\mathbf{U}.$$

Show that the definition of A' does not depend on the particular orthonormal bases chosen, and so is a coordinate-free Euclidean concept.

3.4.10 Suppose that $\mathscr{E}$ is a Euclidean space with an inner product denoted by π^*. Suppose that π denotes a new inner product defined over $\mathscr{E}$, and that $\mathbf{Q}$ denotes the inner product matrix of the new inner product relative to a basis $\mathbf{V}$ which is orthonormal relative to the original inner product. Show that the linear transformation

$$\mathbf{V} \rightarrow \mathbf{QV}$$

is coordinate-free, i.e., does not depend on the particular choice of a π^*-orthonormal $\mathbf{V}$.

3.4.11 The concept of a pseudoinverse B of a given linear transformation A from $\mathscr{E}$ to $\mathscr{F}$ was defined in Section 2.6. When $\mathscr{E}$ and $\mathscr{F}$ are Euclidean spaces it is natural to choose one such pseudoinverse and call it *the* pseudoinverse. Recall that B was defined in terms of subspaces $\mathscr{U}^*$ and $\mathscr{V}^*$ complementary to $\mathscr{U}$ and $\mathscr{V}$ in $\mathscr{E}$ and $\mathscr{F}$, respectively, where $\mathscr{U}$ and $\mathscr{V}$ are determined by A. *The pseudoinverse* B *of* A may be defined as the special case where $\mathscr{U}^*$ and $\mathscr{V}^*$ are chosen to be *the* orthogonal complements of $\mathscr{U}$ and $\mathscr{V}$, respectively. Correspondingly, given any $p \times q$ matrix $\mathbf{A}$, the pseudoinverse $\mathbf{B}$ of $\mathbf{A}$ may be defined by asserting that

$$\mathbf{W} \rightarrow \mathbf{BU}$$

is *the* pseudoinverse of

$$\mathbf{U} \rightarrow \mathbf{AW},$$

where $\mathbf{U}$ and $\mathbf{W}$ are orthonormal bases of $\mathscr{E}$ and $\mathscr{F}$, respectively. Show that $\mathbf{B}$ is the pseudoinverse of $\mathbf{A}$ if and only if it can be represented in the form (2.6.10) and (2.6.11) with $\mathbf{G}$ and $\mathbf{H}$ both orthogonal matrices.

3.4.12 Show that $\mathbf{G} = \mathbf{G}' = \mathbf{G}^{-1}$ for an elementary orthogonal matrix $\mathbf{G}$. What is the geometric explanation for this?

3.5.1 Show that the volume of the simplex $\sum_1^r c_i W_i$ where $c_i \geq 0$ for $i = 1, 2, \ldots, r$ and $\sum_1^r c_i \leq 1$ is $1/r!$ times the volume of the parallelotope $\sum_1^r c_i W_i$ where $0 \leq c_i \leq 1$ for $i = 1, 2, \ldots, r$.

3.6.1 Derive the formulas (3.6.2) and (3.6.3).

3.6.2 Make a drawing of the ellipsoid of an inner product when $p = 3$ and $f = 2$.

3.6.3 Show that Equation (3.1.8) may be interpreted by saying that an inner product of rank p may be expressed as a sum of p inner products each of rank 1. Show that the sum of p arbitrary inner products may be an inner product of any rank from 1 to p.

3.6.4 Suppose that $\mathscr{U}$, $\mathscr{V}$, and $\mathbf{V}$ are as defined in the discussion preceding (3.6.7). Show that (3.6.8) defines *the* pseudoinverse of $\mathbf{Q}$ if $\mathscr{V}$ is the orthogonal complement of $\mathscr{U}$ according to the inner product which takes $\mathbf{V}$ to be orthonormal (cf. Exercises 3.4.10 and 3.4.11).

3.6.5 Suppose that $\mathscr{V}_1$ is any subspace of $\mathscr{E}$ such that all non-$\emptyset$ vectors in $\mathscr{V}_1$ have nonzero norm. Show that whatever the rank of the inner product, there is a unique decomposition of any vector V in $\mathscr{E}$ into a component in $\mathscr{V}_1$ and a component orthogonal to $\mathscr{V}_1$. (Assume, of course, the same result for the case of a full rank inner product.)

3.6.6 Show that if (3.6.9) is satisfied for any two different $p \times f$ matrices $\mathbf{D}_1$ and $\mathbf{D}_1^*$, then $\mathbf{D}_1 = \mathbf{D}_1^* \mathbf{G}_{11}$ for some $f \times f$ orthogonal matrix $\mathbf{G}_{11}$. [*Hint:* express the desired relations first in terms of a basis **U** with inner product matrix $\mathbf{I}_f$ rather than in terms of **V** with inner product matrix **Q**.]

3.6.7 Suppose that A denotes a linear transformation of rank r from a p-dimensional vector space $\mathscr{E}$ to a q-dimensional vector space $\mathscr{E}^*$. Show that $(\mathsf{A}U, \mathsf{A}V)^*$ defines a rank r inner product over $\mathscr{E}$ if $(U^*, V^*)^*$ denotes a rank q inner product over $\mathscr{E}^*$. What is the rank of the induced inner product over $\mathscr{E}$ if the given inner product over $\mathscr{E}^*$ has rank $f < q$?

CHAPTER 4

SUCCESSIVE ORTHOGONALIZATION AND RELATED THEORY

4.1 THE PROCESS OF SUCCESSIVE ORTHOGONALIZATION

This chapter defines and explores a tool of great importance for working with Euclidean spaces, both for deriving mathematical theory and for carrying out computations with numerical data. Essentially, it is a process for using an ordered set of vectors $U_1, U_2, \ldots, U_s$ to produce a set of mutually orthogonal vectors.

Consider a set of vectors $U_1, U_2, \ldots, U_s$ in a Euclidean space $\mathscr{E}$ of dimension p. More general theory is outlined in Section 4.4, but here for simplicity it will be assumed that $U_1, U_2, \ldots, U_s$ are linearly independent and that the inner product over $\mathscr{E}$ has full rank p. Often $s = p$ in applications so that $U_1, U_2, \ldots, U_s$ is a basis of $\mathscr{E}$. From $U_1, U_2, \ldots, U_s$ *define in succession the set of vectors* $U_1^*, U_2^*, \ldots, U_s^*$ *as follows*:

$$
\begin{aligned}
U_1^* &= U_1 \\
U_2^* &= U_2 - \frac{(U_2, U_1^*)}{(U_1^*, U_1^*)} U_1^* \\
&\cdot \\
&\cdot \\
&\cdot \\
U_r^* &= U_r - \sum_{j=1}^{r-1} \frac{(U_r, U_j^*)}{(U_j^*, U_j^*)} U_j^* \qquad (4.1.1) \\
&\cdot \\
&\cdot \\
&\cdot \\
U_s^* &= U_s - \sum_{j=1}^{s-1} \frac{(U_s, U_j^*)}{(U_j^*, U_j^*)} U_j^*.
\end{aligned}
$$

This process of producing $U_1^*, U_2^*, \ldots, U_s^*$ from the ordered set $U_1, U_2, \ldots, U_s$ will be called the *process of successive orthogonalization*. To justify this terminology, it will be proved in the next paragraph that $U_1^*, U_2^*, \ldots, U_s^*$ are mutually orthogonal. In passing, note that the process of successive orthogonalization of $U_1, U_2, \ldots, U_s$ includes the process of successive orthogonalization of $U_1, U_2, \ldots, U_t$ for $t = 1, 2, \ldots, s$ and that the U_j^* produced by these processes, for a given j, are identical.

An inductive proof that $U_1^*, U_2^*, \ldots, U_s^*$ are mutually orthogonal may be based on the following useful theorem: *if $U_1^*, U_2^*, \ldots, U_{r-1}^*$ form any set of $r - 1$ mutually orthogonal vectors, V is any vector, and*

$$\dot{V} = \sum_{j=1}^{r-1} \frac{(V, U_j^*)}{(U_j^*, U_j^*)} U_j^*, \tag{4.1.2}$$

then $V - \dot{V}$ is orthogonal to each of $U_1^*, U_2^*, \ldots, U_{r-1}^*$ and therefore to the subspace spanned by $U_1^*, U_2^*, \ldots, U_{r-1}^*$.

The theorem follows from the direct calculation that

$$\begin{aligned}(V - \dot{V}, U_i^*) &= (V, U_i^*) - (\dot{V}, U_i^*) \\ &= (V, U_i^*) - \sum_{j=1}^{r-1} \frac{(V, U_j^*)}{(U_j^*, U_j^*)} (U_j^*, U_i^*) \\ &= (V, U_i^*) - \frac{(V, U_i^*)}{(U_i^*, U_i^*)} (U_i^*, U_i^*) \\ &= 0,\end{aligned} \tag{4.1.3}$$

for $i = 1, 2, \ldots, r - 1$. The theorem may be applied $s - 1$ times in succession where V is chosen to be $U_2, U_3, \ldots, U_s$ and $r - 1$ is chosen to be $1, 2, \ldots, s - 1$, respectively. The first application of the theorem shows that U_2^* is orthogonal to U_1^*. The second application shows that, assuming U_2^* and U_1^* to be orthogonal, U_3^* is orthogonal to U_1^* and U_2^*. In general, the $(r - 1)$st application shows that, assuming $U_1^*, U_2^*, \ldots, U_{r-1}^*$ to be mutually orthogonal, $U_1^*, U_2^*, \ldots, U_r^*$ are mutually orthogonal. Thus, from $s - 1$ applications, it follows that $U_1^*, U_2^*, \ldots, U_s^*$ are mutually orthogonal, as required.

An important detail was neglected in the preceding. If $(U_r^*, U_r^*) = 0$ for some r, then the definition (4.1.1) breaks down for $t \geq r$. Actually, if this should occur, then the terms involving such U_r^* may simply be omitted from the right hand side of (4.1.1) to provide a modified and foolproof definition of $U_1^*, U_2^*, \ldots, U_s^*$. However, this difficulty does not arise when the inner product has full rank and $U_1, U_2, \ldots, U_s$ are linearly independent. For under these conditions $(U_r^*, U_r^*) = 0$ implies that $U_r^* = \emptyset$, and this together with the modified (4.1.1) would mean that $U_1, U_2, \ldots, U_s$ could be expressed in terms of fewer than s nonzero U_j^* which would imply linear dependence among $U_1, U_2, \ldots, U_s$.

The process of successive orthogonalization provides proofs for several assertions left unproved in Chapter 3. First, it shows that every Euclidean space possesses an orthogonal basis, for the $U_1^*, U_2^*, \ldots, U_p^*$ constructed as above from any basis $U_1, U_2, \ldots, U_p$ constitute an orthogonal basis. Further, one may define

$$U_j^{**} = [(U_j^*, U_j^*)^{-1/2}]U_j^* \tag{4.1.4}$$

for $j = 1, 2, \ldots, p$ so that $U_1^{**}, U_2^{**}, \ldots, U_p^{**}$ constitute an orthonormal basis. Finally, in connection with the definition of an orthogonal projection in Section 3.3 it is required to show that the subspace $\mathscr{V}$ of vectors orthogonal to a given subspace $\mathscr{U}$ is complementary to $\mathscr{U}$, i.e., to show that the notion of orthogonal complement is properly defined. To prove this, suppose that $\mathscr{U}$ has dimension s, that $U_1, U_2, \ldots, U_s$ is a basis of $\mathscr{U}$, and that $U_1, U_2, \ldots, U_p$ is a basis of the whole space $\mathscr{E}$ which includes the basis $U_1, U_2, \ldots, U_s$ of $\mathscr{U}$. From these, construct the orthogonal basis $U_1^*, U_2^*, \ldots, U_p^*$ of $\mathscr{E}$ as in (4.1.1). It is clear from the construction that $U_1^*, U_2^*, \ldots, U_s^*$ is an orthogonal basis of $\mathscr{U}$. Also $U_{s+1}^*, U_{s+2}^*, \ldots, U_p^*$ clearly span a $(p - s)$-dimensional space both orthogonal to and complementary to $\mathscr{U}$. It remains only to show that any V orthogonal to $\mathscr{U}$ lies in the subspace spanned by $U_{s+1}^*, U_{s+2}^*, \ldots, U_p^*$. Certainly V may be written $V = \alpha_1^* U_1^* + \alpha_2^* U_2^* + \cdots + \alpha_p^* U_p^*$. But, taking inner products of each side with U_i^* yields $\alpha_1^* = 0$ for $i = 1, 2, \ldots, s$, as required.

The operation of orthogonal projection into a subspace $\mathscr{U}$ is especially easy to carry out when an orthogonal basis of $\mathscr{U}$ is available. For, suppose that $U_1^*, U_2^*, \ldots, U_s^*$ is an orthogonal basis of $\mathscr{U}$ and that $U_{s+1}^*, U_{s+2}^*, \ldots, U_p^*$ is an orthogonal basis of the orthogonal complement $\mathscr{V}$ of $\mathscr{U}$. Then any vector W may be written

$$W = \sum_{i=1}^{p} \frac{(W, U_i^*)}{(U_i^*, U_i^*)} U_i^* = \dot{W} + W^*, \tag{4.1.5}$$

where

$$\dot{W} = \sum_{i=1}^{s} \frac{(W, U_i^*)}{(U_i^*, U_i^*)} U_i^* \tag{4.1.6}$$

is the orthogonal projection of W into $\mathscr{U}$ or the component of W along $\mathscr{U}$, and

$$W^* = \sum_{i=s+1}^{p} \frac{(W, U_i^*)}{(U_i^*, U_i^*)} U_i^* \tag{4.1.7}$$

is the component of W orthogonal to $\mathscr{U}$. The proofs of these assertions are left to the reader. Note that the coordinates of any vector relative to an orthogonal basis are very simply expressed in terms of inner products, and that each coordinate multiplied by its associated basis vector simply gives the orthogonal projection of W into the one-dimensional subspace spanned by that basis vector.

The stepwise construction (4.1.1) of successive orthogonalization is a very important computational device, and is explored further from the computational viewpoint in Section 4.3. For pure mathematics, the ability to construct an orthonormal basis for an arbitrary inner product has led to the derivation of important theory such as the theorem: *given any inner product defined on a* *vector space $\mathscr{E}$ there exists a basis such that the inner product is defined by formula* (3.1.8) *in terms of that basis, and furthermore such a basis can be constructed from an arbitrary basis in a finite number of steps.*

The theorem on the existence of an orthonormal basis corresponds to the geometric theorem that *every ellipsoid has a set of p conjugate axes.* In matrix algebra, this existence theorem corresponds to the following famous result: *if $\mathbf{Q}$ is any positive definite symmetric matrix, then there exists a nonsingular $p \times p$ matrix $\mathbf{C}$ such that*

$$\mathbf{CQC}' = \mathbf{I}. \tag{4.1.8}$$

To see this, suppose that $\mathbf{Q}$ is the inner product matrix of a basis $\mathbf{V}$. Then there exists a basis $\mathbf{U} = \mathbf{CV}$ with inner product matrix $\mathbf{I}$ and (4.1.8) is simply an application of (3.4.4).

It should be noted that the result of successive orthogonalization depends in general on the order in which the vectors are presented. Thus, with p vectors $U_1, U_2, \ldots, U_p$ there are in general $p!$ different orders of possible successive orthogonalization. Although the theory is always presented using a given order, the reader should keep in mind that in applications an order different from an arbitrary given order may often be appropriate.

4.2 SOME MATRIX THEORY RELATED TO SUCCESSIVE ORTHOGONALIZATION

Suppose that $\mathbf{Q}$ is a $p \times p$ positive definite symmetric matrix. By the device of regarding $\mathbf{Q}$ to be the inner product matrix relative to some basis of a vector space $\mathscr{E}$ and then applying successive orthogonalization to this basis, one is led to a wealth of identities all based on the elements of $\mathbf{Q}$. To begin, suppose that

$$\mathbf{U} = \begin{bmatrix} U_1 \\ U_2 \\ \cdot \\ \cdot \\ \cdot \\ U_p \end{bmatrix} \quad \text{and} \quad \mathbf{U}^* = \begin{bmatrix} U_1^* \\ U_2^* \\ \cdot \\ \cdot \\ \cdot \\ U_p^* \end{bmatrix} \tag{4.2.1}$$

denote the basis of $\mathscr{E}$ and its orthogonalization defined by (4.1.1) with $r = p$. In matrix notation (4.1.1) may be written

$$\mathbf{U} = \mathbf{BU}^*, \tag{4.2.2}$$

where $\mathbf{B}$ is a $p \times p$ triangular matrix with elements zero above the diagonal and unity along the diagonal. It is clear from (4.1.1) that $\mathbf{B}$ is uniquely determined by the inner product over $\mathscr{E}$ and therefore by $\mathbf{Q}$.

For simplicity of notation, the inverse matrix of $\mathbf{B}$ will be denoted by $\mathbf{A}$, so that

$$\mathbf{U}^* = \mathbf{AU}. \tag{4.2.3}$$

A may be found from **B** by a process of successive substitution to solve the equations (4.1.1) or (4.2.2) for **U*** in terms of **U**, i.e., the first row of (4.1.1) yields the first row of (4.2.3), the second row of (4.2.3) is found by substituting the first row of (4.2.3) into the second row of (4.1.1), the third row of (4.2.3) is found by substituting the already found first two rows of (4.2.3) into the third row of (4.1.1), and so on. It is clear from this process of construction that **A** like **B** is a triangular matrix with elements zero above the diagonal and unity along the diagonal.

A matrix **T** may be defined as the inner product matrix of **U***, where, of course, **T** is a diagonal matrix with diagonal elements (U_s^*, U_s^*) in the (s, s) position for $s = 1, 2, \ldots, p$. It follows from (4.2.2) that

$$\mathbf{Q} = \mathbf{BTB}'. \tag{4.2.4}$$

The inverse of **Q** will be denoted by **P**, and, by inverting both sides of (4.2.4) and replacing $\mathbf{B}^{-1}$ by **A**, it follows that

$$\mathbf{P} = \mathbf{A}'\mathbf{T}^{-1}\mathbf{A}. \tag{4.2.5}$$

The above formulas also yield det **Q** as a by-product. For, since **B** is triangular with diagonal elements unity, det **B** = 1, and hence

$$\begin{aligned} \det \mathbf{Q} &= \det \mathbf{BTB}' \\ &= \det \mathbf{B} \det \mathbf{T} \det \mathbf{B}' \\ &= \det \mathbf{T} \\ &= \prod_{s=1}^{p} (U_s^*, U_s^*). \end{aligned} \tag{4.2.6}$$

As discussed in Section 3.5, det **Q** may be interpreted as the squared volume of the parallelotope generated by the basis $U_1, U_2, \ldots, U_p$. Formula (4.2.6) has special interest in this regard as the generalization to p dimensions of the formula "Area = base × height" for a parallelogram. In fact, the product of the first $p - 1$ terms of (4.2.6) simply gives the square of the $(p - 1)$-dimensional volume of the $(p - 1)$-dimensional parallelotope based on $U_1, U_2, \ldots, U_{p-1}$. This corresponds to the "base." The "height" is given by the component of U_p orthogonal to $U_1, U_2, \ldots, U_{p-1}$, and the squared length of this component is given by the last term of (4.2.6). Thus by repeated application of the "base × height" formula to the parallelotopes spanned by $U_1, U_2, \ldots, U_s$ for $s = 2, 3, \ldots, p$ one achieves an illuminating explanation of formula (4.2.6).

The remainder of this section is devoted to a set of relationships concerning the first s and last $p - s$ elements of **U** and **U***. These will be of use in understanding the computational aspects of successive orthogonalization to be discussed in Section 4.3. For any $p \times 1$ column vector **G**, denote the first s rows by $\mathbf{G}_1$ and the last $p - s$ rows by $\mathbf{G}_2$, so that

$$\mathbf{G} = \begin{bmatrix} \mathbf{G}_1 \\ \mathbf{G}_2 \end{bmatrix}. \tag{4.2.7}$$

Similarly, for a $p \times p$ matrix **K**, write

$$\mathbf{K} = \begin{bmatrix} \mathbf{K}_{11} & \mathbf{K}_{12} \\ \mathbf{K}_{21} & \mathbf{K}_{22} \end{bmatrix}, \tag{4.2.8}$$

where $\mathbf{K}_{11}$, $\mathbf{K}_{12}$, $\mathbf{K}_{21}$, and $\mathbf{K}_{22}$ are $s \times s$, $s \times (p - s)$, $(p - s) \times s$, and $(p - s) \times (p - s)$ matrices, respectively. This notation will be applied in particular to the $p \times 1$ vectors **U** and **U***, and to the $p \times p$ matrices **B**, **A**, **Q**, **P**, and **T**. Note that $\mathbf{A}_{12}$ and $\mathbf{B}_{12}$ consist entirely of zeros, and that $\mathbf{A}_{11}$, $\mathbf{A}_{22}$, $\mathbf{B}_{11}$, and $\mathbf{B}_{22}$ are triangular like **A** and **B**. In addition, the notation $\mathbf{U}_{2.1}$ will be used for the vector of components of $\mathbf{U}_2$ orthogonal to $\mathbf{U}_1$, i.e.,

$$\mathbf{U}_{2.1} = \begin{bmatrix} U_{s+1.12...s} \\ U_{s+2.12...s} \\ \cdot \\ \cdot \\ \cdot \\ U_{p.12...s} \end{bmatrix}, \tag{4.2.9}$$

where $U_{r.12...s}$ denotes the component of U_r orthogonal to the subspace spanned by $U_1, U_2, \ldots, U_s$. Finally, the inner product matrix of $\mathbf{U}_{2.1}$ will be denoted by $\mathbf{Q}_{22.1}$. Observe that the notation of this paragraph assumes a fixed p and s.

One may now write (4.2.2) as

$$\mathbf{U}_1 = \mathbf{B}_{11}\mathbf{U}_1^* \quad \text{and} \quad \mathbf{U}_2 = \mathbf{B}_{21}\mathbf{U}_1^* + \mathbf{B}_{22}\mathbf{U}_2^*, \tag{4.2.10}$$

and (4.2.3) as

$$\mathbf{U}^* = \mathbf{A}_{11}\mathbf{U}_1 \quad \text{and} \quad \mathbf{U}_2^* = \mathbf{A}_{21}\mathbf{U}_1 + \mathbf{A}_{22}\mathbf{U}_2. \tag{4.2.11}$$

By substituting (4.2.10) into (4.2.11), one may express the submatrices of **A** in terms of the submatrices of **B** as

$$\begin{aligned} \mathbf{A}_{11} &= \mathbf{B}_{11}^{-1}, \\ \mathbf{A}_{21} &= -\mathbf{B}_{22}^{-1}\mathbf{B}_{21}\mathbf{B}_{11}^{-1}, \quad \text{and} \\ \mathbf{A}_{22} &= \mathbf{B}_{22}^{-1}. \end{aligned} \tag{4.2.12}$$

Similarly, one has

$$\begin{aligned} \mathbf{B}_{11} &= \mathbf{A}_{11}^{-1}, \\ \mathbf{B}_{21} &= -\mathbf{A}_{22}^{-1}\mathbf{A}_{21}\mathbf{A}_{11}^{-1}, \quad \text{and} \\ \mathbf{B}_{22} &= \mathbf{A}_{22}^{-1}. \end{aligned} \tag{4.2.13}$$

From (4.2.12)

$$\mathbf{A}_{21}\mathbf{A}_{11}^{-1} = -\mathbf{B}_{22}^{-1}\mathbf{B}_{21} = \mathbf{A}_{21}\mathbf{B}_{11} = -\mathbf{A}_{22}\mathbf{B}_{21}, \tag{4.2.14}$$

and from (4.2.13)

$$\mathbf{B}_{21}\mathbf{B}_{11}^{-1} = -\mathbf{A}_{22}^{-1}\mathbf{A}_{21} = \mathbf{B}_{21}\mathbf{A}_{11} = -\mathbf{B}_{22}\mathbf{A}_{21}. \tag{4.2.15}$$

It will be convenient in the sequel to use the special notation $\mathbf{H}_{21}$ *for the matrix expressed by* (4.2.15). Two special properties of $\mathbf{H}_{21}$ are:

i) *the first row of* $\mathbf{H}_{21}$ *is the negative of the first row of* $\mathbf{A}_{21}$

ii) *the last column of* $\mathbf{H}_{21}$ *is the last column of* $\mathbf{B}_{21}$.

These follow easily from the relations $\mathbf{H}_{21} = -\mathbf{B}_{22}\mathbf{A}_{21}$ and $\mathbf{H}_{21} = \mathbf{B}_{21}\mathbf{A}_{11}$, respectively. Property (i) may be generalized by noting from (4.2.10) that

$$\mathbf{U}_{2.1} = \mathbf{B}_{22}\mathbf{U}_2^*, \tag{4.2.16}$$

and thence from (4.2.16) and (4.2.11) that

$$\mathbf{U}_{2.1} = \mathbf{U}_2 - \mathbf{H}_{21}\mathbf{U}_1. \tag{4.2.17}$$

Thus the rows of $\mathbf{H}_{21}$ *determine the linear combinations of* $U_1, U_2, \ldots, U_s$ *which are the components of* $U_{s+1}, U_{s+2}, \ldots, U_p$ *along the subspace spanned by* $U_1, U_2, \ldots, U_s$.

It is of interest to express $\mathbf{Q}_{11}$, $\mathbf{Q}_{21}$, $\mathbf{Q}_{22}$, and $\mathbf{Q}_{22.1}$ in terms of $\mathbf{B}$ and $\mathbf{T}$. From (4.2.10) it follows that

$$\begin{aligned} \mathbf{Q}_{11} &= \mathbf{B}_{11}\mathbf{T}_{11}\mathbf{B}_{11}', \\ \mathbf{Q}_{21} &= \mathbf{B}_{21}\mathbf{T}_{11}\mathbf{B}_{11}', \qquad \text{and} \\ \mathbf{Q}_{22} &= \mathbf{B}_{21}\mathbf{T}_{11}\mathbf{B}_{21}' + \mathbf{B}_{22}\mathbf{T}_{22}\mathbf{B}_{22}'. \end{aligned} \tag{4.2.18}$$

Also, from (4.2.16) it follows that the inner product matrix $\mathbf{Q}_{22.1}$ of $\mathbf{U}_{2.1}$ is given by

$$\mathbf{Q}_{22.1} = \mathbf{B}_{22}\mathbf{T}_{22}\mathbf{B}_{22}'. \tag{4.2.19}$$

From (4.2.19) it is clear that the first and second terms in the expression for $\mathbf{Q}_{22}$ in (4.2.18) represent the contributions to the inner product matrix of $\mathbf{U}_2$ from the components of $\mathbf{U}_2$ along the subspace spanned by $\mathbf{U}_1$, and from the components of $\mathbf{U}_2$ orthogonal to the subspace spanned by $\mathbf{U}_1$, respectively.

Matrix formulas are often seen which contain the products $\mathbf{Q}_{21}\mathbf{Q}_{11}^{-1}$ or $\mathbf{Q}_{21}\mathbf{Q}_{11}^{-1}\mathbf{Q}_{12}$. It will be useful therefore to note the following alternative expressions:

$$\mathbf{Q}_{21}\mathbf{Q}_{11}^{-1} = \mathbf{B}_{21}\mathbf{B}_{11}^{-1} = \mathbf{H}_{21}, \tag{4.2.20}$$

and

$$\mathbf{Q}_{21}\mathbf{Q}_{11}^{-1}\mathbf{Q}_{12} = \mathbf{H}_{21}\mathbf{Q}_{12} = \mathbf{B}_{21}\mathbf{T}_{11}\mathbf{B}_{21}' = \mathbf{Q}_{22} - \mathbf{Q}_{22.1}. \tag{4.2.21}$$

The reader may have noticed a duality between the formulas (4.2.4) and (4.2.5) and between the sets of formulas (4.2.12) and (4.2.13). The nature of this duality will be elaborated in Chapter 6, but it will be useful to give dual formulas here for (4.2.18) and (4.2.19). From (4.2.5), rewritten as

$$\begin{bmatrix} \mathbf{P}_{11} & \mathbf{P}_{12} \\ \mathbf{P}_{21} & \mathbf{P}_{22} \end{bmatrix} = \begin{bmatrix} \mathbf{A}_{11} & \mathbf{0} \\ \mathbf{A}_{21} & \mathbf{A}_{22} \end{bmatrix}' \begin{bmatrix} \mathbf{T}_{11}^{-1} & \mathbf{0} \\ \mathbf{0} & \mathbf{T}_{22}^{-1} \end{bmatrix} \begin{bmatrix} \mathbf{A}_{11} & \mathbf{0} \\ \mathbf{A}_{21} & \mathbf{A}_{22} \end{bmatrix},$$

it follows that

$$\begin{aligned} \mathbf{P}_{11} &= \mathbf{A}_{21}'\mathbf{T}_{22}^{-1}\mathbf{A}_{21} + \mathbf{A}_{11}'\mathbf{T}_{11}^{-1}\mathbf{A}_{11}, \\ \mathbf{P}_{12} &= \mathbf{A}_{21}'\mathbf{T}_{22}^{-1}\mathbf{A}_{22}, \quad \text{and} \\ \mathbf{P}_{22} &= \mathbf{A}_{22}'\mathbf{T}_{22}^{-1}\mathbf{A}_{22}. \end{aligned} \tag{4.2.22}$$

The right side of the last line of (4.2.22) is now seen to be the inverse of the right side of (4.2.19), so that

$$\mathbf{Q}_{22.1} = \mathbf{P}_{22}^{-1}. \tag{4.2.23}$$

Dually, then, one might define

$$\mathbf{P}_{11.2} = \mathbf{Q}_{11}^{-1}, \tag{4.2.24}$$

and by inverting the first line of (4.2.18) find the dual formula of (4.2.19) to be

$$\mathbf{P}_{11.2} = \mathbf{A}_{11}'\mathbf{T}_{11}^{-1}\mathbf{A}_{11}. \tag{4.2.25}$$

Note that the duality here interchanges the roles of **B**, **Q**, and **T** with their transposed inverses, and also replaces the subscripts 1 and 2 with 2 and 1, respectively.

The formulas of this section all have analogues where the orthonormal basis $\mathbf{U}^{**}$ is used in place of $\mathbf{U}^*$. Here

$$\mathbf{U}^* = \mathbf{R}\mathbf{U}^{**}, \tag{4.2.26}$$

where **R** is the $p \times p$ diagonal matrix with diagonal elements $(U_s^*, U_s^*)^{1/2}$. Consequently

$$\mathbf{U} = \mathbf{D}\mathbf{U}^{**} \tag{4.2.27}$$

and

$$\mathbf{U}^{**} = \mathbf{C}\mathbf{U}, \tag{4.2.28}$$

where

$$\mathbf{C} = \mathbf{D}^{-1}, \qquad \mathbf{D} = \mathbf{B}\mathbf{R}, \qquad \text{and} \qquad \mathbf{C} = \mathbf{R}^{-1}\mathbf{A}. \tag{4.2.29}$$

In words, this formula says that **D** is found by multiplying each column of **B** by the corresponding element of **R**, and **C** is found by multiplying each row of **A** by the corresponding element of $\mathbf{R}^{-1}$. Thus, **D** and **C** are triangular like **B** and **A**, but with the diagonal elements of **R** and $\mathbf{R}^{-1}$, respectively. In place of (4.2.4) and (4.2.5), one now has

$$\mathbf{Q} = \mathbf{D}\mathbf{D}' \tag{4.2.30}$$

and

$$\mathbf{P} = \mathbf{C}'\mathbf{C}, \tag{4.2.31}$$

and, in place of (4.2.10) and (4.2.11), one now has

$$\mathbf{U}_1 = \mathbf{D}_{11}\mathbf{U}_1^{**} \qquad \text{and} \qquad \mathbf{U}_2 = \mathbf{D}_{21}\mathbf{U}_1^{**} + \mathbf{D}_{22}\mathbf{U}_2^{**}, \tag{4.2.32}$$

and also

$$\mathbf{U}_1^{**} = \mathbf{C}_{11}\mathbf{U}_1 \qquad \text{and} \qquad \mathbf{U}_2^{**} = \mathbf{C}_{21}\mathbf{U}_1 + \mathbf{C}_{22}\mathbf{U}_2. \tag{4.2.33}$$

The analogues of formulas (4.2.12), (4.2.13), (4.2.14), (4.2.15), (4.2.18), (4.2.19),

(4.2.22), and (4.2.25) are found by replacing **B** with **D**, **A** with **C**, and **T** with **I**. These analogues are left for the reader to write down and check.

4.3 COMPUTATIONAL METHODS RELATED TO SUCCESSIVE ORTHOGONALIZATION

Positive definite or semi-definite symmetric matrices may be computed from multivariate data in many ways, usually in the context of covariance matrices or their inverses. These ways will, of course, be discussed in detail in later chapters. Certain much-used further computations with such matrices are closely related to the process of successive orthogonalization. Beginning from a given **Q**, the computations proceed by stages to produce the matrices which appear in the various identities of Section 4.2. Many of these matrices have important statistical interpretations and it is therefore important to have efficient computing methods suitable for an electronic computer. Besides, these computing methods often have a simplicity and elegance which is not obvious from the definitions and identities of Section 4.2.

Q will denote throughout Section 4.3 a $p \times p$ symmetric positive definite matrix of full rank p.

4.3.1. Elimination procedures. Following the rows of (4.1.1) in order to find $U_2^*, U_3^*, \ldots, U_p^*$ corresponds to computing the rows of **B** in order. Such a direct approach is possible and is presented in Section 4.3.3, but a more convenient and widely used scheme computes the columns of **B** in order. The latter scheme and various natural extensions of it are the subject of Section 4.3.1.

The idea behind elimination procedures is a set of $p - 1$ stages where at stage s all of the terms in U_s^* on the right side of (4.1.1) are subtracted out at once, for $s = 1, 2, \ldots, p - 1$. After s such stages, one has in hand U_1^*, U_2^*, $\ldots$, U_s^* in the first s rows of (4.1.1), $U_{s+1}^* = U_{s+1.12\ldots s}$ in row $s + 1$, and $U_{r.12\ldots s}$ in row r for $r = s + 2, s + 3, \ldots, p$. In geometric language, the procedure uses orthogonal projection to *eliminate* at stage s the components of $U_{s+1}, U_{s+2}, \ldots, U_p$ along U_s^* so that after s stages only the components of each of $U_{s+1}, U_{s+2}, \ldots, U_p$ perpendicular to all of $U_1, U_2, \ldots, U_s$ remain.

The computations will be described in three layers whose complexity increases as more quantities are carried along in the calculations. In the first layer, the main objective is simply to calculate **B** from **Q** by producing the columns of **B** one at a time. It turns out to be convenient to compute simultaneously the inner product matrices $\mathbf{Q}_{22.1}$ of $U_{s+1.12\ldots s}$ $(= U_{s+1}^*)$, $U_{s+2.12\ldots s}$, $\ldots$, $U_{p.12\ldots s}$, for $s = 1, 2, \ldots, p - 1$. Thus, after s stages of the first layer, one has in hand the first s columns of **B**, namely $\mathbf{B}_{11}$ and $\mathbf{B}_{21}$, together with $\mathbf{Q}_{22.1}$.

Consider now how to carry out the computations of stage $s + 1$ of the first layer while having in hand the output of stage s. Suppose that b_{ij} denotes the

(i, j) element of $\mathbf{B}$ and that the elements of $\mathbf{Q}_{22.1}$ are denoted by $q_{ij.12...s}$ for i and $j = s + 1, s + 2, \ldots, p$. Suppose also that the elements of the analogue of $\mathbf{Q}_{22.1}$ with s raised to $s + 1$ are denoted by $q_{ij.12...\overline{s+1}}$ for i and $j = s + 2, s + 3, \ldots, p$.

From (4.1.1)

$$\begin{aligned} b_{i\,\overline{s+1}} &= \frac{(U_i, U^*_{s+1})}{(U^*_{s+1}, U^*_{s+1})} = \frac{(U_{i.12...s}, U^*_{s+1})}{(U^*_{s+1}, U^*_{s+1})} \\ &= \frac{q_{i\,\overline{s+1}.12...s}}{q_{\overline{s+1}\,\overline{s+1}.12...s}} \end{aligned} \tag{4.3.1}$$

for $i = s + 2, s + 3, \ldots, p$. This provides the nontrivial elements of column $s + 1$ of $\mathbf{B}$. The justification of the first step in (4.3.1) is that $U_i - U_{i.12...s}$ consists of components along $U^*_1, U^*_2, \ldots, U^*_s$ which are orthogonal to U^*_{s+1} and therefore $(U_i - U_{i.12...s}, U^*_{s+1}) = 0$ or $(U_i, U^*_{s+1}) = (U_{i.12...s}, U^*_{s+1})$, as required. Similarly

$$\begin{aligned} q_{ij.12...\overline{s+1}} &= (U_{i.12...\overline{s+1}}, U_{j.12..\overline{s+1}}) \\ &= (U_{i.12...s} - b_{i\,\overline{s+1}}U^*_{s+1}, U_{j.12...s} - b_{j\,\overline{s+1}}U^*_{s+1}) \\ &= q_{ij.12...s} - b_{i\,\overline{s+1}}q_{j\,\overline{s+1}.12...s} - b_{j\,\overline{s+1}}q_{i\,\overline{s+1}.12...s} \\ &\qquad + b_{i\,\overline{s+1}}b_{j\,\overline{s+1}}q_{\overline{s+1}\,\overline{s+1}.12...s}. \end{aligned} \tag{4.3.2}$$

From (4.3.1), the last three terms here are equal apart from sign, and thus

$$q_{ij.12...\overline{s+1}} = q_{ij.12...s} - \frac{q_{i\,\overline{s+1}.12...s}\,q_{j\,\overline{s+1}.12...s}}{q_{\overline{s+1}\,\overline{s+1}.12...s}} \tag{4.3.3}$$

or

$$q_{ij.12...\overline{s+1}} = q_{ij.12...s} - b_{i\,\overline{s+1}}q_{j\,\overline{s+1}.12...s}, \tag{4.3.4}$$

for i and $j = s + 2, s + 3, \ldots, p$. Formula (4.3.3) shows how to upstage $\mathbf{Q}_{22.1}$ from s to $s + 1$, but (4.3.4) is computationally more convenient assuming that column $s + 1$ of $\mathbf{B}$ has already been computed from (4.3.1). The calculation indicated by (4.3.3) is often called *pivotal condensation*. This completes the discussion of stage $s + 1$ of the first layer of the elimination procedure.

The second layer has the basic objective of computing $\mathbf{A} = \mathbf{B}^{-1}$ along with $\mathbf{B}$. Recall that $\mathbf{A}$ may be found in stages by solving (4.2.2) to produce (4.2.3) where, at stage s, rows $1, 2, \ldots, s$ of (4.2.3) are substituted into row $s + 1$ of (4.2.2) to produce row $s + 1$ of $\mathbf{A}$. Under the elimination approach, it is more natural at stage s to substitute row s of (4.2.3) into rows $s + 1, s + 2, \ldots, p$ of (4.2.2), i.e., to *eliminate* U^*_s from the right side of (4.2.2). After s stages of this elimination approach one has produced the first s rows of (4.2.3) from the first s rows of (4.2.2), i.e., one has the first s rows $\mathbf{A}_{11}$ of $\mathbf{A}$. Also, one has modified the last $p - s$ rows of (4.2.2) into expressions for $U_{s+1}, U_{s+2}, \ldots, U_p$ in terms of $U_1, U_2, \ldots, U_s$ and $U^*_{s+1}, U^*_{s+2}, \ldots, U^*_p$, i.e., for $\mathbf{U}_2$ in terms of $\mathbf{U}_1$ and

$\mathbf{U}_{2.1}$. From (4.2.17) the coefficients of $\mathbf{U}_1$ here form $\mathbf{H}_{21}$. Thus, after s stages of the second layer of the elimination method, one may expect to have $\mathbf{A}_{11}$ and $\mathbf{H}_{21}$ together with the output $\mathbf{B}_{11}$, $\mathbf{B}_{21}$, and $\mathbf{Q}_{22.1}$ of the first layer.

Consider now how to upstage $\mathbf{A}_{11}$ and $\mathbf{H}_{21}$ from s to $s + 1$. Finding row $s + 1$ of $\mathbf{A}$ is trivial, for, as pointed out in Section 4.2 as property (i) of $\mathbf{H}_{21}$, the first s elements of row $s + 1$ of $\mathbf{A}$ are simply the negatives of the first row of $\mathbf{H}_{21}$ while the remaining $p - s$ elements are simply a one followed by zeros. It remains therefore to consider only $\mathbf{H}_{21}$. Suppose that the elements of $\mathbf{H}_{21}$ are denoted by h_{ij} for $i = s + 1, s + 2, \ldots, p$ and $j = 1, 2, \ldots, s$, and the elements after upstaging s to $s + 1$ are denoted by h^+_{ij} for $i = s + 2, s + 3, \ldots, p$ and $j = 1, 2, \ldots, s + 1$. Now the stage $s + 1$ elimination procedure alters the expression

$$U_i = \sum_{j=1}^{s} h_{ij} U_j + \sum_{t=s+1}^{i} b_{it} U_t^* \tag{4.3.5}$$

into

$$U_i = \sum_{j=1}^{s+1} h^+_{ij} U_j + \sum_{t=s+2}^{i} b_{it} U_t^* \tag{4.3.6}$$

for $i = s + 2, s + 3, \ldots, p$, by substituting

$$U^*_{s+1} = U_{s+1} + \sum_{j=1}^{s} a_{\overline{s+1}\,j} U_j = U_{\overline{s+1}} - \sum_{j=1}^{s} h_{\overline{s+1}\,j} U_j. \tag{4.3.7}$$

Carrying out the substitution and comparing coefficients with (4.3.6) one finds

$$h^+_{ij} = h_{ij} - b_{i\,\overline{s+1}} h_{\overline{s+1}\,j} \tag{4.3.8}$$

for $i = s + 2, s + 3, \ldots, p$ and $j = 1, 2, \ldots, s$. An alternative to (4.3.8) derived from (4.3.1) is

$$h^+_{ij} = h_{ij} - \frac{q_{i\,\overline{s+1}.12\ldots s}\, h_{\overline{s+1}\,j}}{q_{\overline{s+1}\,\overline{s+1}.12\ldots s}}. \tag{4.3.9}$$

Formulas (4.3.8) and (4.3.9) are analogous to (4.3.4) and (4.3.3), respectively; the first is computationally more direct, assuming that $b_{i\,\overline{s+1}}$ has already been computed. This completes the discussion of stage $s + 1$ of the second layer of the elimination procedure.

The third layer when added to the first two brings $\mathbf{Q}^{-1}$ (= $\mathbf{P}$) into the system by finding after s stages $\mathbf{Q}_{11}^{-1}$ (= $\mathbf{P}_{11.2}$) and upstaging it from s to $s + 1$. Denote the elements of $\mathbf{Q}_{11}^{-1}$ by $p_{ij.\overline{s+1}\,\overline{s+2}\ldots p}$ for i and $j = 1, 2, \ldots, s$ and the upstaged elements by $p_{ij.\overline{s+2}\,\overline{s+3}\ldots p}$ for i and $j = 1, 2, \ldots, s + 1$. Now $\mathbf{Q}_{11}^{-1}$ could have been calculated from (4.2.25) and the upstaged $\mathbf{Q}_{11}^{-1}$ could be calculated from the upstaged (4.2.25). Note, however, that most of the labor in calculating the upstaged (4.2.25) was involved in calculating the original (4.2.25). Indeed, by careful comparison of these two versions of (4.2.25) the reader may check that

$$\begin{aligned} p_{ij.\overline{s+2}\,\overline{s+3}\ldots p} &= p_{ij.\overline{s+1}\,\overline{s+2}\ldots p} + \frac{a_{\overline{s+1}\,i}a_{\overline{s+1}\,j}}{q_{\overline{s+1}\,\overline{s+1}.12\ldots s}} \\ &= p_{ij.\overline{s+1}\,\overline{s+2}\ldots p} + \frac{h_{\overline{s+1}\,i}h_{\overline{s+1}\,j}}{q_{\overline{s+1}\,\overline{s+1}.12\ldots s}} \end{aligned} \tag{4.3.10}$$

for i and $j = 1, 2, \ldots, s$, and

$$p_{ij.\overline{s+2}\,\overline{s+3}\ldots p} = \frac{a_{\overline{s+1}\,i}a_{\overline{s+1}\,j}}{q_{\overline{s+1}\,\overline{s+1}.\,2\ldots s}} \tag{4.3.11}$$

when either i or j or both are $s + 1$. Note that (4.3.11) may be explicitly written

$$p_{i\,\overline{s+1}.\overline{s+2}\,\overline{s+3}\ldots p} = -\frac{h_{\overline{s+1}\,i}}{q_{\overline{s+1}\,\overline{s+1}.12\ldots s}} = p_{\overline{s+1}\,i.\overline{s+2}\,\overline{s+3}\ldots p}$$

for $i = 1, 2, \ldots, s$, and (4.3.12)

$$p_{\overline{s+1}\,\overline{s+1}.\overline{s+2}\,\overline{s+3}\ldots p} = \frac{1}{q_{\overline{s+1}\,\overline{s+1}.12\ldots s}}.$$

Formulas (4.3.10) and (4.3.12) express the upstaged $\mathbf{Q}_{11}^{-1}$ in terms of the output of layers 1, 2, and 3 of the first s stages of the elimination procedures. This process of upstaging $\mathbf{Q}_{11}^{-1}$ is sometimes called *bordering*.

The foregoing formulas provide computational routines for essentially all of the matrices discussed in Section 4.2. Note that the first diagonal element of $\mathbf{Q}_{22.1}$ is (U_{s+1}^*, U_{s+1}^*) which is the $(s + 1, s + 1)$ element of $\mathbf{T}$, so that the elements of $\mathbf{T}$ may be picked off from the successive $\mathbf{Q}_{22.1}$ as s increases. Knowing $\mathbf{T}$, det $\mathbf{Q}$ may easily be computed from (4.2.6). From $\mathbf{A}$, $\mathbf{B}$, and $\mathbf{T}$ one has $\mathbf{R}$, and thence $\mathbf{C}$ and $\mathbf{D}$ from (4.2.29).

Before illustrating these calculations it will be helpful to provide a very simple means of describing them.

4.3.2. The sweep operator. A $p \times p$ matrix $\mathbf{M}$ will be said to have been *swept on row k and column k* if $\mathbf{M}$ is replaced by another $p \times p$ matrix $\mathbf{N}$ whose (i, j) elements n_{ij} are related to the (i, j) elements m_{ij} of $\mathbf{M}$ as follows:

$$\begin{aligned} n_{kk} &= -1/m_{kk} \\ n_{ik} &= m_{ik}/m_{kk} \\ n_{kj} &= m_{kj}/m_{kk} \\ n_{ij} &= m_{ij} - m_{ik} \cdot m_{kj}/m_{kk}, \end{aligned} \tag{4.3.13}$$

for $i \neq k$ and $j \neq k$. For brevity $\mathbf{N}$ will be denoted by $\mathrm{SWP}[k]\mathbf{M}$ and the result of successively applying the operations $\mathrm{SWP}[k_1]$, $\mathrm{SWP}[k_2], \ldots, \mathrm{SWP}[k_t]$ to $\mathbf{M}$ will be denoted by $\mathrm{SWP}[k_1, k_2, \ldots, k_t]$. The terminology here is borrowed from Beaton (1964).

With an electronic computer the operations (4.3.13) would usually be carried out as follows, beginning from a set of p^2 registers containing the elements of **M**. First, m_{kk} is replaced by $n_{kk} = -1/m_{kk}$. Second, the remaining elements m_{ik} of column k are replaced by $n_{ik} = -m_{ik}n_{kk}$. Third, the elements m_{ij} in neither row k nor column k are replaced by $n_{ij} = m_{ij} - n_{ik}m_{kj}$. Finally, the remaining elements m_{kj} in row k are replaced by $n_{kj} = -m_{kj}n_{kk}$. Each stage here is designed to use only the output of the previous stages, so that no waste motion of saving numbers in special registers is needed. Note, however, that in the primary applications of this book **M** is a symmetric matrix, whence (4.3.13) shows that **N** is also a symmetric matrix. It follows that only $p(p + 1)/2$ registers are required to store **M**, and the foregoing routine may be altered slightly to fit this circumstance. In any case, it is clear that a computer subroutine can be readily programmed to carry out the sweep operations one at a time and thence successively, i.e., SWP$[k_1, k_2, \ldots, k_t]$**M** is quite amenable to electronic computation.

The calculations of each stage of the elimination procedure of Section 4.3.1 may be viewed simply as a sweep operation. To see this, set

$$\mathbf{Q}_{(012\ldots s)} = \begin{bmatrix} -\mathbf{Q}_{11}^{-1} & \mathbf{H}_{12} \\ \mathbf{H}_{21} & \mathbf{Q}_{22.1} \end{bmatrix} \tag{4.3.14}$$

where $\mathbf{H}_{12} = \mathbf{H}'_{21}$. (The remaining notation was introduced in Section 4.2.) The notation (4.3.14) should be construed to include the limiting cases

$$\mathbf{Q}_{(0)} = \mathbf{Q} \tag{4.3.15}$$

and

$$\mathbf{Q}_{(012\ldots p)} = -\mathbf{Q}^{-1}. \tag{4.3.16}$$

The reason for the notation (4.3.14) is the following simple but powerful theorem which is an immediate consequence of (4.3.1), (4.3.3), (4.3.9), (4.3.10), and (4.3.12) together with the definition (4.3.13).

Theorem 4.3.1.

$$\mathbf{Q}_{(012\ldots\overline{s+1})} = \text{SWP}[s + 1]\mathbf{Q}_{(012\ldots s)} \tag{4.3.17}$$

for $s = 0, 1, 2, \ldots, p - 1$ *and consequently*

$$\mathbf{Q}_{(012\ldots s)} = \text{SWP}[1, 2, \ldots, s]\mathbf{Q} \tag{4.3.18}$$

for $s = 1, 2, \ldots, p$

The remarkable feature of Theorem 4.3.1 is that it shows how the same computing operation is involved at each stage s. By simply carrying out the operations SWP[1], SWP[2], . . . , SWP[p], one can pick up **A**, **B**, and **T** along the way and finally arrive at SWP$[1, 2, \ldots, p]\mathbf{Q} = -\mathbf{Q}^{-1}$. (Recall that the first diagonal element of $\mathbf{Q}_{22.1}$ is (U^*_{s+1}, U^*_{s+1}), that column s of $\mathbf{H}_{21}$ is that part of column s of **B** below the diagonal, and that the first row of $\mathbf{H}_{21}$ is the negative of that part of row $s + 1$ of **A** to the left of the diagonal.)

Example 4.3 The following is a 4 × 4 sample covariance matrix:

$$\mathbf{Q} = \begin{bmatrix} 19.1434 & 9.0356 & 9.7634 & 3.2394 \\ 9.0356 & 11.8658 & 4.6232 & 2.4746 \\ 9.7634 & 4.6232 & 12.2978 & 3.8794 \\ 3.2394 & 2.4746 & 3.8794 & 2.4604 \end{bmatrix}.$$

The calculations of the elimination procedure to find **B**, **T**, **A**, and $\mathbf{Q}^{-1}$ will be illustrated on this **Q**. The reader should attempt to reproduce the numbers in the subsequent matrices.

The first stage is essentially to compute

$$\text{SWP}[1]\mathbf{Q} = \begin{bmatrix} -0.0522373 & 0.471995 & 0.510014 & 0.169218 \\ 0.471995 & 7.60104 & 0.01492 & 0.94562 \\ 0.510014 & 0.01492 & 7.31833 & 2.22726 \\ 0.169218 & 0.94562 & 2.22726 & 1.91224 \end{bmatrix}.$$

At this stage one knows that

$$\mathbf{T} = \begin{bmatrix} 19.1434 & 0 & 0 & 0 \\ 0 & 7.60104 & 0 & 0 \\ 0 & 0 & ? & 0 \\ 0 & 0 & 0 & ? \end{bmatrix},$$

$$\mathbf{B} = \begin{bmatrix} 1 & 0 & 0 & 0 \\ 0.471995 & 1 & 0 & 0 \\ 0.510014 & ? & 1 & 0 \\ 0.169218 & ? & ? & 1 \end{bmatrix},$$

$$\mathbf{A} = \begin{bmatrix} 1 & 0 & 0 & 0 \\ -0.471995 & 1 & 0 & 0 \\ ? & ? & 1 & 0 \\ ? & ? & ? & 1 \end{bmatrix},$$

and $19.1434^{-1} = 0.0522373$.

The second stage is to compute

$$\text{SWP}[1, 2]\mathbf{Q} = \text{SWP}[2]\text{SWP}[1]\mathbf{Q}$$

$$= \begin{bmatrix} -0.0815463 & 0.0620961 & 0.509088 & 0.110499 \\ 0.0620961 & -0.131561 & 0.0019629 & 0.1294067 \\ 0.509088 & 0.0019629 & 7.318301 & 2.22574 \\ 0.110499 & 0.1244067 & 2.22574 & 1.79460 \end{bmatrix}$$

from which

$$\mathbf{T} = \begin{bmatrix} 19.1434 & 0 & 0 & 0 \\ 0 & 7.60104 & 0 & 0 \\ 0 & 0 & 7.318301 & 0 \\ 0 & 0 & 0 & ? \end{bmatrix},$$

$$\mathbf{B} = \begin{bmatrix} 1 & 0 & 0 & 0 \\ 0.471995 & 1 & 0 & 0 \\ 0.510014 & 0.0019629 & 1 & 0 \\ 0.169218 & 0.1244067 & ? & 0 \end{bmatrix},$$

$$\mathbf{A} = \begin{bmatrix} 1 & 0 & 0 & 0 \\ -0.471995 & 1 & 0 & 0 \\ -0.509088 & -0.0019629 & 1 & 0 \\ ? & ? & ? & 1 \end{bmatrix},$$

and

$$\begin{bmatrix} 19.1434 & 9.0356 \\ 9.0356 & 11.8658 \end{bmatrix}^{-1} = \begin{bmatrix} 0.0815463 & -0.0620961 \\ -0.0620961 & 0.131561 \end{bmatrix}.$$

The third stage produces

$$\mathrm{SWP}[1, 2, 3]\mathbf{Q} = \mathrm{SWP}[3]\mathrm{SWP}[1, 2]\mathbf{Q}$$

$$= \begin{bmatrix} -0.1169601 & 0.0619596 & 0.0695633 & -0.044331 \\ 0.0619596 & -0.131562 & 0.0002682 & 0.123810 \\ 0.0695633 & 0.0002682 & -0.136643 & 0.304132 \\ -0.044331 & 0.123810 & 0.304132 & 1.11768 \end{bmatrix},$$

from which

$$\mathbf{T} = \begin{bmatrix} 19.1434 & 0 & 0 & 0 \\ 0 & 7.60104 & 0 & 0 \\ 0 & 0 & 7.318301 & 0 \\ 0 & 0 & 0 & 1.11768 \end{bmatrix},$$

$$\mathbf{B} = \begin{bmatrix} 1 & 0 & 0 & 0 \\ 0.471995 & 1 & 0 & 0 \\ 0.510014 & 0.0019629 & 1 & 0 \\ 0.169218 & 0.1244067 & 0.304132 & 1 \end{bmatrix},$$

$$\mathbf{A} = \begin{bmatrix} 1 & 0 & 0 & 0 \\ -0.471995 & 1 & 0 & 0 \\ -0.509088 & -0.0019629 & 1 & 0 \\ 0.044331 & -0.123810 & -0.304132 & 1 \end{bmatrix},$$

and

$$\begin{bmatrix} 19.1434 & 9.0356 & 9.7634 \\ 9.0356 & 11.8658 & 4.6232 \\ 9.7634 & 4.6232 & 12.2978 \end{bmatrix}^{-1} = \begin{bmatrix} 0.1169601 & -0.0619596 & -0.0695633 \\ -0.0619596 & 0.131562 & -0.0002682 \\ -0.0695633 & -0.0002682 & 0.136643 \end{bmatrix}.$$

If desired, a final stage may be added to yield

$$\mathbf{Q}^{-1} = -\mathrm{SWP}[4]\mathrm{SWP}[1, 2, 3]\mathbf{Q}$$

$$= \begin{bmatrix} 0.118718 & -0.066871 & -0.081626 & 0.039663 \\ -0.066871 & 0.145277 & 0.033422 & -0.110774 \\ -0.081626 & 0.033422 & 0.219400 & -0.272110 \\ 0.039663 & 0.110774 & -0.272110 & 0.894710 \end{bmatrix}.$$

Other quantities of interest might be $\det \mathbf{Q} = \det \mathbf{T} = 1190.04$ and the square roots of $\mathbf{T}$, namely,

$$\mathbf{R} = \begin{bmatrix} 4.3753 & 0 & 0 & 0 \\ 0 & 2.7570 & 0 & 0 \\ 0 & 0 & 2.7052 & 0 \\ 0 & 0 & 0 & 1.0572 \end{bmatrix}.$$

From (4.2.9), $\mathbf{D}$ is found from $\mathbf{B}$ by multiplying each column of $\mathbf{B}$ by the corresponding element of $\mathbf{R}$, giving

$$\mathbf{D} = \begin{bmatrix} 4.3753 & 0 & 0 & 0 \\ 2.0651 & 2.7570 & 0 & 0 \\ 2.2315 & 0.0054 & 2.7052 & 0 \\ 0.5712 & 0.3430 & 0.8277 & 1.0572 \end{bmatrix}.$$

Similarly, $\mathbf{C}$ is found from $\mathbf{A}$ by dividing each row of $\mathbf{A}$ by the corresponding element of $\mathbf{R}$, giving

$$\mathbf{C} = \begin{bmatrix} 0.22855 & 0 & 0 & 0 \\ -0.17120 & 0.36271 & 0 & 0 \\ -0.18819 & -0.00073 & 0.36966 & 0 \\ 0.04193 & -0.11711 & -0.28768 & 0.94589 \end{bmatrix}.$$

These calculations were performed on a desk calculator. Variations on the calculations—to be exhibited later in Section 4.3—were performed independently on a desk calculator and show minor deviations from those given above due to rounding error.

Two important properties of the sweep operator will now be demonstrated. The first of these is commutativity, i.e.,

$$\mathrm{SWP}[i, j]\mathbf{M} = \mathrm{SWP}[j, i]\mathbf{M}, \tag{4.3.19}$$

from which it follows that

$$\mathrm{SWP}[i_1, i_2, \ldots, i_t]\mathbf{M} = \mathrm{SWP}[j_1, j_2, \ldots, j_t]\mathbf{M}, \tag{4.3.20}$$

where $i_1, i_2, \ldots, i_t$ and $j_1, j_2, \ldots, j_t$ are permutations of the same set of integers. Formula (4.3.19) may be deduced directly from (4.3.13), but it is interesting to note also that it can be deduced from (4.3.18). The point is that while all of the parts $-\mathbf{Q}_{11}^{-1}$, $\mathbf{H}_{21}$, and $\mathbf{Q}_{22.1}$ of $\mathbf{Q}_{(012\ldots s)}$ depend on the parts $\mathbf{U}_1$ and $\mathbf{U}_2$ of the basis $\mathbf{U}$ they do not depend on the order of the basis elements of $\mathbf{U}_1$, at least not in any meaningful sense. Thus $\mathbf{Q}_{11}^{-1}$ is the inverse of the inner product matrix of $\mathbf{U}_1$, and if $\mathbf{Q}_{11}^{-1}$ is computed using the basis elements in one order it can equally well be computed using the basis elements in any other order. Similar remarks apply to $\mathbf{H}_{21}$ via (4.2.17) and to $\mathbf{Q}_{22.1}$ which is the inner product matrix of the components of $\mathbf{U}_2$ orthogonal to $\mathbf{U}_1$. These computations using the basis elements in a different order are, however, nothing more than the application of the sweep operators SWP[1], SWP[2], . . . , SWP[s] in a different order. Consequently, permuting the order of these operations cannot affect the outcome.

The second property of the sweep operator is that it is very easily undone. Indeed, the equations (4.3.13) may be solved to yield

$$\begin{aligned} m_{kk} &= -1/n_{kk} \\ m_{ik} &= -n_{ik}/n_{kk} \\ m_{kj} &= -n_{kj}/n_{kk} \\ m_{ij} &= n_{ij} - n_{ik}n_{kj}/n_{kk} \end{aligned} \tag{4.3.21}$$

for $j \neq i$ and $k \neq i$. The operator defined by (4.3.21) may be denoted by

$$\mathbf{M} = \mathrm{RSW}[k]\mathbf{N} \tag{4.3.22}$$

and may be called the *reverse sweep operator on row and column k*. RSW operators commute with each other, and as with SWP operators, RSW$[k_1, k_2, \ldots, k_t]$ will denote the result of successively applying RSW$[k_1]$, RSW$[k_2]$, . . . , RSW$[k_t]$ in any order.

The formulas

$$\begin{aligned} &\mathrm{SWP}[1, 2, \ldots, s]\begin{bmatrix} \mathbf{Q}_{11} & \mathbf{Q}_{12} \\ \mathbf{Q}_{21} & \mathbf{Q}_{22} \end{bmatrix} = \begin{bmatrix} -\mathbf{Q}_{11}^{-1} & \mathbf{Q}_{11}^{-1}\mathbf{Q}_{12} \\ \mathbf{Q}_{21}\mathbf{Q}_{11}^{-1} & \mathbf{Q}_{22} - \mathbf{Q}_{21}\mathbf{Q}_{11}^{-1}\mathbf{Q}_{12} \end{bmatrix} \text{ and} \\ &\mathrm{RSW}[1, 2, \ldots, s]\begin{bmatrix} \mathbf{Q}_{11} & \mathbf{Q}_{12} \\ \mathbf{Q}_{21} & \mathbf{Q}_{22} \end{bmatrix} = \begin{bmatrix} -\mathbf{Q}_{11}^{-1} & -\mathbf{Q}_{11}^{-1}\mathbf{Q}_{12} \\ -\mathbf{Q}_{21}\mathbf{Q}_{11}^{-1} & \mathbf{Q}_{22} - \mathbf{Q}_{21}\mathbf{Q}_{11}^{-1}\mathbf{Q}_{12} \end{bmatrix} \end{aligned} \tag{4.3.23}$$

are useful mathematical characterizations of the general SWP and RSW operators.

4.3.3. The assimilation operator. In place of the elimination procedure described above, it is possible to proceed in stages which produce after stage s the successive orthogonalization of $U_1, U_2, \ldots, U_s$ without having touched $U_{s+1}, U_{s+2}, \ldots, U_p$. At stage s, U_{s+1} is *assimilated* into the picture, for $s = 1, 2, \ldots, p - 1$. First, however, a more general assimilation problem is considered.

Suppose that computations on $\mathbf{Q}$ have proceeded to the stage SWP[1, 2, . . . , s]$\mathbf{Q}$ when the p-dimensional space $\mathscr{E}$ with basis $U_1, U_2, \ldots, U_p$ is enlarged to a $(p + r)$-dimensional space $\mathscr{E}^*$ by the addition of new basis variables $U_{p+1}, U_{p+2}, \ldots, U_{p+r}$. At the same time the $p \times p$ inner product matrix

$$\mathbf{Q} = \begin{bmatrix} \mathbf{Q}_{11} & \mathbf{Q}_{12} \\ \mathbf{Q}_{21} & \mathbf{Q}_{22} \end{bmatrix} \tag{4.3.24}$$

is enlarged to the $(p + r) \times (p + r)$ inner product matrix

$$\mathbf{Q}^* = \begin{bmatrix} \mathbf{Q}_{11} & \mathbf{Q}_{12} & \mathbf{Q}_{13} \\ \mathbf{Q}_{21} & \mathbf{Q}_{22} & \mathbf{Q}_{23} \\ \mathbf{Q}_{31} & \mathbf{Q}_{32} & \mathbf{Q}_{33} \end{bmatrix}. \tag{4.3.25}$$

The basic computing task considered here is to produce SWP$[1, 2, \ldots, s]\mathbf{Q}^*$ from SWP$[1, 2, \ldots, s]\mathbf{Q}$ and the last r rows and columns of $\mathbf{Q}^*$, i.e., to pass from

$$\begin{bmatrix} -\mathbf{Q}_{11}^{-1} & \mathbf{H}_{12} & \mathbf{Q}_{13} \\ \mathbf{H}_{21} & \mathbf{Q}_{22.1} & \mathbf{Q}_{23} \\ \mathbf{Q}_{31} & \mathbf{Q}_{32} & \mathbf{Q}_{33} \end{bmatrix} \tag{4.3.26}$$

to

$$\begin{bmatrix} -\mathbf{Q}_{11}^{-1} & \mathbf{H}_{12} & \mathbf{H}_{13} \\ \mathbf{H}_{21} & \mathbf{Q}_{22.1} & \mathbf{Q}_{23.1} \\ \mathbf{H}_{31} & \mathbf{Q}_{32.1} & \mathbf{Q}_{33.1} \end{bmatrix}, \tag{4.3.27}$$

where, from (4.3.18),

$$\mathbf{H}_{13} = \mathbf{H}_{31}' = \mathbf{Q}_{11}^{-1}\mathbf{Q}_{13}, \tag{4.3.28}$$

$$\mathbf{Q}_{23.1} = \mathbf{Q}_{32.1}' = \mathbf{Q}_{23} - \mathbf{H}_{21}\mathbf{Q}_{13}, \tag{4.3.29}$$

and

$$\mathbf{Q}_{33.1} = \mathbf{Q}_{33} - \mathbf{H}_{31}\mathbf{Q}_{13}. \tag{4.3.30}$$

It is convenient to introduce the operator notation ASM$[p + 1, p + 2, \ldots, p + r; 1, 2, \ldots, s]$ for the passage from (4.3.26) to (4.3.27) defined by (4.3.28), (4.3.29), and (4.3.30). In general terms, the operator may be written

$$\text{ASM}[p + 1, p + 2, \ldots, p + r; 1, 2, \ldots, s] \begin{bmatrix} \mathbf{K}_{11} & \mathbf{K}_{12} & \mathbf{K}_{13} \\ \mathbf{K}_{21} & \mathbf{K}_{22} & \mathbf{K}_{23} \\ \mathbf{K}_{31} & \mathbf{K}_{32} & \mathbf{K}_{33} \end{bmatrix}$$

$$= \begin{bmatrix} \mathbf{K}_{11} & \mathbf{K}_{12} & -\mathbf{K}_{11}\mathbf{K}_{13} \\ \mathbf{K}_{21} & \mathbf{K}_{22} & \mathbf{K}_{23} - \mathbf{K}_{21}\mathbf{K}_{13} \\ -\mathbf{K}_{31}\mathbf{K}_{11} & \mathbf{K}_{32} - \mathbf{K}_{31}\mathbf{K}_{12} & \mathbf{K}_{33} + \mathbf{K}_{31}\mathbf{K}_{11}\mathbf{K}_{13} \end{bmatrix}. \tag{4.3.31}$$

The notation ASM stands for *assimilate*; more fully, the assimilation operator ASM$[p + 1, p + 2, \ldots, p + r; 1, 2, \ldots, s]$ assimilates $U_{p+1}, U_{p+2}, \ldots, U_{p+r}$ into a situation where $U_1, U_2, \ldots, U_s$ have already been swept out.

Two alternative characterizations of the ASM operator follow. First, it is clear that the assimilation of $U_{p+1}, U_{p+2}, \ldots, U_{p+r}$ may itself be carried out in r steps. Thus ASM$[p + 1, p + 2, \ldots, p + r; 1, 2, \ldots, s]$ may be described as the result of applying in order ASM$[p + 1; 1, 2, \ldots, s]$ to the first $p + 1$ rows and columns, ASM$[p + 2; 1, 2, \ldots, s]$ to the first $p + 2$ rows and columns, and so on to ASM$[p + r; 1, 2, \ldots, s]$ applied to the whole matrix. This is the direct way to program the ASM operator for an electronic computer. The second characterization of the ASM$[p + 1, p + 2, \ldots, p + r; 1, 2, \ldots, s]$ operator is that it is the result of applying RSW$[1, 2, \ldots, s]$ to the first p rows and columns followed by SWP$[1, 2, \ldots, s]$ applied to the whole matrix. The first step here returns the first p rows and columns of (4.3.25) to $\mathbf{Q}$, and the second step then finds SWP$[1, 2, \ldots, s]\mathbf{Q}^*$ directly from $\mathbf{Q}^*$. This second characterization of the ASM operator is given for its mathematical interest; it is clearly an inefficient way to carry out the calculations.

As an example of the ASM operator consider the following operations applied in sequence to $\mathbf{Q}$:

SWP[1] applied to the upper left 1×1 submatrix,
ASM[2; 1] applied to the upper left 2×2 submatrix,
SWP[2] applied to the upper left 2×2 submatrix,

.
.
.

ASM[s; 1, 2, . . . , $s - 1$] applied to the upper left $s \times s$ submatrix,
SWP[s] applied to the upper left $s \times s$ submatrix,

.
.
.

ASM[p; 1, 2, . . . , $p - 1$] applied to the whole matrix,
SWP[p] applied to the whole matrix.

Just before the SWP[s] operation, row s provides the negative of row s of $\mathbf{A}$. Just after the SWP[s] operation, the upper left $s \times s$ submatrix provides $-\mathbf{Q}_{11}^{-1}$. The final result of the sequence of operations is $-\mathbf{Q}^{-1}$.

Example 4.3 (*First continuation*) The computing sequence just described is applied to the 4×4 matrix $\mathbf{Q}$ used to illustrate the SWP operator:

$$-0.052237,$$

$$\begin{bmatrix} -0.052237 & 0.471993 \\ 0.471993 & 7.601060 \end{bmatrix},$$

$$\begin{bmatrix} -0.081546 & 0.062096 \\ 0.062096 & -0.131561 \end{bmatrix},$$

$$\begin{bmatrix} -0.081546 & 0.062096 & 0.509084 \\ 0.062096 & -0.131561 & 0.001965 \\ 0.509084 & 0.001965 & 7.318324 \end{bmatrix},$$

$$\begin{bmatrix} -0.116959 & 0.061959 & 0.069563 \\ 0.061959 & -0.131562 & 0.000269 \\ 0.069563 & 0.000269 & -0.136643 \end{bmatrix},$$

$$\begin{bmatrix} -0.116959 & 0.061959 & 0.069563 & -0.044310 \\ 0.061959 & -0.131562 & 0.000269 & 0.123809 \\ 0.069563 & 0.000269 & -0.136643 & 0.304085 \\ -0.04431 & 0.123809 & 0.304085 & 1.117893 \end{bmatrix},$$

$$\begin{bmatrix} -0.118715 & 0.066866 & 0.081616 & -0.039637 \\ 0.066866 & -0.145274 & -0.033409 & 0.110752 \\ 0.081616 & -0.033409 & -0.219359 & 0.272016 \\ -0.039637 & 0.110752 & 0.272016 & -0.894540 \end{bmatrix}.$$

The final result here is $-\mathbf{Q}^{-1}$. The reader should also locate in this sequence the elements of $\mathbf{A}$ and $\mathbf{T}$.

4.3.4. The multistandardize operator (cf. Beaton, 1964). For later computations involving eigenvalues and eigenvectors (to be discussed in Chapter 5) it is often desirable to have in hand an inner product matrix where a subset of the vectors $\mathbf{U}$ has been replaced by an orthonormal set spanning the same subspace as the original subset. Usually any orthonormal set of linear combinations of the specified subset will suffice, and the process of successive orthogonalization is a convenient means to such an end.

Suppose that $\mathbf{Q}$ is the inner product matrix for a basis $\mathbf{U}$ and, for simplicity, that the subset $\mathbf{U}_1$ is to be replaced by the orthonormal subset $\mathbf{U}_1^{**}$ found by orthogonalizing $\mathbf{U}_1$ in the given order. The objectives are to find two $p \times p$ matrices $\mathbf{Q}_{[012...s]}$ and $\mathbf{C}_{[012...s]}$ where $\mathbf{Q}_{[012...s]}$ is the inner product matrix of the new basis $[\mathbf{U}_1^{**}, \mathbf{U}_2]'$ and $\mathbf{C}_{[012...s]}$ expresses the basis $[\mathbf{U}_1^{**}, \mathbf{U}_2]'$ in terms of $\mathbf{U}$, i.e.,

$$\begin{bmatrix} \mathbf{U}_1^{**} \\ \mathbf{U}_2 \end{bmatrix} = \mathbf{C}_{[012...s]}\mathbf{U}. \tag{4.3.32}$$

The limiting cases $\mathbf{Q}_{[0]}$ and $\mathbf{C}_{[0]}$ will be taken to be $\mathbf{Q}$ and $\mathbf{I}$.

The *multistandardize operator* $\text{MST}[1, 2, \ldots, s]$ is a computation which modifies the pair $[\mathbf{Q}, \mathbf{I}]$ in a set of $2p^2$ registers into the pair $[\mathbf{Q}_{[012...s]}, \mathbf{C}_{[012...s]}]$. It does this in s stages where stage $r + 1$ for $r = 0, 1, \ldots, s - 1$ modifies $[\mathbf{Q}_{[012...r]}, \mathbf{C}_{[012...r]}]$ into $[\mathbf{Q}_{[012...\overline{r+1}]}, \mathbf{C}_{[012...\overline{r+1}]}]$. The following four paragraphs will describe how to carry out stage $r + 1$ in such a multistandardize operation.

First note that, when $\mathbf{Q}_{[012...s]}$ and $\mathbf{C}_{[012...s]}$ are partitioned in the usual way, only one part of each is unknown at the outset. Thus

$$\mathbf{Q}_{[012...s]} = \begin{bmatrix} \mathbf{I} & \mathbf{Q}_{12}^{**} \\ \mathbf{Q}_{21}^{**} & \mathbf{Q}_{22} \end{bmatrix}, \tag{4.3.33}$$

where $\mathbf{I}$ and $\mathbf{Q}_{22}$ are the known inner product matrices of $\mathbf{U}_1^{**}$ and $\mathbf{U}_2$ and where $\mathbf{Q}_{21}^{**}$ or its transpose $\mathbf{Q}_{12}^{**}$ contain the unknown inner products between $\mathbf{U}_1^{**}$ and $\mathbf{U}_2$. Similarly

$$\mathbf{C}_{[012...s]} = \begin{bmatrix} \mathbf{C}_{11} & \mathbf{0}' \\ \mathbf{0} & \mathbf{I} \end{bmatrix}, \tag{4.3.34}$$

where $\mathbf{C}_{11}$ is the part of $\mathbf{C}$ which expresses $\mathbf{U}_1^{**}$ in terms of $\mathbf{U}_1$ as in (4.2.33), and where $\mathbf{0}$ and its transpose consist of zeros and $\mathbf{I}$ is the $(p - s) \times (p - s)$ identity which expresses $\mathbf{U}_2$ in terms of $\mathbf{U}_2$. These partitions may also be applied with s replaced by r for $r = 0, 1, 2, \ldots, s - 1$.

Suppose that (U_i, U_j^{**}) is denoted by q_{ij}^{**} for $i \geq j$. The formulas underlying the computations at stage $r + 1$ are

$$U_{r+1}^{*} = U_{r+1} - q_{\overline{r+1}1}^{**}U_1^{**} - q_{\overline{r+1}2}^{**}U_2^{**} - \cdots - q_{\overline{r+1}r}^{**}U_r^{**} \tag{4.3.35}$$

and

$$U_{\overline{r+1}}^{**} = (U_{r+1}^{*}, U_{r+1}^{*})^{-1/2}U_{r+1}^{*}. \tag{4.3.36}$$

From (4.3.35),

$$(U_{r+1}^{*}, U_{r+1}^{*}) = q_{\overline{r+1}\,\overline{r+1}} - (q_{\overline{r+1}\,1}^{**})^2 - (q_{\overline{r+1}\,2}^{**})^2 - \cdots - (q_{\overline{r+1}\,r}^{**})^2, \tag{4.3.37}$$

and from (4.3.36)

$$q_{i\,\overline{r+1}}^{**} = (q_{i\,\overline{r+1}} - q_{\overline{r+1}1}^{**}q_{i1}^{**} - q_{\overline{r+1}2}^{**}q_{i2}^{**} - \cdots - q_{\overline{r+1}\,r}^{**}q_{ir}^{**})/(U_{r+1}^{*}, U_{r+1}^{*})^{1/2} \tag{4.3.38}$$

for $i = r + 2, r + 3, \ldots, p$.

Passage from $\mathbf{Q}_{[012\ldots r]}$ to $\mathbf{Q}_{[012\ldots\overline{r+1}]}$ requires only modification of row and column $r + 1$. The last $(p - r - 1)$ elements of row and column $r + 1$ are modified by replacing $q_{i\,\overline{r+1}} = q_{\overline{r+1}\,i}$ by $q_{i\,\overline{r+1}}^{**}$ calculated from (4.3.38) with $i = r + 2, r + 3, \ldots, p$. Note that (4.3.38) requires preliminary computation of $(U_{r+1}^{*}, U_{r+1}^{*})$ via (4.3.37). The remaining elements of row and column $r + 1$ are modified to zeros except for the diagonal element which becomes unity.

From (4.3.32) it is seen that linear combinations of the vectors $\mathbf{U}_1^{**}$ and $\mathbf{U}_2$ correspond to linear combinations of rows of $\mathbf{C}_{[012\ldots s]}$. It is therefore clear from (4.3.35) and (4.3.36) that $\mathbf{C}_{[012\ldots\overline{r+1}]}$ is produced from $\mathbf{C}_{[012\ldots r]}$ by altering row $r + 1$ of $\mathbf{C}_{[012\ldots r]}$ as follows: first replace row $r + 1$ of $\mathbf{C}_{[012\ldots r]}$ by

$$\begin{aligned}&[\text{row } r + 1 \text{ of } \mathbf{C}_{[012\ldots r]}] - q_{\overline{r+1}\,1}^{**}[\text{row 1 of } \mathbf{C}_{[012\ldots r]}] \\ &\quad - q_{\overline{r+1}\,2}^{**}[\text{row 2 of } \mathbf{C}_{[012\ldots r]}] - \cdots - q_{\overline{r+1}\,r}^{**}[\text{row } r \text{ of } \mathbf{C}_{[012\ldots r]}],\end{aligned} \tag{4.3.39}$$

and then divide through the resulting row $r + 1$ by $(U_{r+1}^{*}, U_{r+1}^{*})^{1/2}$.

This completes the definition of the multistandardize operator MST$[1, 2, \ldots, s]$ with the property

$$\text{MST}[1, 2, \ldots, s][\mathbf{Q}, \mathbf{I}] = [\mathbf{Q}_{[012\ldots s]}, \mathbf{C}_{[012\ldots s]}]. \tag{4.3.40}$$

Example 4.3 (*Second continuation*) Beginning from

$$[\mathbf{Q}, \mathbf{I}] = \begin{bmatrix} 19.1434 & 9.0356 & 9.7634 & 3.2394 & 1 & 0 & 0 & 0 \\ 9.0356 & 11.8658 & 4.6232 & 2.4746 & 0 & 1 & 0 & 0 \\ 9.7634 & 4.6232 & 12.2978 & 3.8794 & 0 & 0 & 1 & 0 \\ 3.2394 & 2.4746 & 3.8794 & 2.4604 & 0 & 0 & 0 & 1 \end{bmatrix},$$

the multistandardize operations will be applied to yield in succession $[\mathbf{Q}_{[01]}, \mathbf{C}_{[01]}]$, $[\mathbf{Q}_{[012]}, \mathbf{C}_{[012]}]$, $[\mathbf{Q}_{[0123]}, \mathbf{C}_{[0123]}]$, and $[\mathbf{Q}_{[01234]}, \mathbf{C}_{[01234]}] = [\mathbf{I}, \mathbf{C}]$.

The first stage simply replaces U_1 by $U_1^{**} = 0.22855U_1$ whence

$$\mathbf{Q}_{[01]} = \begin{bmatrix} 1 & 2.0651 & 2.2314 & 0.7404 \\ 2.0651 & 11.8658 & 4.6232 & 2.4746 \\ 2.2314 & 4.6232 & 12.2978 & 3.8794 \\ 0.7404 & 2.4746 & 3.8794 & 2.4604 \end{bmatrix}$$

and

$$\mathbf{C}_{[01]} = \begin{bmatrix} 0.22855 & 0 & 0 & 0 \\ 0 & 1 & 0 & 0 \\ 0 & 0 & 1 & 0 \\ 0 & 0 & 0 & 1 \end{bmatrix}.$$

The second stage requires computing from (4.3.37):

$$\begin{aligned}(U_2^*, U_2^*) &= 11.8658 - 4.26460 \\ &= 7.6018, \text{ whence} \\ (U_2^*, U_2^*)^{1/2} &= 2.7571.\end{aligned}$$

Next, following (4.3.33) and (4.3.38),

$$\mathbf{Q}_{[012]} = \begin{bmatrix} 1 & 0 & 2.23143 & 0.74036 \\ 0 & 1 & 0.00548 & 0.34300 \\ 2.23143 & 0.00548 & 12.2978 & 2.8794 \\ 0.74036 & 0.34300 & 3.8794 & 2.4604 \end{bmatrix}.$$

Then, following (4.3.39),

$$\mathbf{C}_{[012]} = \begin{bmatrix} 0.22855 & 0 & 0 & 0 \\ -0.17119 & 0.36270 & 0 & 0 \\ 0 & 0 & 1 & 0 \\ 0 & 0 & 0 & 1 \end{bmatrix}.$$

The third stage follows the same general pattern as the second except with increasing complexity. Thus

$$\begin{aligned}(U_3^*, U_3^*) &= 12.2978 - 4.97928 - 0.00003 \\ &= 7.3185, \text{ whence} \\ (U_3^*, U_3^*)^{1/2} &= 2.7053.\end{aligned}$$

Similarly,

$$\mathbf{Q}_{[0123]} = \begin{bmatrix} 1 & 0 & 0 & 0.74036 \\ 0 & 1 & 0 & 0.34300 \\ 0 & 0 & 1 & 0.82262 \\ 0.74036 & 0.34300 & 0.82262 & 2.4604 \end{bmatrix}$$

and

$$\mathbf{C}_{[0123]} = \begin{bmatrix} 0.22855 & 0 & 0 & 0 \\ -0.17119 & 0.36270 & 0 & 0 \\ -0.18817 & -0.00074 & 0.36964 & 0 \\ 0 & 0 & 0 & 1 \end{bmatrix}.$$

The final stage differs in that $\mathbf{Q}_{[01234]}$ is known to be simply $\mathbf{I}$. Thus, one needs

$$(U_4^*, U_4^*) = 1.11791,$$
$$(U_4^*, U_4^*)^{1/2} = 1.0573,$$

and

$$\mathbf{C} = \mathbf{C}_{[01234]} = \begin{bmatrix} 0.22855 & 0 & 0 & 0 \\ -0.17119 & 0.36270 & 0 & 0 \\ -0.18817 & -0.00074 & 0.36964 & 0 \\ 0.04190 & -0.11709 & -0.28759 & 0.94581 \end{bmatrix}.$$

It is clear that the rows and columns $1, 2, \ldots, s$ were arbitrarily chosen and that the definition may be extended to define $\text{MST}[i_1, i_2, \ldots, i_s]$ where $i_1, i_2, \ldots, i_s$ are any subset of the integers $1, 2, \ldots, p$. The vectorial definitions all proceed as before except that $U_1, U_2, \ldots, U_s$ are replaced by $U_{i_1}, U_{i_2}, \ldots, U_{i_s}$ and the desired orthonormal basis is that arising from the orthogonalization of $U_{i_1}, U_{i_2}, \ldots, U_{i_s}$ in this order. Precise details are left to the reader, but clearly (4.3.39) easily generalizes to

$$\text{MST}[i_1, i_2, \ldots, i_s][\mathbf{Q}, \mathbf{I}] = [\mathbf{Q}_{[0\, i_1 i_2 \ldots i_s]}, \mathbf{C}_{[0\, i_1 i_2 \ldots i_s]}]. \qquad (4.3.41)$$

The definitions were originally given in the special case only because the partitions (4.3.33) and (4.3.34) are more easily displayed in that case.

A further observation is that the definition of the operator does not require the initial pair to be $[\mathbf{Q}, \mathbf{I}]$; rather, any $p \times p$ matrix $\mathbf{K}$ may be substituted for $\mathbf{I}$. It follows that (4.3.41) generalizes to

$$\text{MST}[i_1, i_2, \ldots, i_s][\mathbf{Q}, \mathbf{K}] = [\mathbf{Q}_{[0\, i_1 i_2 \ldots i_s]}, \mathbf{C}_{[0\, i_1 i_2 \ldots i_s]}\mathbf{K}]. \qquad (4.3.42)$$

The idea behind definition (4.3.42) is that the basis $\mathbf{U}$ may have been derived from an initial basis $\mathbf{V}$ where $\mathbf{U} = \mathbf{KV}$. Then (4.3.42) extends to

$$\begin{bmatrix} \mathbf{U}_1^{**} \\ \mathbf{U}_2 \end{bmatrix} = \mathbf{C}_{[012\ldots s]}\mathbf{KV} \qquad (4.3.43)$$

so that $\mathbf{C}_{[012\ldots s]}\mathbf{K}$ is an important matrix for relating back to the original basis $\mathbf{V}$. If (4.3.43) is used in place of (4.3.32) throughout the foregoing discussion, one is naturally led to the generalization (4.3.42) rather than (4.3.41).

The term *multistandardize* was suggested by Beaton (1964) who recognized the usefulness of the MST operator. The term arises as follows: if a single vector U_i in a basis $\mathbf{U}$ is replaced by $(U_i, U_i)^{-1/2}U_i$ having a unit norm, then the inner product matrix $\mathbf{Q}$ of $\mathbf{U}$ is replaced by dividing row and column i of $\mathbf{Q}$ by $(U_i, U_i)^{-1/2}$. This is the same as the operation MST$[i]$ applied to $\mathbf{Q}$. In the statistical context where U_i is a variable, the transformation $U_i \to (U_i, U_i)^{-1/2}U_i$ reduces U_i to a rescaled variable with unit norm or standard deviation which is often called a *standardized* variable, and so MST$[i]$ is closely related to the *standardization* of variable i. The term *multistandardize* is a generalization referring to standardizing not a single variable but a block of variables, producing not a single variable with unit norm but a block of orthonormal variables.

4.4 SITUATIONS WITH LESS THAN FULL RANK

In Section 4.1 it was pointed out that the definition (4.1.1) for $U_1^*, U_2^*, \ldots, U_r^*$ may be made more general by agreeing to drop from the right side of (4.1.1) any term which is a multiple of U_s^* for any s such that $(U_s^*, U_s^*) = 0$. By similarly dropping terms in U_j^* where $(U_j^*, U_j^*) = 0$ on the right sides of (4.1.2) and (4.1.3) it is easily proved that $U_1^*, U_2^*, \ldots, U_r^*$ are mutually orthogonal in the general case. Recall, of course, that any U_s^* such that $(U_s^*, U_s^*) = 0$ is orthogonal to every V in $\mathscr{E}$.

The condition $(U_s^*, U_s^*) = 0$ means either that $U_s^* = \emptyset$, or that the inner product is of less than full rank, or both.

The possibility $U_s^* = \emptyset$ implies linear dependence among $U_1, U_2, \ldots, U_s$. More precisely, *if the inner product over $\mathscr{E}$ has full rank, if the subspace spanned by $U_1, U_2, \ldots, U_r$ has dimension $s \leq r$, and if the number of U_j^* different from $\emptyset$ is q, then $s = q$ and the subset of q non-$\emptyset$ U_j^* constitute an orthogonal basis of the subspace spanned by $U_1, U_2, \ldots, U_r$.* To prove this it will be shown that the subspaces spanned by $U_1, U_2, \ldots, U_r$ and $U_1^*, U_2^*, \ldots, U_r^*$ are identical. Clearly the latter is contained in the former because linear combinations of $U_1, U_2, \ldots, U_r$ are used to define the latter. Also (4.1.1) expresses each U_i in terms of the $U_1^*, U_2^*, \ldots, U_r^*$, so that the former subspace is contained in the latter, as required. To prove that the dimension of this subspace is q, one need only show that the s non-$\emptyset$ U_j^* which span it are linearly independent. (This was left to the reader as Exercise 3.1.7.)

The theorem just proved shows how the process of successive orthogonalization may, in principle, be used to check on the linear dependence of a set of vectors and to find the dimension of the subspace spanned by these vectors. Since the successive orthogonalization of $U_1, U_2, \ldots, U_r$ contains the successive orthogonalization of $U_1, U_2, \ldots, U_t$ for every $t \leq r$, it produces as a by-product the dimension of each of the subspaces spanned by $U_1, U_2, \ldots, U_t$ for $t = 1, 2, \ldots, r$. It is of interest to note that while the dimensions of these subspaces are affine properties, the structure of Euclidean vector spaces was used in finding them. It follows that if the inner product were changed, resulting in general in a different set of $U_1^*, U_2^*, \ldots, U_r^*$, the property of whether a particular $U_j^* = \emptyset$ or not would not be changed.

Turning now to the possibility that the inner product over $\mathscr{E}$ has less than full rank, suppose that $U_1, U_2, \ldots, U_p$ is a basis of $\mathscr{E}$ and that the inner product has rank f so that the inner product matrix $\mathbf{Q}$ of the basis $\mathbf{V}$ is positive semi-definite symmetric of rank f. Since, as before, the $U_1^*, U_2^*, \ldots, U_p^*$ defined by the general version of (4.1.1) span the same space as $U_1, U_2, \ldots, U_p$, it must be that $U_1^*, U_2^*, \ldots, U_p^*$ form a basis of $\mathscr{E}$, and $U_s^* = \emptyset$ is impossible for any s. Furthermore, it is clear that the set of U_s^* such that $(U_s^*, U_s^*) = 0$ must span the $(p-f)$-dimensional subspace $\mathscr{U}$ of vectors with zero norm and that the remaining U_s^* span a complementary f-dimensional subspace $\mathscr{V}$. In particular, it follows that the number of U_s^* with positive norm must be f. This result shows how in principle to compute the rank of a given positive semi-definite symmetric matrix $\mathbf{Q}$.

The general definition of $\mathbf{U}^*$ discussed above requires that $\mathbf{U} = \mathbf{B}\mathbf{U}^*$ where the elements b_{is} of $\mathbf{B}$ for $i > s$ are chosen to be zero when $(U_s^*, U_s^*) = 0$. However, if such zero elements were to be replaced by arbitrary numbers, the $\mathbf{U}_j^*$ would be altered only by the addition of vectors of zero norm. In particular, the diagonal inner product matrix of $\mathbf{T}$ of $\mathbf{U}^*$ would be the same for each such choice of $\mathbf{B}$, and therefore (4.2.4) would continue to hold. Also, any such $\mathbf{B}$ is triangular with elements unity along the main diagonal and zero above, so that $\mathbf{B}$ has a unique inverse $\mathbf{A}$. Defining $\dot{\mathbf{T}}$ to be the matrix formed by inverting the nonzero elements of $\mathbf{T}$, it follows from (2.6.10) and (2.6.11) that

$$\dot{\mathbf{Q}} = \mathbf{A}'\dot{\mathbf{T}}\mathbf{A} \tag{4.4.1}$$

is a pseudoinverse of $\mathbf{Q}$ for any of the choices of $\mathbf{B}$ and thence of $\mathbf{A}$. Formula (4.4.1) is a generalization of (4.2.5).

The theory of this section has practical implications of several kinds. It is sometimes convenient in statistics to consider sets of variables including some which are known to be linear combinations of others; in effect, this means that linear dependence is built in. In such situations care must be taken not to program an electronic computer to carry out (4.1.1) in its original form, since the attempt to divide by zero will either produce wild results due to rounding error or will stop the machine.

Another possible complication arises when the input variables are not linearly dependent and small values of (U_s^*, U_s^*) are encountered due to empirical relationships among variables. In such situations, blind following of (4.1.1) may again lead to trouble because the value (U_s^*, U_s^*) used at stage s may consist largely of rounding error. In situations where the order of orthogonalization has some latitude, programs may be written which determine the order as the calculation proceeds in a way which controls the problem of small (U_s^*, U_s^*). But if the problem becomes too severe, the computation may need to be abandoned or its precision increased. For the most part, such questions of accuracy of computed values are beyond the scope of this book.

4.5 EXERCISES

4.1.1 Show that the successive orthogonalization of U_1, U_2 in general produces different vectors from the successive orthogonalization of U_2, U_1. What is the exceptional case? Illustrate your answer with a plane diagram.

4.1.2 Show that the subspace spanned by $U_1^*, U_2^*, \ldots, U_s^*$ defined by (4.1.1) is the same as the subspace spanned by $U_1, U_2, \ldots, U_s$.

4.1.3 For any $t \leq s$, show that

$$U_s - \sum_{j=1}^{t-1} \frac{(U_s, U_j^*)}{(U_j^*, U_j^*)} U_j^* \qquad \text{and} \qquad \sum_{j=1}^{t-1} \frac{(U_s, U_j^*)}{(U_j^*, U_j^*)} U_j^*$$

denote the components of U_s along and orthogonal to the subspace spanned by U_1, $U_2, \ldots, U_{t-1}$. In particular, deduce that the mapping $U_s \to U_s^*$ is the orthogonal projection of U_s into the subspace orthogonal to $U_1, U_2, \ldots, U_{s-1}$.

4.1.4 Show that, if $\mathscr{V}$ is the orthogonal complement of $\mathscr{U}$, then $\mathscr{U}$ is the orthogonal complement of $\mathscr{V}$.

4.2.1 Show that, given any basis $\mathbf{U}$ of a p-dimensional Euclidean space $\mathscr{E}$, there exists one and only one *orthogonal* basis $\mathbf{U}^* = \mathbf{AU}$ such that $\mathbf{A}$ is triangular with elements unity along the diagonal and zero above the diagonal. Show also that there exists one and only one *orthonormal* basis $\mathbf{U}^{**} = \mathbf{CU}$ such that $\mathbf{C}$ is triangular with elements zero above the diagonal.

4.2.2 In the notation of Section 4.2, show that

$$\mathbf{T} = \mathbf{AQA}' \qquad \text{and} \qquad \mathbf{T}^{-1} = \mathbf{B}'\mathbf{PB}.$$

4.2.3 Write down the analogues of (4.2.12), (4.2.13), (4.2.14), (4.2.15), (4.2.18), (4.2.19), (4.2.22), and (4.2.25) in terms of $\mathbf{C}$, $\mathbf{D}$, and $\mathbf{I}$ in place of $\mathbf{A}$, $\mathbf{B}$, and $\mathbf{T}$. Show that these may be derived from (4.2.32) and (4.2.33) in the same way that their analogues were derived from (4.2.10) and (4.2.11). Show also that they may be derived alternatively by the direct substitution of $\mathbf{A} = \mathbf{RC}$, $\mathbf{B} = \mathbf{DR}^{-1}$, and $\mathbf{T} = \mathbf{RR}$ into the analogous formulas.

4.2.4 Show that $\mathbf{Q}_{21}\mathbf{Q}_{11}^{-1} = \mathbf{B}_{21}\mathbf{B}_{11}^{-1} = -\mathbf{A}_{22}^{-1}\mathbf{A}_{21} = \mathbf{D}_{21}\mathbf{D}_{11}^{-1} = -\mathbf{C}_{22}^{-1}\mathbf{C}_{21}$ and dually that $\mathbf{P}_{12}\mathbf{P}_{22}^{-1} = \mathbf{A}_{21}'\mathbf{A}_{22}'^{-1} = -\mathbf{B}_{11}'^{-1}\mathbf{B}_{21}' = \mathbf{C}_{21}'\mathbf{C}_{22}'^{-1} = \mathbf{D}_{11}'^{-1}\mathbf{D}_{21}'$.

4.2.5 Show directly that $\mathbf{U}_2 - \mathbf{Q}_{21}\mathbf{Q}_{11}^{-1}\mathbf{U}_1$ is orthogonal to $\mathbf{U}_1$, and hence must be $\mathbf{U}_{2.1}$. Then show that the inner product matrix of $\mathbf{U}_2 - \mathbf{Q}_{21}\mathbf{Q}_{11}^{-1}\mathbf{U}_1$ is $\mathbf{Q}_{21}\mathbf{Q}_{11}^{-1}\mathbf{Q}_{12}$ and deduce that $\mathbf{Q}_{22.1} = \mathbf{Q}_{22} - \mathbf{Q}_{21}\mathbf{Q}_{11}^{-1}\mathbf{Q}_{12}$.

4.2.6 Show that $\mathbf{U}_2 = \mathbf{B}_{21}\mathbf{B}_{11}^{-1}\mathbf{U}_1 + \mathbf{B}_{22}\mathbf{U}_2^*$, and by looking at the expression for U_{s+1} given by the first row of this equality, show that the first row of $\mathbf{B}_{21}\mathbf{B}_{11}^{-1}$ consists of

$$[-a_{\overline{s+1}\,1}, -a_{\overline{s+1}\,2}, \ldots, -a_{\overline{s+1}\,s}],$$

i.e., of the negatives of the first s elements of row $s + 1$ of $\mathbf{A}$. Note that the remaining elements are known, for $a_{\overline{s+1}\,\overline{s+1}} = 1$ and $a_{\overline{s+1}\,t} = 0$ for $t > s + 1$.

4.2.7 By writing $\mathbf{B}_{21}\mathbf{B}_{11}^{-1} = \mathbf{B}_{21}\mathbf{A}_{11}$, show directly that the last column of $\mathbf{B}_{21}\mathbf{B}_{11}^{-1}$ consists of $[b_{\overline{s+1}\,s}, b_{\overline{s+2}\,s}, \ldots, b_{p\,s}]$, i.e., of the elements below the diagonal element of the $(s + 1)$st column of $\mathbf{B}$.

4.2.8 From Exercises 4.2.6 and 4.2.7 deduce that

$$a_{\overline{s+1}\,s} = -b_{\overline{s+1}\,s} \quad \text{for} \quad s = 1, 2, \ldots, p-1.$$

4.2.9 What are the dual results of Exercises 4.2.6 and 4.2.7?

4.2.10 Show that $\mathbf{Q}_{22.1} = \mathbf{Q}_{22} - \mathbf{H}_{21}\mathbf{Q}_{11}\mathbf{H}_{21}'$ and dually that $\mathbf{Q}_{11}^{-1} = \mathbf{P}_{11} - \mathbf{H}_{21}'\mathbf{P}_{22}\mathbf{H}_{21}$.

4.3.1 How many additions or subtractions and how many multiplications or divisions are required to compute **B** and **T** by the elimination procedure of Section 4.3.1? How many are required to compute **B**, **T**, and **A**? How many are required to compute **B**, **T**, **A**, and $\mathbf{Q}^{-1}$? Compare the number of multiplications and divisions in each of these three categories with the number of multiplications required to multiply two $p \times p$ matrices, especially for p large.

4.3.2 The elimination method of Section 4.3.1 may be modified into the *square root method.* This approach bypasses **B** and **A** and finds **D** and **C** directly. Finding **D** by this method may be described as finding the coefficients in the set of equations

$$\begin{aligned}
d_{11}U_1^{**} &= U_1^* = U_1 \\
d_{22}U_2^{**} &= U_2^* = U_2 - d_{21}U_1^{**} \\
&\vdots \\
d_{pp}U_p^{**} &= U_p^* = U_p - d_{p1}U_1^{**} - d_{p2}U_2^{**} \cdots - d_{p\,\overline{p-1}}U_{p-1}^{**}.
\end{aligned}$$

Show that the column of coefficients of U_1^{**} may be computed directly from **Q** as $(U_s, U_1)/(U_1, U_1)^{1/2}$ for $s = 2, 3, \ldots, p$. Show that this column multiplied by its transpose may be subtracted from the last $p - 1$ rows and columns of **Q** to yield $\mathbf{Q}_{22.1}$ with $s = 1$, which completes the first stage of the square root version of the elimination method of finding **D**. Describe the remaining steps required to find **D**, **C**, and $\mathbf{Q}^{-1}$ by this method, illustrating your answer with the matrix **Q** of Example 4.3.

4.3.3 *Triangularization.* The process of successive orthogonalization leads to a somewhat different set of computational procedures when the computations are based directly on the coordinates of the set **U** relative to an orthonormal basis **W** of $\mathscr{E}$ rather than on the inner product matrix **Q** of the set **U**. As in the text, there is a choice between expressions involving $\mathbf{U}^*$, and hence **A** and **B**, or expressions involving $\mathbf{U}^{**}$, and hence **C** and **D**. Because of the convenience of having orthogonal matrices represent relations between the orthonormal sets **W** and $\mathbf{U}^{**}$, the latter representation is used here.

Suppose that **E** is any $s \times p$ matrix of maximum rank s for some s on $1 \leq s \leq p$. Then **E** may viewed as defining a set of linearly independent vectors $\mathbf{U} = \mathbf{EW}$ where **W** is an orthonormal basis of $\mathscr{E}$. The orthonormal set $\mathbf{U}^{**}$ produced by successive orthogonalization of **U** may be expressed as $\mathbf{U}^{**} = \mathbf{GW}$ where **G** is an $s \times p$ matrix obeying $\mathbf{GG}' = \mathbf{I}$. Since $\mathbf{U} = \mathbf{D}_{11}\mathbf{U}^{**}$ where $\mathbf{D}_{11}$ is lower triangular,

$$\mathbf{E} = \mathbf{D}_{11}\mathbf{G} \tag{4.5.1}$$

which may be called the *triangularization* of **E**.

There are various ways to compute **G** and $\mathbf{D}_{11}$ of which three will be sketched here. The reader is asked to supply missing details as an exercise.

a) *Triangularization by assimilation.* Suppose that the rows of $\mathbf{E}$ are denoted by $\mathbf{E}_1, \mathbf{E}_2, \ldots, \mathbf{E}_s$, that the rows of $\mathbf{G}$ are denoted by $\mathbf{G}_1, \mathbf{G}_2, \ldots, \mathbf{G}_s$, and that the (i,j) element of $\mathbf{D}_{11}$ is denoted by d_{ij} with $d_{ij} = 0$ for $j > i$. From (4.5.1), $\mathbf{E}_1 = d_{11}\mathbf{G}_1$ and, since $\mathbf{G}_1\mathbf{G}_1' = 1$, $d_{11} = \pm(\mathbf{E}_1\mathbf{E}_1')^{1/2}$, thus determining $\mathbf{G}_1$. Now suppose that the first s rows of both $\mathbf{D}_{11}$ and $\mathbf{G}$ are determined. Then $\mathbf{G}_{r+1}\mathbf{W}$ is found by removing from $\mathbf{E}_{r+1}\mathbf{W}$ components along $\mathbf{G}_1\mathbf{W}, \mathbf{G}_2\mathbf{W}, \ldots, \mathbf{G}_r\mathbf{W}$ and scaling for unit length. Thus

$$k\mathbf{G}_{r+1} = \mathbf{E}_{r+1} - (\mathbf{E}_{r+1}\mathbf{G}_1')\mathbf{G}_1 - (\mathbf{E}_{r+1}\mathbf{G}_2')\mathbf{G}_2 \cdots - (\mathbf{E}_{r+1}\mathbf{G}_r')\mathbf{G}_r, \qquad (4.5.2)$$

and after computing the right side of (4.5.2) one finds k from $k^2 = (\mathbf{G}_{r+1}\mathbf{G}_{r+1}')$. Note that row $r + 1$ of $\mathbf{D}_{11}$ is given by $[\mathbf{E}_{r+1}\mathbf{G}_1', \mathbf{E}_{r+1}\mathbf{G}_2', \ldots, \mathbf{E}_{r+1}\mathbf{G}_r', k]$.

b) *Triangularization by elimination.* After finding $\mathbf{G}_1$, the components of each of $\mathbf{E}_2, \mathbf{E}_3, \ldots, \mathbf{E}_s$ along $\mathbf{G}_1$ may be removed yielding, say, $\mathbf{E}_{2.1}, \mathbf{E}_{3.1}, \ldots, \mathbf{E}_{s.1}$. After scaling, $\mathbf{E}_{2.1}$ yields $\mathbf{G}_2$. Components of $\mathbf{E}_{3.1}, \mathbf{E}_{4.1}, \ldots, \mathbf{E}_{s.1}$ along $\mathbf{G}_2$ are then removed, and so on. Further details are left to the reader.

c) *Triangularization by Householder transformations* (Householder, 1958). This method produces an $s \times p$ matrix $\mathbf{D}^*$ and a $p \times p$ orthogonal matrix $\mathbf{G}^*$ such that $\mathbf{E} = \mathbf{D}^*\mathbf{G}^*$ and the (i,j) elements of $\mathbf{D}^*$ are zero for $j > i$. Dropping the last $p - s$ columns of $\mathbf{D}^*$ yields $\mathbf{D}_{11}$ and dropping the last $p - s$ rows of $\mathbf{G}^*$ yields $\mathbf{G}$ where (4.5.1) holds. Because the last $p - s$ columns of $\mathbf{D}^*$ are all $\mathbf{0}$, dropping them along with the last $p - s$ rows of $\mathbf{G}^*$ does not affect the product $\mathbf{D}^*\mathbf{G}^*$, but the truncated product is then in the form required of $\mathbf{D}_{11}\mathbf{G}$ and so must be $\mathbf{D}_{11}\mathbf{G}$. $\mathbf{D}^*$ and $\mathbf{G}^*$ are found using a sequence of $p \times p$ orthogonal matrices $\mathbf{H}_1, \mathbf{H}_2, \ldots, \mathbf{H}_s$ and successively writing $\mathbf{E} = (\mathbf{E})(\mathbf{I}) = (\mathbf{E}\mathbf{H}_1')(\mathbf{H}_1) = (\mathbf{E}\mathbf{H}_1'\mathbf{H}_2')(\mathbf{H}_2\mathbf{H}_1) = \cdots = (\mathbf{E}\mathbf{H}_1'\mathbf{H}_2' \cdots \mathbf{H}_s')(\mathbf{H}_s\mathbf{H}_{s-1} \cdots \mathbf{H}_1)$ where $\mathbf{D}^* = \mathbf{E}\mathbf{H}_1'\mathbf{H}_2' \cdots \mathbf{H}_s'$ and $\mathbf{G}^* = \mathbf{H}_s\mathbf{H}_{s-1} \cdots \mathbf{H}_1$. $\mathbf{H}_1$ is chosen to be an elementary orthogonal matrix such that $\mathbf{E}\mathbf{H}_1'$ has a first row whose only nonzero element is its first. In other words, the linear transformation $\mathbf{X} \to \mathbf{X}\mathbf{H}_1'$ carries $\mathbf{E}_1 \to [k, 0, 0, \ldots, 0]$, or, since such transformations are self-inverting, carries $[k, 0, 0, \ldots, 0] \to \mathbf{E}_1$. The construction of such an $\mathbf{H}_1$ was described in Section 3.4. More generally, $\mathbf{E}\mathbf{H}_1'\mathbf{H}_2' \cdots \mathbf{H}_r'$ has the property that its (i,j) elements are zero for $j > i$ and $i = 1, 2, \ldots, r$. Then $\mathbf{H}_{r+1}$ is chosen to be a matrix whose first r rows and columns are like an identity matrix but whose remaining part is an $(s - r) \times (s - r)$ elementary orthogonal matrix such that the superdiagonal elements of row $r + 1$ of $\mathbf{E}\mathbf{H}_1'\mathbf{H}_2' \cdots \mathbf{H}_r'$ are eliminated when multiplied by $\mathbf{H}_{r+1}'$. The definition of $\mathbf{H}_{r+1}$ for $r = 1, 2, \ldots, s - 1$ is essentially the same as that of $\mathbf{H}_1$ in a different context. The reader is invited to supply further details.

4.3.4 In addition to the sweep operator SWP[i], define the following operators on $p \times p$ matrices:

IOP: the identity operation.
NOP: the operator which changes all signs.
MOP[i]: the operator which changes the signs of the off-diagonal elements in row and column i.
POP[i]: the operator which changes the signs of the (i, i) element and the elements (j, k) with $j \neq i$ and $k \neq i$.

Suppose that the operator defined by the successive application of the operators $A, B, \ldots, C$ is denoted by $C \cdots BA$. Show that

$$\begin{aligned}
\text{SWP}[i]\text{SWP}[i] &= \text{MOP}[i] \\
\text{MOP}[i]\text{SWP}[i] &= \text{SWP}[i]\text{MOP}[i] \\
\text{SWP}[i]\text{POP}[i] &= \text{NOPSWP}[i] \\
\text{SWP}[i]\text{NOP} &= \text{POP}[i]\text{SWP}[i] \\
\text{NOP} &= \text{SWP}[i]\text{NOPSWP}[i].
\end{aligned}$$

What are the analogous identities involving RSW[i] instead of SWP[i]? Show that the SWP[i] and RSW[j] commute except for confusion of signs. Describe this sign confusion in detail.

4.3.5 *Inversion of nonsymmetric matrices.* Suppose that $\mathbf{G}$ is a $p \times p$ nonsingular matrix and is regarded as carrying the basis $\mathbf{V}$ of a vector space $\mathscr{E}$ into a basis $\mathbf{W} = \mathbf{GV}$ of $\mathscr{E}$. Suppose that $\mathbf{U}^{(s)}$ is the set of vectors $W_1, W_2, \ldots, W_s, V_{s+1}, \ldots, V_p$, and suppose that $\mathbf{U}^{(s)}$ is a basis of $\mathscr{E}$ for $s = 1, 2, \ldots, p - 1$. The basis $\mathbf{V}$ may be modified by stages into $\mathbf{W}$ via

$$\mathbf{V} = \mathbf{U}^{(0)} \to \mathbf{U}^{(1)} \to \mathbf{U}^{(2)} \to \cdots \to \mathbf{U}^{(p)} = \mathbf{W}.$$

Define $\mathbf{H}^{(s)}$ to be a matrix with (i, j) element $h_{ij}^{(s)}$ whose row i for $i = 1, 2, \ldots, s$ expresses $-V_i$ in terms of $\mathbf{U}^{(s)}$ and for $i = s + 1, s + 2, \ldots, p$ expresses W_i in terms of $\mathbf{U}^{(s)}$, i.e.,

$$-V_i = \sum_{j=1}^{s} h_{ij}^{(s)} W_j + \sum_{j=s+1}^{p} h_{ij}^{(s)} V_j$$

for $i = 1, 2, \ldots, p$, and

$$W_i = \sum_{j=1}^{s} h_{ij}^{(s)} W_j + \sum_{j=s+1}^{p} h_{ij}^{(s)} V_j$$

for $i = s + 1, s + 2, \ldots, p$. Show that $\mathbf{H}^{(s+1)} = \text{SWP}[s + 1]\mathbf{H}^{(s)}$, and deduce that $\mathbf{G}^{-1} = -\text{SWP}[1, 2, \ldots, p]\mathbf{G}$.

4.3.6 *Solution of linear equations.* The formulation of Exercise 4.3.5 will be continued here. Suppose that $\mathbf{Y}$ is a $q \times p$ matrix; consider finding a $q \times p$ matrix $\mathbf{X}$ such that

$$\mathbf{XG} = \mathbf{Y}.$$

The problem is thus to solve a collection of q sets of linear equations each having p unknowns and each having the same matrix of coefficients $\mathbf{G}$. In vector terms, $\mathbf{YV}$ determines q points in $\mathscr{E}$, and the problem is to express these q points as $\mathbf{XW}$ in terms of the basis $\mathbf{W} = \mathbf{GV}$. Suppose these q points are $\mathbf{Z}^{(s)}\mathbf{U}^{(s)}$ in terms of the basis $\mathbf{U}^{(s)}$. Then passage from $\mathbf{Y}$ to $\mathbf{X}$ may be achieved via

$$\mathbf{Y} = \mathbf{Z}^{(0)} \to \mathbf{Z}^{(1)} \to \mathbf{Z}^{(2)} \to \cdots \to \mathbf{Z}^{(p)} = \mathbf{X}.$$

Show that

$$\begin{bmatrix} \mathbf{H}^{(s+1)} \\ \mathbf{Z}^{(s+1)} \end{bmatrix} = \text{SWP}[s + 1]\begin{bmatrix} \mathbf{H}^{(s)} \\ \mathbf{Z}^{(s)} \end{bmatrix},$$

so that

$$\begin{bmatrix} -\mathbf{G}^{-1} \\ \mathbf{X} \end{bmatrix} = \text{SWP}[1, 2, \ldots, p]\begin{bmatrix} \mathbf{G} \\ \mathbf{Y} \end{bmatrix}.$$

Note that although the sweep operator was defined in Section 4.3.2 for square matrices, the same definition is used here for a $(p + q) \times p$ matrix.

4.3.7 The computational methods in Exercises 4.3.5 and 4.3.6 may not be applied with arbitrary **G** because the sets $\mathbf{U}^{(s)}$ are not necessarily linearly independent. Show that the method may be applied for some rearrangement of the rows of **G**, i.e., that for some $W_{\pi(1)}$ the set $W_{\pi(1)}, V_2, \ldots, V_p$ must be a basis such that given such a $W_{\pi(1)}$ there must be a $W_{\pi(2)}$ such that the set $W_{\pi(1)}, W_{\pi(2)}, V_3, \ldots, V_p$ is a basis, and so on. Show that this leads to performance of a sweeping operation at stage s where the row $\pi(s)$ and the column s selected for special treatment are in general different, i.e., the definition of sweep operations must be slightly generalized. It may be further shown that $\pi(s)$ may be chosen to be any i such that $h_{is}^{(s-1)} \neq 0$, where $h_{is}^{(s-1)}$ refers to the generalized process with rows taken in the order $\pi(1), \pi(2), \ldots, \pi(s-1)$. It should now be clear how to carry out matrix inversion and solution of linear equations for arbitrary **G**.

4.3.8 Describe in detail the set of calculations required to carry out the ASM$[p+1, p+2, \ldots, p+r; 1, 2, \ldots, s]$ operator using the scheme of r successive stages.

4.3.9 Suppose that RSM$[p+1, p+2, \ldots, p+r; 1, 2, \ldots, s]$ denotes the operator inverse of ASM$[p+1, p+2, \ldots, p+r; 1, 2, \ldots, s]$. Describe the three characterizations of the RSM operator analogous to the three characterizations of the ASM operator given in Section 4.3.3.

4.3.10 What are the special features of the output of

$$\text{MST}[1, 2, \ldots, s]\text{MST}[s+1, s+2, \ldots, p][\mathbf{Q}, \mathbf{I}]$$

and

$$\text{MST}[1]\text{MST}[2] \ldots \text{MST}[p][\mathbf{Q}, \mathbf{I}]?$$

4.4.1 Suppose that the vectors U_1, U_2, U_3, U_4, U_5 are all nonzero and span a two-dimensional subspace of a three-dimensional Euclidean space. How many and which of the $U_1^*, U_2^*, \ldots, U_5^*$ produced by successive orthogonalization are $\varnothing$? Suppose that **Q** denotes the 5×5 inner product matrix of $U_1, U_2, \ldots, U_5$. Show that **Q** is a positive semi-definite symmetric matrix of rank 2.

4.4.2 Describe a computing procedure to determine the rank of a symmetric positive semi-definite matrix **Q**.

4.4.3 Suppose that a positive semi-definite symmetric matrix

$$\mathbf{Q} = \begin{bmatrix} \mathbf{Q}_{11} & \mathbf{Q}_{12} \\ \mathbf{Q}_{21} & \mathbf{Q}_{22} \end{bmatrix}$$

of rank f is regarded as an inner product matrix relative to a basis

$$\mathbf{U} = \begin{bmatrix} \mathbf{U}_1 \\ \mathbf{U}_2 \end{bmatrix} \text{ of a vector space } \mathscr{E},$$

where the partitions refer as usual to s and $p - s$ rows and columns. Suppose that $\mathscr{U}_1$ denotes the intersection of the subspace $\mathscr{U}$ of $\mathscr{E}$ of vectors with zero norm with the subspace spanned by $\mathbf{U}_1$. Suppose that $\mathscr{V}_1$ is any complementary subspace to $\mathscr{U}_1$ in the subspace spanned by $\mathbf{U}_1$. Show that $\mathscr{U}_1$ consists of vectors with zero norm and $\mathscr{V}_1$ consists of vectors with nonzero norm. Show that the dimension f_1 of $\mathscr{V}_1$ is the same as the rank of $\mathbf{Q}_{11}$ and that $f_1 \leq s$ and $f_1 \leq f$. Show that any V in $\mathscr{E}$ decomposes uniquely into a component in $\mathscr{V}_1$ and a component orthogonal to $\mathscr{V}_1$ (cf. Exercise 3.6.5), and define the latter set of components of $\mathbf{U}_2$ to be $\mathbf{U}_{2.1}$. Show that the definitions of $\mathbf{U}_{2.1}$ differ for different $\mathscr{V}_1$ but only by vectors of zero norm. Show that the inner product matrix $\mathbf{Q}_{22.1}$ of $\mathbf{U}_{2.1}$ is consequently well-defined in the sense of not depending on the choice of $\mathscr{V}_1$.

4.4.4 Following the notation of Exercise 4.4.3, suppose that $\dot{\mathbf{Q}}_{11}$ is a pseudoinverse of $\mathbf{Q}_{11}$ defined as in (3.6.8) with the roles of $\mathbf{Q}$, $\mathscr{U}$, and $\mathscr{V}$ played here by $\mathbf{Q}_{11}$, $\mathscr{U}_1$, and $\mathscr{V}_1$. Show that

$$\mathbf{Q}_{22.1} = \mathbf{Q}_{22} - \mathbf{Q}_{21}\dot{\mathbf{Q}}_{11}\mathbf{Q}_{12}.$$

In particular, $\dot{\mathbf{Q}}_{11}$ may be taken as (4.4.1) with any choice of the null columns of $\mathbf{B}$, in which case

$$\mathbf{Q}_{22.1} = \mathbf{B}_{22}\mathbf{T}_{22}\mathbf{B}'_{22}.$$

In another particular case $\dot{\mathbf{Q}}_{11}$ may be *the* pseudoinverse of $\mathbf{Q}_{11}$ (cf. Exercise 3.6.4).

4.4.5 Suppose that the first s rows and columns of $\mathbf{Q}$ in Exercise 4.4.3 are further partitioned into $s = f_1 + (s - f_1)$ so that

$$\mathbf{Q} = \begin{bmatrix} \mathbf{Q}_{111} & \mathbf{Q}_{112} & \mathbf{Q}_{121} \\ \mathbf{Q}_{121} & \mathbf{Q}_{122} & \mathbf{Q}_{122} \\ \mathbf{Q}_{211} & \mathbf{Q}_{212} & \mathbf{Q}_{22} \end{bmatrix}$$

where

$$\mathbf{Q}_{11} = \begin{bmatrix} \mathbf{Q}_{111} & \mathbf{Q}_{112} \\ \mathbf{Q}_{121} & \mathbf{Q}_{122} \end{bmatrix}$$

and

$$\mathbf{Q}_{21} = [\mathbf{Q}_{211}, \mathbf{Q}_{212}] = \begin{bmatrix} \mathbf{Q}_{121} \\ \mathbf{Q}_{122} \end{bmatrix}' = \mathbf{Q}'_{12}.$$

Suppose also that the first s rows and columns are arranged such that $\mathbf{Q}_{111}$ has full rank f_1.

Show that SWP$[1, 2, \ldots, f_1]\mathbf{Q}$ has the form

$$\begin{bmatrix} -\mathbf{Q}_{111}^{-1} & \mathbf{H}_{112} & \mathbf{H}_{121} \\ \mathbf{H}_{121} & \mathbf{0} & \mathbf{0} \\ \mathbf{H}_{211} & \mathbf{0} & \mathbf{Q}_{22.1} \end{bmatrix}$$

where $[\mathbf{H}_{211}, \mathbf{0}] = \begin{bmatrix} \mathbf{H}_{121} \\ \mathbf{0} \end{bmatrix}'$ is one choice for $\mathbf{H}_{21}$ in Exercise 4.4.3 and $\mathbf{Q}_{22.1}$ is the uniquely defined inner product matrix of $\mathbf{U}_{2.1}$ arising from any choice of $\mathbf{H}_{21}$. Note that in computational practice a subset of f_1 of the first s rows and columns having a full rank inner product matrix may not be known. In this case one need only set out to perform SWP[1], SWP[2], . . . , SWP[s] in order, omitting any operation which is undefined because of a zero element in the pivotal diagonal position. As a result one will carry out just f_1 sweeping operations and arrive at a matrix like SWP$[1, 2, \ldots, f_1]\mathbf{Q}$ above, except that generally a different subset of f_1 of the first s rows and columns will have been swept.

4.4.6 Supposing that $\mathbf{A}$ is any $p \times q$ matrix of rank $q < p$, show how the idea of triangularization may be used to find the pseudoinverse of $\mathbf{A}$ defined in Exercise 3.4.11.

CHAPTER 5

THE RELATION BETWEEN TWO INNER PRODUCTS

5.1 BASIC THEORY

The statistical techniques of canonical correlation analysis, multiple linear discriminant analysis, and principal component analysis are the most sophisticated methods of multivariate statistical analysis considered in this book. Each of these techniques may be naturally viewed as relating two different inner products on the same vector space $\mathscr{E}$. Consideration of such relationships leads to a mathematical theory of *eigenvalues* and *eigenvectors* (sometimes called *characteristic values* and *characteristic vectors*, *proper values* and *proper vectors*, or *latent roots* and *latent vectors*) in Euclidean spaces.

Suppose that π_1 and π_2 are symbols for two different inner product functions on a p-dimensional vector space $\mathscr{E}$, and suppose that the inner product of U and V according to π_i is denoted by $(U, V)_i$ for $i = 1, 2$. One might ask: for what vectors V in $\mathscr{E}$ is the ratio

$$\lambda = (V, V)_1/(V, V)_2 \tag{5.1.1}$$

maximized or minimized? The answer to this question and many related questions comes from the following theory which indicates that in terms of a specially chosen basis $\mathbf{W}$ of $\mathscr{E}$ the relationship between π_1 and π_2 is simply and clearly displayed. Until stated otherwise, π_1 and π_2 will be assumed to have full rank p.

The theory depends on the following simple lemmas.

Lemma 5.1.1. *The supremum of the ratio* (5.1.1) *is achieved for at least one vector V in $\mathscr{E}$.*

In proving this lemma, one need only consider vectors V such that $(V, V)_2 = 1$, for the ratio (5.1.1) is invariant under multiplication of V by a scalar; consequently any value of (5.1.1) taken on by some U in $\mathscr{E}$ is also taken on by $V = (U, U)_2^{-1/2}U$, satisfying $(V, V)_2 = 1$. In analytic terms, with reference to an orthonormal basis of π_2, the problem is to find $\boldsymbol{\alpha}$ which maximizes $\boldsymbol{\alpha}\mathbf{Q}_1\boldsymbol{\alpha}'$ subject to the restriction $\boldsymbol{\alpha}\boldsymbol{\alpha}' = 1$. The existence of such an $\boldsymbol{\alpha}$ follows because the function $\boldsymbol{\alpha}\mathbf{Q}_1\boldsymbol{\alpha}'$ is continuous and finite over the closed domain $\boldsymbol{\alpha}\boldsymbol{\alpha}' = 1$.

Lemma 5.1.2. *Suppose that W_1 is a vector which maximizes* (5.1.1) *over all V in $\mathscr{E}$. Then any vector orthogonal to W_1 according to π_1 is also orthogonal to W_1 according to π_2 and vice versa, i.e., the $(p-1)$-dimensional subspace $\mathscr{V}_1$ of $\mathscr{E}$ orthogonal to W_1 is the same for π_1 and π_2.*

The lemma will be proved by contradiction. Suppose that $\mathscr{V}_{1i}$ is the subspace of $\mathscr{E}$ orthogonal to W_1 according to π_i, for $i = 1, 2$, and suppose that $\mathscr{V}_{11}$ and $\mathscr{V}_{12}$ are different. This would imply that a vector W_1^* orthogonal to $\mathscr{V}_{11}$ according to π_2 is not a multiple of W_1. Thus W_1 may be decomposed into

$$W_1 = W_{11} + W_{12}, \tag{5.1.2}$$

where W_{11} lies along W_2^*, W_{12} lies in $\mathscr{V}_{11}$, and $(W_{11}, W_{12})_2 = 0$. Also, since $\mathscr{V}_{11}$ and $\mathscr{V}_{12}$ are different, W_{12} is different from $\emptyset$. Thus

$$(W_1, W_1)_2 = (W_{11}, W_{11})_2 + (W_{12}, W_{12})_2,$$

whence

$$(W_{11}, W_{11})_2 < (W_1, W_1)_2. \tag{5.1.3}$$

On the other hand, according to π_1, W_1 and W_{12} are orthogonal, so that $(W_{11}, W_{11})_1 = (W_1, W_1)_1 + (W_{12}, W_{12})_1$, whence

$$(W_{11}, W_{11})_1 > (W_1, W_1)_1. \tag{5.1.4}$$

From (5.1.3) and (5.1.4) it follows that

$$\frac{(W_{11}, W_{11})_1}{(W_{11}, W_{11})_2} > \frac{(W_1, W_1)_1}{(W_1, W_1)_2}, \tag{5.1.5}$$

which is impossible since W_1 maximizes (5.1.1). Thus the lemma is proved by contradiction.

Lemmas 5.1.1 and 5.1.2 are used to prove:

Theorem 5.1.1. *There exists a basis $\mathbf{W}$ of $\mathscr{E}$ which is orthogonal according to both π_1 and π_2.*

The existence of such a basis is demonstrated by constructing it. For W_1 take any vector which maximizes (5.1.1). Suppose that $\mathscr{V}_1$ is the subspace orthogonal to W_1 according to both π_1 and π_2. Now consider π_1 and π_2 as inner products over $\mathscr{V}_1$. Choose W_2 to be any vector in $\mathscr{V}_1$ which maximizes (5.1.1) over V in $\mathscr{V}_1$. Suppose that $\mathscr{V}_2$ is the subspace of $\mathscr{V}_1$ orthogonal to W_2 according to both π_1 and π_2. Choose W_3 to be any vector in $\mathscr{V}_2$ which maximizes (5.1.1) over V in $\mathscr{V}_2$. Continue thus until $\mathbf{W}$ with the required property is constructed.

The vectors $W_1, W_2, \ldots, W_p$ of a basis $\mathbf{W}$ which is orthogonal relative to both π_1 and π_2 will be called *eigenvectors of* π_1 *relative to* π_2. The corresponding

$$\lambda_i = (W_i, W_i)_1/(W_i, W_i)_2 \tag{5.1.6}$$

will be called *eigenvalues of* π_1 *relative to* π_2. The constructive proof of Theorem 5.1.1 leaves some latitude in the choice of eigenvectors. Theorem 5.1.2 will describe in detail the range of possible bases $\mathbf{W}$ allowed by this constructive proof and will show that the construction always produces the same set of ordered eigenvalues $\lambda_1, \lambda_2, \ldots, \lambda_p$. Theorem 5.1.3 will show that, apart from order, any basis of eigenvectors must belong to the class of such bases specified in Theorem 5.1.2, and consequently that the set of eigenvalues of π_1 relative to π_2, again apart from order, is uniquely determined.

If $[W_1, W_2, \ldots, W_p]$ is a basis orthogonal relative to both π_1 and π_2 and if $[c_1, c_2, \ldots, c_p]$ is any set of nonzero coefficients, then $[c_1W_1, c_2W_2, \ldots, c_pW_p]$ is also a basis orthogonal relative to both π_1 and π_2. The latter basis will be called a *scaled* version of the former. It follows that a basis of eigenvectors may be unique only up to arbitrary changes of scale. In other words, it is possible only that the set of p one-dimensional subspaces spanned by $W_1, W_2, \ldots, W_p$ can be uniquely determined. Necessary and sufficient conditions that such uniqueness obtains are implied by the following theorem.

Theorem 5.1.2. *Suppose that* $\lambda_1, \lambda_2, \ldots, \lambda_p$ *and* $W_1, W_2, \ldots, W_p$ *denote a particular set of eigenvalues and corresponding eigenvectors of* π_1 *relative to* π_2 *found by the construction procedure used in the proof of Theorem* 5.1.1. *Then any other realization of the construction procedure (resulting from an alternative choice of* W_i *at any stage) yields the same set of* $\lambda_1, \lambda_2, \ldots, \lambda_p$. *Suppose that* $s_1 < s_2 < \cdots < s_r$ *denote the set of indices such that*

$$\begin{aligned} &\lambda_1 = \cdots = \lambda_{s_1} \\ &>\lambda_{s_1+1} = \cdots = \lambda_{s_2} \\ &>\lambda_{s_2+1} = \cdots = \lambda_{s_3} \\ &\cdots \\ &>\lambda_{s_r+1} = \cdots = \lambda_p. \end{aligned} \tag{5.1.7}$$

Then the subspaces $\mathcal{W}_1, \mathcal{W}_2, \ldots, \mathcal{W}_{r+1}$ *spanned by* $[W_1, \ldots, W_{s_1}]$, $[W_{s_1+1}, \ldots, W_{s_2}], \ldots, [W_{s_r+1}, \ldots, W_p]$ *are uniquely determined under any realization of the construction procedure. The inner product* π_1 *is a multiple of* π_2 *over each of* $\mathcal{W}_1, \mathcal{W}_2, \ldots, \mathcal{W}_{r+1}$. *The sets* $[W_1, \ldots, W_{s_1}]$, $[W_{s_1+1}, \ldots, W_{s_2}], \ldots, [W_{s_r+1}, \ldots, W_p]$ *are any orthogonal bases of their corresponding subspaces. In particular, if*

$$\lambda_1 > \lambda_2 > \cdots > \lambda_p, \tag{5.1.8}$$

then $W_1, W_2, \ldots, W_p$ *are uniquely determined up to a set of scale factors.*

The proof of Theorem 5.1.2 is omitted, but requires only a careful following-out of the constructive proof of Theorem 5.1.1. The difference is that one must now check into the uniqueness of W_s at each stage and show that the range of possibilities is as specified by the theorem in terms of subspaces $\mathscr{W}_1, \mathscr{W}_2, \ldots, \mathscr{W}_{r+1}$ over which the ratio of norms is constant.

Theorem 5.1.3. *The class of bases* **W** *defined as in Theorem* 5.1.2 *may be characterized as the only bases which are orthogonal relative to both* π_1 *and* π_2. *Consequently, the eigenvalues of* π_1 *relative to* π_2 *are a well-defined set of numbers.*

The proof will show that any contemplated basis element $\boldsymbol{\delta}\mathbf{W}$ must be a member of a basis in the permitted class, where $\boldsymbol{\delta} = [\delta_1, \delta_2, \ldots, \delta_p]$ and $\mathbf{W}$ is a basis in the permitted class which is orthonormal relative to π_2. The subspace of vectors orthogonal to $\boldsymbol{\delta}\mathbf{W}$ according to π_2 consists of those $\boldsymbol{\alpha}\mathbf{W}$ satisfying

$$\sum_{i=1}^{p} \delta_i \alpha_i = 0. \tag{5.1.9}$$

Similarly

$$\sum_{i=1}^{p} \lambda_i \delta_i \alpha_i = 0 \tag{5.1.10}$$

is the condition for $\boldsymbol{\delta}\mathbf{W}$ and $\boldsymbol{\alpha}\mathbf{W}$ to be orthogonal relative to π_1. Since $\boldsymbol{\delta}\mathbf{W}$ is a member of a doubly orthogonal basis, the vectors $\boldsymbol{\alpha}\mathbf{W}$ satisfying (5.1.9) must coincide with those satisfying (5.1.10). When the λ_i are distinct, (5.1.9) and (5.1.10) define the same subspaces only when all the δ_i are zero except one, i.e., $\boldsymbol{\delta}\mathbf{W}$ is simply an element of $\mathbf{W}$ rescaled. If equality holds for a set of λ_i, then the corresponding δ_i for this set may be nonzero while the remaining δ_i are zero. Again $\boldsymbol{\delta}\mathbf{W}$ is an element of a permitted basis. Thus Theorem 5.1.3 is proved.

It is often convenient to fix the arbitrary scaling of a basis $\mathbf{W}$ of eigenvectors by making it orthonormal according to π_1 or π_2. For example, if $\mathbf{W}$ is scaled so that $(W_i, W_i)_2 = 1$ for $i = 1, 2, \ldots, p$, then $(W_i, W_i)_1 = \lambda_i$ for $i = 1, 2, \ldots, p$, i.e., $\mathbf{W}$ has inner product matrix $\mathbf{L}$ according to π_1 where $\mathbf{L}$ is a diagonal matrix with diagonal elements $\lambda_1, \lambda_2, \ldots, \lambda_p$. In this case, if $U = \boldsymbol{\alpha}\mathbf{W}$ and $V = \boldsymbol{\beta}\mathbf{W}$, then

$$(U, V)_1 = \sum_{i=1}^{p} \lambda_i \alpha_i \beta_i, \tag{5.1.11}$$

whereas

$$(U, V)_2 = \sum_{i=1}^{p} \alpha_i \beta_i. \tag{5.1.12}$$

Formula (5.1.11) shows that π_1 and π_2 are differently weighted sums of p semi-definite inner products each of rank 1, i.e., defining

$$(U, V)_{(i)} = \alpha_i \beta_i \qquad \text{for} \qquad i = 1, 2, \ldots, p, \tag{5.1.13}$$

it follows that

$$(U, V)_1 = \sum_{i=1}^{p} \lambda_i (U, V)_{(i)} \tag{5.1.14}$$

and

$$(U, V)_2 = \sum_{i=1}^{p} (U, V)_{(i)}.$$

The requirement that π_1 and π_2 both have full rank will now be relaxed. In the full rank case, each λ_i must be finite and nonzero. If π_1 or π_2 or both are semi-definite, and if no non-$\emptyset$ V has zero norm relative to both π_1 and π_2, then it may be checked that the full rank theory goes through unchanged except that zero and infinite values of the λ_i are allowed. Finally, suppose that $\mathscr{U}_i$ is the subspace with zero norm according to π_i for $i = 1, 2$, and suppose that $\mathscr{U}_1 \cap \mathscr{U}_2$ is larger than $\emptyset$. Then it may be checked that the theory goes through in any subspace $\mathscr{V}$ complementary to $\mathscr{U}_1 \cap \mathscr{U}_2$. Moreover, the eigenvalues do not depend on the choice of $\mathscr{V}$ and the eigenvectors for different choices of $\mathscr{V}$ differ by arbitrary zero-norm vectors in $\mathscr{U}_1 \cap \mathscr{U}_2$.

The theory of this section treats π_1 and π_2 asymmetrically only in that the ratios of norms had π_1 in the numerator and π_2 in the denominator. It is clear that reversing the roles of π_1 and π_2 results in reciprocal values for eigenvalues but does not affect the eigenvectors.

5.2 RELATIONS BETWEEN TWO ELLIPSOIDS

Given an affine space $\mathscr{E}$, two inner products π_1 and π_2 on $\mathscr{E}$ may be defined by specifying their respective ellipsoids in $\mathscr{E}$. The symbols π_1 and π_2 may be used to denote the ellipsoids as well as the inner products. In ellipsoid language, Theorem 5.1.1 may be expressed as:

> ***Theorem 5.2.1.*** *Given any two p-dimensional ellipsoids π_1 and π_2 with a common center, there exists a set of p lines through the center which define sets of conjugate axes for both π_1 and π_2.*

The directions of these p lines are determined by the line segments $\emptyset W_1$, $\emptyset W_2, \ldots, \emptyset W_p$ where $W_1, W_2, \ldots, W_p$ is a basis of eigenvectors of π_1 relative to π_2. The eigenvalue λ_i is the ratio of the squared length of the semi-axis of π_2 in the direction of W_i to the squared length of the semi-axis of π_1 in the same direction for $i = 1, 2, \ldots, p$. This situation is pictured in Fig. 5.2.1 in two dimensions. It is left to the reader to rewrite similarly Theorems 5.1.2 and 5.1.3 in ellipsoid terms.

Consider the geometric picture of the ellipsoids π_1 and π_2 when $\mathscr{E}$ is regarded as a Euclidean space with inner product π_2. In this Euclidean space, π_2 becomes the unit sphere, and the special conjugate axes of π_1 are called *principal axes.* The eigenvalues λ_i are the inverses of the squared lengths of the *principal semi-axes*. These concepts are familiar in two dimensions, as illustrated in Fig. 5.2.2.

Note that, if equality among eigenvalues occurs so that the norms are in a constant ratio over a subspace $\mathscr{W}$ as in Theorem 5.1.2, then the intersections of the ellipsoids π_1 and π_2 with $\mathscr{W}$ are ellipsoids which differ only by a scale factor.

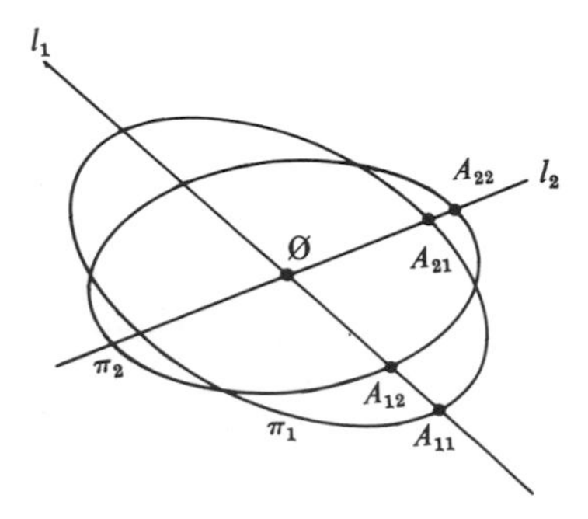

Fig. 5.2.1. Ellipses π_1 and π_2 centered at Ø in the plane. Lines l_1 and l_2 define a pair of common conjugate axes. The eigenvalues of π_1 relative to π_2 are $\lambda_i = [ØA_{i2}/ØA_{i1}]^2$ for $i = 1, 2$.

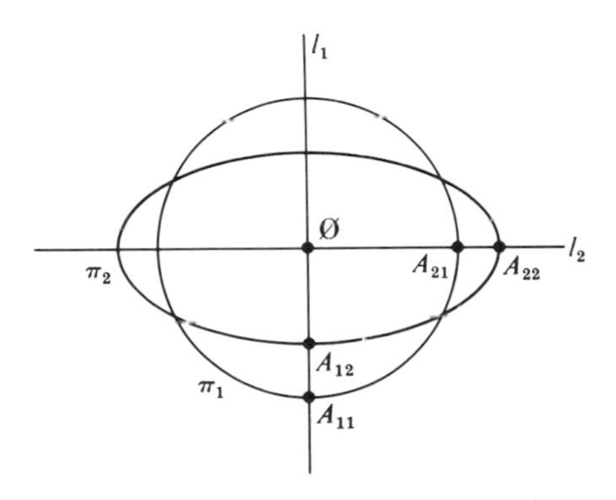

Fig. 5.2.2. The same picture as Fig. 5.2.1 drawn with $ØA_{21}$ and $ØA_{11}$ perpendicular with the same (unit) length, so that π_1 is a (unit) circle.

5.3 RELATED MATRIX THEORY

The basic theory of Section 5.1 can be used to derive corresponding and equivalent theory relating positive definite symmetric matrices. Suppose that $\mathbf{V}$ is any basis of a vector space $\mathscr{E}$, and that inner products π_1 and π_2 are defined in $\mathscr{E}$ using positive definite matrices $\mathbf{Q}_1$ and $\mathbf{Q}_2$ as inner product matrices relative to $\mathbf{V}$. For a basis $\mathbf{W} = \mathbf{AV}$ the corresponding inner product matrices are $\mathbf{AQ}_1\mathbf{A}'$ and $\mathbf{AQ}_2\mathbf{A}'$. Theorem 5.1.1 then yields the purely analytic theorem:

> ***Theorem 5.3.1.*** *Given any pair* $\mathbf{Q}_1$ *and* $\mathbf{Q}_2$ *of positive definite symmetric matrices, there exists a nonsingular matrix* $\mathbf{A}$ *such that both* $\mathbf{AQ}_1\mathbf{A}'$ *and* $\mathbf{AQ}_2\mathbf{A}'$ *are diagonal matrices with positive diagonal elements.*

Alternatively, the two inner products π_1 and π_2 could be defined relative to a basis $\mathbf{U}$ which is orthonormal relative to π_2, so that only the inner product matrix $\mathbf{Q}$ of π_1 relative to $\mathbf{U}$ is needed to specify both π_1 and π_2. If Theorem 5.1.1 is applied in this case, and if the basis $\mathbf{W}$ is scaled to be orthonormal according to π_2, then $\mathbf{W} = \mathbf{CU}$ for some orthogonal matrix $\mathbf{C}$. Thus:

Theorem 5.3.2. *Given any positive definite symmetric matrix* $\mathbf{Q}$*, there exists an orthogonal matrix* $\mathbf{C}$ *such that* $\mathbf{CQC}'$ *is a diagonal matrix with positive diagonal elements.*

The reader may check that Theorems 5.3.1 and 5.3.2 can be deduced from each other and so are equivalent, and that either Theorem 5.3.1 or 5.3.2 implies Theorem 5.1.1.

Suppose that the diagonal elements of $\mathbf{AQ}_1\mathbf{A}'$ and $\mathbf{AQ}_2\mathbf{A}'$ as found in Theorem 5.3.1 are denoted by $\mu_{11}, \mu_{12}, \ldots, \mu_{1p}$ and $\mu_{21}, \mu_{22}, \ldots, \mu_{2p}$. Then one may define

$$\lambda_i = \frac{\mu_{1i}}{\mu_{2i}} \tag{5.3.1}$$

for $i = 1, 2, \ldots, p$ and, if desired, the rows of $\mathbf{A}$ may be arranged so that $\lambda_1 \geq \lambda_2 \geq \cdots \geq \lambda_p$. Note that the individual rows $\boldsymbol{\alpha}_1, \boldsymbol{\alpha}_2, \ldots, \boldsymbol{\alpha}_p$ of $\mathbf{A}$ determine the individual μ_{1i}, μ_{2i}, and λ_i because $\boldsymbol{\alpha}_i\mathbf{Q}_1\boldsymbol{\alpha}_i' = \mu_{1i}$ and $\boldsymbol{\alpha}_i\mathbf{Q}_2\boldsymbol{\alpha}_i' = \mu_{2i}$, so that

$$\lambda_i = \frac{\boldsymbol{\alpha}_i\mathbf{Q}_1\boldsymbol{\alpha}_i'}{\boldsymbol{\alpha}_i\mathbf{Q}_2\boldsymbol{\alpha}_i'}. \tag{5.3.2}$$

If $\mathbf{Q}_1$ and $\mathbf{Q}_2$ are regarded as the inner product matrices of two inner products π_1 and π_2 relative to a basis $\mathbf{V}$ of a vector space $\mathscr{E}$, then it is clear that $\boldsymbol{\alpha}_1\mathbf{V}$, $\boldsymbol{\alpha}_2\mathbf{V}, \ldots, \boldsymbol{\alpha}_p\mathbf{V}$ form an orthogonal basis relative to π_1 and π_2 and

$$\lambda_i = \frac{\boldsymbol{\alpha}_i\mathbf{Q}_1\boldsymbol{\alpha}_i'}{\boldsymbol{\alpha}_i\mathbf{Q}_2\boldsymbol{\alpha}_i'} = \frac{(\boldsymbol{\alpha}_i\mathbf{V}, \boldsymbol{\alpha}_i\mathbf{V})_1}{(\boldsymbol{\alpha}_i\mathbf{V}, \boldsymbol{\alpha}_i\mathbf{V})_2}. \tag{5.3.3}$$

Thus the basis $\mathbf{W} = \mathbf{AV}$ consists of the eigenvectors of π_1 relative to π_2 and $\lambda_1, \lambda_2, \ldots, \lambda_p$ are the corresponding eigenvalues. Since they relate to the corresponding vector space quantities, it is natural to say that $\lambda_1, \lambda_2, \ldots, \lambda_p$ defined by (5.3.1) are the *eigenvalues of* $\mathbf{Q}_1$ *relative to* $\mathbf{Q}_2$ and that the rows $\boldsymbol{\alpha}_1, \boldsymbol{\alpha}_2, \ldots, \boldsymbol{\alpha}_p$ of $\mathbf{A}$ are the *associated eigenvectors of* $\mathbf{Q}_1$ *relative to* $\mathbf{Q}_2$.

If $\mathbf{Q}_2 = \mathbf{I}$ the eigenvalues and eigenvectors of $\mathbf{Q}_1$ relative to $\mathbf{I}$ are referred to simply as the *eigenvalues* and *eigenvectors* of $\mathbf{Q}_1$ (with no reference to $\mathbf{Q}_2$). Thus it may be checked that the rows of $\mathbf{C}$ in Theorem 5.3.2 are a set of eigenvectors of $\mathbf{Q}$, and the associated eigenvalues are given by the diagonal elements of $\mathbf{CQC}'$.

If the eigenvalues of a positive definite symmetric matrix $\mathbf{Q}$ are denoted by $\lambda_1, \lambda_2, \ldots, \lambda_p$, and if corresponding orthonormal eigenvectors are denoted by $\boldsymbol{\gamma}_1, \boldsymbol{\gamma}_2, \ldots, \boldsymbol{\gamma}_p$, then

$$\mathbf{CQC}' = \mathbf{L} \tag{5.3.4}$$

where $\mathbf{C}$ is an orthogonal matrix with rows $\boldsymbol{\gamma}_1, \boldsymbol{\gamma}_2, \ldots, \boldsymbol{\gamma}_p$ and $\mathbf{L}$ is a diagonal matrix with diagonal elements $\lambda_1, \lambda_2, \ldots, \lambda_p$. From (5.3.4),

$$\mathbf{C}'\mathbf{C}\mathbf{Q}\mathbf{C}'\mathbf{C} = \mathbf{C}'\mathbf{L}\mathbf{C}, \qquad \text{or}$$

$$\mathbf{Q} = \sum_{i=1}^{p} \lambda_i \boldsymbol{\gamma}_i' \boldsymbol{\gamma}_i. \tag{5.3.5}$$

This formula is equivalent to (5.1.11) or (5.1.14).

5.4 COMPUTATIONAL METHODS

5.4.1. A brief description of some basic approaches. The eigenvalues and eigenvectors of a given $\mathbf{Q}$ may *not* be computed in a finite number of steps based on the arithmetic operations of adding, multiplying, dividing, and extracting roots, except when $p \leq 4$ and the approach of Section 5.5 is followed. This is an important difference from the theory of Chapter 4. As a result, the practical determination of eigenvalues and eigenvectors must ultimately involve some iterative procedure of successive approximations, and this is rarely feasible except with an electronic computer. There are many competing approaches which have different advantages in different situations. The subject is highly developed and highly technical; consequently, this section will attempt only to convey some understanding without complete details of two methods, namely the Jacobi and QR methods, which have seen considerable use in recent years. Further theory, methods, and details may be found in Wilkinson (1965).

The method of Jacobi (1846) is easily described from first principles. It applies to any real symmetric matrix $\mathbf{Q}$. The aim is to find an orthogonal matrix $\mathbf{C}$ such that $\mathbf{L} = \mathbf{C}\mathbf{Q}\mathbf{C}'$ is a diagonal matrix. Or in geometric terms, the aim is to pass from an original orthonormal basis $\mathbf{U}$ of a Euclidean space $\mathscr{E}$ to a new orthonormal basis $\mathbf{W} = \mathbf{C}\mathbf{U}$ such that the inner product defined by the inner product matrix $\mathbf{Q}$ relative to $\mathbf{U}$ has a diagonal inner product matrix $\mathbf{C}\mathbf{Q}\mathbf{C}'$ relative to $\mathbf{W}$. In these terms, the approach is to find a sequence of orthonormal bases $\mathbf{U} = \mathbf{U}^{(0)} \to \mathbf{U}^{(1)} \to \mathbf{U}^{(2)} \to \cdots$ such that $\lim_{s\to\infty} \mathbf{U}^{(s)} = \mathbf{W}$. This means that the corresponding sequence of orthogonal $\mathbf{C}^{(s)}$ defined by $\mathbf{U}^{(s)} = \mathbf{C}^{(s)}\mathbf{U}$ converges to $\mathbf{C}$ and the sequence $\mathbf{Q}^{(s)} = \mathbf{C}^{(s)}\mathbf{Q}\mathbf{C}^{(s)\prime}$ converges to $\mathbf{C}\mathbf{Q}\mathbf{C}' = \mathbf{L}$.

This basic idea is to make each transformation $\mathbf{U}^{(s)} \to \mathbf{U}^{(s+1)}$ a plane rotation affecting only a pair of elements of $\mathbf{U}^{(s)}$. Thus at stage s, one chooses indices r and t and defines

$$\begin{aligned} U_r^{(s+1)} &= \cos\theta U_r^{(s)} + \sin\theta U_t^{(s)}, \\ U_t^{(s+1)} &= -\sin\theta U_r^{(s)} + \cos\theta U_t^{(s)}, \qquad \text{and} \\ U_j^{(s+1)} &= U_j^{(s)} \qquad \text{for} \qquad j \neq r, j \neq t. \end{aligned} \tag{5.4.1}$$

The angle θ is chosen to carry out the two-dimensional eigenvalue computation in the space spanned by $U_r^{(s)}$ and $U_t^{(s)}$, i.e., θ is determined by the requirement that $\mathbf{Q}^{(s+1)}$ shall have zeros in the symmetric (r, t) and (t, r) positions. (See Exercise 5.4.1.) A rule must be established for determining r and t at each stage s, but the choice of a rule is not generally critical for convergence and many such rules will be apparent once the proof of convergence is understood.

Passage from $\mathbf{Q}^{(s)}$ to $\mathbf{Q}^{(s+1)}$ annihilates one pair of off-diagonal elements (r, t) and (t, r), but a later stage involving one of r and t will in general bring back a nonzero value in the (r, t) and (t, r) positions. This explains why a finite number of stages cannot be used to annihilate one by one all the symmetric pairs of off-diagonal elements. Nevertheless there is a very simple sense in which each stage brings one measurably closer to the limiting diagonal form. The theory depends on a lemma which asserts:

Lemma 5.4.1. *The sum of squares of the p^2 elements of $\mathbf{Q}^{(s+1)}$ is identical to the sum of squares of the p^2 elements of $\mathbf{Q}^{(s)}$, so that this sum of squares is constant through all the stages. Moreover, at stage s, the invariant sum may be broken into three sums each of which is invariant, these parts consisting of the sum of squares of the* 4 *elements in both rows and columns r or t, the sum of squares of the $(p-2)^2$ elements in neither rows nor columns r or t, and the sum of squares of the remaining $2(p-2)$ elements in rows r or t but not columns r or t or in columns r or t but not rows r or t.*

From the lemma it may be easily seen that one effect of the passage from $\mathbf{Q}^{(s)}$ to $\mathbf{Q}^{(s+1)}$ is to reduce the sum of squares of the off-diagonal elements by $2q_{rt}^{(s)2}$ while increasing the sum of squares of the diagonal elements by the same amount, where $q_{rt}^{(s)}$ denotes the (r, t) element of $\mathbf{Q}^{(s)}$.

It is natural, in view of the above lemma to measure the distance from $\mathbf{U}^{(s)}$ to $\mathbf{W}$ by the sum of squares of the off-diagonal elements of $\mathbf{Q}^{(s)}$, for, if this sum could be reduced to zero, then the required diagonalization would be precisely achieved. Also, it is clear that many rules of choosing r and t at stage s will result in this distance tending to zero as $s \to \infty$. The most obvious rule is to choose r and t $(r \neq t)$ to maximize $|q_{rt}^{(s)}|$. However, for large p, an electronic computer may find it wasteful of time to locate this maximum for each s. Consequently, a rule taking any (r, t) pair such that $|q_{rt}^{(s)}|$ exceeds some assigned threshold is often used. When no values of $|q_{rt}^{(s)}|$ exceed the threshold, then the threshold may be lowered, and so on, until the distance from $\mathbf{U}^{(s)}$ to $\mathbf{W}$ is arbitrarily small.

In the practical application of the method, one starts with $\mathbf{Q}$ and $\mathbf{I}$ in a set of memory locations in a computer. The contents of these registers are then altered by stages so that $[\mathbf{Q}, \mathbf{I}] \to [\mathbf{Q}^{(1)}, \mathbf{C}^{(1)}] \to [\mathbf{Q}^{(2)}, \mathbf{C}^{(2)}] \to \cdots$, finally stopping at a stage for which $\mathbf{Q}^{(s)}$ is acceptably close to diagonal. For further details see Exercise 5.4.1.

Example 5.4. The eigenvalues and eigenvectors of

$$\mathbf{Q} = \begin{bmatrix} 19.1434 & 9.0356 & 9.7634 & 3.2394 \\ 9.0356 & 11.8658 & 4.6232 & 2.4746 \\ 9.7634 & 4.6232 & 12.2978 & 3.8794 \\ 3.2394 & 2.4746 & 3.8794 & 2.4604 \end{bmatrix}$$

were computed as below by the Jacobi method:

$$\mathbf{Q}^{(1)} = \begin{bmatrix} 25.245387 & 0 & 10.678569 & 4.0694975 \\ 0 & 5.7638128 & -1.6328245 & 0.2377977 \\ 10.678569 & -1.6328245 & 12.297800 & 3.879400 \\ 4.0694975 & 0.2377977 & 3.879400 & 2.460400 \end{bmatrix},$$

$$\mathbf{C}^{(1)} = \begin{bmatrix} 0.8287229 & 0.5596592 & 0 & 0 \\ -0.5596592 & 0.8287229 & 0 & 0 \\ 0 & 0 & 1.0 & 0 \\ 0 & 0 & 0 & 1.0 \end{bmatrix},$$

$$\mathbf{Q}^{(2)} = \begin{bmatrix} 31.259260 & -0.8012371 & 0 & 5.4495008 \\ -0.8012371 & 5.7638128 & -1.4227210 & 0.2377977 \\ 0 & -1.4227210 & 6.2839258 & 1.3832912 \\ 5.4495008 & 0.2377977 & 1.3832912 & 2.460400 \end{bmatrix},$$

$$\mathbf{C}^{(2)} = \begin{bmatrix} 0.7220871 & 0.4876451 & 0.4907062 & 0 \\ -0.5596592 & 0.8287229 & 0 & 0 \\ -0.4066594 & -0.2746282 & 0.8713251 & 0 \\ 0 & 0 & 0 & 1.0 \end{bmatrix},$$

$$\mathbf{Q}^{(3)} = \begin{bmatrix} 32.255954 & -0.7453803 & 0.2488708 & 0 \\ -0.7453803 & 5.7638128 & -1.4227210 & 0.3780697 \\ 0.2488708 & -1.4227210 & 6.2839258 & 1.3607196 \\ 0 & 0.3780697 & 1.3607196 & 1.4637057 \end{bmatrix},$$

$$\mathbf{C}^{(3)} = \begin{bmatrix} 0.7103045 & 0.4796880 & 0.4826991 & 0.179912 \\ -0.5596592 & 0.8287229 & 0 & 0 \\ -0.4066594 & -0.2746282 & 0.8713251 & 0 \\ -0.1299122 & -0.08773323 & -0.08828395 & 0.9836827 \end{bmatrix},$$

and so on to

$$\mathbf{Q}^{(16)} = \begin{bmatrix} 32.280122 & -0.0000016 & 0 & 0 \\ -0.0000016 & 4.9317448 & 0 & -0.0000005 \\ 0 & 0 & 7.5673957 & 0 \\ 0 & -0.0000005 & 0 & 0.9881297 \end{bmatrix},$$

$$\mathbf{C}^{(16)} = \begin{bmatrix} 0.7214751 & 0.4526087 & 0.4921702 & 0.1799647 \\ -0.6868510 & 0.4923919 & 0.4466156 & 0.2938031 \\ -0.03142772 & -0.7305346 & 0.6688321 & 0.1341453 \\ 0.08198438 & -0.1378935 & -0.3331163 & 0.9291380 \end{bmatrix},$$

$$\mathbf{Q}^{(17)} = \begin{bmatrix} 32.280121 & 0 & 0 & 0 \\ 0 & 4.9317446 & 0 & -0.0000005 \\ 0 & 0 & 7.5673957 & 0 \\ 0 & -0.0000005 & 0 & 0.9881297 \end{bmatrix},$$

$$\mathbf{C}^{(17)} = \begin{bmatrix} 0.7214751 & 0.4526087 & -0.4921702 & 0.1799647 \\ -0.6868510 & 0.4923919 & 0.4466156 & 0.2938031 \\ -0.03142772 & -0.7305346 & 0.6688321 & 0.1341453 \\ -0.08198438 & -0.1378935 & -0.3331163 & 0.9291380 \end{bmatrix}.$$

At this point the iterations were stopped and $\mathbf{Q}^{(17)}$ declared diagonal to the order of accuracy carried in these calculations. The diagonal elements of $\mathbf{Q}^{(17)}$ are the computed (approximate) eigenvalues, and $\mathbf{C}^{(17)}$ is the computed (approximate) matrix of eigenvectors.

The QR method of Francis (1961, 1962) is a modern refinement of a very old concept called *powering*. The idea is best understood in terms of the linear transformation $\mathbf{U} \to \mathbf{QU}$ (cf. Exercise 3.4.10) which sends the eigenvectors $\mathbf{W} = \mathbf{CU}$ into $\mathbf{CQU} = \mathbf{CQC'W} = \mathbf{LW}$, i.e., this is the transformation which simply stretches the component along each eigenvector by a factor which is the corresponding eigenvalue. In other terms, the transformation carries

$$\boldsymbol{\alpha}\mathbf{U} \to \beta_1\lambda_1 W_1 + \beta_2\lambda_2 W_2 + \cdots + \beta_p\lambda_p W_p \tag{5.4.2}$$

where $\boldsymbol{\beta} = \boldsymbol{\alpha}\mathbf{C}'$ expresses the $\mathbf{W}$ coordinates of $\boldsymbol{\alpha}\mathbf{U}$. Moreover, the result of successively applying this transformation s times, namely $\mathbf{U} \to \mathbf{Q}^s\mathbf{U}$, carries

$$\boldsymbol{\alpha}\mathbf{U} \to \beta_1\lambda_1^s W_1 + \beta_2\lambda_2^s W_2 + \cdots + \beta_p\lambda_p^s W_p. \tag{5.4.3}$$

Assuming for simplicity the strict ordering $\lambda_1 > \lambda_2 > \cdots > \lambda_p$, it is clear that, provided $\boldsymbol{\alpha}$ is chosen so that $\beta_1 \neq 0$, the first coefficient $\beta_1\lambda_1^s$ in (5.4.3) comes to dominate all the others as $s \to \infty$. Thus, the sequence of vectors $\boldsymbol{\alpha}\mathbf{Q}, \boldsymbol{\alpha}\mathbf{Q}^2, \ldots, \boldsymbol{\alpha}\mathbf{Q}^s, \ldots$ must tend, after scaling for unit norm, to the first eigenvector, which is the first row of $\mathbf{C}$. At the same time the ratio of the norms of $\boldsymbol{\alpha}\mathbf{Q}^{s+1}$ and $\boldsymbol{\alpha}\mathbf{Q}^s$ tends to λ_1. This is an old method of computing the largest eigenvalue and its associated eigenvector. It may be applied again to the right side of (5.3.5) with the first term removed to yield the second eigenvalue and eigenvector, and so on.

Instead of starting from a single vector $\boldsymbol{\alpha}\mathbf{U}$, the QR method starts from a basis $\mathbf{AU}$ and determines all the eigenvectors in one sequence of iterations. Formula (5.4.3) generalizes to

$$\mathbf{AU} \to \begin{bmatrix} b_{11}\lambda_1^s W_1 + b_{12}\lambda_2^s W_2 + \cdots + b_{1p}\lambda_p^s W_p \\ b_{21}\lambda_1^s W_1 + b_{22}\lambda_2^s W_2 + \cdots + b_{2p}\lambda_p^s W_p \\ \cdot \\ \cdot \\ \cdot \\ b_{p1}\lambda_1^s W_1 + b_{p2}\lambda_2^s W_2 + \cdots + b_{pp}\lambda_p^s W_p^s \end{bmatrix}, \tag{5.4.4}$$

where $\mathbf{B} = \mathbf{AC}'$. Assuming for $r = 1, 2, \ldots, p$ that the first r rows and columns of $\mathbf{B}$ define a nonsingular $r \times r$ matrix, because $\lambda_1 > \lambda_2 > \cdots > \lambda_p$ it is clear that for $r = 1, 2, \ldots, p$ the subspace spanned by the first r elements in the right side of (5.4.4) tends as $s \to \infty$ to the subspace spanned by $W_1, W_2, \ldots, W_r$. It follows that, if the basis on the right side of (5.4.4) is orthogonalized to yield an orthonormal basis, the sequence of orthonormal bases thus defined for $s = 0, 1, 2, \ldots$ tends to the basis $\mathbf{W}$ of eigenvectors as $s \to \infty$. This sequence of bases will be denoted by $\mathbf{U}^{(s)} = \mathbf{C}^{(s)}\mathbf{U}$ for $s = 0, 1, 2, \ldots$ where the coordinate matrices $\mathbf{C}^{(s)}$ tend to $\mathbf{C}$ and the inner product matrices $\mathbf{Q}^{(s)} = \mathbf{C}^{(s)}\mathbf{QC}^{(s)\prime}$ tend to $\mathbf{L}$ as $s \to \infty$.

The computations are carried out by following the steps $[\mathbf{A}, \mathbf{Q}] \to [\mathbf{C}^{(0)}, \mathbf{Q}^{(0)}] \to [\mathbf{C}^{(1)}, \mathbf{Q}^{(1)}] \to \cdots$, and these computations are conveniently described using the concept of triangularization discussed in Exercise 4.3.3. Thus $\mathbf{C}^{(0)}$ is defined by

$$\mathbf{A} = \mathbf{DC}^{(0)}, \tag{5.4.5}$$

where $\mathbf{D}$ is triangular with zeros above the diagonal, and

$$\mathbf{Q}^{(0)} = \mathbf{C}^{(0)}\mathbf{QC}^{(0)\prime}. \tag{5.4.6}$$

For $s = 0, 1, 2, \ldots$, the orthogonal matrix $\mathbf{K}^{(s)}$ such that $\mathbf{U}^{(s+1)} = \mathbf{K}^{(s)}\mathbf{U}^{(s)}$ may be defined by

$$\mathbf{Q}^{(s)} = \mathbf{D}^{(s)}\mathbf{K}^{(s)}, \tag{5.4.7}$$

where again $\mathbf{D}^{(s)}$ is triangular with zeros above the diagonal. Having $\mathbf{K}^{(s)}$, one finds

$$\mathbf{C}^{(s+1)} = \mathbf{K}^{(s)}\mathbf{C}^{(s)} \tag{5.4.8}$$

and

$$\mathbf{Q}^{(s+1)} = \mathbf{K}^{(s)}\mathbf{Q}^{(s)}\mathbf{K}^{(s)\prime} = \mathbf{K}^{(s)}\mathbf{D}^{(s)}, \tag{5.4.9}$$

and is ready for the next stage. The justification of (5.4.7) is provided by showing that it leads to the correct $\mathbf{C}^{(s)}$, i.e., that

$$\mathbf{AQ}^{s} = \mathbf{FC}^{(s)}, \tag{5.4.10}$$

where $\mathbf{F}$ is a triangular matrix with zeros above the diagonal. To demonstrate (5.4.10), note that

$$\begin{aligned} \mathbf{Q}^{(s)} &= \mathbf{K}^{(s-1)}\mathbf{Q}^{(s-1)}\mathbf{K}^{(s-1)\prime} \\ &= \mathbf{K}^{(s-1)}\mathbf{K}^{(s-2)}\mathbf{Q}^{(s-2)}\mathbf{K}^{(s-2)\prime}\mathbf{K}^{(s-1)\prime} \\ &\;\cdot \\ &\;\cdot \\ &\;\cdot \\ &= \mathbf{K}^{(s-1)}\ldots\mathbf{K}^{(1)}\mathbf{C}^{(0)}\mathbf{QC}^{(0)\prime}\mathbf{K}^{(1)\prime}\ldots\mathbf{K}^{(s-1)\prime} \\ &= \mathbf{C}^{(s)}\mathbf{QC}^{(s)\prime} \end{aligned} \tag{5.4.11}$$

from which

$$\mathbf{Q}^{(s)}\mathbf{C}^{(s)} = \mathbf{C}^{(s)}\mathbf{Q}. \tag{5.4.12}$$

Applying (5.4.8), (5.4.7), and (5.4.12) in order yields

$$\mathbf{D}\mathbf{D}^{(0)}\mathbf{D}^{(1)}\cdots\mathbf{D}^{(s)}\mathbf{C}^{(s+1)} = [\mathbf{D}\mathbf{D}^{(0)}\mathbf{D}^{(1)}\ldots\mathbf{D}^{(s-1)}\mathbf{C}^{(s+1)}]\mathbf{Q} \qquad (5.4.13)$$

and applying (5.4.13) for $s - 1, s - 2, \ldots, 0$ followed by (5.4.5) yields

$$\mathbf{D}\mathbf{D}^{(0)}\mathbf{D}^{(1)}\ldots\mathbf{D}^{(s-1)}\mathbf{C}^{(s)} = \mathbf{A}\mathbf{Q}^{s}, \qquad (5.4.14)$$

which is in the form (5.4.10) with

$$\mathbf{F} = \mathbf{D}\mathbf{D}^{(0)}\mathbf{D}^{(1)}\ldots\mathbf{D}^{(s-1)}.$$

Obviously, the initial choice of **A** can greatly affect the rate of convergence of the QR method. For example, if by a lucky guess **A** were exactly **C** then one iteration would produce the exact correct answer. Likewise, if **A** were near **C** in some sense then one would expect fewer iterations to be needed. The usefulness of the QR method is greatly enhanced by a trick choice of **A** which *tridiagonalizes* **Q**.

The $p \times p$ symmetric matrix **Q** is said to be *tridiagonalized* by the orthogonal matrix **G** provided that

$$\mathbf{T} = \mathbf{G}\mathbf{Q}\mathbf{G}' \qquad (5.4.15)$$

has (i, j) elements $t_{ij} = 0$ if $|j - i| > 1$.

A happy combination of circumstances makes this idea important for eigenvalue calculations. First, it may be carried out by a succession of $p - 1$ elementary orthogonal transformations and is therefore computationally highly tractable. Second, it obviously yields an inner product matrix **T** which will in general be much closer to the derived **L** than is the original **Q**, so that it is attractive as a first step in several approaches to eigenvalue computation. Third, the QR method has the property that, if $\mathbf{Q}^{(0)}$ is tridiagonal, then the whole sequence $\mathbf{Q}^{(s)}$ for $s = 1, 2, \ldots$ is tridiagonal, so that the choice of **A** to be the tridiagonalizing **G** of (5.4.15) means that the whole QR iteration procedure involves only tridiagonal inner product matrices. This may be especially important for large p because it means that $\mathbf{Q}^{(s)}$ may be stored in $2p - 1$ memory registers of a computer rather than the $p(p + 1)/2$ registers required in general. The procedure for tridiagonalizing **Q** by Householder transformations will be described in the following paragraph. For a proof that the QR method preserves the tridiagonal form the reader is referred to Wilkinson (1965).

T in (5.4.15) is produced by a sequence of steps $\mathbf{T} = \mathbf{T}^{(0)} \to \mathbf{T}^{(1)} \to \cdots \to \mathbf{T}^{(p-1)} = \mathbf{T}$, where $\mathbf{T}^{(s-1)}$ has zeros in positions (i, j) and (j, i) for $j > i + 1$ and $i = 1, 2, \ldots, s - 1$. The next stage uses an orthogonal matrix $\mathbf{J}^{(s)}$ to create $\mathbf{T}^{(s)} = \mathbf{J}^{(s)}\mathbf{T}^{(s-1)}\mathbf{J}^{(s)\prime}$ which has the required zeros in the sth row and column. The end result after $p - 1$ stages is then (5.4.15) with

$$\mathbf{G} = \mathbf{J}^{(p-1)}\mathbf{J}^{(p-2)}\ldots\mathbf{J}^{(1)}.$$

$\mathbf{J}^{(s)}$ has the form

$$\mathbf{J}^{(s)} = \begin{bmatrix} \mathbf{I} & \mathbf{0} \\ \mathbf{0} & \mathbf{L}^{(s)} \end{bmatrix}, \tag{5.4.16}$$

where $\mathbf{I}$ has dimensions $s \times s$ and $\mathbf{L}^{(s)}$ is a $(p - s) \times (p - s)$ elementary orthogonal matrix. $\mathbf{J}^{(s)}$ carries the basis $\mathbf{V}^{(s-1)}$ with inner product matrix $\mathbf{T}^{(s-1)}$ into the basis $\mathbf{V}^{(s)} = \mathbf{J}^{(s)}\mathbf{V}^{(s-1)}$ with inner product matrix $\mathbf{T}^{(s)}$ but operates only on the last $p - s$ elements of $\mathbf{V}^{(s-1)}$. Consider any orthogonal transformation leaving $V_1^{(s-1)}, \ldots, V_s^{(s-1)}$ fixed and sending $V_{s+1}^{(s-1)}$ into $V = \sum_{s+1}^{p} t_{si}^{(s-1)} V_i^{(s-1)}$, where $t_{ij}^{(s-1)}$ denotes the (i, j) element of $\mathbf{T}^{(s-1)}$. Any vector $W = \sum_{s+1}^{p} c_{s+i} V_{s+i}^{(s-1)}$ is orthogonal to V according to the original inner product if and only if $\sum_{s+1}^{p} c_{s+i} t_{si}^{(s-1)} = 0$ and is orthogonal to $V_s^{(s-1)}$ if and only if $[0, 0, \ldots, 0, c_{s+i}, \ldots, c_p]\mathbf{T}^{(s-1)}[0, 0, \ldots, 1, 0, \ldots, 0]' = 0$. But these two conditions are identical, so that any transformation of this type is a candidate for $\mathbf{J}^{(s)}$. The suggested $\mathbf{J}^{(s)}$ employs for $\mathbf{L}^{(s)}$ in (5.4.16) the $(p - s) \times (p - s)$ elementary orthogonal matrix which reflects in the bisector of the angle between $V_{s+1}^{(s-1)}$ and $\sum_{s+1}^{p} t_{si}^{(s-1)} V_i^{(s-1)}$.

The QR method may be conveniently and elegantly carried out using a long sequence of Householder transformations. The first $p - 1$ of these reduce $\mathbf{Q}$ to tridiagonal form. Then each iteration of the QR method proper requires a triangularization which can be carried out by $p - 1$ Householder transformations as described in part (*c*) of Exercise 4.3.3. The QR method now appears to be favored by numerical analysts, since it generally performs well, regarding both speed and round-off error. Because of its dependence on powering, however, the rate of convergence of the QR method is sensitive to the ratios among $\lambda_1, \lambda_2, \ldots, \lambda_p$, which are of course initially unknown. For example, if $\lambda_1/\lambda_2 \gg 1$ and $\lambda_2/\lambda_3 \gg 1$ but $\lambda_3, \lambda_4, \ldots, \lambda_p$ have ratios close to unity, then the QR method will quickly find the first two eigenvalues and eigenvectors, but may be slow to converge to the rest.

The Jacobi method was used in the examples of Chapter 9, 10, and 11.

5.4.2. The SDG operator. The computing operation of finding $\mathbf{L}$ and $\mathbf{C}$ from $\mathbf{Q}$ will be written in this book as an operator SDG applied to the pair $[\mathbf{Q}, \mathbf{I}]$ yielding the pair $[\mathbf{L}, \mathbf{C}]$. SDG abbreviates step-diagonalize as in Beaton (1964). More precisely, the notation

$$[\mathbf{L}, \mathbf{C}] = \mathrm{SDG}[1, 2, \ldots, p][\mathbf{Q}, \mathbf{I}] \tag{5.4.17}$$

will be used. The bracket $[1, 2, \ldots, p]$ indicates that all p rows and columns of $\mathbf{Q}$ were used. In many statistical applications, the eigenvalue analysis is applied only to a subset of the rows and columns of $\mathbf{Q}$. For example, selecting rows and columns $1, 2, \ldots, s$, one would write

$$[\dot{\mathbf{L}}, \dot{\mathbf{C}}] = \mathrm{SDG}[1, 2, \ldots, s][\mathbf{Q}, \mathbf{I}], \tag{5.4.18}$$

where

$$\dot{\mathbf{C}} = \begin{bmatrix} \mathbf{C}_{11} & \mathbf{0} \\ \mathbf{0} & \mathbf{I} \end{bmatrix} \tag{5.4.19}$$

with $\mathbf{C}_{11}$ the matrix of eigenvectors of $\mathbf{Q}_{11}$ and

$$\dot{\mathbf{L}} = \dot{\mathbf{C}}\mathbf{Q}\dot{\mathbf{C}}', \tag{5.4.20}$$

the partitions referring in the obvious way to the first s and last $p - s$ rows and columns. The extension of the SDG operator to any subset of rows and columns should now be clear.

One further extension of the operator notion is often used. For any $p \times p$ matrix $\mathbf{K}$, define

$$[\dot{\mathbf{L}}, \dot{\mathbf{K}}] = \mathrm{SDG}[1, 2, \ldots, s][\mathbf{Q}, \mathbf{K}] \tag{5.4.21}$$

to be a generalization of (5.4.16) where $\dot{\mathbf{K}} = \dot{\mathbf{C}}\mathbf{K}$. Thus, if the eigenvalue analysis starts with a basis $\mathbf{U} = \mathbf{KV}$, then the SDG operator (5.4.21) produces the bases $\dot{\mathbf{W}} = \dot{\mathbf{C}}\mathbf{U} = \dot{\mathbf{C}}\mathbf{KV}$ directly in terms of $\mathbf{V}$. For example, if $\mathbf{Q}_1$ and $\mathbf{Q}_2$ are inner product matrices relative to a basis $\mathbf{V}$ and if the eigenvalues and eigenvectors of $\mathbf{Q}_1$ relative to $\mathbf{Q}_2$ are required, then one might first compute $\mathrm{MST}[1, 2, \ldots, p][\mathbf{Q}_2, \mathbf{I}] = [\mathbf{I}, \mathbf{K}]$. In terms of the basis $\mathbf{U} = \mathbf{KV}$, one then needs the eigenvalues of $\mathbf{KQ}_1\mathbf{K}'$ relative to $\mathbf{I}$, so the operator $\mathrm{SDG}[1, 2, \ldots, p]$ $[\mathbf{KQ}_1\mathbf{K}', \mathbf{K}]$ produces $[\mathbf{L}, \mathbf{CK}]$ where $\mathbf{CK}$ expresses the eigenvectors in terms of the original basis $\mathbf{V}$.

5.5 AN ANALYTIC DEFINITION OF EIGENVALUES AND EIGENVECTORS

Eigenvalues are often defined as roots of a certain determinantal equation, and the corresponding eigenvectors are defined by a corresponding set of linear equations. Since different definitions have been given already, these analytic definitions may be derived as a theorem.

Theorem 5.5.1. *Suppose that $\mathbf{Q}_1$ and $\mathbf{Q}_2$ are positive definite symmetric matrices, that $\lambda_1, \lambda_2, \ldots, \lambda_p$ are the eigenvalues of $\mathbf{Q}_1$ relative to $\mathbf{Q}_2$, and that $\boldsymbol{\alpha}_1, \boldsymbol{\alpha}_2, \ldots, \boldsymbol{\alpha}_p$ are corresponding eigenvectors. Then $\lambda_1, \lambda_2, \ldots, \lambda_p$ are the roots of the equation*

$$\det(\mathbf{Q}_1 - \lambda\mathbf{Q}_2) = 0, \tag{5.5.1}$$

and $\boldsymbol{\alpha}_1, \boldsymbol{\alpha}_2, \ldots, \boldsymbol{\alpha}_p$ satisfy the equations

$$\boldsymbol{\alpha}_i(\mathbf{Q}_1 - \lambda_i\mathbf{Q}_2) = \mathbf{0} \tag{5.5.2}$$

for $i = 1, 2, \ldots, p$.

To prove this theorem, think of $\mathbf{Q}_1$ and $\mathbf{Q}_2$ as inner product matrices of π_1 and π_2 relative to a basis $\mathbf{V}$ of $\mathscr{E}$. Then consider changing to the basis $\mathbf{W} = \mathbf{AV}$

where the rows of $\mathbf{A}$ are $\boldsymbol{\alpha}_1, \boldsymbol{\alpha}_2, \ldots, \boldsymbol{\alpha}_p$, i.e., $\mathbf{W}$ is the basis of eigenvectors $\boldsymbol{\alpha}_1\mathbf{V}, \boldsymbol{\alpha}_2\mathbf{V}, \ldots, \boldsymbol{\alpha}_p\mathbf{V}$. The inner product matrices of π_1 and π_2 relative to $\mathbf{W}$ are $\mathbf{M}_1 = \mathbf{A}\mathbf{Q}_1\mathbf{A}'$ and $\mathbf{M}_2 = \mathbf{A}\mathbf{Q}_2\mathbf{A}'$, where $\mathbf{M}_1$ and $\mathbf{M}_2$ are diagonal matrices with diagonal elements $\mu_{11}, \mu_{12}, \ldots, \mu_{1p}$ and $\mu_{21}, \mu_{22}, \ldots, \mu_{2p}$ such that $\lambda_i = \mu_{1i}/\mu_{2i}$ for $i = 1, 2, \ldots, p$. Thus

$$\begin{aligned}
\det(\mathbf{Q}_1 - \lambda\mathbf{Q}_2) &= \det(\mathbf{A}^{-1}\mathbf{A}(\mathbf{Q}_1 - \lambda\mathbf{Q}_2)\mathbf{A}'\mathbf{A}'^{-1}) \\
&= [\det \mathbf{A}]^{-2} \det(\mathbf{A}\mathbf{Q}_1\mathbf{A}' - \lambda\mathbf{A}\mathbf{Q}_2\mathbf{A}') \\
&= [\det \mathbf{A}]^{-2} \det(\mathbf{M}_1 - \lambda\mathbf{M}_2) \\
&= [\det \mathbf{A}]^{-2} \prod_{i=1}^{p} (\mu_{1i} - \lambda\mu_{2i}) \\
&= (-1)^p[\det \mathbf{A}]^{-2} \prod_{i=1}^{p} \mu_{2i} \prod_{i=1}^{p} (\lambda - \lambda_i),
\end{aligned} \tag{5.5.3}$$

so that the roots of (5.5.1) are $\lambda_1, \lambda_2, \ldots, \lambda_p$. Similarly

$$\begin{aligned}
\boldsymbol{\alpha}_i(\mathbf{Q}_1 - \lambda_i\mathbf{Q}_2) &= \boldsymbol{\alpha}_i\mathbf{A}^{-1}\mathbf{A}(\mathbf{Q}_1 - \lambda_i\mathbf{Q}_2)\mathbf{A}'\mathbf{A}'^{-1} \\
&= \mu_i\mathbf{1}_i(\mathbf{M}_1 - \lambda_i\mathbf{M}_2)\mathbf{A}'^{-1} \\
&= \mathbf{0}\mathbf{A}'^{-1} = \mathbf{0},
\end{aligned} \tag{5.5.4}$$

where $\mathbf{1}_i$ is the ith row of $\mathbf{I}$. The only unexplained step in (5.5.4) is the step $\boldsymbol{\alpha}_i\mathbf{A}^{-1} = \mu_i\mathbf{1}_i$. If $\boldsymbol{\alpha}$ denotes coordinates relative to $\mathbf{V}$ and $\boldsymbol{\beta}$ denotes coordinates relative to $\mathbf{W} = \mathbf{A}\mathbf{V}$, then $\boldsymbol{\beta} = \boldsymbol{\alpha}\mathbf{A}^{-1}$. But relative to $\mathbf{W}$, the ith eigenvector has coordinates $\mu_i\mathbf{1}_i$, and hence $\boldsymbol{\alpha}_i\mathbf{A}^{-1} = \mu_i\mathbf{1}_i$ for some μ_i. This completes the proof of the theorem. Theorem 5.5.1 is often given in the special case where $\mathbf{Q}_2 = \mathbf{I}$.

It is not necessary that π_1 should be of full rank, i.e., $\mathbf{Q}_1$ need only be *positive semi-definite* of rank r. In this case there are r nonzero eigenvalues, i.e., the equation (5.5.1) has a zero root of multiplicity $p - r$.

The equations (5.5.1) provide an alternative to the iterative method of computation. Given $\mathbf{Q}_1$ and $\mathbf{Q}_2$, however, it is not easy to compute the left side of (5.5.1). As with the iterative computational methods, difficulties may be eased by changing to a basis $\mathbf{U} = \mathbf{K}\mathbf{V}$ which is orthonormal according to π_2. This requires finding $\mathbf{K}$ such that $\mathbf{K}\mathbf{Q}_2\mathbf{K}' = \mathbf{I}$ and then finding $\mathbf{Q} = \mathbf{K}\mathbf{Q}_1\mathbf{K}'$. Applying (5.5.1) and (5.5.2) to the simplified situation leads to

$$\det(\mathbf{Q} - \lambda\mathbf{I}) = 0 \tag{5.5.5}$$

and

$$\boldsymbol{\gamma}_i(\mathbf{Q} - \lambda_i\mathbf{I}) = \mathbf{0}, \tag{5.5.6}$$

where the roots of (5.5.5) are the same as those of (5.5.1), and the $\boldsymbol{\gamma}_i$ found from (5.5.6) are related to the $\boldsymbol{\alpha}_i$ in (5.5.1) via $\mathbf{U} = \mathbf{K}\mathbf{V}$, i.e.,

$$\boldsymbol{\alpha}_i = \boldsymbol{\gamma}_i\mathbf{K}. \tag{5.5.7}$$

Even in this form it is not easy to compute the polynomial $\det(\mathbf{Q} - \lambda\mathbf{I})$. A further simplification is produced by the tridiagonalization device of (5.4.14).

Thus (5.5.5) may be transformed further into

$$\det(\mathbf{T} - \lambda\mathbf{I}) = 0, \tag{5.5.8}$$

which, being the determinant of a tridiagonal matrix, is more easily computed. The eigenvectors are then determined by

$$\boldsymbol{\delta}_i(\mathbf{T} - \lambda_i\mathbf{I}) = \mathbf{0}, \tag{5.5.9}$$

where

$$\boldsymbol{\alpha}_i = \boldsymbol{\delta}_i\mathbf{GK}. \tag{5.5.10}$$

According to (5.5.5) or (5.5.8) the eigenvalues may be found as the roots of a polynomial of degree p in λ. Having these roots, each corresponding eigenvector may be deduced from a set of linear equations as in (5.5.6) or (5.5.9). Note that only $p - 1$ of the equations (5.5.6) or (5.5.9) for a given i are linearly independent and that, because of the arbitrary scale factor, any element of $\boldsymbol{\gamma}_i$ or $\boldsymbol{\delta}_i$ may be arbitrarily fixed, yielding $p - 1$ equations in $p - 1$ unknowns.

This approach to computing eigenvalues and eigenvectors is not pursued in detail because for most statistical purposes one requires both eigenvalues and eigenvectors, and the methods of Section 5.4.1 are generally faster.

5.6 AN APPLICATION TO ANGLES BETWEEN SUBSPACES OF A EUCLIDEAN SPACE

Consider a p-dimensional Euclidean space $\mathscr{E}$ with two specified subspaces $\mathscr{U}$ and $\mathscr{V}$ of dimensions m and n, respectively. The theory of eigenvectors and eigenvalues provides an easy means to an understanding of the system of angles between the hyperplanes $\mathscr{U}$ and $\mathscr{V}$. One may ask, for example, what is the smallest angle between $\mathscr{U}$ and $\mathscr{V}$? In other words, how does one find a vector U in $\mathscr{U}$ and a vector V in $\mathscr{V}$ such that the angle between U and V is minimum, and what is the angle?

Given any U in $\mathscr{U}$, a vector in $\mathscr{V}$ making the smallest angle with U is given by the orthogonal projection of U into $\mathscr{V}$, which may be denoted by $\dot{U}$. Moreover, if θ is the angle from U to $\dot{U}$

$$\cos^2\theta = \frac{(\dot{U}, \dot{U})}{(U, U)}, \tag{5.6.1}$$

and the problem is to choose U to maximize $\cos^2\theta$. To place the problem in the same form as that considered at the start of this chapter, one need only define a pair of inner products π_1 and π_2 over $\mathscr{U}$ where, for any U and W in $\mathscr{U}$,

$$(U, W)_1 = (\dot{U}, \dot{W}) \tag{5.6.2}$$

and

$$(U, W)_2 = (U, W). \tag{5.6.3}$$

Here, the brackets subscripted by i refer to π_i for $i = 1, 2$ and the brackets without subscripts refer to the inner product implied by the assertion that $\mathscr{E}$ is

Euclidean. As before, $\dot{U}$ and $\dot{W}$ refer to the orthogonal projection of U and W into $\mathscr{V}$. The reader should check that π_2 as defined in (5.6.3) is an inner product, albeit possibly semi-definite. It follows that the largest eigenvalue of π_1 relative to π_2 maximizes $\cos^2\theta$ in (5.6.1). The general picture is provided by the following theorem.

Theorem 5.6.1. *Suppose that $\mathscr{U}$ and $\mathscr{V}$ are subspaces of dimensions m and n of a p-dimensional Euclidean space $\mathscr{E}$ where $m \leq n$. Then there exist an orthonormal basis $U_1, U_2, \ldots, U_m$ of $\mathscr{U}$ and an orthonormal basis $V_1, V_2, \ldots, V_n$ of $\mathscr{V}$ with the properties that*

$$(U_i, V_j) = 0 \quad \text{for} \quad i \neq j. \tag{5.6.4}$$

If the angles θ_i between U_i and V_i for $i = 1, 2, \ldots, m$ are ordered so that

$$\theta_1 \leq \theta_2 \leq \cdots \leq \theta_m, \tag{5.6.5}$$

then θ_1 is the smallest angle between $\mathscr{U}$ and $\mathscr{V}$, θ_2 is the smallest angle between the subspace of $\mathscr{U}$ orthogonal to U_1 and the subspace of $\mathscr{V}$ orthogonal to V_1, and so on. If the inequalities in (5.6.5) *are strict inequalities, then the orthonormal sets $U_1, U_2, \ldots, U_m$ and $V_1, V_2, \ldots, V_m$ satisfying* (5.6.4) *are unique. On the other hand, if for some s and t,*

$$\theta_{s-1} < \theta_s = \theta_{s+1} = \cdots = \theta_{s+t-1} < \theta_{s+t}, \tag{5.6.6}$$

then only the subspaces spanned by $U_s, U_{s+1}, \ldots, U_{s+t-1}$ and $V_s, V_{s+1}, \ldots, V_{s+t-1}$ are uniquely determined, and any orthonormal basis of one such t-dimensional subspace corresponds to an orthonormal basis of the other such t-dimensional subspace satisfying (5.6.4) *and* (5.6.5). *In either case, any orthogonal transformation of the set $V_{m+1}, V_{m+2}, \ldots, V_n$ leads to another possible choice of $V_{m+1}, V_{m+2}, \ldots, V_n$, whose only requirement from* (5.6.4) *is that they shall be orthogonal to $\mathscr{U}$.*

As already indicated, the basic idea leading to this theorem is that $U_1, U_2, \ldots, U_m$ shall be taken as a basis of eigenvectors of π_1 relative to π_2. For some s on $0 \leq s \leq m$, the orthogonal projections $\dot{U}_1, \dot{U}_2, \ldots, \dot{U}_s$ will have positive length, and $V_1, V_2, \ldots, V_s$ may be taken to be that orthonormal set found by rescaling $\dot{U}_1, \dot{U}_2, \ldots, \dot{U}_s$ to unit length. It follows that the subspace of $\mathscr{V}$ orthogonal to $V_1, V_2, \ldots, V_s$ is orthogonal to $\mathscr{U}$, and any orthonormal sets $U_{s+1}, U_{s+2}, \ldots, U_m$ and $V_{s+1}, V_{s+2}, \ldots, V_n$ may be chosen to complete the required bases of $\mathscr{U}$ and $\mathscr{V}$. The uniqueness properties claimed for the bases $U_1, U_2, \ldots, U_m$ and $V_1, V_2, \ldots, V_n$ in the theorem follow directly from Theorems 5.1.1, 5.1.2, and 5.1.3. The extremal properties of $\theta_1, \theta_2, \ldots$ follow from the constructive proof of Theorem 5.1.1 (cf. Exercise 5.1.3).

In this geometric framework, the powering procedures of Section 5.4.1 have a simple, elegant interpretation. Because the bases $U_1, U_2, \ldots, U_m$ and

$V_1, V_2, \ldots, V_n$ are orthonormal, the orthogonality relations imply that $\dot{U}_i = \cos\theta_i V_i$ for $i = 1, 2, \ldots, m$. Thus, if A is any vector in $\mathscr{U}$ and $A = \sum_1^m a_i U_i$, then the orthogonal projection $\dot{A}$ of A into $\mathscr{V}$ is given by

$$\dot{A} = \sum_{i=1}^{m} a_i \dot{U}_i = \sum_{i=1}^{m} [a_i \cos\theta_i] V_i. \tag{5.6.7}$$

Similarly, if $B = \sum_1^n b_i V_i$ is any vector in $\mathscr{V}$ and the orthogonal projection of B into $\mathscr{U}$ is denoted by $\ddot{B}$, then one may deduce that $\ddot{V}_i = \cos\theta_i U_i$ for $i = 1, 2, \ldots, m$ and $\ddot{V}_i = \emptyset$ for $i = m + 1, \ldots, n$. Thence

$$\ddot{B} = \sum_{i=1}^{n} b_i \ddot{V}_i = \sum_{i=1}^{m} [b_i \cos\theta_i] U_i. \tag{5.6.8}$$

If one performs the transformations $A \to \dot{A}$ and $B \to \ddot{B}$ in succession one has

$$\sum_{i=1}^{m} a_i U_i \to \sum_{i=1}^{m} [a_i \cos\theta_i] V_i \to \sum_{i=1}^{m} [a_i \cos^2\theta_i] U_i, \tag{5.6.9}$$

which has the form of the transformation $\mathbf{U} \to \mathbf{QU}$ considered in connection with the powering methods. It follows in particular that if a vector A_0 is projected orthogonally into $\mathscr{V}$, then back into $\mathscr{U}$ and so on back and forth, the pair of vectors in $\mathscr{U}$ and $\mathscr{V}$ converges to a pair of vectors which make the smallest angle between $\mathscr{V}$ and $\mathscr{U}$.

In the sequel it will be convenient to call the angles $\theta_1, \theta_2, \ldots, \theta_m$ in (5.6.5) the *canonical angles* between $\mathscr{U}$ and $\mathscr{V}$. Corresponding bases $\mathbf{U}$ and $\mathbf{V}$ as in (5.6.4) will be called *canonical bases*. The angles $\theta_{m+1}, \theta_{m+2}, \ldots, \theta_n$ between $V_{m+1}, V_{m+2}, \ldots, V_n$ and $\mathscr{U}$ are all $\pi/2$, but may also be called canonical angles.

5.7 EXERCISES

5.1.1 Suppose that λ_1 and λ_p are the largest and smallest eigenvalues, respectively, of π_1 relative to π_2. Show that any value of $\lambda = (V, V)_1/(V, V)_2$ between λ_1 and λ_p occurs for some V in $\mathscr{E}$.

5.1.2 Suppose that $\lambda_1, \lambda_2, \ldots, \lambda_p$ denote the eigenvalues of π_1 relative to π_2. For any U and V in $\mathscr{E}$, define π_3 from

$$(U, V)_3 = c_1(U, V)_1 + c_2(U, V)_2.$$

What is the condition on $c_1, c_2, \lambda_1, \lambda_2, \ldots, \lambda_p$ such that $(V, V)_3 > 0$ for all V in $\mathscr{E}$ and $(U, V)_3$ defines an inner product? Show that any basis orthogonal relative to both π_1 and π_2 is orthogonal relative to π_3, whether or not π_3 defines a proper inner product. What are the eigenvalues of π_3 relative to π_2?

5.1.3 Suppose that $W_{(1)}, W_{(2)}, \ldots, W_{(r)}$ denote a subset of a set of eigenvectors of π_1 relative to π_2, where the corresponding eigenvalues $\lambda_{(1)}, \lambda_{(2)}, \ldots, \lambda_{(p)}$ are taken in non-increasing order. Suppose that $\mathscr{U}$ denotes the subspace of $\mathscr{E}$ spanned by $W_{(1)}, W_{(2)}, \ldots,$

$W_{(r)}$. Show that $(V, V)_1/(V, V)_2$ has maximum value $\lambda_{(1)}$ and minimum value $\lambda_{(r)}$ for V in $\mathscr{U}$.

5.1.4 Prove Theorem 5.1.2.

5.1.5 Characterize the set of all inner products π_2 which have a given set of eigenvalues relative to a given inner product π_1.

5.2.1 Suppose that the ellipsoid π_1 has eigenvalues $\lambda_1, \lambda_2, \ldots, \lambda_p$ relative to the ellipsoid π_2 in affine space $\mathscr{E}$. Show that the affine ratio of the volume of π_1 to the volume of π_2 is given by

$$\left[\prod_{i=1}^{p} \lambda_i\right]^{-1/2}.$$

Consequently, deduce that, if $\mathbf{Q}_1$ and $\mathbf{Q}_2$ are inner product matrices of π_1 and π_2 relative to a basis $\mathbf{U}$, then the product $\prod_{i=1}^{p} \lambda_i$ may be expressed as $\det \mathbf{Q}_1/\det \mathbf{Q}_2$.

5.2.2 Consider a general ellipsoid π in a Euclidean space $\mathscr{E}$. Show that any axis of the ellipsoid which is perpendicular to the tangent plane at its intersection with the ellipsoid is a principal axis of the ellipsoid.

5.3.1 Suppose that $\mathbf{Q}_1$ and $\mathbf{Q}_2$ are positive definite symmetric matrices. Given the theory proving the existence of an orthogonal basis of a Euclidean vector space, show that the problem of finding a $1 \times p$ matrix $\boldsymbol{\alpha}$ to maximize $\boldsymbol{\alpha}\mathbf{Q}_1\boldsymbol{\alpha}'/\boldsymbol{\alpha}\mathbf{Q}_2\boldsymbol{\alpha}'$ can be reduced to the problem of finding a $1 \times p$ matrix $\boldsymbol{\beta}$ to maximize $\boldsymbol{\beta}\mathbf{Q}\boldsymbol{\beta}'$ subject to the condition $\boldsymbol{\beta}\boldsymbol{\beta}' = 1$, where $\mathbf{Q}$ is a certain positive definite symmetric matrix.

5.3.2 Show that a positive definite symmetric matrix $\mathbf{Q}$ has the same eigenvalues as $\mathbf{DQD}'$ if and only if $\mathbf{D}$ is orthogonal. Show also that if the eigenvectors of $\mathbf{Q}$ are denoted by the rows of a $p \times p$ matrix $\mathbf{C}$, then the eigenvectors of $\mathbf{DQD}'$ for orthogonal $\mathbf{C}$ are given by the rows of $\mathbf{CD}'$.

5.3.3 State and prove the extension of Theorem 5.3.2 to cover positive semi-definite symmetric matrices.

5.3.4 Suppose that $\mathbf{P}$ is any symmetric $p \times p$ matrix, and that

$$\mu = \inf\,[\boldsymbol{\beta}\mathbf{P}\boldsymbol{\beta}'],$$

where $\boldsymbol{\beta}$ ranges over all row vectors such that $\boldsymbol{\beta}\boldsymbol{\beta}' = 1$. Set

$$\mathbf{Q} = \mathbf{P} + \nu\mathbf{I},$$

where ν is any real number greater than μ. Show that $\mathbf{Q}$ is positive definite symmetric. Deduce also that there exists an orthogonal matrix $\mathbf{C}$ such that

$$\mathbf{CPC}' = \mathbf{L},$$

where $\mathbf{L}$ is a diagonal matrix whose diagonal elements $\nu_1, \nu_2, \ldots, \nu_p$ are not necessarily positive.

5.3.5 Suppose that the positive definite symmetric matrix $\mathbf{Q}$ is operated on by the orthogonal matrix $\mathbf{C}$ to produce $\mathbf{CQC}'$. Show that $\mathbf{Q}$ and $\mathbf{CQC}'$ have the same trace, i.e., the same sum of diagonal elements. Deduce that the sum of the eigenvalues of $\mathbf{Q}$ is given by the trace of $\mathbf{Q}$. Can this result be extended to any symmetric matrix $\mathbf{P}$ (cf. Exercise 5.3.4)?

5.3.6 Suppose that a positive definite symmetric $p \times p$ matrix $\mathbf{Q}$ is the sum $\mathbf{Q}_1 + \mathbf{Q}_2 + \cdots + \mathbf{Q}_p$ of p positive semi-definite matrices each of rank 1. Show that the $\mathbf{Q}_i$ are necessarily the terms in the sum (5.3.5) corresponding to an eigenvalue analysis of $\mathbf{Q}$ (Cochran's theorem).

5.4.1 Show that the angle θ in (5.4.1) is determined by the equation

$$q_{rt}^{(s)} \cos^2 \theta + [q_{tt}^{(s)} - q_{rr}^{(s)}] \cos \theta \sin \theta - q_{rt}^{(s)} \sin^2 \theta = 0,$$

and that the following relations describe how to compute $\mathbf{Q}^{(s+1)}$ from $\mathbf{Q}^{(s)}$ and θ:

$$\begin{aligned}
q_{rr}^{(s+1)} &= q_{rr}^{(s)} \cos^2 \theta + 2q_{rt}^{(s)} \cos \theta \sin \theta + q_{tt}^{(s)} \sin^2 \theta, \\
q_{tt}^{(s+1)} &= q_{rt}^{(s)} \sin^2 \theta - 2q_{rt}^{(s+1)} \cos \theta \sin \theta + q_{tt}^{(s)} \cos^2 \theta, \\
q_{rt}^{(s+1)} &= q_{tr}^{(s+1)} = 0, \\
q_{ir}^{(s+1)} &= q_{ri}^{(s+1)} = q_{ir}^{(s)} \cos \theta + q_{it}^{(s)} \sin \theta \quad \text{for} \quad i \neq r, t, \\
q_{it}^{(s+1)} &= q_{ti}^{(s+1)} = -q_{ir}^{(s)} \sin \theta + q_{it}^{(s)} \cos \theta \quad \text{for} \quad i \neq r, t, \\
q_{ij}^{(s+1)} &= q_{ij}^{(s)} \quad \text{for} \quad i \neq r, t, \quad \text{and} \quad j \neq r, t.
\end{aligned}$$

Check also that the rows of $\mathbf{C}^{(s+1)}$ are computed from the rows of $\mathbf{C}^{(s)}$ in the same way that the rows of $\mathbf{U}^{(s+1)}$ are computed from the rows of $\mathbf{U}^{(s)}$, as in (5.4.1).

5.4.2 Suppose that $\mathbf{D}$ is any $q \times q$ orthogonal matrix and $\mathbf{P}$ is any $q \times q$ symmetric matrix. Show that the sum of squares of the elements of $\mathbf{P}$ and of $\mathbf{DPD}'$ are the same. Show how this result can be applied to prove Lemma 5.4.1.

5.4.3 Check the first stage of computation in Example 5.4.

5.4.4 Carry out the tridiagonalization of $\mathbf{Q}$ in Example 5.4 using a pair of elementary orthogonal transformations.

5.4.5 Starting from the tridiagonalized version of $\mathbf{Q}$ computed in Exercise 5.4.4, carry out one stage of the *QR* method.

5.5.1 Show how to compute directly from determinants of submatrices of $\mathbf{Q}$ the elementary symmetric functions of the eigenvalues of $\mathbf{Q}$, namely,

$$\sum_{i=1}^{p} \lambda_i$$

$$\sum_{i=1}^{p} \sum_{j=i}^{p} \lambda_i \lambda_j$$

$$\vdots$$

$$\lambda_1 \lambda_2 \cdots \lambda_p.$$

5.5.2 Use the calculus method of Lagrange multipliers to show that the maximum of the quadratic form $\boldsymbol{\alpha}\mathbf{Q}\boldsymbol{\alpha}'$, subject to the condition $\boldsymbol{\alpha}\boldsymbol{\alpha}' = 1$, must satisfy

$$\boldsymbol{\alpha}\mathbf{Q} = \lambda\boldsymbol{\alpha}, \tag{5.7.1}$$

where λ satisfies

$$\det(\mathbf{Q} - \lambda\mathbf{I}) = 0. \tag{5.7.2}$$

Show also that the resulting maximum is λ.

5.5.3 Show that eigenvectors γ_i and γ_j satisfying (5.5.6) for eigenvalues λ_i and λ_j satisfying $\lambda_i \neq \lambda_j$ must also satisfy

$$\gamma_i\mathbf{Q}\gamma_j = 0. \tag{5.7.3}$$

5.5.4 Suppose (5.7.1) and (5.7.2) are used to define eigenvectors and eigenvalues for an arbitrary matrix $\mathbf{Q}$. Show that, in general, the eigenvectors $\gamma_1^*, \gamma_2^*, \ldots, \gamma_p^*$ of $\mathbf{Q}'$ are different from the eigenvectors $\gamma_1, \gamma_2, \ldots, \gamma_p$ of $\mathbf{Q}$, but that

$$\gamma_i\mathbf{Q}\gamma_j^{*\prime} = 0 \quad \text{if} \quad \lambda_i \neq \lambda_j \tag{5.7.4}$$

is the appropriate generalization of (5.7.3).

5.5.5 Show, as an alternative to (5.5.5) and (5.5.6), that formulas (5.5.1) and (5.5.2) may be written

$$\det(\mathbf{Q}_1\mathbf{Q}_2^{-1} - \lambda\mathbf{I}) = 0 \tag{5.7.5}$$

and

$$\gamma_i(\mathbf{Q}_1\mathbf{Q}_2^{-1} - \lambda_i\mathbf{I}) = \mathbf{0}. \tag{5.7.6}$$

Show that $\mathbf{Q}_1\mathbf{Q}_2^{-1}$ is not in general a symmetric matrix, so that its eigenvalues as defined by $\mathbf{Q}_1\mathbf{Q}_2^{-1}$ may not be found by iterative methods designed for symmetric matrices.

5.6.1 What becomes of the theorem of Section 5.6 when $m = 1$?

5.6.2 Show that (5.6.4) defines a definite or semi-definite inner product over $\mathscr{U}$.

5.6.3 Show that the inner products defined in (5.6.4) and (5.6.5) satisfy $(W, W)_1/(W, W)_2 \leq 1$ and that such ratios may be interpreted as $\cos^2\theta$ for some θ.

5.6.4 Show that the angles $\theta_1, \theta_2, \ldots, \theta_m$ defined in Section 5.6 may all be zero, may all be $\pi/2$, or more generally may all be equal to any θ on $0 \leq \theta \leq \pi/2$. Relate the number of θ_i which are zero to the dimension of the intersection of $\mathscr{U}$ and $\mathscr{V}$.

5.6.5 Suppose that $\mathbf{U}$ denotes a basis of $\mathscr{U}$ and $\mathbf{V}$ a basis of $\mathscr{V}$. Suppose that the orthogonal projections of $\mathbf{U}$ into $\mathscr{V}$ into $\mathscr{U}$ are denoted by $\mathbf{SV}$ and $\mathbf{RU}$, respectively, where $\mathbf{U}$, $\mathbf{V}$, $\mathbf{R}$, and $\mathbf{S}$ have dimensions $m \times 1$, $n \times 1$, $n \times m$, and $m \times n$. Show that the iteration procedure is equivalent to computing a product of the form $\mathbf{SRSR} \ldots \mathbf{SR}$. What would be an efficient way to compute such a product?

CHAPTER 6

DUAL SPACES

6.1 BASIC DEFINITIONS AND THEORY

Given any vector space $\mathscr{E}$, it is possible to define as follows a new vector space $\mathscr{F}$ whose elements consist of the set of all linear functionals over $\mathscr{E}$. A *linear functional* over $\mathscr{E}$ is a real-valued function $v(V)$, defined for all V in $\mathscr{E}$, which satisfies the requirement that

$$v(\alpha_1 V_1 + \alpha_2 V_2) = \alpha_1 v(V_1) + \alpha_2 v(V_2) \tag{6.1.1}$$

for all vectors V_1 and V_2 in $\mathscr{E}$ and all real numbers α_1 and α_2. The addition of two linear functionals to give a linear functional and the multiplication of a linear functional by a real number to give a linear functional are both defined in the obvious manner, i.e., the relation $v_3 = \beta_1 v_1 + \beta_2 v_2$ for linear functionals v_1, v_2 and v_3 and real numbers β_1 and β_2 means that

$$v_3(V) = \beta_1 v_1(V) + \beta_2 v_2(V) \tag{6.1.2}$$

for all V in $\mathscr{E}$. It is easily checked that the set of linear functionals forms a vector space under the operations defined by (6.1.2), and this defines the vector space $\mathscr{F}$, as promised above.

The mathematical interest in considering $\mathscr{F}$ is that $\mathscr{E}$ and $\mathscr{F}$ have the mathematical properties of what will be called a pair of dual vector spaces. An abstract definition of this concept will be given shortly. The statistical interest in considering $\mathscr{F}$ is that if $\mathscr{E}$ is taken to be the variable-space of Example 2.1.1, then $\mathscr{F}$ is essentially the individual-space of Example 2.1.2. Note that any observation vector $[x_1, x_2, \ldots, x_p]$ on a basic set of variables $[V_1, V_2, \ldots, V_p]'$ defines an observation $\boldsymbol{\alpha}\mathbf{x}'$ on any variable $\boldsymbol{\alpha}\mathbf{V}$ in $\mathscr{E}$, and that the observation $\boldsymbol{\alpha}\mathbf{x}'$ may be regarded as the value of a functional v, where

$$v(\boldsymbol{\alpha}\mathbf{V}) = \boldsymbol{\alpha}\mathbf{x}'. \tag{6.1.3}$$

It may easily be checked that the functional v defined by (6.1.3) obeys (6.1.1), and so is a linear functional. Moreover, the vector operations for observation vectors defined in Example 2.1.2 and the vector operations for functionals defined in (6.1.2) determine the same operations on the functionals defined by (6.1.3), so that the concepts of individual-space and the space of linear functionals over variable-space are abstractly identical.

Returning to duality in general, any two vector spaces $\mathscr{E}$ and $\mathscr{F}$ will be called *dual* with respect to each other if they are related by a proper bilinear product function. A *bilinear product function* is a real-valued function $\{V, v\}$ defined for each V in $\mathscr{E}$ and v in $\mathscr{F}$, which satisfies the pair of linearity requirements that

$$\{\alpha_1 V_1 + \alpha_2 V_2, v\} = \alpha_1\{V_1, v\} + \alpha_2\{V_2, v\} \tag{6.1.4}$$

and

$$\{V, \beta_1 v_1 + \beta_2 v_2\} = \beta_1\{V, v_1\} + \beta_2\{V, v_2\}, \tag{6.1.5}$$

where α_1, α_2, β_1, and β_2 denote any real numbers, where V_1, V_2, and V denote any vectors in $\mathscr{E}$, and where v_1, v_2, and v denote any vectors in $\mathscr{F}$. From (6.1.4) and (6.1.5), it is clear that for each fixed v the relation

$$f_v(V) = \{V, v\} \tag{6.1.6}$$

defines a linear functional f_v over $\mathscr{E}$, and that for each fixed V the relation

$$F_V(v) = \{V, v\} \tag{6.1.7}$$

defines a linear functional F_V over $\mathscr{F}$. Furthermore, the mapping

$$v \rightarrow f_v \tag{6.1.8}$$

from the space $\mathscr{F}$ to the space of linear functionals over $\mathscr{E}$ is a linear transformation. Similarly the mapping

$$V \rightarrow F_V \tag{6.1.9}$$

from the space $\mathscr{E}$ to the space of linear functionals over $\mathscr{F}$ is a linear transformation. If the mappings (6.1.8) and (6.1.9) are both one-one in the sense that they define an isomorphism between one vector space and the space of linear functionals over another vector space, then the bilinear product $\{V, v\}$ is here called *proper*, and, in this case, the spaces $\mathscr{E}$ and $\mathscr{F}$ are dual spaces.

The definition of dual spaces treats $\mathscr{E}$ and $\mathscr{F}$ symmetrically, so that $\mathscr{F}$ dual to $\mathscr{E}$ implies $\mathscr{E}$ dual to $\mathscr{F}$. Unfortunately, however, it is not immediately clear that individual-space $\mathscr{F}$ and variable-space $\mathscr{E}$ are dual according to the definition. Specifically, it is clear that (6.1.8) is one-one but not that (6.1.9) is one-one. In other words, it needs to be shown that each linear functional over $\mathscr{F}$ corresponds to exactly one variable in $\mathscr{E}$ whose values are those given by the linear functional over $\mathscr{F}$. The missing link is provided by:

Lemma 6.1. *Suppose that two vector spaces $\mathscr{E}$ and $\mathscr{F}$ are related by a bilinear product $\{V, v\}$ such that one of the mappings* (6.1.8) *and* (6.1.9) *is one-one. Then the other mapping is also one-one, and $\mathscr{E}$ and $\mathscr{F}$ are dual spaces.*

It need only be proved that if (6.1.8) is a one-one mapping then (6.1.9) is also, for the symmetry of the hypotheses will then imply that the converse is also true. Assuming that (6.1.8) is one-one, it follows that $\mathscr{F}$ is abstractly identical to the space of linear functionals over $\mathscr{E}$, so it may be assumed that $\mathscr{F}$ is this space of linear functionals and that (6.1.6) holds. It is required to show that only one V corresponds to a given F_V, or that the relation $\{V_1, v\} = \{V_2, v\}$ for all v implies that $V_1 = V_2$, or, finally, that the relation $v(V_1) = v(V_2)$ for all linear functionals v implies that $V_1 = V_2$. But this last version is obvious, for, given $V_1 \neq V_2$, one can easily construct a linear functional v such that $v(V_1) \neq v(V_2)$, and so the lemma is proved by contradiction.

It is now clear that the space $\mathscr{F}$ of linear functionals over $\mathscr{E}$ should be regarded as a dual space for $\mathscr{E}$ according to the bilinear product

$$\{V, v\} = v(V) \tag{6.1.10}$$

for V in $\mathscr{E}$ and v in $\mathscr{F}$. The relations (6.1.1) and (6.1.2) imply (6.1.4) and (6.1.5), so that $\{V, v\}$ in (6.1.10) defines a bilinear product. Moreover, from (6.1.6) and (6.1.10) the functionals v and f_v are identical, so that (6.1.8) is trivially a one-one linear transformation, as required.

According to the given definition of dual spaces, it is possible for a given vector space $\mathscr{E}$ to be dual to a number of different vector spaces, or even dual to a given vector space $\mathscr{F}$ in a number of different ways corresponding to different bilinear product functions. Still, it makes sense to speak of *the* dual space $\mathscr{F}$ of a given vector space $\mathscr{E}$. The reason for this terminology is essentially given by the one-one relation (6.1.8) which asserts that all dual spaces are isomorphic to the dual space of linear functionals according to an isomorphism which preserves the values of the bilinear product function.

Virtually every concept and entity concerning a vector space $\mathscr{E}$ has a corresponding and generally different concept and entity in the dual space $\mathscr{F}$. Consequently, any statement concerning a vector space $\mathscr{E}$ may be rewritten as an equivalent but apparently different statement concerning the dual space $\mathscr{F}$. This translation is a useful device because certain statements may seem more familiar and therefore more comprehensible in terms of one space than in terms of the other. Some of these corresponding dual entities will be derived in the remainder of this section, beginning with dual bases and dual subspaces.

Suppose that $\mathbf{V} = [V_1, V_2, \ldots, V_p]'$ is any basis of a vector space $\mathscr{E}$ whose dual space is $\mathscr{F}$. Then a basis $\mathbf{v} = [v_1, v_2, \ldots, v_p]'$ of $\mathscr{F}$ dual to the basis $\mathbf{V}$ of $\mathscr{E}$ may be defined by the relations

$$\begin{aligned} \{V_i, v_j\} &= 1 \quad \text{if} \quad i = j \\ &= 0 \quad \text{if} \quad i \neq j, \end{aligned} \tag{6.1.11}$$

for i and $j = 1, 2, \ldots, p$. Note that the set of relations (6.1.11), as i ranges while j is fixed, determines the values of the functional v_j in $\mathscr{F}$ for the basis elements $V_1, V_2, \ldots, V_p$ in $\mathscr{E}$. Consequently, $v_j(V)$ is determined for any V in $\mathscr{E}$. The reader may easily check that the $v_1, v_2, \ldots, v_p$ defined in this way are linearly independent and that any v in $\mathscr{F}$ may be expressed as a linear combination of $v_1, v_2, \ldots, v_p$. In other words, $\mathbf{v}$ is in fact a basis of $\mathscr{F}$ and the concept of dual basis is well-defined. It follows incidentally that $\mathscr{E}$ and its dual space $\mathscr{F}$ have the same dimension, a fact already illustrated in the examples of variable-space and its dual individual-space.

Suppose that $\mathscr{U}$ is an r-dimensional subspace of a p-dimensional vector space $\mathscr{E}$ whose dual space is $\mathscr{F}$. A $(p-r)$-dimensional subspace $\mathscr{U}_d$ of $\mathscr{F}$ dual to $\mathscr{U}$ in $\mathscr{E}$ may be defined by the condition that v is in $\mathscr{U}_d$ if

$$\{V, v\} = 0 \qquad \text{for all } V \text{ in } \mathscr{U}. \tag{6.1.12}$$

Relation (6.1.5) is enough to ensure that $\mathscr{U}_d$ is a subspace of $\mathscr{F}$. To show that $\mathscr{U}_d$ has dimension $p - r$, suppose that $\mathbf{V} = [V_1, V_2, \ldots, V_p]'$ is a basis of $\mathscr{E}$ such that $V_1, V_2, \ldots, V_r$ span $\mathscr{U}$. It follows from (6.1.11) and (6.1.12) that the elements $v_{r+1}, v_{r+2}, \ldots, v_p$ of the dual basis $\mathbf{v} = [v_1, v_2, \ldots, v_p]'$ of $\mathscr{F}$ lie in $\mathscr{U}_d$. Moreover, for any $v = x_1v_1 + x_2v_2 + \cdots + x_rv_r$ with some $x_i \neq 0$, there exists a V in $\mathscr{U}$, for example V_i, such that $\{V, v\} \neq 0$. Consequently $\mathscr{U}_d$ is the subspace spanned by $v_{r+1}, v_{r+2}, \ldots, v_p$ and has dimension $p - r$.

A limiting case of the duality between $\mathscr{U}$ and $\mathscr{U}_d$ occurs when $\mathscr{U}$ is taken to be the subspace consisting only of $\emptyset$ in $\mathscr{E}$; then $\mathscr{U}_d$ is the subspace consisting of the whole of $\mathscr{F}$. Another important property of the duality is that, if $\mathscr{U}_d$ and $\mathscr{V}_d$ in $\mathscr{F}$ are the duals of $\mathscr{U}$ and $\mathscr{V}$ in $\mathscr{E}$, then $\mathscr{U}_d \cap \mathscr{V}_d$ in $\mathscr{F}$ is the dual of $\mathscr{U} \oplus \mathscr{V}$ in $\mathscr{E}$. Of course, if $\mathscr{U}_d$ is the dual of $\mathscr{U}$, then $\mathscr{U}$ is the dual of $\mathscr{U}_d$.

Suppose that A is a narrow sense linear transformation from $\mathscr{E}$ to $\mathscr{E}^*$ whose dual spaces are $\mathscr{F}$ and $\mathscr{F}^*$, corresponding to bilinear products $\{V, v\}$ and $\{V^*, v^*\}^*$, respectively. Then there is a unique narrow sense linear transformation A_d from $\mathscr{F}^*$ to $\mathscr{F}$ which satisfies

$$\{V, v\} = \{V^*, v^*\}^* \tag{6.1.13}$$

for all V in $\mathscr{E}$ and v^* in $\mathscr{F}^*$, where $V^* = \mathsf{A}V$ and $v = \mathsf{A}_d v^*$. The proof of this assertion requires only simple checking: (a) that $\{\mathsf{A}V, v^*\}^*$ defines a linear functional over $\mathscr{E}$ for each v^*, i.e., defines a member v of $\mathscr{F}$ for each v^*, and (b) that the mapping $v^* \to v = \mathsf{A}_d v^*$ so defined is a linear transformation. The linear transformation A_d will be called the *dual linear transformation of* A. Clearly, if A_d is the dual of A, then A is the dual of A_d. If $\mathscr{U}$ is the subspace in $\mathscr{E}$ which maps under A into the origin in $\mathscr{E}^*$ while $\mathscr{V}^*$ is the range space in $\mathscr{E}^*$ of the transformation A, then $\mathscr{V}_d^*$ is the subspace of $\mathscr{F}^*$ which maps under A_d into the origin in $\mathscr{F}$ and $\mathscr{U}_d$ is the range space in $\mathscr{F}$ of the transformation A_d.

Given an inner product function (V, U) defined for each pair V, U in $\mathscr{E}$, the next task is to define the dual inner product $(v, u)_d$ for each pair v, u in the dual space $\mathscr{F}$ of $\mathscr{E}$. For any v in $\mathscr{F}$, there exists a hyperplane of dimension $p - 1$ in $\mathscr{E}$ such that $\{V, v\} = 1$ for all V in the hyperplane, and V^* may be defined to be the orthogonal projection of $\emptyset$ into this hyperplane. Similarly, for u in $\mathscr{F}$ a corresponding U^* in $\mathscr{E}$ may be defined. With this structure in hand the dual inner product is defined by

$$(v, u)_d = \frac{(V^*, U^*)}{(V^*, V^*)(U^*, U^*)}. \tag{6.1.14}$$

To check that (6.1.14) defines an inner product, and incidentally to provide a simple alternative definition, consider any orthonormal basis $\mathbf{V}$ of $\mathscr{E}$ and the dual basis $\mathbf{v}$ of $\mathscr{F}$. Representing $v = \mathbf{xv}$, the hyperplane in $\mathscr{E}$ whose points V satisfy $\{V, v\} = 1$ may be represented analytically as the set of points $V = \boldsymbol{\alpha}\mathbf{V}$ such that $\boldsymbol{\alpha}\mathbf{x}' = 1$; the point V^* on this hyperplane which is closest to the origin is given by

$$V^* = [(\mathbf{xx}')^{-1}\mathbf{x}]\mathbf{V}. \tag{6.1.15}$$

Similarly, representing $u = \mathbf{yv}$, the corresponding

$$U^* = [(\mathbf{yy}')^{-1}\mathbf{y}]\mathbf{V}. \tag{6.1.16}$$

From (6.1.14), (6.1.15), and (6.1.16), together with the orthonormality of $\mathbf{V}$, one finds

$$\begin{aligned}(v, u)_d &= \frac{[(\mathbf{xx}')^{-1}\mathbf{x}][(\mathbf{yy}')^{-1}\mathbf{y}]'}{[(\mathbf{xx}')^{-1}\mathbf{x}][(\mathbf{xx}')^{-1}\mathbf{x}]' \cdot [(\mathbf{yy}')^{-1}\mathbf{y}][(\mathbf{yy}')^{-1}\mathbf{y}]'} \\ &= \mathbf{xy}'. \end{aligned} \tag{6.1.17}$$

It follows that $(v, u)_d$ as originally defined in (6.1.14) is identical to the inner product defined by asserting that $\mathbf{v}$ is orthonormal. Having thus shown that the coordinate-free definition (6.1.14) is legitimate, it follows that the dual basis $\mathbf{v}$ of *any* orthonormal basis $\mathbf{V}$ is orthonormal according to the dual inner product.

A Euclidean vector space $\mathscr{E}$ with a proper inner product is self-dual where the bilinear product relating $\mathscr{E}$ with itself is simply the given inner product over $\mathscr{E}$ which makes $\mathscr{E}$ Euclidean. The inner product is clearly a bilinear product and a proper one because $(V, W_1) = (V, W_2)$ for all V implies that $W_1 = W_2$. The one-one correspondence between $\mathscr{E}$ and the space of linear functionals over $\mathscr{E}$ implied by the representation of the dual space as $\mathscr{E}$ is

$$W \leftrightarrow v_W, \tag{6.1.18}$$

where

$$v_W(V) = (W, V) \tag{6.1.19}$$

for V and W in $\mathscr{E}$. If $\mathbf{W}$ is an orthonormal basis of $\mathscr{E}$, the isomorphism (6.1.18) carries

$$\mathbf{W} \leftrightarrow \mathbf{w}, \tag{6.1.20}$$

where $\mathbf{w}$ is the dual orthonormal basis of the space of linear functionals over $\mathscr{E}$. In this sense there is a natural isomorphism between any Euclidean vector space and its dual Euclidean vector space which carries every orthonormal basis into its dual orthonormal basis.

The foregoing theory provides an inner product defined on individual-space dual to a given covariance inner product on variable-space. Such a dual inner product will be called a *concentration inner product* in Chapter 7 and is an important concept in multivariate statistical theory.

6.2 DUAL GEOMETRIC SPACES

The idea of duality is often introduced in simple discussions of geometry. For example, in plane geometry the concept of a line is thought of as the dual of the concept of a point, the set of points on a line is the dual of a pencil of lines through a point, and the proposition that every two points define a line joining them is the dual of the proposition that every two lines intersect in a point. When this kind of duality is applied to p-dimensional space it asserts that points are dual to $(p - 1)$-dimensional hyperplanes, or, more generally, that r-dimensional hyperplanes are dual to $(p - r - 1)$-dimensional hyperplanes for $r = 0, 1, 2, \ldots, p - 1$.

To arrive at such duality concepts in vector space terms, the dual of a point V in a vector space $\mathscr{E}$ may be defined to be the $(p - 1)$-dimensional hyperplane consisting of points v in the dual space $\mathscr{F}$ of $\mathscr{E}$ which satisfy $\{V, v\} = 1$. The dual of a hyperplane in $\mathscr{E}$ may then be defined as the hyperplane of intersection of the family of $(p - 1)$-dimensional hyperplanes in $\mathscr{F}$ dual to the points of its original hyperplane in $\mathscr{E}$. The reader may wish to show that in this way a one-one correspondence is defined between r-dimensional hyperplanes in $\mathscr{E}$ and $(p - r - 1)$-dimensional hyperplanes in $\mathscr{F}$, and that, if two hyperplanes intersect in a third, then the duals of these two hyperplanes determine the dual of the third as the smallest hyperplane containing them both.

Note that the above concept of dual pairs of hyperplanes does not apply to hyperplanes through the origin, and is different from the concept of dual pairs of subspaces (i.e., hyperplanes through the origin) defined in Section 6.1. To see the relationship between these two types of duals, suppose that $u + \mathscr{V}$ in $\mathscr{F}$ denotes the dual hyperplane for the point V in $\mathscr{E}$. It is easily checked that, if $\mathscr{U}$ in $\mathscr{E}$ denotes the one-dimensional subspace consisting of the points αV for $-\infty < \alpha < \infty$, then $\mathscr{U}$ and $\mathscr{V}$ are a pair of dual subspaces in the sense of Section 6.1. Moreover, the dual hyperplane of αV is $\alpha^{-1}u + \mathscr{V}$. In other words, as V moves along a line towards the origin, the dual hyperplanes are a progression of parallel hyperplanes moving away from the origin, and vice versa. If V were to reach the origin then $u + \mathscr{V}$ would need to be a hyperplane at infinity. The concept of hyperplane at infinity is rigorously introduced in affine geometry, but need not be pursued here.

In this way the duality concept shows how the set of $(p - 1)$-dimensional hyperplanes of a given vector space $\mathscr{E}$ may themselves be regarded as forming a vector space, i.e., one need only consider the corresponding operations on the points of the dual space $\mathscr{F}$. Multiplying a hyperplane by α results in a hyperplane $1/\alpha$ times as distant from the origin, and the zero hyperplane is the hyperplane at infinity.

The dual of an origin-centered ellipsoid π in $\mathscr{E}$ is an origin-centered ellipsoid π_d in $\mathscr{F}$, where π and π_d are symbols for a pair of dual inner products or for their corresponding ellipsoids. However, the dual of a point on the surface of an ellipsoid π is a $(p-1)$-dimensional hyperplane tangent to the dual ellipsoid π_d. To see this, consider any point V on the surface of π, i.e., a point such that $(V, V) = 1$ according to π. Then V corresponds to a hyperplane $v_V + \mathscr{F}_V$ in $\mathscr{F}$, where v_V may be chosen orthogonal to $\mathscr{F}_V$ according to π_d. Applying the dual form of (6.1.14) yields

$$1 = (V, V) = \frac{(v_V, v_V)_d}{(v_V, v_V)_d(v_V, v_V)_d} = (v_V, v_V)_d^{-1} = (v_V, v_V)_d, \qquad (6.2.1)$$

so that v_V lies on the surface of π_d. Since $\mathscr{F}_V$ is orthogonal to v_V according to π_d, $v_V + \mathscr{F}_V$ is tangent to π_d at v_V, as required. It follows that the dual ellipsoid π_d may be regarded as the envelope of the family of $(p-1)$-dimensional hyperplanes which are the duals of the points on π.

It is illuminating to describe how to determine the length of line segment $\emptyset W$ in $\mathscr{E}$ from the dual ellipsoid π_d. Recall that the length of $\emptyset W$ may be regarded as the affine ratio of the length of $\emptyset W$ to the length of the semi-axis of π in the same direction, i.e., as the ratio of the length of $\emptyset W$ to the length of $\emptyset V$ where $V = \alpha W$ and $\alpha = (W, W)^{-1/2}$. To dualize this characterization, consider the dual $v_W + \mathscr{F}_W$ of W where v_W is orthogonal to $\mathscr{F}_W$ according to π_d. The corresponding dual of $V = \alpha W$ is $\alpha^{-1}v_W + \mathscr{F}_W$. Thus the length of W is the ratio of $v_V = \alpha^{-1}v_W$ on π_d to the length of v_W. This is pictured in Fig. 6.2.1 in two dimensions. Note that, as pictured in Fig. 6.2.1, $v_W + \mathscr{F}_W$

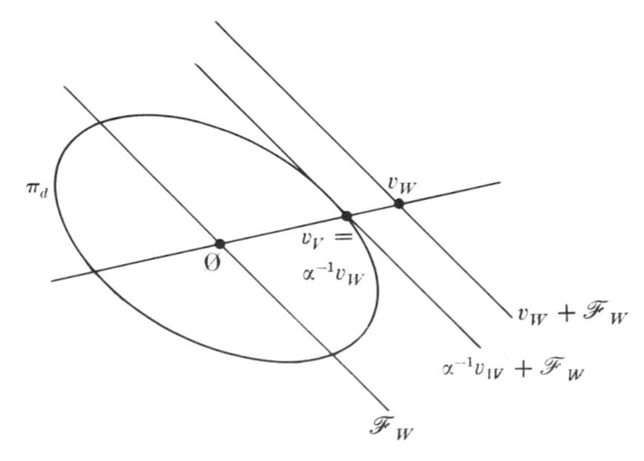

Fig. 6.2.1. The dual hyperplanes $v_W + \mathscr{F}_W$ and $\alpha^{-1}v_W + \mathscr{F}_W$ of the points W and V. The length of W is the ratio of the length of $\emptyset v_W$ to the length of $\emptyset v_V$.

lies outside π_d, which implies that W has length *less* than unity. In general, the farther from the origin that $v_W + \mathscr{F}_W$ moves, the smaller the length of W becomes.

From (6.1.14) it is clear that if the inner product π is scaled, i.e., multiplied by a factor λ, then the dual inner product is scaled by the factor λ^{-1}. At the same time, the ellipsoid π in $\mathscr{E}$ is scaled by the factor $\lambda^{-1/2}$, i.e., the length of each axis is multiplied by $\lambda^{-1/2}$, but the ellipsoid π_d in $\mathscr{F}$ is scaled by the direct factor $\lambda^{1/2}$.

6.3 SOME RELATED MATRIX THEORY

Suppose that $\mathbf{V} = [V_1, V_2, \ldots, V_p]'$ and $\mathbf{W} = [W_1, W_2, \ldots, W_p]'$ are two bases of $\mathscr{E}$ related by

$$\mathbf{V} = \mathbf{AW}, \qquad \boldsymbol{\beta} = \boldsymbol{\alpha}\mathbf{A}, \tag{6.3.1}$$

where $\boldsymbol{\alpha}$ and $\boldsymbol{\beta}$ denote coordinates of points of $\mathscr{E}$ relative to $\mathbf{V}$ and $\mathbf{W}$ respectively. Then the corresponding dual bases $\mathbf{v} = [v_1, v_2, \ldots, v_p]'$ and $\mathbf{w} = [w_1, w_2, \ldots, w_p]'$ of $\mathscr{F}$ are related by

$$\mathbf{w} = \mathbf{A}'\mathbf{v}, \qquad \mathbf{x} = \mathbf{y}\mathbf{A}', \tag{6.3.2}$$

where $\mathbf{x}$ and $\mathbf{y}$ are the coordinates of points of $\mathscr{F}$ relative to $\mathbf{v}$ and $\mathbf{w}$, respectively. To see this, note that either of the equations of (6.3.2) implies the other, and that the second equation of (6.3.2) is an immediate consequence of the first equation of (6.3.1); for, in the language of variable-space and individual-space, if variables obey a certain linear relation $\mathbf{V} = \mathbf{AW}$, then values of those variables obey the same linear relation $\mathbf{x}' = \mathbf{A}\mathbf{y}'$.

In matrix terms the concept of a dual linear transformation is very simple. Suppose that A is a linear transformation from a p-dimensional space $\mathscr{E}$ to a q-dimensional space $\mathscr{E}^*$, and that A is represented by

$$\mathbf{V} \to \mathbf{AW}, \tag{6.3.3}$$

where $\mathbf{V}$ is a basis of $\mathscr{E}$, $\mathbf{W}$ is a basis of $\mathscr{E}^*$, and $\mathbf{A}$ is the $p \times q$ matrix which determines A relative to these bases. It is easily checked from (6.1.13) that the dual linear transformation A_d may be represented by

$$\mathbf{w} \to \mathbf{A}'\mathbf{v}, \tag{6.3.4}$$

where $\mathbf{v}$ and $\mathbf{w}$ are the dual bases of $\mathbf{V}$ and $\mathbf{W}$ in the dual spaces $\mathscr{F}$ and $\mathscr{F}^*$ of $\mathscr{E}$ and $\mathscr{E}^*$, respectively.

Suppose that an inner product π on $\mathscr{E}$ has the inner product matrix $\mathbf{Q}$ relative to a basis $\mathbf{V}$. Then an important matrix result is that *the dual inner product* π_d *in* $\mathcal{F}$ *has the inner product matrix* $\mathbf{Q}^{-1}$ *relative to the dual basis* $\mathbf{v}$ *corresponding to* $\mathbf{V}$. To see this, suppose that $\mathbf{U} = \mathbf{CV}$ is orthonormal relative to π, so that

$$\mathbf{CQC}' = \mathbf{I} \qquad \text{or} \qquad \mathbf{Q} = [\mathbf{C}'\mathbf{C}]^{-1}. \tag{6.3.5}$$

Then the corresponding $\mathbf{u}$, where $\mathbf{v} = \mathbf{C}'\mathbf{u}$, is known to be orthonormal relative to π_d. Thus, if π_d has inner product matrix $\mathbf{P}$ relative to $\mathbf{v}$, then

$$\mathbf{P} = \mathbf{C}'\mathbf{IC} = \mathbf{C}'\mathbf{C}. \tag{6.3.6}$$

From (6.3.5) and (6.3.6),

$$\mathbf{P} = \mathbf{Q}^{-1}, \tag{6.3.7}$$

as required.

6.4 DUALITY ASPECTS OF THE PROCESS OF SUCCESSIVE ORTHOGONALIZATION

Another example of the inversion phenomena experienced in passing from one space to its dual is given by:

> ***Theorem 6.4.*** *Suppose that the basis* $\mathbf{U}$ *of a Euclidean space* $\mathcal{E}$ *is orthogonalized as in Section* 4.1 *to produce an orthogonal basis* $\mathbf{U}^*$ *and then an orthonormal basis* $\mathbf{U}^{**}$. *Suppose that* $\mathbf{U}$, $\mathbf{U}^*$, *and* $\mathbf{U}^{**}$ *have dual bases* $\mathbf{u}$, $\mathbf{u}^*$, *and* $\mathbf{u}^{**}$, *respectively, in the dual Euclidean space* $\mathcal{F}$ *of* $\mathcal{E}$. *Then, if the basis* $\mathbf{u}$ *is orthogonalized in the reverse of the given order, the resulting orthogonal basis is* $\mathbf{u}^*$ *and the corresponding orthonormal basis is* $\mathbf{u}^{**}$.

Since $\mathbf{U}^*$ is orthogonal in $\mathcal{E}$, its dual $\mathbf{u}^*$ is known to be orthogonal in $\mathcal{F}$, and similarly, $\mathbf{u}^{**}$ is known to be orthonormal in $\mathcal{F}$. Thus it remains only to show that $\mathbf{u}^*$ and $\mathbf{u}^{**}$ are the specific orthogonal bases indicated by the theorem. Using the notation of Section 4.3, it is known that

$$\mathbf{U}^* = \mathbf{AU} \tag{6.4.1}$$

may be characterized as that orthogonal basis of $\mathcal{E}$ such that $\mathbf{A}$ is a triangular matrix with unity along the main diagonal and zero above the main diagonal. Similarly

$$\mathbf{U}^{**} = \mathbf{CU} \tag{6.4.2}$$

may be characterized as that orthonormal basis of $\mathcal{E}$ such that $\mathbf{C}$ is triangular with zero elements above the main diagonal. From (6.3.2),

$$\mathbf{u}^* = \mathbf{B}'\mathbf{u} \qquad \text{and} \qquad \mathbf{u}^{**} = \mathbf{D}'\mathbf{u}, \tag{6.4.3}$$

where

$$\mathbf{B} = \mathbf{A}^{-1} \qquad \text{and} \qquad \mathbf{D} = \mathbf{C}^{-1}. \tag{6.4.4}$$

Thus $\mathbf{B}'$ is triangular with unity along the main diagonal and zero *below* the main diagonal and, similarly, $\mathbf{D}'$ is triangular with zero below the main diagonal.

These properties of $\mathbf{B}'$ and $\mathbf{D}'$ are sufficient to imply, respectively, that $\mathbf{u}^*$ and $\mathbf{u}^{**}$ are the particular reverse order bases specified in the theorem.

Theorem 6.4 supplies a concise explanation of the dual formulas which were profusely displayed in Section 4.2. Any formula involving $\mathbf{Q}$, $\mathbf{P}$, $\mathbf{T}$, $\mathbf{T}^{-1}$, $\mathbf{B}$, $\mathbf{A}$, $\mathbf{D}$, and $\mathbf{C}$ may be regarded as describing aspects of a basis $\mathbf{U}$ of a Euclidean space $\mathscr{E}$, where $\mathbf{U}$ has the inner product matrix $\mathbf{Q}$. The same formulas may equally well be applied to yield similar descriptions of the basis $\mathbf{u}$ of $\mathscr{F}$, treating the elements of $\mathbf{u}$ in the opposite order from the elements of $\mathbf{U}$. Thus, the dual of any formula may be immediately written down simply by replacing $\mathbf{Q}$, $\mathbf{P}$, $\mathbf{T}$, $\mathbf{T}^{-1}$, $\mathbf{B}$, $\mathbf{A}$, $\mathbf{D}$, and $\mathbf{C}$ by $\mathbf{P}^*$, $\mathbf{Q}^*$, $\mathbf{T}^{*-1}$, $\mathbf{T}^*$, $\mathbf{A}^*$, $\mathbf{B}^*$, $\mathbf{C}^*$, and $\mathbf{D}^*$, respectively, where the star notation means that the order of the rows and columns has been reversed, i.e., $\mathbf{P}^*$ is the same as $\mathbf{P}$ except for the reversing of the order of the rows and columns of $\mathbf{P}$, and so on.

Theorem 6.4 also suggests that the computational routines applicable to $\mathbf{Q}$, as described in Section 4.3, should also be interesting when applied to $\mathbf{P} = \mathbf{Q}^{-1}$. In particular, the dual of successively applying the sweep operator of (4.3.13) to the rows and columns of $\mathbf{Q}$ in order is the operation of successively applying the sweep operator to the rows and columns of $\mathbf{P}$ in reverse order. After s stages of the former, one has (4.3.14), which may be written

$$\begin{bmatrix} -\mathbf{Q}_{11}^{-1} & \mathbf{Q}_{11}^{-1}\mathbf{Q}_{12} \\ \mathbf{Q}_{21}\mathbf{Q}_{11}^{-1} & \mathbf{Q}_{22.1} \end{bmatrix}. \tag{6.4.5}$$

It follows dually that after $p - s$ stages of the latter, one must have

$$\begin{bmatrix} \mathbf{P}_{11.2} & \mathbf{P}_{12}\mathbf{P}_{22}^{-1} \\ \mathbf{P}_{22}^{-1}\mathbf{P}_{21} & -\mathbf{P}_{22}^{-1} \end{bmatrix}. \tag{6.4.6}$$

From the relations in Section 4.2, it follows that (6.4.5) is simply the negative of (6.4.6). Thus, the dual of the computations of the elimination method yields the same quantities as the original except for the changed signs and reversed order.

6.5 DUALITY RELATIONS CONCERNING A PAIR OF INNER PRODUCTS

Suppose that π_1 and π_2 are two inner products defined over $\mathscr{E}$ with dual inner products π_{1d} and π_{2d} defined over the dual space $\mathscr{F}$ of $\mathscr{E}$. If $\mathbf{W}$ is an orthogonal basis according to both π_1 and π_2, then the dual basis $\mathbf{W}$ of $\mathscr{F}$ is orthogonal according to both π_{1d} and π_{2d}, i.e., the dual of a basis of eigenvectors is also a basis of eigenvectors for the dual space. The eigenvalues of π_{1d} relative to π_{2d} are, however, the inverses of the eigenvalues of π_1 relative to π_2. To see this, suppose that $\mathbf{W}$ is scaled to be orthonormal relative to π_2. Then, relative to π_1,

$$\begin{aligned} (W_i, W_i)_1 &= \lambda_i, \qquad \text{for} \quad i = 1, 2, \ldots, p, \\ (W_i, W_j)_1 &= 0, \qquad \text{for} \quad i \neq j, \end{aligned} \tag{6.5.1}$$

where $\lambda_1, \lambda_2, \ldots, \lambda_p$ are the eigenvalues of π_1 relative to π_2. From (6.1.11), $\mathbf{w}$ is orthonormal relative to π_{2d}, but

$$\begin{aligned} (w_i, w_i)_{1d} &= \frac{1}{\lambda_i} \qquad \text{for} \qquad i = 1, 2, \ldots, p, \\ (w_i, w_j)_{1d} &= 0 \qquad \text{for} \qquad i \neq j, \end{aligned} \tag{6.5.2}$$

whence the eigenvalues of π_{1d} relative to π_{2d} are $1/\lambda_1, 1/\lambda_2, \ldots, 1/\lambda_p$.

Geometrically, the basis $\mathbf{W}$ determines sets of conjugate axes for both of the ellipsoids π_1 and π_2 in $\mathscr{E}$, while $\mathbf{w}$ does the same for the dual ellipsoids π_{1d} and π_{2d} in $\mathscr{F}$. However, the ratio of the lengths of such principal axes is inverted by the passage from one space to its dual.

The inversion of the eigenvalues is also clear analytically. For suppose that $\mathbf{Q}_1$ and $\mathbf{Q}_2$ are the inner product matrices of π_1 and π_2 relative to a basis $\mathbf{U}$ of $\mathscr{E}$. Then the eigenvalues are roots of the equation

$$\det(\mathbf{Q}_1 - \lambda \mathbf{Q}_2) = 0. \tag{6.5.3}$$

This equation is equivalent to

$$\lambda^p \det \mathbf{Q}_1\mathbf{Q}_1^{-1}\left(\frac{1}{\lambda}\mathbf{Q}_1 - \mathbf{Q}_2\right)\mathbf{Q}_2^{-1}\mathbf{Q}_2 = 0, \qquad \text{or}$$

$$(-\lambda)^p \det \mathbf{Q}_1 \det \mathbf{Q}_2 \det\left(\mathbf{Q}_1^{-1} - \frac{1}{\lambda}\mathbf{Q}_2^{-1}\right) = 0, \qquad \text{or}$$

$$\det\left(\mathbf{Q}_1^{-1} - \frac{1}{\lambda}\mathbf{Q}_2^{-1}\right) = 0, \tag{6.5.4}$$

which means that the inverses $1/\lambda_i$ are the roots of the determinantal equation relative to the dual basis $\mathbf{u}$ for the eigenvalues of π_{1d} relative to π_{2d}.

To pursue the analytic approach further, suppose that $\mathbf{V}$ is orthonormal relative to π_2, and has the inner product matrix $\mathbf{Q}$ according to π_1. Then the eigenvalues are the roots of the equation

$$\det(\mathbf{Q} - \lambda \mathbf{I}) = 0, \tag{6.5.5}$$

which is the standard form for solution. If the eigenvectors $\mathbf{W}$ are also chosen to be orthonormal according to π_2, then

$$\mathbf{W} = \mathbf{EV}, \tag{6.5.6}$$

where $\mathbf{E}$ is an orthogonal matrix whose rows give the coordinates of $W_1, W_2, \ldots, W_p$ relative to $\mathbf{V}$. It is interesting to note that, since from (6.3.2)

$$\mathbf{v} = \mathbf{E}'\mathbf{w} \qquad \text{or} \qquad \mathbf{w} = \mathbf{E}\mathbf{v}, \tag{6.5.7}$$

the rows of $\mathbf{E}$ are also the coordinates of the dual eigenvectors $w_1, w_2, \ldots, w_p$ relative to $\mathbf{v}$.

A quite different theory relating two sets of eigenvalues will now be presented. Suppose that π denotes an inner product over a p-dimensional space $\mathscr{E}$, and that π_d denotes the dual inner product over $\mathscr{F}$. Next, consider a separate q-dimensional Euclidean space $\mathscr{E}^*$ whose inner product is denoted by π^* and whose dual and dual inner product are denoted by $\mathscr{F}^*$ and π_d^*. Suppose that A denotes a linear transformation from $\mathscr{E}^*$ to $\mathscr{E}$. With this structure a second inner product π_{A} may be defined over $\mathscr{E}$ from

$$(U, V)_{\mathsf{A}} = (\mathsf{A}U, \mathsf{A}V)^*. \tag{6.5.8}$$

Dually, a second inner product $\pi_{\mathsf{A}_d}^*$ may be defined over $\mathscr{F}^*$ from

$$(u^*, v^*)_{\mathsf{A}_d}^* = (\mathsf{A}_d u^*, \mathsf{A}_d v^*)_d. \tag{6.5.9}$$

Finally, suppose that A has rank $r \leq \min(p, q)$. *Then there are r nonzero eigenvalues of π_{A} relative to π, and $p - r$ zero eigenvalues. These same nonzero eigenvalues $\lambda_1, \lambda_2, \ldots, \lambda_r$ together with $q - r$ zeros make up the eigenvalues of $\pi_{\mathsf{A}_d}^*$ relative to π_d^*. If W_i denotes an eigenvector in $\mathscr{E}$ associated with λ_i, for $i = 1, 2, \ldots, r$, then an eigenvector w_i^* in $\mathscr{F}^*$ also corresponding to λ_i may be constructed by passing from W_i in $\mathscr{E}$ to w_i in $\mathscr{F}$ defined by the natural isomorphism* (6.1.18) *and then setting*

$$w_i^* = \mathsf{A}_d w_i. \tag{6.5.10}$$

The proof requires constructing a π^*-orthonormal basis $\mathbf{W}^*$ of $\mathscr{E}^*$ such that A may be described as

$$\mathbf{W}^* \rightarrow \mathbf{JW}, \tag{6.5.11}$$

where $\mathbf{W}$ is a π-orthonormal basis of $\mathscr{E}$ whose first r elements $W_1, W_2, \ldots, W_r$ are eigenvectors as above and where $\mathbf{J}$ is a $q \times p$ matrix whose elements are all zero except that the (i, i) element is $\lambda_i^{1/2}$ for $i = 1, 2, \ldots, r$. The construction proceeds as follows: $W_{r+1}^*, W_{r+2}^*, \ldots, W_q^*$ is any π^*-orthonormal basis of the $(q - r)$-dimensional subspace of $\mathscr{E}^*$ which maps into $\emptyset$ in $\mathscr{E}$ under A. The r-dimensional subspace spanned by $W_1^*, W_2^*, \ldots, W_r^*$ is then determined as the π^*-orthogonal complement of the subspace spanned by $W_{r+1}^*, W_{r+2}^*, \ldots, W_q^*$. Under A, this r-dimensional subspace of $\mathscr{E}^*$ is in one-one correspondence with an r-dimensional range space in $\mathscr{E}$, and from (6.5.8) this range space must be the space spanned by $W_1, W_2, \ldots, W_r$. Finally $W_1^*, W_2^*, \ldots, W_r^*$ may be defined from (6.5.11), and the π^*-orthonormality of $W_1^*, W_2^*, \ldots, W_r^*$ follows from (6.5.8) together with the eigenvalue properties $(W_i, W_j)_{\mathsf{A}} = \lambda_i$ or 0 depending on whether $i = j$ or $i \neq j$.

In terms of the dual bases $\mathbf{w}^*$ and $\mathbf{w}$ of $\mathbf{W}^*$ and $\mathbf{W}$, the dual of (6.5.11) may be written

$$\mathbf{w} \rightarrow \mathbf{J}'\mathbf{w}^*. \tag{6.5.12}$$

It follows directly from (6.5.9) and (6.5.12) that the eigenvalues and eigenvectors of $\pi_{\mathsf{A}_d}^*$ relative to π_d^* are as stated.

The theorem just proved may be stated more simply in purely analytical terms as follows.

Theorem 6.5. *If* $\mathbf{A}$ *is a given* $q \times p$ *matrix of rank* r, *then the* r *nonzero eigenvalues* $\lambda_1, \lambda_2, \ldots, \lambda_r$ *of* $\mathbf{A}'\mathbf{A}$ *are the same as the* r *nonzero eigenvalues of* $\mathbf{AA}'$. *Moreover, if a set of eigenvectors of* $\mathbf{A}'\mathbf{A}$ *is given by the rows of an* $r \times p$ *matrix* $\mathbf{C}_1$, *then corresponding eigenvectors of* $\mathbf{AA}'$ *are given by the rows of the* $r \times q$ *matrix* $\mathbf{C}_1\mathbf{A}'$.

The proof here requires simply that $\mathbf{A}$ be interpreted as a linear transformation $\mathbf{V}^* \to \mathbf{AV}$ from a Euclidean space $\mathscr{E}^*$ with π^*-orthonormal basis $\mathbf{V}^*$ to a Euclidean space $\mathscr{E}$ with a π-orthonormal basis $\mathbf{V}$. Then $\mathbf{A}'\mathbf{A}$ is the inner product matrix of π_{A} relative to the bases $\mathbf{V}$ and, dually, $\mathbf{AA}'$ is the inner product matrix of $\pi^*_{\mathsf{A}_d}$ relative to the basis $\mathbf{v}^*$ of $\mathscr{F}^*$ dual to $\mathbf{V}^*$ in $\mathscr{E}^*$. With this identification, Theorem 6.5 is simply an analytic statement of the preceding vector result.

6.6 THE DUAL OF A SEMI-DEFINITE INNER PRODUCT

The definition (6.1.14) of the dual inner product assumed that $(V, V) > 0$ for all V. Suppose that an inner product π over $\mathscr{E}$ is of rank $f < p$ and that $(V, V) = 0$ for V in the $(p - f)$-dimensional subspace $\mathscr{U}$ of $\mathscr{E}$. The dual of $\mathscr{U}$ is an f-dimensional subspace $\mathscr{U}_d$ in $\mathscr{F}$. The natural dual of the semi-definite inner product π is a *partial inner product* π_d, defined only over the subspace $\mathscr{U}_d$ of $\mathscr{F}$.

Consider any basis $\mathbf{W}$ of $\mathscr{E}$ such that $W_1, W_2, \ldots, W_f$ span a subspace of $\mathscr{E}$ complementary to $\mathscr{U}$ and $W_{f+1}, W_{f+2}, \ldots, W_p$ span $\mathscr{U}$. Since the inner product has full rank over this f-dimensional subspace, the first set $W_1, W_2, \ldots, W_f$ may be chosen to be orthonormal according to π, while $W_{f+1}, W_{f+2}, \ldots, W_p$ must have zero norms and zero inner products with every V in $\mathscr{E}$. The dual basis $w_1, w_2, \ldots, w_p$ has the property that $w_1, w_2, \ldots, w_f$ span $\mathscr{U}_d$, so that an inner product may be defined over $\mathscr{U}_d$ taking $w_1, w_2, \ldots, w_f$ to be orthonormal, thus defining the dual partial inner product mentioned above. The reader may check that any basis $\mathbf{W}$ such that $W_1, W_2, \ldots, W_f$ are orthonormal according to π produces the same inner product π_d on $\mathscr{U}_d$, so that the definition is unique. He should also show that the uniqueness property does not hold if $w_1, w_2, \ldots, w_p$ are taken to be orthonormal to define an inner product over all of $\mathscr{F}$.

Conversely, if a partial inner product is defined over an f-dimensional subspace of $\mathscr{F}$, then one may recover the dual semi-definite inner product in $\mathscr{E}$ by specifying a basis $w_1, w_2, \ldots, w_p$ of $\mathscr{F}$ such that $w_1, w_2, \ldots, w_f$ are orthonormal according to the partial inner product. Note that $w_1, w_2, \ldots, w_f$ uniquely determine the $(p - f)$-dimensional subspace of $\mathscr{E}$ spanned by $W_{f+1}, W_{f+2}, \ldots, W_p$ so that the subspace $\mathscr{U}$ of $\mathscr{E}$ on which $(V, V) = 0$ is uniquely determined. The reader may check that any orthogonal transformation of $w_1, w_2, \ldots, w_f$ yields the same semi-definite inner product over $\mathscr{E}$ when $W_1, W_2, \ldots, W_f$ are taken to be orthonormal and $\mathscr{U}$ is uniquely determined as described.

Geometrically, the above theory states that the dual of an ellipsoidal cylinder extending to infinity along a family of $(p - f)$-dimensional hyperplanes is an ellipsoid lying in an f-dimensional hyperplane. This might have been expected, since to stretch an ellipsoid along conjugate axes by given factors is to shrink the dual ellipsoid along the dual conjugate axes by the same factors, so that infinite length axes in the original ellipsoid should result in zero length axes in the dual ellipsoid. Note also that, although the dual inner product is defined only over the hyperplane $\mathscr{U}_d$ through the origin, it can be used to define the concepts of length, volume, and angle in any hyperplane $v + \mathscr{U}_d$ parallel to $\mathscr{U}_d$. One need only translate the geometric figures in $v + \mathscr{U}_d$ back to $\mathscr{U}_d$ and use the definitions applicable in $\mathscr{U}_d$.

Some related analytic theory follows. Suppose that $\mathbf{Q}$ is a positive semi-definite $p \times p$ symmetric matrix of rank f which is regarded as an inner product matrix relative to the basis $\mathbf{U}$ of $\mathscr{E}$. It may be of interest to locate the subspace $\mathscr{U}_d$ of $\mathscr{F}$ over which the partial inner product is defined. A way to do this is to find a $p \times f$ matrix $\mathbf{D}_1$ such that

$$[w_1, w_2, \ldots, w_f]' = \mathbf{D}_1'\mathbf{u}, \tag{6.6.1}$$

where $\mathbf{u}$ is the dual basis of $\mathbf{U}$ and $w_1, w_2, \ldots, w_f$ is an orthonormal set spanning $\mathscr{U}_d$ as above. It will now be proved that a $p \times f$ *matrix* $\mathbf{D}_1$ *obeys the relation* (6.6.1) *for some choice of* $w_1, w_2, \ldots, w_f$ *if and only if*

$$\mathbf{Q} = \mathbf{D}_1\mathbf{D}_1'. \tag{6.6.2}$$

Suppose first that (6.6.1) holds. Then $\mathbf{D}_1$ is the first f columns of a matrix $\mathbf{D}$ such that $\mathbf{w} = \mathbf{D}'\mathbf{u}$ or equivalently that $\mathbf{U} = \mathbf{DW}$. Now $\mathbf{W}$ has the inner product matrix $\mathbf{I}_f$ whose first f diagonal elements are unity and whose remaining elements are zero. It follows that $\mathbf{Q} = \mathbf{DI}_f\mathbf{D}'$. But $\mathbf{DI}_f\mathbf{D}' = \mathbf{D}_1\mathbf{D}_1'$ and thus (6.6.2) follows. To prove the converse result, noting that (6.6.2) implies that $\mathbf{D}_1$ has rank f, add any $p - f$ columns to $\mathbf{D}_1$ to make it a $p \times p$ nonsingular matrix $\mathbf{D}$. Then the argument simply operates in reverse.

The computations required to produce an instance of $\mathbf{D}_1$ from a given $\mathbf{Q}$ were essentially given in Section 1.4. By carrying out successive orthogonalization on $\mathbf{Q}$, one gets f columns of $\mathbf{B}$ corresponding to nonzero (U_s^*, U_s^*). Dividing these f columns by the corresponding $(U_s^*, U_s^*)^{-1/2}$ gives a particular choice of $\mathbf{D}_1$.

In Section 3.6 it was shown that a linear transformation may be used to carry an inner product in the reverse direction in a natural way. Dualizing that theory shows how to carry a partial inner product in the forward direction into another partial inner product. Specifically, suppose that A_d denotes any linear transformation from $\mathscr{F}$ to $\mathscr{F}^*$ and that π_d is a partial inner product over $\mathscr{F}$. Denoting the duals of A_d, $\mathscr{F}$, $\mathscr{F}^*$, and π_d by A, $\mathscr{E}$, $\mathscr{E}^*$, and π, the theory of

Section 3.6 shows how the transformation A from $\mathscr{E}^*$ to $\mathscr{E}$ induces from π a wide sense inner product π^* over $\mathscr{E}^*$, whose dual in turn defines the desired partial inner product π_d^* over $\mathscr{F}^*$ induced by A_d from π_d.

The roundabout definition of π_d^* from π_d via dual theory may be replaced by the simple and direct geometric characterization given in Theorem 6.6 which follows. Let π_d and π_d^* denote ambiguously either the partial inner products π_d and π_d^* or their corresponding ellipsoids lying in the subspaces over which the partial inner products are defined. Define the *shadow of* π_d *in* $\mathscr{F}$ *under the transformation* A_d to be the set of points in $\mathscr{F}^*$ which are the transforms of some point in π_d.

Theorem 6.6. *π_d^* is the shadow of π_d under the transformation A_d.*

In other words, the set of points v in $\mathscr{F}$ for which $(v, v)_d$ is defined and less than or equal to unity maps into the set of points v^* in $\mathscr{F}^*$ for which $(v^*, v^*)_d^*$ is defined and less than or equal to unity. The proof requires consideration of several subspaces: the subspace $\mathscr{W}_d$ in $\mathscr{F}$ in which π_d lies, the subspace $\mathscr{V}_d$ in $\mathscr{F}$ which maps into the origin in $\mathscr{F}^*$ under A_d, the subspace $\mathscr{N}_d$ of $\mathscr{W}_d$ orthogonal to $\mathscr{W}_d \cap \mathscr{U}_d$ according to π_d^*, and the subspace $\mathscr{U}_d^*$ of $\mathscr{F}^*$ consisting of the maps of points in $\mathscr{U}_d$, this being the subspace in which the shadow lies. Perhaps the most straightforward approach is to set up an orthonormal coordinate system in $\mathscr{W}_d$ a part of which spans $\mathscr{U}_d$ and a subpart of which transforms into the range space $\mathscr{U}_d^*$. In these terms it is obvious that the shadow π_d^* of π_d is an ellipsoid in $\mathscr{U}_d^*$. To check that π_d^* is the right ellipsoid requires carefully setting up dual concepts and checking out the original definition of π_d^* by the roundabout route. Further details are left to the reader.

It is worth stating formally that:

Corollary 6.6. *The shadow of any ellipsoid in a hyperplane under a linear transformation is again an ellipsoid in a hyperplane. The center of the shadow ellipsoid is the transform of the center of the original ellipsoid.*

For hyperplanes through the origin and narrow sense linear transformations the corollary is an immediate consequence of Theorem 6.6. But the corollary is obvious for translations of a space into itself, and so holds for wide sense linear transformations and for ellipsoids in arbitrary hyperplanes with arbitrary centers.

Corollary 6.6 is illustrated in Figure 7.3.2.

6.7 EXERCISES

6.1.1 Show that a linear functional v defined over a vector space $\mathscr{E}$ is uniquely determined by its values over any basis of $\mathscr{E}$.

6.1.2 What is meant by the assertion that two linear functionals v_1 and v_2 over $\mathscr{E}$ are different? Show that v_1 and v_2 may agree on a subspace of dimension $p - 1$ and still be different.

6.1.3 Suppose that $\{V, v\}$ is defined to be zero for all V in $\mathscr{E}$ and v in $\mathscr{F}$. Does this define a bilinear product over $\mathscr{E}$ and $\mathscr{F}$? If so, can this bilinear product be used in showing that $\mathscr{E}$ and $\mathscr{F}$ are dual?

6.1.4 Suppose that $V_1, V_2, \ldots, V_p$ is a basis of $\mathscr{E}$ and $v_1, v_2, \ldots, v_p$ is the dual basis in $\mathscr{F}$. Express in terms of $v_1, v_2, \ldots, v_p$ the dual basis in $\mathscr{F}$ of the basis V_1, $V_2 + V_1$, $V_3 + V_1, \ldots, V_p + V_1$ in $\mathscr{E}$.

6.1.5 Suppose that $\mathscr{U}$ and $\mathscr{V}$ are complementary subspaces of $\mathscr{E}$. Show that the dual subspaces $\mathscr{U}_d$ and $\mathscr{V}_d$ are complementary in $\mathscr{F}$.

6.1.6 Show that the isomorphism between $\mathscr{E}$ and $\mathscr{F}$ defined by

$$\boldsymbol{\alpha}'\mathbf{V} \rightarrow \boldsymbol{\alpha}'\mathbf{v},$$

where **V** and **v** are dual bases, is not coordinate-free. Show further that the isomorphism is the same for a basis $\mathbf{W} = \mathbf{CV}$ and its dual **w** if and only if **C** is an orthogonal matrix.

6.1.7 Since variable-space is the dual of individual-space, it must follow that variable-space has a natural isomorphism to the space of linear functionals over individual-space. What is this isomorphism, and what is the bilinear product which it preserves? In other words, how does a linear functional over individual-space determine a variable?

6.1.8 Suppose that $\mathscr{E}$ and $\mathscr{F}$ are dual spaces with bilinear product $\{V, v\}$. Suppose that $V_1, V_2, \ldots, V_p$ and $v_1, v_2, \ldots, v_p$ are dual bases of $\mathscr{E}$ and $\mathscr{F}$, and that a is any element of $\mathscr{F}$. Show that

$$a = \sum_{i=1}^{p} \{V_i, a\} v_i.$$

What is the statistical interpretation of this formula? What is the dual formula and what is the statistical interpretation of the dual formula?

6.1.9 Suppose that $\mathscr{E}$ and $\mathscr{F}$ are dual spaces with bilinear product function $\{V, v\}$. Show that $\mathscr{E}$ and $\mathscr{F}$ are also dual spaces with the rescaled bilinear product function $\lambda\{V, v\}$ for any $\lambda \neq 0$. Show that the duality of a pair of subspaces $\mathscr{U}$ and $\mathscr{U}_d$ is not affected by rescaling the bilinear product function, but that the concepts of dual basis and dual inner product are also subject to rescaling.

6.1.10 Show that the natural isomorphism between a pair $\mathscr{E}$ and $\mathscr{F}$ of dual Euclidean spaces defined in Section 6.1 is simply the identity relationship when $\mathscr{E}$ is regarded as self-dual.

6.1.11 Show that a definition of dual inner product alternative to (6.1.14) is given by

$$(v, v)_d = \sup_V \frac{\{V, v\}^2}{(V, V)}.$$

6.2.1 What is the dual of the parallelotope in $\mathscr{E}$ with vertices $W + \sum_1^p c_i V_i$ where each c_i is 0 or 1?

6.2.2 The dual of a pair of r-dimensional hyperplanes lying in an $(r + 1)$-dimensional hyperplane through the origin is a pair of $(p - r - 1)$-dimensional hyperplanes with a common intersection in the hyperplane at infinity. Show that these two $(p - r - 1)$-dimensional hyperplanes are parallel.

6.2.3 Suppose that V in $\mathscr{E}$ and v in $\mathscr{F}$ are said to be *biorthogonal* if $\{V, v\} = 0$. Show that V and v are biorthogonal if and only if the line V is parallel to the dual hyperplane in $\mathscr{E}$ of v in $\mathscr{F}$. A subspace $\mathscr{U}$ of $\mathscr{E}$ is said to be *biorthogonal* to a subspace $\mathscr{V}$ of $\mathscr{F}$ if $\{V, v\} = 0$ for all V in $\mathscr{U}$ and v in $\mathscr{V}$. What is the geometric interpretation in $\mathscr{E}$ of the relationship between $\mathscr{U}$ and the dual of $\mathscr{V}$?

6.3.1 Suppose that $\mathscr{E}$ and $\mathscr{F}$ are dual p-dimensional spaces with bilinear product function $\{V, v\}$ for V in $\mathscr{E}$ and v in $\mathscr{F}$. Suppose that $\mathbf{V}$ is any basis in $\mathscr{E}$ and $\mathbf{w}$ any basis in $\mathscr{F}$. Define the bilinear product matrix $\mathbf{R}$ of $\mathbf{V}$ and $\mathbf{w}$ to be a $p \times p$ matrix whose (i, j) element is $\{V_i, w_j\}$. Show how to express $\{\boldsymbol{\alpha}\mathbf{V}, \boldsymbol{\beta}\mathbf{w}\}$ in terms of $\boldsymbol{\alpha}$, $\boldsymbol{\beta}$, and $\mathbf{R}$. How is $\mathbf{R}$ related to the bilinear product matrix of bases $\mathbf{V}^* = \mathbf{AV}$ and $\mathbf{w}^* = \mathbf{Bw}$? What is the bilinear product matrix of a pair of dual bases?

6.3.2 Suppose that $\mathbf{V}$ and $\mathbf{W}$ are any two orthonormal bases of a Euclidean space $\mathscr{E}$, and that $\mathbf{v}$ and $\mathbf{w}$ are the corresponding dual bases of $\mathscr{F}$. Show directly that the inner products defined by regarding $\mathbf{v}$ or $\mathbf{w}$ to be orthonormal are identical. Show likewise that the isomorphisms between $\mathscr{E}$ and $\mathscr{F}$ defined by $\mathbf{V} \to \mathbf{v}$ or $\mathbf{W} \to \mathbf{w}$ are identical.

6.3.3 A linear transformation of $\mathscr{E}$ into itself has rank p when it carries a basis $\mathbf{V}$ of $\mathscr{E}$ into another basis $\mathbf{V}^*$ of $\mathscr{E}$. The dual linear transformation carries the dual basis $\mathbf{v}$ of $\mathbf{V}$ into the dual basis $\mathbf{v}^*$ of $\mathbf{V}^*$. Show that the correspondence between points of $\mathscr{E}$ and $(p - 1)$-dimensional hyperplanes of $\mathscr{F}$ is preserved after dual linear transformations are applied to both $\mathscr{E}$ and $\mathscr{F}$.

6.4.1 Show that $\mathbf{Q}$ is a positive definite symmetric matrix if and only if $\mathbf{Q}^{-1}$ is also.

6.4.2 Show that the dual of formula (4.2.17) is

$$\mathbf{u}_{1.2} = \mathbf{u}_1 + \mathbf{H}_{21}'\mathbf{u}_2.$$

6.5.1 Draw the duals of Figs. 5.2.1 and 5.2.2, showing λ_1 and λ_2 as ratios of lengths in $\mathscr{F}$.

6.5.2 Give a purely analytic proof of Theorem 6.5.

6.6.1 Check the statements made in the last two sentences of paragraph two of Section 6.6, and in the last sentence of paragraph three.

6.6.2 Show how definition (6.1.14) may be modified to provide alternative definitions of the dual of a semi-definite inner product and the dual of a partial inner product.

6.6.3 Suppose that $\mathbf{D}_1$ and $\mathbf{D}_1^*$ are both $p \times f$ matrices satisfying (6.6.2). Show that $\mathbf{D}_1 = \mathbf{D}_1^*\mathbf{G}'$ for some orthogonal matrix $\mathbf{G}$.

6.6.4 Suppose that $\dot{\mathbf{Q}}$ is a pseudoinverse of a positive semi-definite symmetric $p \times p$ matrix $\mathbf{Q}$. The inner products π and $\dot{\pi}$ defined by $\mathbf{Q}$ and $\dot{\mathbf{Q}}$ relative to a pair $\mathbf{V}$ and $\mathbf{v}$ of dual bases are both semi-definite. How does $\dot{\pi}$ relate to the partial inner product π_d?

6.6.5 Suppose that $\mathscr{E}$ and $\mathscr{F}$ are a pair of dual spaces with full rank inner products π and π_d. Suppose that π^* is an inner product of rank $r \leq p$ over $\mathscr{E}$ and that π^* is its dual (partial) inner product over $\mathscr{F}$. Show that the r nonzero eigenvalues of π^* relative to π are the inverses of the r eigenvalues of π^* relative to π_d in the subspace over which π^* is defined. Show also that the isomorphism (6.1.18) carries corresponding sets of eigenvectors into one another, where if one set is π-orthonormal its image is π_d-orthonormal.

6.6.6 Demonstrate Corollary 6.6 directly.

6.6.7 Complete the proof of Theorem 6.6.

PART 3

DATA ANALYSIS

CHAPTER 7

ONE SAMPLE OF INDIVIDUALS: BASIC THEORY

7.1 INTRODUCTION

This is a purely theoretical chapter, while the remaining chapters of Part 2 mix theory with examples presenting analyses of observed data. The concern of this chapter is to introduce various concepts related to the sample mean and sample covariance of a sample of n individuals each observed on a set of p variables. The sample individuals will be denoted by $a_1, a_2, \ldots, a_n$ and the observable variables by $V_1, V_2, \ldots, V_p$. The term *p-variate sample of size n* will be used to describe the resulting data.

Such a sample may be identified mathematically with a set of points $a_1, a_2, \ldots, a_n$ in the individual-space $\mathscr{F}$ dual to the variable-space $\mathscr{E}$ spanned by $V_1, V_2, \ldots, V_p$. The theory of Chapters 7 through 11 is completely derived from this simple mathematical formulation.

The variables $V_1, V_2, \ldots, V_p$ and individuals $a_1, a_2, \ldots, a_n$ define $p \times n$ *quantities* or *statistics*. The quantity associated with V_i and a_j may be denoted by $V_j^{(i)}$, and the value of $V_j^{(i)}$ may be denoted by $X_j^{(i)}$ for $i = 1, 2, \ldots, n$ and $j = 1, 2, \ldots, p$. In principle any numerical operation with the $X_j^{(i)}$ defines the value of another quantity which is a function of the $V_j^{(i)}$.

In practice it is unwieldy to carry along double notation and terminology for such quantities and their values. Consequently, accepting the lesser evil of some ambiguity, symbols appropriate to the values of quantities will be used throughout. At the same time the names of quantities may be used in reference to the values of those quantities. For example, $\bar{\mathbf{X}}$ will be used to denote a $1 \times p$ vector of sample mean values, but for brevity $\bar{\mathbf{X}}$ will usually be referred to simply as the sample mean vector.

Note that the methods of Chapters 7 through 11 may be applied to a finite population in place of a finite sample. The methods can also be extended to infinite populations through a limiting argument, but this is usually done within the framework of probability theory, i.e., the concept of an infinite population may be related to the concept of a probability distribution. In this sense, the discussion of infinite populations is postponed until Chapter 12.

7.2 DEFINITIONS

The *sample mean* (*individual*) m of a given sample $a_1, a_2, \ldots, a_n$ is

$$m = \frac{1}{n} \sum_{i=1}^{n} a_i. \tag{7.2.1}$$

The value of m on a variable V in variable-space $\mathscr{E}$ will be denoted by $m(V)$ and should be called the *sample mean* (*value*) *of the variable* V. If the values of the individuals $a_1, a_2, \ldots, a_n$ on a variable V are denoted by $X^{(1)}, X^{(2)}, \ldots, X^{(n)}$, then from (6.1.2) and (7.2.1)

$$m(V) = \frac{1}{n} \sum_{i=1}^{n} X^{(i)}, \tag{7.2.2}$$

where the right side of (7.2.2) is often abbreviated to $\bar{X}$. The idea here is simple and familiar, but note the distinction between a sample mean m, which is a point in the individual-space $\mathscr{F}$ dual to $\mathscr{E}$, and a value $\bar{X}$ of such a sample mean.

For purposes of computation rather than interpretation, it is convenient to have terminology for an alternative but equivalent linear quantity and its associated value. These are the *sample sum individual*

$$t = \sum_{i=1}^{n} a_i = nm \tag{7.2.3}$$

and its associated *sample sum value*

$$t(V) = \sum_{i=1}^{n} X^{(i)} = n\bar{X}, \tag{7.2.4}$$

for the variable V.

The *sample covariance* is an inner product function defined over variable-space $\mathscr{E}$. If the sample values of the variables V and W on individuals $a_1, a_2, \ldots, a_n$ are denoted by $X^{(1)}, X^{(2)}, \ldots, X^{(n)}$ and $Y^{(1)}, Y^{(2)}, \ldots, Y^{(n)}$, respectively then the *sample covariance* (*value*) *of* V *and* W *is defined to be*

$$\operatorname{cov}(V, W) = \frac{1}{n-1} \sum_{i=1}^{n} (X^{(i)} - \bar{X})(Y^{(i)} - \bar{Y}) = \frac{1}{n-1} \left[\sum_{i=1}^{n} X^{(i)} Y^{(i)} - n\bar{X}\bar{Y} \right]. \tag{7.2.5}$$

In the special case where V and W are the same, covariance is called *variance* and is written $\operatorname{cov}(V, V) = \operatorname{var}(V)$. The square root of $\operatorname{var}(V)$, which is a quantity in the same units as V, is called the *standard deviation* of V. The reader should recheck that the sample covariance defined by (7.2.5) satisfies the requirements for an inner product over $\mathscr{E}$, where this inner product may be definite or semi-definite.

Terminology for several related sample-based inner products will also be useful. The *sample raw sum inner product* may be defined, in the notation of (7.2.5), by

$$(V, W)_Q = \sum_{i=1}^{n} X^{(i)} Y^{(i)}, \tag{7.2.6}$$

and similarly the *sample corrected sum inner product* may be defined by

$$(V, W)_T = \sum_{i=1}^{n} (X^{(i)} - \bar{X})(Y^{(i)} - \bar{Y}). \tag{7.2.7}$$

These different inner products are related by

$$(n - 1) \operatorname{cov}(V, W) = (V, W)_T = (V, W)_Q - nm(V)m(W). \tag{7.2.8}$$

The definitions of sample mean, sample covariance, and related concepts have been given in coordinate-free terms. Most often, however, a sample is specified by its $n \times p$ *data matrix* $\mathbf{X}$ whose (i, j) element $X_j^{(i)}$ gives the observed value of the variable V_j on the sample individual a_i, for $i = 1, 2, \ldots, n$ and $j = 1, 2, \ldots, p$.

The sample mean individual m is determined by its $1 \times p$ coordinate vector $\bar{\mathbf{X}}$ relative to the basis $\mathbf{v}$ in $\mathscr{F}$ dual to $\mathbf{V}$ in $\mathscr{E}$, i.e., by

$$m = \bar{\mathbf{X}}\mathbf{v}. \tag{7.2.9}$$

If the rows of $\mathbf{X}$ are denoted by $\mathbf{X}^{(i)}$ for $i = 1, 2, \ldots, n$, then the sample individual a_i may be expressed as

$$a_i = \mathbf{X}^{(i)}\mathbf{v} \tag{7.2.10}$$

for $i = 1, 2, \ldots, n$ (cf. Exercise 6.1.8), whence $\bar{\mathbf{X}}$ in (7.2.9) is given by the ordinary mean of the n rows of $\mathbf{X}$, i.e., by

$$\bar{\mathbf{X}} = \frac{1}{n} \sum_{i=1}^{n} \mathbf{X}^{(i)}. \tag{7.2.11}$$

The elements of $\bar{\mathbf{X}}$ are the values of m for the basis $\mathbf{V}$ of $\mathscr{E}$, so that the value $m(V)$ for any $V = \boldsymbol{\alpha}\mathbf{V}$ in $\mathscr{E}$ is given by

$$m(V) = \boldsymbol{\alpha}\bar{\mathbf{X}}'. \tag{7.2.12}$$

The formulas analogous to (7.2.9), (7.2.11), and (7.2.12) when m is replaced by the sample sum individual t are left for the reader to express.

Similarly, the sample covariance inner product is determined by its inner product matrix $\mathbf{S}$ relative to a basis $\mathbf{V}$, i.e., by the matrix $\mathbf{S}$ whose (i, j) element S_{ij} is given by

$$S_{ij} = \operatorname{cov}(V_i, V_j). \tag{7.2.13}$$

$\mathbf{S}$ will be called the *sample covariance matrix* of the set of variables $\mathbf{V}$. For any $V = \boldsymbol{\alpha}\mathbf{V}$ and $W = \boldsymbol{\beta}\mathbf{V}$ in $\mathscr{E}$,

$$\operatorname{cov}(V, W) = \boldsymbol{\alpha}\mathbf{S}\boldsymbol{\beta}' \tag{7.2.14}$$

as in (3.1.7), i.e., as with any inner product only the covariance matrix for any basis is required to determine the covariance between any pair of variables.

The additional inner products $(V, W)_Q$ and $(V, W)_T$ defined in (7.2.6) and (7.2.7) have inner product matrices relative to **V** which will be denoted by **Q** and **T**, respectively. In matrix terms, **Q** and **T** may be expressed using the data matrix **X** via

$$\mathbf{Q} = \sum_{i=1}^{n} \mathbf{X}^{(i)\prime}\mathbf{X}^{(i)} = \mathbf{X}'\mathbf{X} \tag{7.2.15}$$

and

$$\mathbf{T} = \sum_{i=1}^{n} (\mathbf{X}^{(i)} - \bar{\mathbf{X}})'(\mathbf{X}^{(i)} - \bar{\mathbf{X}}) = \mathbf{X}'\mathbf{X} - n\bar{\mathbf{X}}'\bar{\mathbf{X}}, \tag{7.2.16}$$

while the relations (7.2.8) may be written

$$(n - 1)\mathbf{S} = \mathbf{T} = \mathbf{Q} - n\bar{\mathbf{X}}'\bar{\mathbf{X}}. \tag{7.2.17}$$

The dual of the sample covariance inner product over $\mathscr{E}$ will be called the *sample concentration inner product* over $\mathscr{F}$. If the sample covariance matrix is **S** relative to a basis **V** of $\mathscr{E}$, and if the sample covariance has full rank p, then the inner product matrix of the sample concentration relative to the dual basis **v** in $\mathscr{F}$ of **V** in $\mathscr{E}$ is given by $\mathbf{S}^{-1}$. The case of semi-definite sample covariance is pursued further in Section 7.7. Dual inner products to the sample raw sum inner product and the sample corrected sum inner products will occasionally have roles to play, but no specific terminology will be assigned to them.

7.3 REPRESENTATION OF A SAMPLE WITH INDIVIDUALS AS POINTS

A given p-variate sample of size n may be visualized geometrically as consisting of the n points $a_1, a_2, \ldots, a_n$ in the p-dimensional affine individual-space $\mathscr{F}$. The sample mean and sample covariance may be described geometrically by the sample mean point m and the inner product ellipsoid of the sample concentration. This ellipsoid consists of points at unit distance or less from the origin $\varnothing$ in $\mathscr{F}$ according to the concentration inner product, and will be called the (*origin-centered*) *ellipsoid of concentration.* The result of translating this ellipsoid into an ellipsoid with center m will be called the *mean-centered ellipsoid of concentration* (cf. Cramér, 1946). The mean-centered ellipsoid of concentration consists of points at most unit distance from the mean, and provides a method for representing the location and scatter of a sample in a single geometric figure, at least to the extent to which the sample mean and sample covariance alone are able to provide such a representation.

Before illustrating these concepts with drawings it may help to be specific about the mechanics of plotting the n sample points in $\mathscr{F}$ from an $n \times p$ data matrix **X** representing a p-variate sample of size n. Each individual a_i is represented by the corresponding row i of **X**, namely

$$\mathbf{X}^{(i)} = [X_1^{(i)}, X_2^{(i)}, \ldots, X_p^{(i)}], \tag{7.3.1}$$

which gives the coordinates of a_i relative to the dual basis $\mathbf{v}$ of $\mathbf{V}$ as in (7.2.10). The first step in plotting is to lay out the coordinate axes $v_1, v_2, \ldots, v_p$ forming $\mathbf{v}$. This may be done physically on a plane piece of paper if $p = 2$, or in space if $p = 3$, but may only be done conceptually for $p > 3$. The case $p = 2$ is pictured in Fig. 7.3.1 where the axes v_1 and v_2 were first laid down and the points a_i were plotted using the formula $a_i = X_1^{(i)}v_1 + X_2^{(i)}v_2$ together with the standard physical representations of vector multiplication and addition (cf. Fig. 2.4.1). Note that while v_1 and v_2 are pictured in Fig. 7.3.1 as orthogonal, this is merely a convention inessential in such representations of the sample. The sample mean point is plotted in the same way from $m = \bar{\mathbf{X}}\mathbf{v}$. The points $v = \mathbf{x}\mathbf{v}$ belonging to the origin-centered ellipsoid of concentration satisfy the relation

$$\mathbf{x}\mathbf{S}^{-1}\mathbf{x}' \leq 1 \tag{7.3.2}$$

and those belonging to the mean-centered ellipsoid of concentration satisfy the relation

$$(\mathbf{x} - \bar{\mathbf{X}})\mathbf{S}^{-1}(\mathbf{x} - \bar{\mathbf{X}})' \leq 1, \tag{7.3.3}$$

assuming of course that $\mathbf{S}^{-1}$ exists.

The remainder of this section is concerned with the behavior of samples and their associated mean points and concentration ellipsoids under linear transformations operating on $\mathscr{F}$. The important fact here, namely Theorem 7.3, relates the shadow of a sample with the shadow of its mean-centered concentration ellipsoid. Recall the definition and theory of shadows given in Section 6.6.

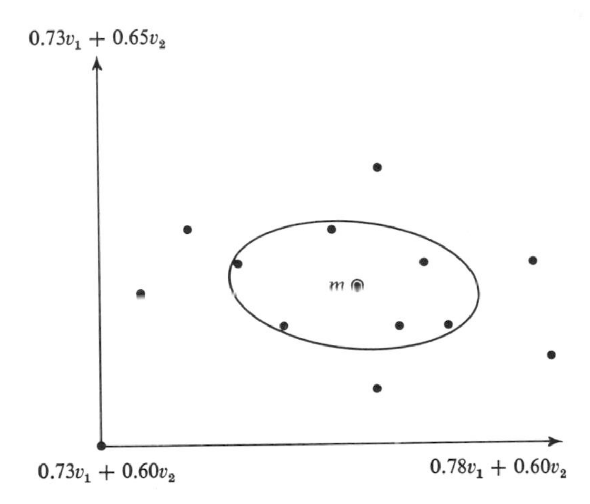

Fig. 7.3.1. The sample data of V_1 and V_2 from Example 8.1 plotted as 12 points in the individual-space dual to the variable-space spanned by V_1, V_2. The mean point and mean-centered concentration ellipse of the sample are also shown.

Theorem 7.3. *Suppose that π_d is the mean-centered ellipsoid of concentration of a sample $a_1, a_2, \ldots, a_n$ in $\mathscr{F}$. Suppose that a linear transformation A_d from $\mathscr{F}$ to $\mathscr{F}^*$ carries the sample $a_1, a_2, \ldots, a_n$ in $\mathscr{F}$ into a sample a_1^*, $a_2^*, \ldots, a_n^*$ in $\mathscr{F}^*$. Then the mean-centered concentration ellipsoid π_d^* of $a_1^*, a_2^*, \ldots, a_n^*$ in $\mathscr{F}^*$ is the shadow of π_d under the transformation A_d.*

This theorem holds when A_d is a wide sense linear transformation, but it is trivial under translations, and so need only be proved when the sample mean in $\mathscr{F}$ is the origin and A_d carries the origin in $\mathscr{F}$ into the origin in $\mathscr{F}^*$. In this case the sample mean of $a_1^*, a_2^*, \ldots, a_n^*$ is the origin in $\mathscr{F}^*$ and both concentration ellipsoids are origin-centered. The individual-spaces $\mathscr{F}$ and $\mathscr{F}^*$ have dual variable-spaces $\mathscr{E}$ and $\mathscr{E}^*$. The transformation A_d determines its dual transformation A from $\mathscr{E}^*$ to $\mathscr{E}$ whose basic property (6.1.13) implies in the present context that the sample values are preserved under the transformation A, i.e., that $a_i(V) = a_i^*(V^*)$ for $i = 1, 2, \ldots, n$ where $V = \mathsf{A}V^*$ and V^* is any variable in $\mathscr{E}^*$. This preservation of sample values means that the inner product over $\mathscr{E}$ induced by A from the covariance inner product over $\mathscr{E}^*$ of the sample a_1^*, $a_2^*, \ldots, a_n^*$ is the sample covariance inner product of the sample $a_1, a_2, \ldots, a_n$. Thus π_d^* may be produced by the roundabout route described in Section 6.6, and Theorem 7.3 follows directly from Theorem 6.6.

The shadow theory is easily visualized when A_d is a linear projection. For example, consider projection along the family of hyperplanes parallel to the subspace spanned by $v_{r+1}, v_{r+2}, \ldots, v_p$ into the subspace spanned by $v_1, v_2, \ldots, v_r$ where $\mathbf{v} = [v_1, v_2, \ldots, v_p]'$ is a basis of $\mathscr{F}$. Of course, any narrow sense linear projection may be defined in this way for properly chosen bases. Such a projection carries the sample defined by the data matrix $\mathbf{X}$ into the sample defined by the same data matrix with the last $p - r$ columns replaced by zeros. Thus the projected sample provides a representation in $\mathscr{F}$ for the reduced sample in which the data are available for $V_1, V_2, \ldots, V_r$ only. Fig. 7.3.2 is a plane drawing for the case $p = 3$ and $r = 2$ of the type of linear projection just described. It also illustrates the shadow theory of Theorem 7.3.

The sample data for $V_1, V_2, \ldots, V_r$ may be equally well represented in $\mathscr{F}$ by projection into any subspace complementary to the subspace spanned by $v_{r+1}, v_{r+2}, \ldots, v_p$ or, more generally, by projection into any hyperplane parallel to such a subspace. For example, one could have projected in Fig. 7.3.2 into any plane making a positive angle with v_3, and the projected sample would have retained essentially the same information. The reason for this is that the subspace spanned by $V_1, V_2, \ldots, V_r$ determines only the dual subspace spanned by $v_{r+1}, v_{r+2}, \ldots, v_p$ on which all of $V_1, V_2, \ldots, V_r$ assume zero values, and consequently the choice of a complementary subspace is left open. In other words, to say that the sample data are available on $V_1, V_2, \ldots, V_r$ is to say not only that the sample data on $V_{r+1}, V_{r+2}, \ldots, V_p$ are unknown but also that the sample data on any complementary subspace to $V_1, V_2, \ldots, V_r$ are unknown.

Sometimes it is helpful to consider projecting a sample into a hyperplane which contains its mean. This provides a representation of the sample data restricted to a subspace of variable-space, where the projected sample has the same mean as the original sample.

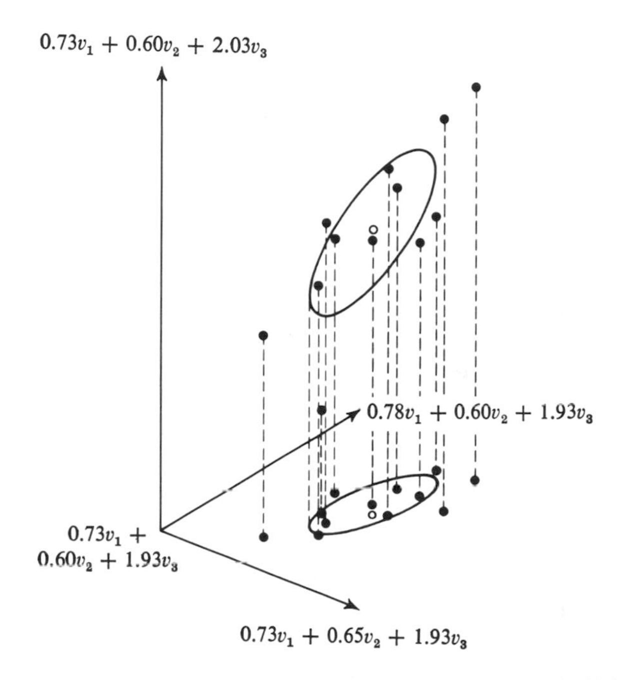

Fig. 7.3.2. The data of Example 8.1 plotted in the 3-dimensional individual-space spanned by v_1, v_2, v_3. The projection along lines of constant x_1 and x_2 into the hyperplane $x_3 = 1.93$ is also shown, along with the original mean-centered ellipsoid of concentration and its shadow.

7.4 REPRESENTATION OF A SAMPLE WITH VARIABLES AS POINTS

In contrast to the geometric representation of Section 7.3, a given p-variate sample of size n may also be regarded as p points plotted in an n-dimensional space, where the points correspond to the basic variables $V_1, V_2, \ldots, V_p$. To achieve this, create an n-dimensional vector space $\mathcal{N}$ by imagining n basis vectors $N_1, N_2, \ldots, N_n$ which correspond to the n sample individuals $a_1, a_2, \ldots, a_n$, and then plot the points

$$P_j = X_j^{(1)}N_1 + X_j^{(2)}N_2 + \cdots + X_j^{(n)}N_n \tag{7.4.1}$$

for $j = 1, 2, \ldots, p$. Here P_j is a geometric representation in $\mathcal{N}$ of V_j whose coordinates are given by the jth column of the data matrix $\mathbf{X}$. More generally, any variable V in $\mathcal{E}$ with sample values $X^{(1)}, X^{(2)}, \ldots, X^{(n)}$ may be represented by

$$P = \sum_{i=1}^{n} X^{(i)} N_i. \tag{7.4.2}$$

From a mathematical point of view, (7.4.2) determines a linear transformation

$$V \to P \tag{7.4.3}$$

from $\mathcal{E}$ to $\mathcal{N}$. It is obvious but worth noting that *knowing the linear transformation* (7.4.3) *is equivalent to knowing the sample data* $\mathbf{X}$. Note also that the range space in $\mathcal{N}$ of the mapping (7.4.3) has at most dimension p which may be much less than n.

The sample mean and sample covariance have special relationships with $\mathcal{N}$, which suggests that $\mathcal{N}$ be regarded as a Euclidean space with inner product defined by regarding $N_1, N_2, \ldots, N_n$ to be orthonormal. Suppose that $\mathcal{N}_I$ denotes the one-dimensional subspace of $\mathcal{N}$ spanned by $\sum_1^n N_j$ and that $\mathcal{N}_{II}$ denotes the $(p-1)$-dimensional subspace of $\mathcal{N}$ orthogonal to $\mathcal{N}_I$ according to the suggested inner product. Then the components of P in (7.4.2) along $\mathcal{N}_I$ and $\mathcal{N}_{II}$ are, respectively,

$$P_I = \sum_{j=1}^{n} \bar{X} N_j \tag{7.4.4}$$

and

$$P_{II} = \sum_{j=1}^{n} (X^{(j)} - \bar{X}) N_j. \tag{7.4.5}$$

From these representations the following theorem is immediately apparent.

Theorem 7.4.1. *Suppose that a given sample is represented by the linear transformation* (7.4.3) *from $\mathcal{E}$ to the Euclidean space $\mathcal{N}$ with orthonormal basis $N_1, N_2, \ldots, N_n$. Suppose that the variables V and W have sample values $X^{(1)}, X^{(2)}, \ldots, X^{(n)}$ and $Y^{(1)}, Y^{(2)}, \ldots, Y^{(n)}$. Suppose that the transforms P and Q of V and W decompose into $P = P_I + P_{II}$ and $Q = Q_I + Q_{II}$ along the orthogonal subspaces $\mathcal{N}_I$ and $\mathcal{N}_{II}$ defined above. Then*

$$|m(V)| = \left[\frac{1}{n}(P_I, P_I)\right]^{1/2} \tag{7.4.6}$$

and similarly for W, while

$$\operatorname{cov}(V, W) = \frac{1}{n-1}(P_{II}, Q_{II}), \tag{7.4.7}$$

where (P_I, P_I) and (P_{II}, Q_{II}) refer to the given inner product over $\mathcal{N}$.

Formula (7.4.6) simply says that the absolute value of $\sqrt{n}m(V)$ is the length of P_I, and this follows directly from (7.4.4). Similarly, from (7.4.5) and its analogue for Q,

$$(P_{II}, Q_{II}) = \sum_{i=1}^{n} (X^{(i)} - \bar{X})(Y^{(i)} - \bar{Y}), \tag{7.4.8}$$

which yields (7.4.7) directly.

Formula (7.4.7) suggests that for certain purposes the linear transformation

$$V \to P_{II} \tag{7.5.9}$$

from $\mathscr{E}$ to $\mathscr{N}_{II}$ may be more useful than (7.4.3). The reader may easily check that the transformation (7.4.9) together with the sample mean uniquely determines the sample, while the transformation (7.4.9) by itself determines the sample covariance. Indeed, the transformation (7.4.9) may be said to induce the inner product $(V, W)_T$ on $\mathscr{E}$ from the given inner product on $\mathscr{N}_{II}$ by setting $(V, W)_T = (P_{II}, Q_{II})$. Recall from (7.2.8) that the inner product $(V, W)_T$ is simply cov (V, W) rescaled by the factor $n - 1$.

The *sample correlation coefficient* between the variables V and W is defined to be

$$r = \frac{\operatorname{cov}(V, W)}{\operatorname{var}(V)^{1/2} \operatorname{var}(W)^{1/2}}. \tag{7.4.10}$$

Alternative expressions for r are

$$\begin{aligned} r &= \frac{(V, W)_T}{(V, V)_T^{1/2}(W, W)_T^{1/2}} \\ &= \frac{(P_{II}, Q_{II})}{(P_{II}, P_{II})^{1/2}(Q_{II}, Q_{II})^{1/2}}. \end{aligned} \tag{7.4.11}$$

Any of the expressions (7.4.10) or (7.4.11) show that r should be thought of as

$$r = \cos \theta, \tag{7.4.12}$$

where θ denotes the angle between V and W in variable-space $\mathscr{E}$ with covariance as inner product, or equivalently θ is the angle between P_{II} and Q_{II} in $\mathscr{N}_{II}$. A sample correlation coefficient between V and W will sometimes be denoted by cor (V, W).

From (7.4.12) it is clear that

$$-1 \leq r \leq 1. \tag{7.4.13}$$

Moreover $r = \pm 1$ if and only if

$$P_{II} = \pm \delta Q_{II} \tag{7.4.14}$$

for some $\delta > 0$. Since $P_{II} = \sum_1^n (X^{(i)} - \bar{X})N_i$ and $Q_{II} = \sum_1^n (Y^{(i)} - \bar{Y})N_i$, the condition (7.4.14) may be written

$$X^{(i)} - \bar{X} = \pm\delta(Y^{(i)} - \bar{Y}) \tag{7.4.15}$$

for $i = 1, 2, \ldots, n$.

Actual graphic plotting of a sample as p points in $\mathscr{N}$ or $\mathscr{N}_{II}$ is impractical since $n = 2$ or $n = 3$ rarely occurs. Such plotting is, however, a useful conceptual device.

7.5 COMPUTATION-ORIENTED THEORY

This section considers some standard computations based on single sample data matrices. The first concern will be to describe the computation of a sample mean vector and a sample covariance matrix in terms of the computing language introduced in Section 4.3. Later, the discussion will turn to deeper matters involving partially swept inner product matrices together with the addition and deletion of either variables or individuals.

Given an $n \times p$ data matrix $\mathbf{X}$, the inner product matrix of the raw sum inner product may be computed as indicated in (7.2.15) by the single matrix multiplication

$$\mathbf{Q} = \mathbf{X}'\mathbf{X}. \tag{7.5.1}$$

Similarly, the mean vector $\bar{\mathbf{X}}$ may be computed as indicated by (7.2.11), and thence $\mathbf{T}$ and $\mathbf{S}$ from $\mathbf{Q}$ and $\bar{\mathbf{X}}$ as indicated by (7.2.17). An alternative computing scheme uses the device of adding a column to $\mathbf{X}$ whose n elements are all unity, thus forming an augmented $n \times (p + 1)$ data matrix $\mathbf{X}_{(+)}$. $\mathbf{X}_{(+)}$ should be regarded as the data matrix for a $(p + 1)$-variate sample whose variables are $V_1, V_2, \ldots, V_p$, and V_0 whose value is unity for all individuals.

Extending (7.5.1) gives an augmented raw sum inner product matrix

$$\mathbf{Q}_{(+)} = \mathbf{X}'_{(+)}\mathbf{X}_{(+)} \tag{7.5.2}$$

of dimension $(p + 1) \times (p + 1)$. It is easily checked that the partition of $\mathbf{Q}_{(+)}$ into p and 1 rows and columns yields

$$\mathbf{Q}_{(+)} = \left[\begin{array}{c|c} & \sum_1^n X_1^{(i)} \\ & \sum_1^n X_2^{(i)} \\ \mathbf{Q} & \vdots \\ & \sum_1^n X_p^{(i)} \\ \hline \sum_1^n X_1^{(i)} \ \sum_1^n X_2^{(i)} \ \ldots \ \sum_1^n X_p^{(i)} & n \end{array}\right] \tag{7.5.3}$$

so that the last row or column of $\mathbf{Q}_{(+)}$ yields the sample sums of the p variables $V_1, V_2, \ldots, V_p$ while the last diagonal element records the sample size. Next, applying the sweep operator SWP$[p + 1]$ defined in Section 4.3.2 yields

$$\text{SWP}[p+1]\mathbf{Q}_{(+)} = \left[\begin{array}{c|c} & \bar{X}_1 \\ & \bar{X}_2 \\ & \cdot \\ \mathbf{T} & \cdot \\ & \cdot \\ & \bar{X}_p \\ \hline \bar{X}_1\ \bar{X}_2 \ldots \bar{X}_p & -1/n \end{array}\right], \tag{7.5.4}$$

where $\mathbf{T}$ denotes the sample corrected sum inner product matrix and $\bar{X}_j$ denotes the sample mean value of V_j for $j = 1, 2, \ldots, p$. Clearly, the computing sequence of finding $\mathbf{Q}_{(+)}$ and then SWP$[p + 1]\mathbf{Q}_{(+)}$ is an easily programmable description of a way to find sample sums, sample means, sample raw sum inner products, and sample corrected sum inner products. The final step of computing $\mathbf{S} = \mathbf{T}/(n - 1)$ is trivial. A word of caution is appropriate here. $\mathbf{T}$ in (7.5.4) is found by subtraction of $n\bar{\mathbf{X}}'\bar{\mathbf{X}}$ from $\mathbf{Q}$ in (7.5.3), and may be a small difference between large values, thus acquiring a large component of rounding error. In practice, therefore, it is usually preferable to compute $\bar{\mathbf{X}}$ directly and thence compute $\mathbf{T}$ directly from the first line of (7.2.16).

A device similar to that of creating $\mathbf{X}_{(+)}$ from $\mathbf{X}$ is to add columns to $\mathbf{X}$ corresponding to individuals in the sample. This device is computationally useful for adding and deleting individuals from a sample. Suppose that the data matrix $\mathbf{X}$ augmented by columns corresponding to individuals $a_{i_1}, a_{i_2}, \ldots, a_{i_r}$ is denoted by

$$\mathbf{X}^* = [\mathbf{X}, \mathbf{1}_{i_1}, \mathbf{1}_{i_2}, \ldots, \mathbf{1}_{i_r}], \tag{7.5.5}$$

where $\mathbf{1}_{i_s}$ denotes an $n \times 1$ vector with zero elements except for unity in position i_s for $s = 1, 2, \ldots, r$. Again, $\mathbf{X}^*$ should be regarded as a data matrix for a sample with additional artificial variables, where the artificial variable corresponding to an individual is the *indicator* variable which takes the value unity for that individual and zero for all other individuals. Next consider

$$\mathbf{Q}^* = \mathbf{X}^{*\prime}\mathbf{X}^* \tag{7.5.6}$$

whose rows and columns may be partitioned into p and r to produce

$$\mathbf{Q}^* = \begin{bmatrix} \mathbf{Q} & \mathbf{F}' \\ \mathbf{F} & \mathbf{I} \end{bmatrix}, \tag{7.5.7}$$

where $\mathbf{F}$ denotes the $r \times p$ data matrix of the individuals $a_{i_1}, a_{i_2}, \ldots, a_{i_r}$ on variables $V_1, V_2, \ldots, V_p$ and $\mathbf{I}$ denotes the $r \times r$ identity matrix.

To see how $\mathbf{Q}^*$ relates to adding and deleting individuals define

$$\dot{\mathbf{Q}}^* = \text{SWP}[p + 1, p + 2, \ldots, p + r]\mathbf{Q}^*, \tag{7.5.8}$$

where, of course,

$$\mathbf{Q}^* = \text{RSW}[p + 1, p + 2, \ldots, p + r]\dot{\mathbf{Q}}^*. \tag{7.5.9}$$

By directly carrying out the sweep operations indicated in (7.5.8), it is easily seen that (7.5.7) is modified into

$$\dot{\mathbf{Q}}^* = \begin{bmatrix} \dot{\mathbf{Q}} & \mathbf{F}' \\ \mathbf{F} & -\mathbf{I} \end{bmatrix}, \tag{7.5.10}$$

where $\dot{\mathbf{Q}}$ denotes the raw sum inner product matrix of the sample of size $n - r$ formed by deleting the individuals $a_{i_1}, a_{i_2}, \ldots, a_{i_r}$ from the given sample. Thus it follows that the operations (7.5.8) and (7.5.9) may be used to delete and add individuals, respectively, from a raw sum inner product matrix.

A somewhat deeper look at the computational problems of adding variables or of adding or deleting individuals is facilitated by the use of the assimilation operator defined in Section 4.3.3. With a given sample of size n, the addition of variables $V_{p+1}, V_{p+2}, \ldots, V_{p+r}$ to a basic set $V_1, V_2, \ldots, V_p$ means that the basic $p \times p$ raw sum inner product matrix $\mathbf{Q}$ acquires r additional rows and columns and becomes a $(p + r) \times (p + r)$ raw sum inner product matrix $\mathbf{Q}^*$. Suppose that earlier statistical analysis of the original p variables has produced $\text{SWP}[1, 2, \ldots, s]\mathbf{Q}$. Then the $\text{ASM}[p + 1, p + 2, \ldots, p + r;\ 1, 2, \ldots, s]$ operator is designed to assimilate the last r rows and columns of $\mathbf{Q}^*$ together with $\text{SWP}[1, 2, \ldots, s]\mathbf{Q}$ to produce $\text{SWP}[1, 2, \ldots, s]\mathbf{Q}^*$.

The ASM operator is also useful in generalizing the operations of passing between (7.5.7) and (7.5.10). The aim of the generalization is to pass back and forth between $\text{SWP}[1, 2, \ldots, s]\mathbf{Q}$ and $\text{SWP}[1, 2, \ldots, s]\dot{\mathbf{Q}}$. The partition of $\text{SWP}[1, 2, \ldots, s]\mathbf{Q}$ will be denoted as usual by

$$\text{SWP}[1, 2, \ldots, s]\mathbf{Q} = \begin{bmatrix} -\mathbf{Q}_{11}^{-1} & \mathbf{H}_{12} \\ \mathbf{H}_{21} & \mathbf{Q}_{22.1} \end{bmatrix}, \tag{7.5.11}$$

and corresponding notation

$$\text{SWP}[1, 2, \ldots, s]\dot{\mathbf{Q}} = \begin{bmatrix} -\dot{\mathbf{Q}}_{11}^{-1} & \dot{\mathbf{H}}_{12} \\ \dot{\mathbf{H}}_{21} & \dot{\mathbf{Q}}_{22.1} \end{bmatrix} \tag{7.5.12}$$

and

$$\mathbf{F} = [\mathbf{F}_1, \mathbf{F}_2] \tag{7.5.13}$$

will be used.

Theorem 7.5. *The operator* $\text{ASM}[p + 1, p + 2, \ldots, p + r;\ 1, 2, \ldots, s]$ *followed by* $\text{SWP}[p + 1, p + 2, \ldots, p + r]$ *carries*

$$\begin{bmatrix} -\mathbf{Q}_{11}^{-1} & \mathbf{H}_{12} & \mathbf{F}_1' \\ \mathbf{H}_{21} & \mathbf{Q}_{22.1} & \mathbf{F}_2' \\ \mathbf{F}_1 & \mathbf{F}_2 & \mathbf{I} \end{bmatrix} \tag{7.5.14}$$

into

$$\begin{bmatrix} -\dot{\mathbf{Q}}_{11}^{-1} & \dot{\mathbf{H}}_{12} & \dot{\mathbf{Q}}_{11}^{-1}\mathbf{F}_1' \\ \dot{\mathbf{H}}_{21} & \dot{\mathbf{Q}}_{22.1} & \mathbf{F}_2' - \dot{\mathbf{H}}_{21}\mathbf{F}_1' \\ \mathbf{F}_1\dot{\mathbf{Q}}_{11}^{-1} & \mathbf{F}_2 - \mathbf{F}_1\dot{\mathbf{H}}_{12} & -\mathbf{I} - \mathbf{F}_1\dot{\mathbf{Q}}_{11}^{-1}\mathbf{F}_1' \end{bmatrix}. \tag{7.5.15}$$

Similarly, the operator ASM$[p+1, p+2, \ldots, p+r; 1, 2, \ldots, s]$ *followed by* SWP$[p+1, p+2, \ldots, p+r]$ *carries*

$$\begin{bmatrix} -\dot{\mathbf{Q}}_{11}^{-1} & \dot{\mathbf{H}}_{12} & \mathbf{F}_1' \\ \dot{\mathbf{H}}_{21} & \dot{\mathbf{Q}}_{22.1} & \mathbf{F}_2' \\ \mathbf{F}_1 & \mathbf{F}_2 & -\mathbf{I} \end{bmatrix} \tag{7.5.16}$$

into

$$\begin{bmatrix} -\mathbf{Q}_{11}^{-1} & \mathbf{H}_{12} & -\mathbf{Q}_{11}^{-1}\mathbf{F}_1' \\ \mathbf{H}_{21} & \mathbf{Q}_{22.1} & -\mathbf{F}_2' + \mathbf{H}_{21}\mathbf{F}_1' \\ -\mathbf{F}_1\mathbf{Q}_{11}^{-1} & -\mathbf{F}_2 + \mathbf{F}_1\mathbf{H}_{12} & \mathbf{I} - \mathbf{F}_1\mathbf{Q}_{11}^{-1}\mathbf{F}_1' \end{bmatrix}. \tag{7.5.17}$$

The first part of Theorem 7.5 is proved by noting that the three steps of passing from (7.5.14) to (7.5.7) to (7.5.10) to (7.5.15) require the successive operations:

$$\begin{aligned} &\text{RSW}[1, 2, \ldots, s] \quad \text{on the upper left } p \times p \text{ part only}, \\ &\text{SWP}[p+1, p+2, \ldots, p+r], \\ &\text{SWP}[1, 2, \ldots, s]. \end{aligned} \tag{7.5.18}$$

The last two operations in (7.5.18) may be carried out in reverse order, since sweep operators commute, and after reversing this order the first two operations combine to form ASM$[p+1, p+2, \ldots, p+r; 1, 2, \ldots, s]$, by the final characterization of the ASM operator given in Section 4.3.3. The second part of the theorem is proved in a similar way, so the details are omitted.

The computing rules of Theorem 7.5 may be made to yield a set of mathematically elegant but computationally inefficient formulas concerning the addition and deletion of individuals. Carrying out the ASM operation as defined by (4.3.31) and the SWP operations as defined by (4.3.23) on (7.5.14) and comparing the result to (7.5.15) yields:

$$\dot{\mathbf{Q}}_{11}^{-1} = \mathbf{Q}_{11}^{-1} + (\mathbf{F}_1\mathbf{Q}_{11}^{-1})'(\mathbf{I} - \mathbf{F}_1\mathbf{Q}_{11}^{-1}\mathbf{F}_1')^{-1}(\mathbf{F}_1\mathbf{Q}_{11}^{-1}), \tag{7.5.19}$$

$$\dot{\mathbf{H}}_{12} = \mathbf{H}_{12} - (\mathbf{F}_1\mathbf{Q}_{11}^{-1})'(\mathbf{I} - \mathbf{F}_1\mathbf{Q}_{11}^{-1}\mathbf{F}_1')^{-1}(\mathbf{F}_2 - \mathbf{F}_1\mathbf{H}_{12}), \tag{7.5.20}$$

$$\dot{\mathbf{Q}}_{22.1} = \mathbf{Q}_{22.1} - (\mathbf{F}_2 - \mathbf{F}_1\mathbf{H}_{12})'(\mathbf{I} - \mathbf{F}_1\mathbf{Q}_{11}^{-1}\mathbf{F}_1')^{-1}(\mathbf{F}_2 - \mathbf{F}_1\mathbf{H}_{12}), \tag{7.5.21}$$

$$\mathbf{F}_1\dot{\mathbf{Q}}_{11}^{-1} = (\mathbf{I} - \mathbf{F}_1\mathbf{Q}_{11}^{-1}\mathbf{F}_1')^{-1}(\mathbf{F}_1\mathbf{Q}_{11}^{-1}), \tag{7.5.22}$$

$$\mathbf{F}_2 - \mathbf{F}_1\dot{\mathbf{H}}_{12} = (\mathbf{I} - \mathbf{F}_1\mathbf{Q}_{11}^{-1}\mathbf{F}_1')^{-1}(\mathbf{F}_2 - \mathbf{F}_1\mathbf{H}_{12}), \tag{7.5.23}$$

and

$$(\mathbf{I} + \mathbf{F}_1\dot{\mathbf{Q}}_{11}^{-1}\mathbf{F}_1') = (\mathbf{I} - \mathbf{F}_1\mathbf{Q}_{11}^{-1}\mathbf{F}_1')^{-1}. \tag{7.5.24}$$

Following a similar procedure with (7.5.16) and (7.5.17) yields

$$\mathbf{Q}_{11}^{-1} = \dot{\mathbf{Q}}_{11}^{-1} - (\mathbf{F}_1\dot{\mathbf{Q}}_{11}^{-1})'(\mathbf{I} + \mathbf{F}_1\dot{\mathbf{Q}}_{11}^{-1}\mathbf{F}_1')^{-1}(\mathbf{F}_1\dot{\mathbf{Q}}_{11}^{-1}), \tag{7.5.25}$$

$$\mathbf{H}_{12} = \dot{\mathbf{H}}_{12} + (\mathbf{F}_1\dot{\mathbf{Q}}_{11}^{-1})'(\mathbf{I} + \mathbf{F}_1\dot{\mathbf{Q}}_{11}^{-1}\mathbf{F}_1')^{-1}(\mathbf{F}_2 - \mathbf{F}_1\dot{\mathbf{H}}_{12}), \tag{7.5.26}$$

and

$$\mathbf{Q}_{22.1} = \dot{\mathbf{Q}}_{22.1} + (\mathbf{F}_2 - \mathbf{F}_1\dot{\mathbf{H}}_{12})'(\mathbf{I} + \mathbf{F}_1\dot{\mathbf{Q}}_{11}^{-1}\mathbf{F}_1')^{-1}(\mathbf{F}_2 - \mathbf{F}_1\dot{\mathbf{H}}_{12}). \tag{7.5.27}$$

The analogues of (7.5.22) and (7.5.23) are formed by substituting (7.5.20) into (7.5.22) and (7.5.23).

Theorem 7.5 and the subsequent formulas are likely to be of most interest and use when $\mathbf{Q}$ is replaced by $\mathbf{Q}_{(+)}$, which means that the artificial variable V_0 is introduced as a $(p + 1)$st variable. The important task is now to pass back and forth between SWP$[p + 1, 1, 2, \ldots, s]\mathbf{Q}_{(+)}$ and SWP$[p + 1, 1, 2, \ldots, s]\dot{\mathbf{Q}}_{(+)}$. The parts of these matrices are worth noting. From SWP$[1, 2, \ldots, s]$ applied to (7.5.4) it follows that

$$\text{SWP}[p + 1, 1, 2, \ldots, s]\mathbf{Q}_{(+)}$$

$$= \begin{bmatrix} -\mathbf{T}_{11}^{-1} & \mathbf{J}_{12} & \mathbf{T}_{11}^{-1}\bar{\mathbf{X}}_1' \\ \mathbf{J}_{21} & \mathbf{T}_{22.1} & \bar{\mathbf{X}}_2' - \mathbf{J}_{21}\bar{\mathbf{X}}_1' \\ \bar{\mathbf{X}}_1\mathbf{T}_{11}^{-1} & \bar{\mathbf{X}}_2 - \bar{\mathbf{X}}_1\mathbf{J}_{12} & -1/n - \bar{\mathbf{X}}_1\mathbf{T}_{11}^{-1}\bar{\mathbf{X}}_1' \end{bmatrix}, \quad (7.5.28)$$

where

$$\mathbf{J}_{12} = \mathbf{J}_{21}' = \mathbf{T}_{11}^{-1}\mathbf{T}_{12} \quad (7.5.29)$$

and

$$\mathbf{T}_{22.1} = \mathbf{T}_{22} - \mathbf{J}_{21}\mathbf{T}_{12}. \quad (7.5.30)$$

Similar formulas could be written down immediately for $\dot{\mathbf{Q}}_{(+)}$ referring to the reduced sample with r fewer individuals.

7.6 PRINCIPAL COMPONENT ANALYSIS

One possible attitude to multivariate statistics might hold that variable-space and individual-space are fundamentally affine spaces and should be regarded as Euclidean spaces only for inner products based on observed data. A different attitude says that it is difficult to contemplate any space of variables without at least some indefinite hints of Euclidean structure present. For example, a plot like Fig. 7.2.1 presumes related scales of measurement in different directions, so as to yield a picture comprehensible to the eye. Likewise, the visual impact of such a picture depends on the initial angle between the coordinate axes v_1 and v_2.

The user of a principal component analysis adopts the second of these two attitudes. In fact, he must promote vague feelings about scales and angles among $v_1, v_2, \ldots, v_p$ into a precise inner product. This inner product is not determined wholly by the sample data, and will be called here a *reference inner product*, where the term will be used either for an inner product over variable-space or for its dual over individual-space. The *principal component analysis* of a given sample relative to a given reference inner product over variable-space consists of finding the eigenvalues and eigenvectors of the sample covariance inner product relative to the reference inner product. The eigenvalues found in this way will be called *sample principal components of total variance relative to the chosen reference inner product* or, more briefly, *principal components*. The corresponding eigenvectors which form a basis of variable-space $\mathscr{E}$ will be called *principal variables*. This terminology is slightly different from and more general than that of Hotelling (1933, 1936) who first introduced the concept of a principal component analysis.

The following discussion first explores the properties of principal components and then finishes with a brief description of their statistical interpretation.

In practice, the reference inner product has usually been chosen in one of two ways. In both of these ways, the directly observed set of variables $V_1, V_2, \ldots, V_p$ is regarded as an orthogonal set, so that only the reference norms of $V_1, V_2, \ldots, V_p$ remain to be chosen. The first method chooses these norms independently of the sample data to represent some vague opinion of what should be comparable scales. Under the second method, the reference norms of $V_1, V_2, \ldots, V_p$ have been taken to be their sample standard deviations, so that the standardized variables $u_i = \text{var}\,(V_i)^{-1/2} V_i$ have unit norms according to the reference inner product. The second method depends on the sample data through the choice of reference norms but not as regards the orthogonality of $\mathbf{V}$, while the first method is entirely free of the particular sample outcomes. Other choices of a reference inner product may be reasonable, but it is clear that arbitrary dependence on the sample data cannot be allowed, since this would permit the user to produce completely arbitrary principal components and variables. Perhaps a reasonable restriction is to require the initial data free selection of *some* basis of variable-space to be an orthogonal basis for the reference inner product, where this basis need not consist of the basic observable variables; the reference norms for the basis may then be chosen in terms of the data.

In computing principal components and variables the first step is generally to find the sample covariance matrix relative to a basis $\mathbf{U}$ orthonormal according to the reference inner product. Calling this covariance matrix $\mathbf{S}^*$, it is clear that the eigenvalues of $\mathbf{S}^*$ are the principal components and the corresponding eigenvectors of $\mathbf{S}^*$ are the coordinate vectors relative to $\mathbf{U}$ of the principal variables. Recall the discussion of Section 5.4 at this point.

If the principal components are denoted by $\lambda_1, \lambda_2, \ldots, \lambda_p$, then

$$\sum_{i=1}^{p} \lambda_i = \text{tr}\,\mathbf{S}^*, \tag{7.6.1}$$

where tr $\mathbf{S}^*$ denotes the sum of the diagonal elements of $\mathbf{S}^*$. Formula (7.6.1) may be proved by showing that tr $\mathbf{S}^* = \text{tr}\,\mathbf{C}\mathbf{S}^*\mathbf{C}'$ for any orthogonal matrix $\mathbf{C}$. Since tr $\mathbf{S}^*$ is a sum of variances, formula (7.6.1) explains the often used term *principal components of total variance*. The λ_i are themselves sample variances of the principal variables. Another relationship similar to (7.6.1) is

$$\prod_{i=1}^{p} \lambda_i = \det \mathbf{S}^*. \tag{7.6.2}$$

Wilks (1932) introduced the term *generalized variance* for the quantity (7.6.2) as a general overall measure of the variability of the set of variables **U**. Neither the total variance (7.6.1) nor the generalized variance (7.6.2) tell the whole story, however, and the generalized variance in particular suffers the disadvantage of being close to zero when any λ_i is close to zero even though the remaining λ_j may be large.

Under the second method of choosing the reference inner product, the orthonormal basis **U** may be defined by $U_i = \text{var}(V_i)^{-1/2} V_i$ for $i = 1, 2, \ldots, p$. In this case the matrix $\mathbf{S}^*$ becomes the *sample correlation matrix* **R** whose (i, j) element is the sample correlation coefficient between V_i and V_j and whose diagonal elements are unity. (See (7.4.10).) In this case

$$\sum_{i=1}^{p} \lambda_i = p \tag{7.6.3}$$

and

$$\prod_{i=1}^{p} \lambda_i = \det \mathbf{R}. \tag{7.6.4}$$

The quantity (7.6.4) is sometimes called a *scatter coefficient* (Frisch, 1929). Since the scatter coefficient is the product of p nonnegative real numbers with a given sum, and since such a product is maximum if and only if the numbers are all equal, it follows that

$$0 \leq \det \mathbf{R} \leq 1. \tag{7.6.5}$$

The idea here is that the scatter coefficient represents a general measure of the degree of correlation among $V_1, V_2, \ldots, V_p$ where the smaller the value, the more correlation is present. Certainly, $\det \mathbf{R} = 1$ if and only if $V_1, V_2, \ldots, V_p$ are uncorrelated. Note, however, that no single index can describe the whole complex of **R** very well. For example, $\det \mathbf{R} = 0$ if any of the λ_i is zero, so that $\det \mathbf{R}$ does not differentiate among the different possible dimensions of scatter as measured by the rank of **R**.

Serious examples of principal component analyses are given in Examples 8.4, 9.1, and 10.3. Figure 7.6.1 shows the same concentration ellipse as Fig. 7.3.1 with the sample points omitted. When V_1 and V_2 are taken to be orthonormal according to the reference inner product, the principal components λ_1 and λ_2 are simply the squared lengths of the major and minor semi-axes of the ellipse, and these axes determine also the dual basis **w** of the principal variable basis **W**.

Finally, consider what meaning a principal component analysis might have. The aim of a principal component analysis is to provide a special basis of uncorrelated variables which provide a maximal range of importance. Usually the eigenvalues are ordered according to $\lambda_1 \geq \lambda_2 \geq \cdots \geq \lambda_p$ and a subset $\lambda_1, \lambda_2, \ldots, \lambda_r$ for $r < p$ is selected as describing most of the variability in the sample. The quantity

$$\sum_{i=1}^{r} \lambda_i \Big/ \sum_{i=1}^{p} \lambda_i \tag{7.6.6}$$

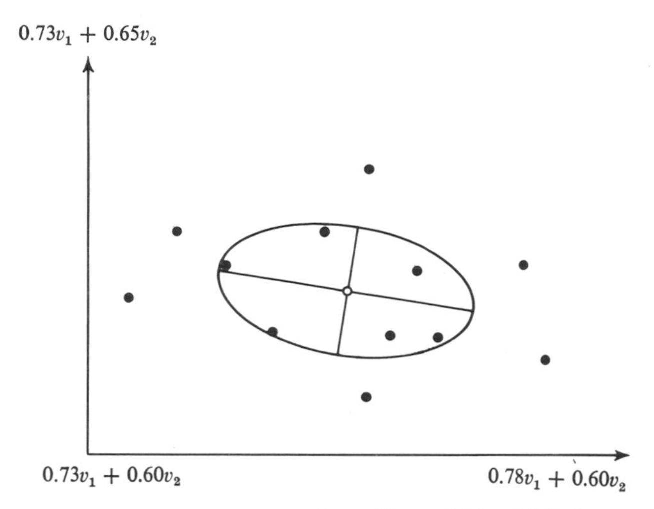

Fig. 7.6.1. The mean-centered concentration ellipse of Fig. 7.3.1 shown together with its major and minor axes which determine principal components of sample variance.

is commonly used to measure the fraction of total variance accounted for by the first r principal variables.

The prime intent of principal component analysis is therefore the attempt to simplify the study of multivariate samples by reducing their dimension in such a way as to lose as little information as possible. Usually it is hoped that the λ_i drop off very rapidly, so that an r of two or three may be selected and the sample represented in a greatly reduced individual-space of two or three dimensions.

There is a strong flavor of vagueness and arbitrariness about the technique of principal component analysis. The reference inner product and the measure (7.6.6) is somewhat arbitrary, and the means of choosing the reduced dimension r is not rationalized. Moreover, the nature of the importance of the first few principal variables is not defined. For example, it is mathematically possible that the last principal variable corresponding to the smallest λ_i should be the only one of use in predicting some separate but scientifically important variable. An empirical basis for the technique is thus seen to rest on whether the first few principal variables are those which are of value for predicting other variables. The data of Examples 8.4 and 9.1 tend to offer limited support for such an empirical basis. The evaluation of a particular sample principal component analysis is further complicated by the presence of sampling variation. Even if a population principal variable were closely aligned with some outside variable, the strength of the relation would be less apparent when the population principal was replaced by a sample analogue.

Principal variables are sometimes referred to as *factors* or *underlying factors*, the idea being that apart from minor disturbances all variables may be represented as linear functions of a few basic underlying variables. Accordingly, principal component analysis is a particular method of *factor analysis*. Attempts are sometimes made to regard the factors found in this way as hard well-defined variables, but such attempts deserve skeptical scrutiny. It may be that principal component analysis will some day be of use in locating hard underlying factors, such as genetically determined factors. At present, however, the uses are largely descriptive, explanatory, and empirical. Sampling theory and formal procedures for drawing inferences from samples to populations are in an underdeveloped and unsatisfactory state, both for principal component analysis and for methods of factor analysis generally. Lawley and Maxwell (1963) and Cattell (1965) are suggested as starting points for the reader wishing to pursue factor analysis further.

7.7 SEMI-DEFINITE SAMPLES

The terminology of Section 3.5 may be extended by defining a p-variate sample to be semi-definite if its sample covariance is a semi-definite inner product. More generally, a p-variate sample will be said to have rank f for $0 \leq f \leq p$ if its sample covariance has rank f.

> ***Theorem** 7.7.1. A p-variate sample of size n has rank f if and only if the n individuals all lie in a hyperplane of dimension f in $\mathscr{F}$ but do not lie in any hyperplane of dimension less than f.*

To assert that n individuals all lie in a hyperplane $u + \mathscr{U}$ in $\mathscr{F}$ is equivalent to asserting that the n individuals have identical observed values for all variables V in the subspace $\mathscr{V}$ in $\mathscr{E}$ dual to $\mathscr{U}$ in $\mathscr{F}$. Consequently the lowest-dimensional hyperplane containing all n individuals has dimension f if and only if the largest subspace of $\mathscr{E}$ on which all n individuals have identical values has dimension $p - f$. But the sample variance of a variable V is zero if and only if all n individuals have identical values on V, so that the subspace of such variables V has dimension $p - f$ if and only if the sample covariance has rank f, as required to prove the theorem.

It follows from the theory of Section 6.6 that the concentration of a semi-definite sample of rank f, being the dual of an inner product of rank f over $\mathscr{E}$, is a partial inner product over an f-dimensional subspace of $\mathscr{F}$. Since this subspace is the dual of the $(p - f)$-dimensional subspace of $\mathscr{E}$ over which the sample variance is zero, it is simply the hyperplane through the origin parallel to the hyperplane containing the sample. Thus, Theorem 7.7.2 which follows is proved.

> ***Theorem** 7.7.2. The concentration inner product of a semi-definite sample of rank f is a partial inner product defined over the f-dimensional subspace $\mathscr{U}$ of $\mathscr{F}$ which is parallel to the f-dimensional hyperplane $u + \mathscr{U}$ which contains the sample. The origin-centered ellipsoid of concentration lies in $\mathscr{U}$ and the mean-centered ellipsoid of concentration lies in $u + \mathscr{U}$.*

A set of n points in $\mathscr{F}$ must lie in some hyperplane of dimension at most $n - 1$. Consequently, if $n - 1 < p$, then the sample must be semi-definite of rank at most $n - 1 < p$. Usually, with observational data, it will turn out that the rank will achieve its maximal value, and, under this circumstance, a sample of size n is semi-definite of rank $n - 1$ if and only if $n - 1 < p$.

The theory of Section 7.3 holds just as well for samples of rank less than p. In particular, the shadow theory of Theorem 7.3 requires no change.

A p-variate sample of size n determines a linear transformation from $\mathscr{E}$ to $\mathscr{N}$ and also a linear transformation from $\mathscr{E}$ to $\mathscr{N}_{II}$ as discussed in Section 7.4. Conversely, the transformation from $\mathscr{E}$ to $\mathscr{N}$ determines the sample. Alternatively, the transformation from $\mathscr{E}$ to $\mathscr{N}_{II}$ together with the sample mean $\boldsymbol{m}$ determines the sample. From the foregoing it is clear that *the transformation from $\mathscr{E}$ to $\mathscr{N}_{II}$ has rank f if and only if the sample has rank f.* Moreover, two variables V and W in $\mathscr{E}$ transform into the same point in $\mathscr{N}_{II}$ if and only if $\operatorname{var}(V - W) = 0$.

Finally, principal component analysis has some special features in the case of a semi-definite sample. Suppose that the reference inner product over $\mathscr{E}$ asserts that $\mathbf{U}$ is an orthonormal basis. Then the principal component analysis simply requires that the eigenvalues and eigenvectors of the sample covariance matrix $\mathbf{S}$ relative to $\mathbf{U}$ shall be found. Alternatively, the matrix $\mathbf{T} = (n - 1)\mathbf{S}$ may be analyzed, since its eigenvalues are simply $(n - 1)$ times those of $\mathbf{S}$ and its eigenvectors are the same as those of $\mathbf{S}$. From (7.2.16)

$$\mathbf{T} = \mathbf{Z}'\mathbf{Z}, \tag{7.7.1}$$

where $\mathbf{Z}$ is the $n \times p$ matrix with rows $\mathbf{X}^{(i)} - \bar{\mathbf{X}}$ for $i = 1, 2, \ldots, n$, i.e., $\mathbf{Z}$ is the data matrix $\mathbf{X}$ with the mean vector $\bar{\mathbf{X}}$ subtracted from each row. From the theory of Section 6.5 it follows that the nonzero eigenvalues of $\mathbf{Z}'\mathbf{Z}$ are identical to the nonzero eigenvalues of $\mathbf{Z}\mathbf{Z}'$ and also that *the eigenvectors of $\mathbf{Z}\mathbf{Z}'$ are simply the sample values of the sample principal variables after the sample means are subtracted out.*

This result holds whether or not the sample is semi-definite, but its practical importance lies in the case where $n - 1 < p$ so that the sample must be semi-definite. In such a case the matrix $\mathbf{Z}\mathbf{Z}'$ is smaller than $\mathbf{Z}'\mathbf{Z}$ and so leads to a more manageable task of computing eigenvalues and eigenvectors. An illustration may be found in Example 10.3.

Semi-definite populations and, more specifically, semi-definite samples are less susceptible to analysis by contemporary multivariate methods than are samples where $n - 1 \geq p$, for reasons which will become apparent in later chapters. Thus, for example, while one might think that as much could be learned, in some rough scale of justice, from a 100-variate sample of size 30 as from a 30-variate sample of size 100, the statistical methodology for handling the former type of data is less well developed and on the whole unsatisfactory.

The method of principal component analysis may be an exception to the rule, but only as an empirical matter to be explored separately by fields of application.

7.8 EXERCISES

7.2.1 Suppose that a given sample $a_1, a_2, \ldots, a_n$ has mean m, and that this sample is translated into the sample $a_1^*, a_2^*, \ldots, a_n^*$ by the translation $a_i \to a_i^* = a_i + b$. Show that the mean of the second sample is given by $m^* = m + b$, but that the covariance inner product of the second example is the same as that of the first sample.

7.2.2 What is the condition on a sample which makes the sample covariance inner product function identically zero?

7.2.3 Show that an alternative to the two expressions (7.2.5) for cov (V, W) is given by

$$\text{cov}\,(V, W) = \frac{1}{n(n-1)} \sum_{i=1}^{n} \sum_{j=1}^{n} (X^{(i)} - X^{(j)})(Y^{(i)} - Y^{(j)}).$$

What is the analogous vector version of (7.2.16)?

7.2.4 For what quantities do the elements of the sample mean vector $\bar{\mathbf{X}}$ and the sample covariance matrix $\mathbf{S}$ represent values?

7.3.1 Suppose that con (a_1, a_2) denotes the sample concentration of the sample individuals a_1 and a_2. Describe how to compute con (a_1, a_2) from the sample data $\mathbf{X}$. Compute con (a_1, a_2) for the data plotted in Fig. 7.3.1.

7.3.2 Make a graphic estimate of $m(V_1 + 2V_2)$ and var $(V_1 + 2V_2)$ from the concentration ellipse plotted in Fig. 7.3.1. Check the estimates by computation.

7.3.3 What is the distance from the origin to the sample mean in Fig. 7.3.1 according to the concentration inner product? For what variable V does this distance equal $m(V)/\text{var}\,(V)^{1/2}$?

7.3.4 Show that there exists a $(p-1)$-dimensional subspace $\mathscr{V}_i$ of variable space $\mathscr{E}$ such that the sample values of individual a_i coincide with those of the sample mean individual. Show that the sample mean values and the sample mean corrected sum inner product both restricted to variables in $\mathscr{V}_i$ are not changed if a_i is removed from the sample. Show that the one-dimensional orthogonal complement $\mathscr{U}_i$ of $\mathscr{V}_i$ according to the sample covariance remains the orthogonal complement according to the sample covariance based on the sample with a_i removed. Thus, if U_i denotes a variable in $\mathscr{U}_i$, the sample mean and sample variance of U_i are altered by removing a_i but the other aspects of the first and second sample moments described above do not change. Use the foregoing theory to describe how the sample mean-centered concentration ellipsoid changes when a_i is removed from the sample.

7.4.1 Show that the subspace $\mathscr{N}_{II}$ defined in Section 7.4 consists of those vectors $\sum_{j=1}^n z_j N_j$ such that $\sum_{j=1}^n z_j = 0$.

7.4.2 Show that the decomposition $P = P_I + P_{II}$ defined by (7.4.4) and (7.4.5) is in fact the desired orthogonal decomposition.

7.4.3 Suppose that the range subspaces in $\mathscr{N}$ of the linear transformations (7.4.3) and (7.4.9) are denoted by $\mathscr{M}$ and $\mathscr{M}_{II}$. What is the maximal dimension of $\mathscr{M}$? Of $\mathscr{M}_{II}$?

7.5.1 Suppose that the $(p + n) \times (p + n)$ matrix

$$\begin{bmatrix} \mathbf{0} & \mathbf{X}' \\ \mathbf{X} & \mathbf{I} \end{bmatrix}$$

is formed from an $n \times p$ sample data matrix $\mathbf{X}$, where $\mathbf{0}$ is a $p \times p$ matrix of zeros and $\mathbf{I}$ is the $n \times n$ identity matrix. What is the result of applying SWP$[p + 1, p + 2, \ldots, p + n]$ to this matrix? Are the computations performed in this way inefficient?

7.5.2 Write out the special application of formulas (7.5.19) through (7.5.27) when $\mathbf{Q}$ is replaced by $\mathbf{Q}_{(+)}$ and the role of indices $1, 2, \ldots, s$ is played by $1, 2, \ldots, s, p + 1$. Note that the latter set of indices partitions naturally into $1, 2, \ldots, s$ and $p + 1$ and that the associated formulas should be further partitioned accordingly. Use the notation of (7.5.28).

7.5.3 Define the augmented data matrix $\mathbf{X}^{(+)}$ to consist of $\mathbf{X}$ with a *first* column of ones adjoined. Suppose that $\mathbf{X}^{(+)\prime} = \mathbf{D}^{(+)}\mathbf{G}$ defines the triangularization of $\mathbf{X}^{(+)\prime}$ as defined in Exercise 4.3.3. Show how to find $\bar{\mathbf{X}}$ and $\mathbf{T}$ from $\mathbf{D}^{(+)}$ and $\mathbf{G}$.

7.6.1 Prove formulas (7.6.1) and (7.6.3).

7.6.2 Show that the product of p positive numbers with a given sum is maximum when and only when the numbers are all equal. Deduce that the scatter coefficient det $\mathbf{R}$ is unity if and only if $\mathbf{R}$ is the identity matrix.

7.6.3 Consider a principal component analysis of the correlation matrix of the pair of variables V_1 and V_2. Show that the principal variables are

$$\frac{1}{\sqrt{\text{var}\,(V_1)}} V_1 \pm \frac{1}{\sqrt{\text{var}\,(V_2)}} V_2.$$

What are the corresponding principal components?

7.7.1 Show that the following three assertions are equivalent:

i) $V - W$ has an observation vector lying along $\mathcal{N}_I$ as defined in Section 7.4,

ii) the observations on V and W differ by a constant for all individuals in the sample, and

iii) var $(V - W) = 0$.

7.7.2 Construct an example of a 4-variate sample of size 3 which has rank 1. Describe simply the set of points lying on the ellipsoid of concentration of this sample.

7.7.3 Suppose that the mapping (7.4.3) from $\mathcal{E}$ to $\mathcal{N}$ has the range space $\mathcal{M}$ of dimension g. Show that the rank of the sample is either $g - 1$ or g depending on whether or not $\mathcal{M}$ contains $\mathcal{N}_I$ as a subspace.

7.7.4 Consider the reduced data matrix $\mathbf{Z}$ with sample means removed. Show that the sample has rank f if and only if $\mathbf{Z}$ has rank f.

7.7.5 Show that $\mathbf{ZZ}'$ can be computed directly from $\mathbf{XX}'$ and describe the required computations.

CHAPTER 8

ONE SAMPLE OF INDIVIDUALS: MULTIPLE REGRESSION AND CORRELATION ANALYSIS

8.1 INTRODUCTION

This chapter is concerned with the prediction of a value for a specified variable given the values of a different set of variables on the same individual. A related concern is with the nature of the covariation which makes such prediction possible. By convention, the variable to be predicted will be denoted by V_p and the variables used for prediction will be denoted by $V_1, V_2, \ldots, V_{p-1}$. In this context V_p will be called a *predictand* or *dependent variable* while $V_1, V_2, \ldots, V_{p-1}$ will be called *predictors* or *independent variables.* It is assumed that an individual a for which a prediction is desired is a member of the same population as that represented by a given sample $a_1, a_2, \ldots, a_n$ of n individuals observed on *all* of the variables $V_1, V_2, \ldots, V_p$. The prediction scheme is to be based on the given sample.

The particular approach to prediction taken here is quite simple. A single unknown value is to be predicted by a single predicted value rather than, for example, by a probability distribution over the possible unknown values. The single predicted value is to be based on a *linear predictor* $w_1V_1 + w_2V_2 + \cdots + w_{p-1}V_{p-1}$ chosen through the principle of *least squares.* The resulting analysis of the given sample will be called *multiple regression analysis* of V_p on $V_1, V_2, \ldots, V_{p-1}$.

The restriction to linearity is not in itself very important, for the variables called $V_1, V_2, \ldots, V_{p-1}$ may be arbitrary functions of any set of directly observable variables. A difficulty may arise, however, because the smaller the sample size n the smaller is the number of predictors which can be used with a given effectiveness. This issue can only be discussed inconclusively, for the art of guessing scientific laws is not governed by well-established rules. In this chapter the choice of $V_1, V_2, \ldots, V_{p-1}$ will be taken as given. Even so, there remain questions concerning which of a possible set $V_1, V_2, \ldots, V_{p-1}$ might better be left out of a linear predictor, and some discussion of this fits naturally into Section 8.3.

The term *multiple regression* is largely a historical accident. Galton (1886) first used the word *regression* in connection with predicting the mature height of children from the heights of their parents. Galton corrected for the sex difference by multiplying all female heights by 1.08, and he used a single predictor variable taken to be the mean of the father's height and corrected mother's height. After some consideration of data it becomes apparent that the heights of children of parents whose height exceeds average by x inches will themselves, on the average, exceed average by less than x inches. In other words, the children *regress* in an average sense back to the mean. By a gradual metamorphosis, the term linear regression analysis came to mean the least squares prediction scheme when $p = 2$, and thence the term multiple regression came to mean the general case with a multiple battery of variables $V_1, V_2, \ldots, V_{p-1}$ available as predictors.

The history of the method, as opposed to that of its common statistical name, is quite different. According to Gauss (1809), he first used the method in 1795 in a different context and under the name *method of least squares*. The early history of the method of least squares is somewhat confused because Gauss did not publish his claim until 1809 and meanwhile Legendre (1806) had independently described the method. According to Eisenhart (1963), the method arose as a natural extension of the principle of averaging the results of several observations of the same quantity to reduce measurement error. It has been widely used in astronomy and the physical sciences since the time of Gauss. It is interesting that the basic computational ideas of Section 4.3 may be traced back to Gauss (1811) who derived them in connection with least squares analysis and illustrated them with the data which he used to identify the orbit of the asteroid Pallas from observations over the period 1803–1809. The Pallas data are used in Example 8.3.

On the history of the correlation coefficient Pearson (1896) wrote:

> The fundamental theorems of correlation were for the first time and almost exhaustively discussed by Bravais ("Analyse mathématique sur les probabilités des erreurs de situation d'un point," *Memoires par divers Savans*, T.IX., Paris, 1846, pp. 255–332) nearly half a century ago. He deals completely with the correlation of two and three variables. Forty years later Mr. J. D. Hamilton Dickson (*Proc. Roy. Soc.*, 1886, p. 63) dealt with a special problem proposed to him by Mr. Galton, and reached on a somewhat narrow basis* (*The coefficient of correlation was assumed to be the same for the arrays of all types, a result which really flows from the normal law of frequency.) some of Bravais' results for correlation of two variables. Mr. Galton at the same time introduced an improved notation which may be summed up in the "Galton function" or coefficient

> of correlation. This indeed appears in Bravais' work, but a single symbol is not used for it. It will be found of great value in the present discussion. In 1892 Professor Edgeworth, also unconscious of Bravais' memoir, dealt in a paper on "Correlated Averages" with correlation for three variables (*Phil. Mag.* **34,** 1892, pp. 194–204). He obtained results identical with Bravais', although expressed in terms of Galton's functions. He indicates also how the method may be extended to higher degrees of correlation. He starts by assuming a general form for the frequency of any complex of n organs each of given size. The form has been deduced on more or less legitimate assumptions by various writers. Several other authors, notably Schols, De Forest, and Czuber, have dealt with the same topic, although little of first-class importance has been added to the researches of Bravais. To Mr. Galton alone is due the idea of applying these results—usually spoken of as "the laws of error in the position of a point in space"—to the problem of correlation in the theory of evolution.

Karl Pearson had much to do with the popularity of the idea among statistical data analysts. See Walker (1931), Seal (1967), and Pearson (1967) for more historical detail.

This introduction concludes with some remarks on the concept of *cause.* The ability to predict one variable from another, which accompanies nontrivial correlation between the variables, is sometimes interpreted by saying that the predictor is having a causal effect on the predictand. It is clear, however, that causal effects should be attributed only with great caution. For example, height and weight will show positive correlation in many human samples. This indicates that either variable can help to predict the other, but it does not indicate that an increase in height causes an increase in weight, or vice versa. It would be more natural to interpret a correlation between height and weight as the result of a common causal factor.

The notion of cause appears to require belief in some mechanism whereby the causal factor is *acting* while the influenced factor is *reacting.* Thus it is a plausible hypothesis that a higher incidence of smoking causes a higher incidence of morbidity of various kinds, and observed correlations do provide evidence for this hypothesis. Such evidence may be challenged on the grounds that the influenced factor is reacting to other causal factors whose variation in the observed sample is not controlled in reaction to that of the alleged causal factor. Such counterarguments may sometimes be finessed in part by the well-known techniques of experimental design in the sense of Fisher (1966), i.e., by the collection of the right sort of data. Sometimes controlled experiments are possible, and sometimes not. The examples in Chapters 8, 9, and 10 are of the latter kind, while in Chapter 11 there are examples of the former kind.

In general, however, the notion of cause is relative and vague, with any cause being partly or wholly replaceable by something more fundamental or more controversial. Issues of causation as distinct from prediction are scarcely mentioned in the sequel.

8.2 BASIC DESCRIPTION

Suppose that $X_1, X_2, \ldots, X_p$ denote the values of $V_1, V_2, \ldots, V_p$ for an individual a, where $X_1, X_2, \ldots, X_{p-1}$ are known and X_p is unknown. The multiple regression analysis of V_p on $V_1, V_2, \ldots, V_{p-1}$ provides a predicted value $\hat{X}_p$ for the unknown value X_p of the form

$$\hat{X}_p = w + w_1X_1 + w_2X_2 + \cdots + w_{p-1}X_{p-1}. \tag{8.2.1}$$

The coefficients $w, w_1, w_2, \ldots, w_{p-1}$ in (8.2.1) are determined from the data on a given p-variate sample of size n to minimize the sum of squares of the n prediction errors resulting from the application of (8.2.1) to the n sample individuals. In symbols, the criterion to be minimized is

$$\sum_{i=1}^{n}(X_p^{(i)} - \hat{X}_p^{(i)})^2, \tag{8.2.2}$$

where

$$\hat{X}_p^{(i)} = w + w_1X_1^{(i)} + w_2X_2^{(i)} + \cdots + w_{p-1}X_{p-1}^{(i)}, \tag{8.2.3}$$

and $X_j^{(i)}$ for $i = 1, 2, \ldots, n$ and $j = 1, 2, \ldots, p$ denotes as in Chapter 7 the (i, j) element of the $n \times p$ data matrix $\mathbf{X}$. The coefficients in (8.2.1), called *regression coefficients*, are chosen according to the *principle of least squares*. When the least squares regression coefficients are used to define $\hat{X}_p^{(i)}$ in (8.2.3) the differences $X_p^{(i)} - \hat{X}_p^{(i)}$ for $i = 1, 2, \ldots, n$ are referred to as *residuals* and the minimized value of the criterion (8.2.2), namely the sum of squares of the residuals, is commonly called the *residual sum of squares*.

In the language of variable-space, the prediction scheme defined above provides the *augmented best linear predictor*

$$\hat{V}_p = wV_0 + w_1V_1 + \cdots + w_{p-1}V_{p-1} \tag{8.2.4}$$

based on the sample data $\mathbf{X}$, where V_0 refers to the artificial variable whose value is always unity. Suppose that $\mathbf{X}_{(+)}$ denotes the augmented data matrix $\mathbf{X}$ with a column of ones added and that $\mathbf{Q}_{(+)} = \mathbf{X}'_{(+)}\mathbf{X}_{(+)}$ denotes the corresponding augmented raw sum inner product matrix, as in (7.5.2). Then the criterion (8.2.2) may be written

$$(\mathbf{X}_{(+)}\mathbf{d}'_{(+)})'(\mathbf{X}_{(+)}\mathbf{d}'_{(+)}) = \mathbf{d}_{(+)}\mathbf{Q}_{(+)}\mathbf{d}'_{(+)}, \tag{8.2.5}$$

where $\mathbf{d}_{(+)}$ is the $1 \times (p + 1)$ vector of coefficients

$$\mathbf{d}_{(+)} = [-w_1, -w_2, \ldots, -w_{p-1}, 1, -w]. \tag{8.2.6}$$

Thus the least squares criterion is a squared length according to the sample raw sum inner product over the augmented variable-space spanned by V_0, V_1,

$V_2, \ldots, V_p$. Furthermore, minimizing this criterion is seen to be equivalent to choosing that variable in the subspace spanned by $V_0, V_1, \ldots, V_{p-1}$ which lies at minimum distance from V_p according to the raw sum inner product over the augmented variable-space. In other words, the *augmented best linear predictor* $\hat{V}_p$ *defined in* (8.2.4) *is the orthogonal projection of* V_p *into the subspace spanned by* $V_0, V_1, \ldots, V_{p-1}$, *and the residual* $V_p - \hat{V}_p$ *is the component of* V_p *orthogonal to each of* $V_0, V_1, V_2, \ldots, V_{p-1}$, *all in terms of the augmented variable-space and an associated sample raw sum inner product.*

The standard computational device for finding such an orthogonal projection is related to the process of successive orthogonalization as described in Chapter 4. Starting from the appropriate inner product matrix $\mathbf{Q}_{(+)}$, the desired computations are provided by $\text{SWP}[p + 1, 1, 2, \ldots, p - 1]\mathbf{Q}_{(+)}$. The off-diagonal elements of row p in the resulting $(p + 1) \times (p + 1)$ matrix are the coefficients of $V_1, V_2, \ldots, V_{p-1}, V_0$ in the orthogonal projection of V_p into the subspace spanned by $V_1, V_2, \ldots, V_{p-1}, V_0$, i.e., they are $w_1, w_2, \ldots, w_{p-1}, w$. The (p, p) diagonal element is the square of the raw sum norm of $V_p - \hat{V}_p$, i.e., it is the residual sum of squares.

The foregoing discussion defines the multiple regression analysis of V_p *on* $V_1, V_2, \ldots, V_{p-1}$, but with the disadvantage of being given largely in terms of the raw sum inner product, while statisticians are more accustomed to looking at sample means and corrected sum or covariance inner products. Consequently, the discussion will now be translated into the latter terms. The bridge is rather easy, since the analysis is provided by

$$\text{SWP}[p + 1, 1, 2, \ldots, p - 1]\mathbf{Q}_{(+)} = \text{SWP}[1, 2, \ldots, p - 1]\text{SWP}[p + 1]\mathbf{Q}_{(+)},$$

and $\text{SWP}[p + 1]\mathbf{Q}_{(+)}$ is expressed in (7.5.4) in the desired terms.

For present purposes it is convenient to partition the rows and columns of the right side of (7.5.4) into $p - 1$, 1, and 1 and to set

$$\text{SWP}[p + 1]\mathbf{Q}_{(+)} = \begin{bmatrix} \mathbf{T}_{11} & \mathbf{T}_{12} & \bar{\mathbf{X}}_1' \\ \mathbf{T}_{21} & t_{pp} & \bar{X}_p \\ \bar{\mathbf{X}}_1 & \bar{X}_p & -1/n \end{bmatrix} \tag{8.2.7}$$

in an obvious notation where, for example, t_{pp} denotes the (p, p) diagonal element of $\mathbf{T}$, and $\bar{\mathbf{X}}_1$ denotes the $1 \times (p - 1)$ vector $[\bar{X}_1, \bar{X}_2, \ldots, \bar{X}_{p-1}]$ of sample means. Performing the $\text{SWP}[1, 2, \ldots, p - 1]$ operation on the right side of (8.2.7) yields

$$\text{SWP}[p + 1, 1, 2, \ldots, p - 1]\mathbf{Q}_{(+)}$$

$$= \begin{bmatrix} -\mathbf{T}_{11}^{-1} & \mathbf{T}_{11}^{-1}\mathbf{T}_{12} & \mathbf{T}_{11}^{-1}\bar{\mathbf{X}}_1' \\ \mathbf{T}_{21}\mathbf{T}_{11}^{-1} & t_{pp} - \mathbf{T}_{21}\mathbf{T}_{11}^{-1}\mathbf{T}_{12} & \bar{X}_p - \mathbf{T}_{21}\mathbf{T}_{11}^{-1}\bar{\mathbf{X}}_1' \\ \bar{\mathbf{X}}_1\mathbf{T}_{11}^{-1} & \bar{X}_p - \bar{\mathbf{X}}_1\mathbf{T}_{11}^{-1}\mathbf{T}_{12} & -1/n - \bar{\mathbf{X}}_1\mathbf{T}_{11}^{-1}\bar{\mathbf{X}}_1' \end{bmatrix}. \tag{8.2.8}$$

From the previous interpretation of row p of $\mathbf{SWP}[p+1, 1, 2, \ldots, p-1]\mathbf{Q}_{(+)}$ it follows that

$$(w_1, w_2, \ldots, w_{p-1}) = \mathbf{T}_{21}\mathbf{T}_{11}^{-1} \tag{8.2.9}$$

and

$$w = \bar{X}_p - \mathbf{T}_{21}\mathbf{T}_{11}^{-1}\bar{\mathbf{X}}_1' = \bar{X}_p - w_1\bar{X}_1 - w_2\bar{X}_2 - \cdots - w_{p-1}\bar{X}_{p-1}, \tag{8.2.10}$$

while the residual sum of squares is given by

$$t_{pp} - \mathbf{T}_{21}\mathbf{T}_{11}^{-1}\mathbf{T}_{12}. \tag{8.2.11}$$

These results lead to the following alternatives to the first two paragraphs of Section 8.2.

The predicted value (8.2.1) may be written as

$$\hat{X}_p = \bar{X}_p + w_1(X_1 - \bar{X}_1) + w_2(X_2 - \bar{X}_2) + \cdots + w_{p-1}(X_{p-1} - \bar{X}_{p-1}), \tag{8.2.12}$$

where $w_1, w_2, \ldots, w_{p-1}$ are chosen to minimize the criterion

$$\sum_{i=1}^{n} [(X_p^{(i)} - \bar{X}_p) - w_1(X_1^{(i)} - \bar{X}_1) - w_2(X_1^{(i)} - \bar{X}_1) - \cdots - w_{p-1}(X_{p-1}^{(i)} - \bar{X}_{p-1})]^2. \tag{8.2.13}$$

The criterion (8.2.13) may also be written

$$\mathbf{dTd}', \tag{8.2.14}$$

where

$$\mathbf{d} = [-w_1, -w_2, \ldots, -w_{p-1}, 1] \tag{8.2.15}$$

and $\mathbf{T}$ denotes the sample corrected sum inner product matrix for the variables $V_1, V_2, \ldots, V_p$. The variable

$$\dot{V}_p = w_1V_1 + w_2V_2 + \cdots + w_{p-1}V_{p-1} \tag{8.2.16}$$

will be called the *best linear predictor* for V_p in terms of $V_1, V_2, \ldots, V_{p-1}$. Note that $\dot{V}_p$ lies in the ordinary p-dimensional variable-space $\mathscr{E}$ in contrast to the augmented best linear predictor $\hat{V}_p$ defined in (8.2.4) which lies in augmented variable-space.

In order to use the best linear predictor for actual prediction it is necessary to know also the vector of sample means, i.e., to know $\hat{V}_p$. On the other hand, $\dot{V}_p$ has an advantage over $\hat{V}_p$ in that it belongs to the familiar variable-space $\mathscr{E}$ on which the notion of covariance is relevant and meaningful. *The best linear predictor $\dot{V}_p$ should be regarded as an orthogonal projection, for from* (8.2.9) *$\dot{V}_p$ and $V_p - \dot{V}_p$ are the components of V_p along and orthogonal to the subspace of $\mathscr{E}$ spanned by $V_1, V_2, \ldots, V_{p-1}$ where the inner product assigned to $\mathscr{E}$ is the* *sample corrected sum inner product. The above orthogonal components* $\dot{V}_p$ and $V_p - \dot{V}_p$ *are the same whether the sample corrected sum inner product or the sample covariance is used, since changes of scale of an inner product have no effect on an orthogonal decomposition.*

The decomposition (8.2.11) of t_{pp} into $\mathbf{T}_{21}\mathbf{T}_{11}^{-1}\mathbf{T}_{12} + (t_{pp} - \mathbf{T}_{21}\mathbf{T}_{11}^{-1}\mathbf{T}_{12})$ is sometimes described in *analysis of variance* terminology (cf. Scheffé, 1959) as the decomposition of the *total sum of squares about the grand mean* into the *fitted or explained sum of squares* plus the residual sum of squares.

In terms of familiar statistical quantities the computations of multiple regression analysis may be described as: (i) finding the sample mean vector $\bar{\mathbf{X}}$, (ii) finding the sample covariance matrix $\mathbf{S}$, and (iii) finding the regression coefficients $\mathbf{S}_{11}^{-1}\mathbf{S}_{12}$ and the residual variance from SWP$[1, 2, \ldots, p-1]\mathbf{S}$. Still, the original description in terms of finding $\mathbf{Q}_{(+)} = \mathbf{X}'_{(+)}\mathbf{X}_{(+)}$ and SWP$[p+1, 1, 2, \ldots, p]\mathbf{Q}_{(+)}$ is computationally more natural.

While both (8.2.1) and (8.2.12) produce identical predicted values, a modified scheme yielding different results is occasionally appropriate. There may sometimes be theoretical reasons for omitting the constant term w from (8.2.1), i.e., for thinking that a predictor of the form

$$X_p^* = w_1^* X_1 + w_2^* X_2 + \cdots + w_{p-1}^* X_{p-1} \tag{8.2.17}$$

may actually improve on the version (8.2.1). In this case the least squares criterion becomes

$$\sum_{i=1}^{n} (X_p^{(i)} - w_1^* X_1^{(i)} - w_2^* X_2^{(i)} - \cdots - w_{p-1}^* X_{p-1}^{(i)})^2 = \mathbf{d}^*\mathbf{Q}\mathbf{d}^{*\prime}, \tag{8.2.18}$$

where

$$\mathbf{d}^* = [-w_1^*, -w_2^*, \ldots, -w_{p-1}^*, 1] \tag{8.2.19}$$

and $\mathbf{Q}$ is the sample raw sum inner product matrix. The required coefficients together with the residual sum of squares here are given by the last row of SWP$[1, 2, \ldots, p-1]\mathbf{Q}$. This produces the *reduced best linear predictor*

$$V_p^* = V_p - w_1^* V_1 - w_2^* V_2 - \cdots - w_{p-1}^* V_{p-1}, \tag{8.2.20}$$

whose interpretation as an orthogonal projection analogous to $\hat{V}_p$ and $\dot{V}_p$ is left to the reader to describe.

Example 8.1. The following data were collected by the author in a kitchen experiment with very rough measuring equipment. The length L in cm, the width W in cm, and the volume V in cc were measured on a dozen grade A large eggs. From the directly observed variables, three transformed variables $V_1 = \log_{10} L$, $V_2 = \log_{10} W$, and $V_3 = \log_{10} (6/\pi)V$ were selected for analysis.

The 12 × 3 data matrix with 12 eggs as individuals and V_1, V_2, V_3 as variables is:

V_1	V_2	V_3
0.7659	0.6360	2.031
0.7353	0.6198	1.982
0.7416	0.6280	1.995
0.7600	0.6280	2.019
0.7861	0.6239	2.031
0.7539	0.6156	1.956
0.7747	0.6156	2.007
0.7718	0.6239	1.995
0.7889	0.6114	1.995
0.7659	0.6072	1.995
0.7689	0.6156	1.995
0.7478	0.6239	2.007

This first example is kept simple so that the reader may try to reproduce the analysis on a desk calculator. The example is not intended to be representative of statistical practice. Note that the sample values are quite discrete, belying the first impression of a glance.

The use of logarithms in defining V_1, V_2, V_3, and the factor $6/\pi$ in the expression for V_3 were suggested by the formula $V = (\pi/6)LW^2$ for the volume of an ellipsoid with two principal axes of length W (i.e., a circular cross-section) and one principal axis of length L. Thus, if the eggs were precisely ellipsoids with circular cross-section, and if the measurements had been made precisely without error, then $V_1 + 2V_2$ would be a perfect predictor for V_3. In the following computations, the predictor $V_1 + 2V_2$ is compared with the two least squares best linear predictors $\hat{V}_3 = wV_0 + w_1V_1 + w_2V_2$ and $V_3^* = w_1^*V_1 + w_2^*V_2$.

The computations begin by finding

$$\mathbf{Q}_{(+)} = \begin{bmatrix} 6.9964 & 5.6861 & 18.3292 & 9.1608 \\ 5.6861 & 4.6246 & 14.9038 & 7.4489 \\ 18.3292 & 14.9038 & 48.0368 & 24.0080 \\ 9.1608 & 7.4489 & 24.0080 & 12.0000 \end{bmatrix}.$$

The computer then applied the operators SWP[1], SWP[2], SWP[3], SWP[4], RSW[3], RSW[2], RSW[1], and RSW[4] and printed out the resulting 8 matrices:

$$\text{SWP}[1]\mathbf{Q}_{(+)} = \begin{bmatrix} -0.1429 & 0.8127 & 2.6198 & 1.3094 \\ 0.8127 & 0.003329 & 0.007217 & 0.003708 \\ 2.6198 & 0.007217 & 0.01756 & 0.008374 \\ 1.3094 & 0.003708 & 0.008374 & 0.005174 \end{bmatrix},$$

$$\text{SWP}[1, 2]\mathbf{Q}_{(+)} = \begin{bmatrix} -198.5754 & 244.1576 & 0.8577 & 0.4040 \\ 244.1576 & -300.4193 & 2.1682 & 1.1139 \\ 0.8577 & 2.1682 & 0.001910 & 0.0003347 \\ 0.4040 & 1.1139 & 0.0003347 & 0.001044 \end{bmatrix},$$

$$\text{SWP}[1, 2, 3]\mathbf{Q}_{(+)} = \begin{bmatrix} -583.3215 & -728.5001 & 448.5989 & 0.2538 \\ -728.5001 & -2759.3479 & 1134.0810 & 0.7342 \\ 448.5989 & 1134.0810 & -523.0488 & 0.1751 \\ 0.2538 & 0.7342 & 0.1751 & 0.0009849 \end{bmatrix},$$

$$\text{SWP}[1, 2, 3, 4]\mathbf{Q}_{(+)} = -\mathbf{Q}_{(+)}^{-1}$$
$$= \begin{bmatrix} -648.7275 & -917.6850 & 403.4707 & 257.6735 \\ -917.6850 & -3306.5594 & 1003.5490 & 745.3128 \\ 403.4707 & 1003.5490 & -554.1859 & 177.7871 \\ 257.6735 & 745.3128 & 177.7871 & -1015.1307 \end{bmatrix},$$

$$\text{SWP}[1, 2, 4]\mathbf{Q}_{(+)} = \begin{bmatrix} -354.9839 & -187.0591 & 0.7280 & 387.1100 \\ -187.0591 & -1489.2800 & 1.8109 & 1067.2590 \\ 0.7280 & 1.8109 & 0.001803 & 0.3208 \\ 387.1100 & 1067.2590 & 0.3208 & -958.0952 \end{bmatrix},$$

$$\text{SWP}[1, 4]\mathbf{Q}_{(+)} = \begin{bmatrix} -331.4886 & -0.1256 & 0.5006 & 253.0584 \\ -0.1256 & 0.0006713 & 0.001216 & 0.7166 \\ 0.5006 & 0.001216 & 0.004005 & 1.6185 \\ 253.0584 & 0.7166 & 1.6185 & -193.2681 \end{bmatrix},$$

$$\text{SWP}[4]\mathbf{Q}_{(+)} = \begin{bmatrix} 0.003017 & -0.0003790 & 0.001510 & 0.7634 \\ -0.0003790 & 0.0007189 & 0.001026 & 0.6207 \\ 0.001510 & 0.001026 & 0.004761 & 2.0007 \\ 0.7634 & 0.6207 & 2.0007 & -0.08333 \end{bmatrix},$$

$$\mathbf{Q}_{(+)} = \begin{bmatrix} 6.9909 & 5.6816 & 18.3148 & 9.1536 \\ 5.6816 & 4.6209 & 14.8921 & 7.4431 \\ 18.3148 & 14.8921 & 47.9990 & 23.9891 \\ 9.1536 & 7.4431 & 23.9891 & 11.9906 \end{bmatrix}.$$

All of this output or even all of this computation is not necessary, but it is shown to emphasize the repetitive nature of the calculation which the machine finds easy. The calculations were done carrying roughly 8 digits; the output shows 4 decimal places for numbers greater than 0.1 and 4 digits otherwise. The final $\mathbf{Q}_{(+)}$ resulting from 8 sweeping operations may be compared with the original $\mathbf{Q}_{(+)}$ to gain some idea of the effect of rounding error on the output. A rounding error of 5 in the fourth digit is roughly typical. The quantities which are interpreted statistically are based on fewer sweeping operations and should in general be correct to 3 digits at least.

From the third line of $\mathbf{SWP}[1, 2, 4]\mathbf{Q}_{(+)}$ it follows that

$$\hat{V}_3 = 0.3208V_0 + 0.7280V_1 + 1.8109V_2$$

while the residual sum of squares is 0.001803. From the third line of $\mathbf{SWP}[1, 2]\mathbf{Q}_{(+)}$ it follows that

$$V_3^* = 0.8577V_1 + 2.1682V_2$$

while the residual sum of squares is 0.001910. Finally, a simple desk calculation on the original data matrix shows that the "theoretical" predictor

$$V_3^{**} = V_1 + 2V_2$$

has a residual sum of squares 0.002226.

The three predictors $\hat{V}_3$, V_3^*, and V_3^{**} when applied to the sample yield the following 3 columns of residuals, each calculated to 3 decimal places:

0.001	−0.005	−0.007
0.004	0.008	0.007
−0.003	−0.003	−0.003
0.008	0.006	0.003
0.008	0.004	−0.003
−0.028	−0.025	−0.029
0.007	0.008	0.011
−0.017	−0.020	−0.025
−0.007	−0.007	−0.017
0.017	0.022	0.015
0.000	0.001	−0.005
0.012	0.013	0.011

In considering these 3 vectors of residuals as points in the 12-dimensional Euclidean space $\mathcal{N}$, it should be remembered that the first is constrained to lie in the 9-dimensional subspace orthogonal to the vectors corresponding to V_0, V_1, and V_2, and similarly that the second is constrained to lie in the 10-dimensional subspace orthogonal to the vectors corresponding to V_1 and V_2. Consequently, the residual sums of squares 0.001803, 0.001910, and 0.002226 are squared lengths constrained to 9, 10, and 12 dimensions, respectively. To make them comparable, they are often divided by their associated dimension or *degree of freedom* number, leading to the three *residual mean squares* 0.0002003, 0.0001910, and 0.0001855. On this measure, the theoretical predictor V_3^{**} appears most accurate, although the differences are slight. Visual inspection of the three columns of residual does not turn up any striking differences in pattern.

Ignoring the crudeness of the data, the example illustrates a difficult scientific question. Is it better to use a theoretical predictor with given regression coefficients or a predictor from a wider model with fitted regression coefficients?

With finite sample sizes the sampling error from fitted regression coefficients may well exceed the actual error of the postulated theoretical regression coefficients, and whether or not this happens is unknown. Consequently, a real dilemma is posed. One imperfect solution to the dilemma is to prefer the theoretical model unless there are sufficient data to contradict the theoretical model in the sense of significance testing. Such significance tests will be discussed briefly in Section 14.2, but meanwhile the analysis should convey the feeling that fitting has not produced any clear cut improvement over the theoretical predictor, and correspondingly no denial of the ellipsoid model for these eggs.

In Example 8.1 use was made of the idea that variables may be represented by points in the n-dimensional space $\mathscr{N}$. For example, various residual sums of squares were interpreted as squared lengths in subspaces of $\mathscr{N}$. The dual geometric representation of multiple regression analysis in p-dimensional individual-space $\mathscr{F}$ is less obvious. Here the sample is represented either by the n sample individuals or by the sample mean-centered concentration ellipsoid. This description is dual to the description already given of $\dot{V}_p$ in $\mathscr{E}$ as the orthogonal projection of V_p into the subspace spanned by $V_1, V_2, \ldots, V_{p-1}$, in accordance with the sample covariance inner product. It is therefore clear at the outset that, whereas in $\mathscr{E}$ projection along a family of parallel lines was involved, in $\mathscr{F}$ projection along a family of parallel $(p-1)$-dimensional hyperplanes will be involved.

Consider the hyperplane in $\mathscr{F}$ consisting of the points $\mathbf{xv}$ where the coordinates $\mathbf{x}$ relative to the basis $\mathbf{v}$ dual to $\mathbf{V}$ in $\mathscr{E}$ satisfy the equation

$$x_p = w + w_1x_1 + \cdots + w_{p-1}x_{p-1}. \tag{8.2.21}$$

According to the criterion (8.2.2), multiple regression analysis may be regarded as the task of finding that hyperplane of the form (8.2.21) such that the sum of squares of the deviations of the sample individuals $a_1, a_2, \ldots, a_n$ from the hyperplane along a direction parallel to v_p is minimized. The resulting optimum hyperplane may be called the *sample regression hyperplane.* Since the sample regression hyperplane may also be expressed by the equation

$$x_p - \bar{X}_p = w_1(x_1 - \bar{X}_1) + w_2(x_2 - \bar{X}_2) + \cdots + w_{p-1}(x_{p-1} - \bar{X}_{p-1}), \tag{8.2.22}$$

it clearly passes through the sample mean point.

For any hyperplane such as (8.2.21), define αv_p to be its intersection with the axis defined by v_p, and define $\alpha_1v_p, \alpha_2v_p, \ldots, \alpha_nv_p$ to be the linear projections of $a_1, a_2, \ldots, a_n$ into the same axis along hyperplanes parallel to (8.2.21). Then the least squares criterion may be expressed as

$$\sum_{i=1}^{n} (\alpha_i - \alpha)^2. \tag{8.2.23}$$

Thus the task of multiple regression analysis is that of finding the hyperplane of the form (8.2.21) such that the projected sample $\alpha_1 v_p, \alpha_2 v_p, \ldots, \alpha_n v_p$ has the smallest clustering in the sense of (8.2.23). Note that for this smallest clustering

$$\alpha = \frac{1}{n} \sum_{i=1}^{n} \alpha_i \tag{8.2.24}$$

because the regression hyperplane is known to pass through the sample mean. Thus, the criterion (8.2.23) to be minimized may also be taken to be

$$\sum_{i=1}^{n} (\alpha_i - \bar{\alpha})^2. \tag{8.2.25}$$

The final geometric characterization dispenses with the points $a_1, a_2, \ldots, a_n$ and makes use only of the sample mean-centered concentration ellipsoid. Theorem 7.3 ensures that the mean-centered concentration ellipsoid of the projected sample $\alpha_1 v_p, \alpha_2 v_p, \ldots, \alpha_n v_p$ is the shadow cast by the mean-centered

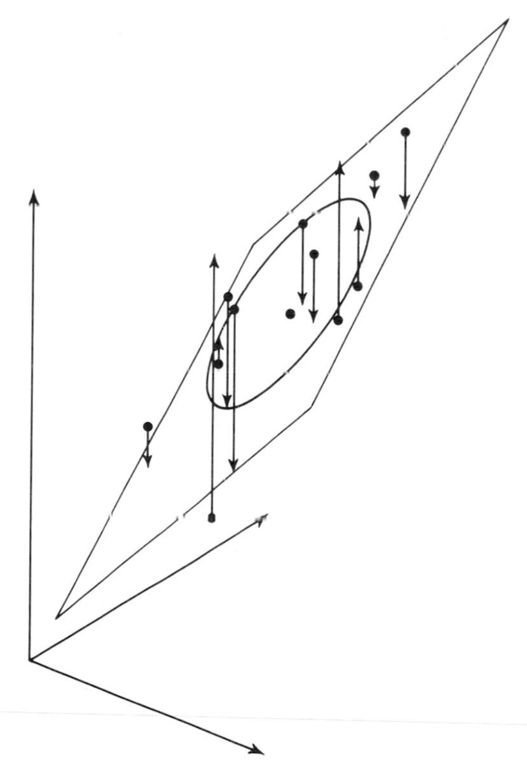

Fig. 8.2.1. The data of Example 8.1 as plotted in Fig. 7.3.2, showing in addition the fitted part of each point (marked by an arrowhead) and the best fitting hyperplane through the sample mean.

ellipsoid of concentration of the full sample under projection along the family of hyperplanes parallel to (8.2.21). It is easily checked that the mean-centered ellipsoid of concentration of the univariate sample $\alpha_1 v_p, \alpha_2 v_p, \ldots, \alpha_n v_p$ consists simply of the line segment joining the two points

$$\left\{\bar{\alpha} \pm \left[\sum_{i=1}^{n}(\alpha_i - \bar{\alpha})^2/(n-1)\right]^{1/2}\right\} v_p. \tag{8.2.26}$$

Consequently, minimizing the criterion (8.2.25) is equivalent to minimizing the length of the shadow (8.2.26). It is easy to see in geometric terms how this shadow is to be minimized. Consider the points $m \pm \beta v_p$ on the mean-centered ellipsoid of concentration of the full sample, i.e., the points where the line through the center of the ellipsoid parallel to v_p meets the ellipsoid. Clearly the shadow cast by the line segment from $m - \beta v_p$ to $m + \beta v_p$ lies in any shadow cast by the ellipsoid. Also, if $m \pm \beta v_p + \mathscr{V}$ denote the tangent hyperplanes of dimension $p - 1$ to the ellipsoid at $m \pm \beta v_p$, then projection along hyperplanes parallel to $\mathscr{V}$ casts a shadow identical to the shadow cast by the line segment from $m - \beta v_p$ to $m + \beta v_p$. It follows that $m + \mathscr{V}$ must be the desired regression hyperplane and, by comparing β with (8.2.26), that

$$\beta = \left[\sum_{i=1}^{n}(\alpha_i - \bar{\alpha})^2/(n-1)\right]^{1/2}, \tag{8.2.27}$$

where the right side of (8.2.27) is the sample standard deviation of the tightest projected sample.

The results of the last three paragraphs are illustrated in Fig. 8.2.1 which takes the data of Example 8.1 as plotted in Fig. 7.3.2 and adds the regression hyperplane.

8.3 REGRESSION COEFFICIENTS, CORRELATION COEFFICIENTS, AND THE MULTIPLE REGRESSION ANALYSIS OF V_p ON A SUBSET OF $V_1, V_2, \ldots, V_{p-1}$

Up to now only the regression analysis of V_p on the whole set $V_1, V_2, \ldots, V_{p-1}$ has been explicitly considered. The realities of data analysis often require or suggest several analyses of the same sample, so that it becomes advisable to understand certain relationships among the regression analyses of V_p on different subsets of $V_1, V_2, \ldots, V_{p-1}$. The relevant quantities here are regression coefficients and correlation coefficients.

In general, consider the multiple regression analysis of V_r on $V_{s_1}, V_{s_2}, \ldots, V_{s_t}$. The best linear predictor for V_r in this analysis will be denoted by

$$\sum_{i=1}^{t} w_{rs_i(s_1 s_2 \ldots s_t)} V_{s_i}, \tag{8.3.1}$$

where $w_{rs_i(s_1 s_2 \ldots s_t)}$ will be called the regression coefficient of V_r on V_{s_i} in the multiple regression analysis of V_r on $V_{s_1}, V_{s_2}, \ldots, V_{s_t}$. In this more general notation, the regression coefficients w_i appearing in (8.2.1), (8.2.4), or (8.2.16) are denoted by $w_{pi(12\ldots\overline{p-1})}$ for $i = 1, 2, \ldots, p-1$.

A regression coefficient such as $w_{rs(s)}$, which refers to the regression analysis of V_r on V_s alone, may be called a *simple regression coefficient* and may be denoted simply by w_{rs}. Thus

$$w_{rs} = w_{rs(s)} = \frac{\operatorname{cov}(V_r, V_s)}{\operatorname{var}(V_s)}. \tag{8.3.2}$$

By contrast the general type of regression coefficient as appears in (8.3.1) with $t \geq 2$ may be called a *joint regression coefficient*. Suppose that $\mathbf{V}^* = \mathbf{AV}$ denotes the basis of variable-space $\mathscr{E}$ resulting from the successive orthogonalization of the basis $\mathbf{V} = [V_1, V_2, \ldots, V_p]'$, where the inner product is defined by the sample covariance. As in Sections 4.2 and 4.3, the matrix $\mathbf{A}$ is a triangular matrix with elements zero above the diagonal and unity along the diagonal. The remaining elements of $\mathbf{A}$ are all joint regression coefficients. In fact, $\mathbf{A}$ may be written

$$\mathbf{A} = \begin{bmatrix} 1 & 0 & \cdots & 0 \\ -w_{21(1)} & 1 & \cdots & 0 \\ -w_{31(12)} & -w_{32(12)} & \cdots & 0 \\ \cdot & \cdot & & \\ \cdot & \cdot & & \\ \cdot & \cdot & & \\ -w_{p1(12\ldots\overline{p-1})} & -w_{p2(12\ldots\overline{p-1})} & \cdots & 1 \end{bmatrix}, \tag{8.3.3}$$

for line r of $\mathbf{A}$ shows that $V_r - V_r^* = w_{r1(12\ldots\overline{r-1})}V_1 + w_{r2(12\ldots\overline{r-1})}V_2 + \cdots + w_{r\overline{r-1}(12\ldots\overline{r-1})}V_{r-1}$ where $V_r - V_r^*$ is the component of V_r along the subspace spanned by $V_1, V_2, \ldots, V_{r-1}$, i.e., $V_r - V_r^*$ is the reduced best linear predictor for V_r in terms of $V_1, V_2, \ldots, V_{r-1}$, as is required to demonstrate (8.3.3).

It is illuminating to introduce a terminology of partial regression coefficients, even though it will subsequently turn out that all *partial* regression coefficients are simply joint regression coefficients in disguise. After removing the components along $V_{s_1}, V_{s_2}, \ldots, V_{s_t}$ from each of $V_r, V_{q_1}, V_{q_2}, \ldots, V_{q_m}$, one may contemplate the regression analysis of $V_{r.s_1s_2\ldots s_t}$ on $V_{q_1.s_1s_2\ldots s_t}$, $V_{q_2.s_1s_2\ldots s_t}, \ldots, V_{q_m.s_1s_2\ldots s_t}$. Actually, since $V_r - V_{r.s_1s_2\ldots s_t}$ is orthogonal to the predictor variables $V_{q_1.s_1s_2\ldots s_t}$, $V_{q_2.s_1s_2\ldots s_t}, \ldots, V_{q_m.s_1s_2\ldots s_t}$, the regression analysis of V_r or $V_{r.s_1s_2\ldots s_t}$ on these predictor variables produces the same best linear predictor whose coefficients may be denoted by

$$w_{rq_i(q_1q_2\ldots q_m).s_1s_2\ldots s_t}, \tag{8.3.4}$$

which represents the general form of a *partial (joint) regression coefficient*. Examples of these are the elements of the matrix $\mathbf{B}$ produced by successive orthogonalization where $\mathbf{V} = \mathbf{BV}^*$, namely

$$\mathbf{B} = \begin{bmatrix} 1 & 0 & 0 & \cdots & 0 \\ w_{21} & 1 & 0 & \cdots & 0 \\ w_{31} & w_{32.1} & 1 & \cdots & 0 \\ \cdot & \cdot & \cdot & & \\ \cdot & \cdot & \cdot & & \\ \cdot & \cdot & \cdot & & \\ w_{p1} & w_{p2.1} & w_{p3.12} & \cdots & 1 \end{bmatrix}. \tag{8.3.5}$$

Formula (8.3.5) follows by noting that column s on the right side of (8.3.5) may be determined from

$$\begin{aligned} w_{rs.12\ldots\overline{s-1}} &= w_{rs(s).12\ldots\overline{s-1}} \\ &= \frac{\operatorname{cov}(V_{r.12\ldots\overline{s-1}}, V_{s.12\ldots\overline{s-1}})}{\operatorname{var}(V_{s.12\ldots\overline{s-1}})} \end{aligned} \tag{8.3.6}$$

for $r = s + 1, s + 2, \ldots, p$, and the rule for computing column s of $\mathbf{B}$ given in Section 4.3.1 agrees with (8.3.6).

It is now time to remark that

$$w_{rq_i(q_1q_2\ldots q_m).s_1s_2\ldots s_t} = w_{rq_i(q_1q_2\ldots q_ms_1s_2\ldots s_t)}, \tag{8.3.7}$$

so that all partial regression coefficients may be interpreted simply as joint regression coefficients, and vice versa. Since dimensions may be relabeled and subscripts may be permuted, it will be sufficient to prove that

$$w_{p\overline{p-1}\,(\overline{s+1}\,\overline{s+2}\ldots\overline{p-1}).12\ldots s} = w_{p\overline{p-1}\,(12\ldots\overline{p-1})}.$$

To prove this, one need only follow through the computation of the right side by successively applying the operations SWP[1], SWP[2], ..., SWP[$p - 1$] in stages to the covariance matrix $\mathbf{S}$. One of the parts of SWP[$1, 2, \ldots, s$]$\mathbf{S}$ which results from the first s stages is the covariance matrix $\mathbf{S}_{(012\ldots s)}$ of the component variables $V_{\overline{s+1}.12\ldots s}, V_{\overline{s+2}.12\ldots s}, \ldots, V_{p.12\ldots s}$, and $w_{p\overline{p-1}(\overline{s+1}\,\overline{s+2}\ldots p).12\ldots s}$ may be calculated by further sweep operations on this $\mathbf{S}_{(012\ldots s)}$. The reader may check that these subsequent sweep operations on $\mathbf{S}_{(012\ldots s)}$ are actually included in the last $(p - s - 1)$ stages of the original $(p - 1)$ stages of sweep operations on $\mathbf{S}$ and consequently produce the same result for $w_{p\overline{p-1}(12\ldots p)}$ or $w_{p\overline{p-1}(\overline{s+1}\,\overline{s+2}\ldots p).12\ldots s}$.

In view of (8.3.7) it may be simpler always to use the joint regression coefficient notation, remembering, for example, that $w_{12(234)} = w_{12.34} = w_{12(23).4} = w_{12(24).3}$. It also follows from (8.3.7) together with (8.3.5) that

$$\mathbf{B} = \begin{bmatrix} 1 & 0 & 0 & 0 & \cdots & 0 \\ w_{21} & 1 & 0 & 0 & \cdots & 0 \\ w_{31} & w_{32(12)} & 1 & 0 & \cdots & 0 \\ w_{41} & w_{42(12)} & w_{43(123)} & 1 & \cdots & 0 \\ \cdot & \cdot & \cdot & \cdot & & \\ \cdot & \cdot & \cdot & \cdot & & \\ \cdot & \cdot & \cdot & \cdot & & \\ w_{p1} & w_{p2(12)} & w_{p3(123)} & w_{p4(1234)} & \cdots & 1 \end{bmatrix}. \tag{8.3.8}$$

From (8.3.8) and (8.3.3), together with $\mathbf{AB} = \mathbf{BA} = \mathbf{I}$, numerous identities involving regression coefficients may be deduced, but these are left for the interested reader to explore.

There is a class of correlation coefficients comparable to the class of regression coefficients relating a set of variables $V_1, V_2, \ldots, V_p$. Simple correlation coefficients have already been defined in (7.4.10). Thus, among $V_1, V_2, \ldots, V_p$ there are $p(p-1)/2$ different simple correlation coefficients

$$\begin{aligned} r_{st} &= \text{cor}\,(V_s, V_t) \\ &= \text{cov}\,(V_s, V_t)/\text{var}\,(V_s)^{1/2}\,\text{var}\,(V_t)^{1/2} \qquad (8.3.9) \\ &= r_{ts} \end{aligned}$$

for $1 \le s < t \le p$. These correlation coefficients together with var (V_s) for $s = 1, 2, \ldots, p$ determine the covariance matrix of $V_1, V_2, \ldots, V_p$. In geometric terms, the correlation coefficient r_{st} with the sample covariance inner product determines the angle between V_s and V_t in variable-space $\mathscr{E}$, as indicated by (7.4.12). Alternatively, r_{st} determines the angle between the corresponding pair of vectors in $\mathscr{N}_{II}$.

The correlation coefficient r_{st} may be regarded as the covariance between the *standardized variables* $U_s = \text{var}\,(V_s)^{-1/2}V_s$ and $U_t = \text{var}\,(V_t)^{-1/2}V_t$. Indeed, the sample correlation matrix $\mathbf{R}$ of $V_1, V_2, \ldots, V_p$ is simply the sample covariance matrix of the standardized basis $U_1, U_2, \ldots, U_p$. It follows easily that r_{st} may also be interpreted as the simple regression coefficient of either U_s on U_t or U_t on U_s.

The *multiple correlation coefficient* $r_{s(t_it_2\ldots t_m)}$ between V_s and a set of m variables $V_{t_1}, V_{t_2}, \ldots, V_{t_m}$ is defined to be the simple correlation coefficient between V_s and the reduced best linear predictor for V_s in terms of $V_{t_1}, V_{t_2}, \ldots, V_{t_m}$. Denote this best linear predictor by $V_{s(t_1t_2\ldots t_m)}$, so that the orthogonal decomposition of V_s along and orthogonal to the subspace spanned by $V_{t_1}, V_{t_2}, \ldots, V_{t_m}$ is given by

$$V_s = V_{s(t_1t_2\ldots t_m)} + V_{s.t_1t_2\ldots t_m}. \qquad (8.3.10)$$

Then

$$r_{s(t_1t_2\ldots t_m)} = \frac{\text{cov}\,(V_s, V_{s(t_1t_2\ldots t_m)})}{\text{var}\,(V_s)^{1/2}\text{var}\,(V_{s(t_1t_2\ldots t_m)})^{1/2}}. \qquad (8.3.11)$$

Since the angle between V_s and $V_{s(t_1t_2\ldots t_m)}$ is no greater than $\pi/2$,

$$0 \le r_{s(t_1t_2\ldots t_m)} \le 1. \qquad (8.3.12)$$

Since cov $(V_s - V_{s(t_1t_2\ldots t_m)}, V_{s(t_1t_2\ldots t_m)}) = 0$, or cov $(V_s, V_{s(t_1t_2\ldots t_m)}) =$ var $(V_{s(t_1t_2\ldots t_m)})$, it follows that

$$r_{s(t_1t_2\ldots t_m)} = \text{var}\,(V_{s(t_1t_2\ldots t_m)})^{1/2}/\text{var}\,(V_s)^{1/2}. \qquad (8.3.13)$$

Or, since $\text{var}(V_s) = \text{var}(V_{s(t_1t_2\ldots t_m)}) + \text{var}(V_{s.t_1t_2\ldots t_m})$, it follows that

$$1 - r^2_{s(t_1t_2\ldots t_m)} = \text{var}(V_{s.t_1t_2\ldots t_m})/\text{var}(V_s). \tag{8.3.14}$$

Note that if $r_{s(t_1t_2\ldots t_m)}$ is regarded as $\cos\theta$, then (8.3.14) is $\sin^2\theta$.

Partial correlation coefficients are simply correlation coefficients among variables from which the same set of components has been removed. Thus $r_{t(q_1q_2\ldots q_u).s_1s_2\ldots s_m}$ is defined to be the multiple correlation coefficient between $V_{t.s_1s_2\ldots s_m}$ and the set $V_{q_1.s_1s_2\ldots s_m}, V_{q_2.s_1s_2\ldots s_m}, \ldots, V_{q_u.s_1s_2\ldots s_m}$. Unlike partial regression coefficients, partial correlation coefficients do not provide quantities directly expressible as multiple correlation coefficients already defined.

It is often convenient to think of a correlation coefficient r in terms of the quantity $1 - r^2$ which may always be regarded as a fraction of variance remaining after fitting a best linear predictor, as in (8.3.14). By considering successive reductions in variance from fitting linear predictors, one may immediately write down such identities as

$$1 - r^2_{t(q_1q_2\ldots q_us_1s_2\ldots s_m)} = (1 - r^2_{t(s_1s_2\ldots s_m)})(1 - r^2_{t(q_1q_2\ldots q_u).s_1s_2\ldots s_m}), \tag{8.3.15}$$

and

$$1 - r^2_{p(12\ldots\overline{p-1})} = \prod_{i=1}^{p-1}(1 - r^2_{pi.12\ldots\overline{i-1}}). \tag{8.3.16}$$

The basic property of correlation coefficients which motivates their definition is that they are dimensionless, i.e., if $r = \text{cor}(V, W)$, then $r = \text{cor}(\mu V, \nu W)$ for any $\mu \neq 0$ and $\nu \neq 0$. In other words, linear changes of scale do not affect a correlation coefficient. The appeal of correlation coefficients as a tool for interpreting data is closely tied to this invariance property.

Regression coefficients, on the other hand, are always measured in the units of a ratio of two variables. For example, if $\hat{V}_3 = w_1V_1 + w_2V_2$ is a predictor for V_3 where V_3 is height in inches and V_1 is weight in pounds, then w_1 must be measured in units of inches per pound. Generally, $w_{st_1(t_1t_2\ldots t_m)}$ is measured in units of V_s divided by V_{t_1}. This dependence on units must be remembered when regression coefficients are regarded as measures of association between variables, for a large regression coefficient may only reflect a particular choice of scale for the variables concerned. In this sense regression coefficients require more careful interpretation than correlation coefficients.

Individual regression coefficients also require careful interpretation because they can depend strongly on the set of variables included as predictors in the multiple regression analysis. For example, although $w_{p1}, w_{p1(12)}, \ldots, w_{p1(12\ldots p-1)}$ all have the same dimensions, they may still vary greatly. The safest attitude to assume toward an individual joint regression coefficient is to regard it as a simple partial regression coefficient, i.e., to regard $w_{rs_1(s_1s_2\ldots s_m)}$ as $w_{rs_1.s_2\ldots s_m}$. In this way $w_{rs_1(s_1s_2\ldots s_m)}$ is seen to be the weight applied to $V_{s_1.s_2\ldots s_m}$ as a single predictor for V_r. In other words, any joint regression coefficient may always be regarded as a weight applied to V_{s_1} after all the other predictors $V_{s_2}, \ldots, V_{s_m}$ have been taken into account.

The multiple regression analysis of V_p on $V_1, V_2, \ldots, V_{p-1}$ has the associated fractional reductions of variance $1 - r^2_{p(s_1 s_2 \ldots s_m)}$ where $s_1, s_2, \ldots, s_m$ is any subset of $1, 2, \ldots, p-1$. There are $2^{p-1} - 1$ such nonempty subsets, and the corresponding set of $2^{p-1} - 1$ fractional reductions in variance provides a clear picture of the interaction of the variables $V_1, V_2, \ldots, V_{p-1}$ in their ability to jointly explain var (V_p). In statistical practice it often happens that a predictor for V_p is chosen which depends only on a subset of the available variables $V_1, V_2, \ldots, V_{p-1}$. The reasons for such a restricted predictor may be of two different sorts. First, for reasons of time, money, or effort it may be deemed impractical to expect anyone to make use of a predictor requiring the observation of the complete set $V_1, V_2, \ldots, V_{p-1}$. In such cases, a loss in prediction accuracy may be judged to be offset by increased practicability. Secondly, it is possible that deleting certain variables may result in an *increase* of prediction accuracy, because predictors based on finite samples find it hard to digest larger and larger numbers of independent variables. This issue was raised briefly in Example 8.1. To take another more extreme example, it may be noted that *multiple regression analysis is not even defined when* $p - 1 > n - 1$. For $\mathbf{S}$ has rank at most $n - 1$, and fitting $n - 1$ predictor variables is sufficient to reduce the residual variance of V_p to zero, so that no further fitting can be done. Theoretical understanding of this phenomenon of diminishing returns for variables introduced remains imperfect, while the phenomenon itself can be demonstrated empirically by making use of different predictors.

There are several standard methods for choosing a subset of the set of possible predictors. To simplify a discussion of these, make the unrealistic assumption that a decision has been made to include precisely k predictors. (This assumption is unrealistic because, for example, only one predictor might be of any value. Or, having chosen k predictors, it might be obvious that great benefits would accrue from the inclusion of a $(k + 1)$st predictor.) There are two popular methods of selecting k predictors. The first, which may be called the *forward method*, selects variables one at a time by the following rule:

i) Choose V_{s_1} out of $V_1, V_2, \ldots, V_{p-1}$ so that $r^2_{ps_1} \geq r^2_{pi}$ for $i = 1, 2, \ldots, p - 1$;

ii) Choose V_{s_2} out of the remaining V_i with $i \neq s_1$ so that $r^2_{ps_2.s_1} \geq r^2_{pi.s_1}$;

iii) Choose V_{s_3} out of the remaining V_i with $i \neq s_1, s_2$ so that $r^2_{ps_3.s_1s_2} \geq r^2_{pi.s_1s_2}$,

and so on until $V_{s_1}, V_{s_2}, \ldots, V_{s_k}$ have been chosen. In other words, the variables are chosen to yield the greatest reduction of residual sum of squares at each step of the introduction of a single predictor variable into the multiple regression analysis. The *backward method* begins from the complete regression analysis with predictor variables $V_1, V_2, \ldots, V_{p-1}$ and deletes one at a time from the analysis in such a way as to leave the minimum residual sum of squares at each stage or, equivalently, to leave the maximum multiple correlation between V_p and the predictor variables remaining at any stage. There are many variations on these methods. For example, the best pair of variables might be included at each stage in the forward method, and a similar modification could be made in the backward method. For a preselected k, it is plausible but computationally burdensome to look at all $\binom{p-1}{k}$ different sets of possible predictors and choose that with the smallest residual sum of squares.

It is nearly obvious that the different selection methods may give different results. For example, with three predictor variables V_1, V_2, and V_3, it may happen that $V_1 - V_2$ is a perfect predictor for V_4 while neither V_1 nor V_2 alone is as good as V_3 alone. To construct such an example suppose that U_1, U_2, U_3 are an orthonormal set of variables and define the set V_1, V_2, V_3, V_4 as follows: $V_4 = U_3$, $V_1 = (U_3 + U_1)/2$, $V_2 = (U_3 - U_1)/2$, and $V_3 = U_3 + U_2/4$. It follows easily that $r^2_{43} = \frac{16}{17}$ while $r^2_{42} = r^2_{41} = \frac{1}{2}$, and yet $r^2_{4(12)} = 1$ while $r^2_{4(13)} = r^2_{4(23)} = \frac{17}{18}$. This example illustrates the dilemma facing the user of either the forward or backward methods—by following down single chains of variables he must exclude examination of many pairs, triples, etc. which may have high predictive content. On the other hand, he may doubt the existence of such hidden combinations and be unwilling or unable to do the computations necessary to find them.

The forward scheme requires the least computing labor and is therefore the most used, especially for large p. Indeed the backward method may be computationally impractical for large p because it requires first carrying out the complete analysis. Theoretical considerations leading to a good method of selection remain generally undiscovered. In many examples, of course, various different methods of selection will produce effectively, if not exactly, the same result.

Example 8.2. This example is based on the data used by Cochran (1938) to illustrate the computations associated with the deletion or addition of a variable in multiple regression analysis. The following description is quoted from Cochran's paper:

> In a study of the effects of weather factors on the numbers of noctuid moths per night caught in a light trap, regressions were worked out on the minimum night temperature, the maximum temperature of the previous day, the average speed of the wind during the night and the amount of rain during the night. The dependent variable was log (number of moths + 1). This was found to be roughly normally distributed, whereas the numbers themselves had an extremely skew distribution. Further, a change in one of the weather factors was likely to produce the same *percentage* change at

different times in the numbers of moths rather than the same *actual* change. Three years' data were included. These were grouped in blocks of nine consecutive days, so as to eliminate as far as possible the effects of the lunar cycle. After the removal of differences between blocks, 72 degrees of freedom remained for the regressions.

Interest centered on the effect of including night cloud cover as a fifth predictor variable. The basic data culled from Cochran's paper is a 6×6 corrected sum inner product matrix, where to correct is to subtract out the block means of each block of nine days. In this way certain dimensions in $\mathcal{N}$ were removed from the data vectors before the analysis started in order to eliminate the influence of factors not relevant to weather. This corrected sum inner product matrix is

T =

0.14029*E* 02	0.56635*E* 01	0.19866*E* 01	0.27330*E* 01	−0.48670*E* 01	0.20744*E* 01
0.56635*E* 01	0.14537*E* 02	0.12710*E*-00	−0.13470*E* 01	0.20600*E*-00	0.15747*E* 01
0.19866*E* 01	0.12710*E*-00	0.20680*E* 01	0.29400*E*-00	−0.54460*E* 00	−0.64400*E* 00
0.27330*E* 01	−0.13470*E* 01	0.29400*E*-00	0.17110*E* 02	−0.54200*E* 01	0.88500*E* 00
−0.48670*E* 01	0.20600*E*-00	−0.54460*E* 00	−0.54200*E* 01	0.78700*E* 01	−0.19330*E* 01
0.20744*E* 01	0.15747*E* 01	−0.64400*E* 00	0.88500*E* 00	−0.19330*E* 01	0.35520*E* 01

The numbers here are in "floating point" computer output where, for example, an exponent *E* 01 means that the given number should be multiplied by $10 = 10^1$ or an exponent *E*-02 means that the given number should be multiplied by $0.01 = 10^{-2}$. The 6 rows and columns of **T** refer to the variables V_1 = minimum night temperature, V_2 = maximum day temperature, V_3 = average night wind speed, V_4 = amount of night rainfall, V_5 = percentage of starlight obscured by clouds in a night sky camera, and V_6 = log (number of moths caught + 1).

The usual step-by-step process of finding the multiple regression analysis of V_6 on V_1, V_2, V_3, V_4, V_5 was carried out in a computer by finding

SWP[1]**T** =

−0.71283*E*-01	0.40371*E*-00	0.14161*E*-00	0.19482*E*-00	−0.34693*E*-00	0.14787*E*-00
0.40371*E*-00	0.12250*E* 02	−0.67491*E* 00	−0.24503*E* 01	0.21709*E* 01	0.73724*E* 00
0.14161*E* 00	−0.67491*E* 00	0.17867*E* 01	−0.93022*E*-01	0.14462*E*-00	−0.93776*E* 00
0.19482*E*-00	−0.24503*E* 01	−0.93022*E*-01	0.16578*E* 02	−0.44718*E* 01	0.48087*E*-00
−0.34693*E*-00	0.21709*E* 01	0.14462*E*-00	−0.44718*E* 01	0.61815*E* 01	−0.12133*E* 01
0.14787*E*-00	0.73724*E* 00	−0.93776*E* 00	0.48087*E*-00	−0.12133*E* 01	0.32453*E* 01

SWP[1, 2]**T** =

−0.84587*E*-01	0.32955*E*-01	0.16385*E*-00	0.27557*E*-00	−0.41847*E*-00	0.12357*E*-00
0.32955*E*-01	−0.81630*E*-01	−0.55093*E*-01	−0.20002*E*-00	0.17721*E*-00	0.60181*E*-01
0.16385*E*-00	−0.55093*E*-01	0.17495*E* 01	−0.22802*E*-00	0.26422*E*-00	−0.89714*E* 00
0.27557*E*-00	−0.20002*E*-00	−0.22802*E*-00	0.16087*E* 02	−0.40376*E* 01	0.62834*E* 00
−0.41847*E*-00	0.17721*E*-00	0.26422*E*-00	−0.40376*E* 01	0.57968*E* 01	−0.13440*E* 01
0.12357*E*-00	0.60181*E*-01	−0.89714*E* 00	0.62834*E* 00	−0.13440*E* 01	0.32009*E* 01

SWP[1, 2, 3]**T** =

−0.99933*E*-01	0.38115*E*-01	0.93657*E*-01	0.29692*E*-00	−0.44322*E*-00	0.20760*E*-00
0.38115*E*-01	−0.83365*E*-01	−0.31491*E*-01	−0.20720*E*-00	0.18553*E*-00	0.31929*E*-01
0.93657*E*-01	−0.31491*E*-01	−0.57159*E* 00	−0.13033*E*-00	0.15103*E*-00	−0.51280*E* 00
0.29692*E*-00	−0.20720*E*-00	−0.13033*E*-00	0.16058*E* 02	−0.40032*E* 01	0.51141*E* 00
−0.44322*E*-00	0.18553*E*-00	0.15103*E*-00	−0.40032*E* 01	0.57569*E* 01	−0.12085*E* 01
0.20760*E*-00	0.31929*E*-01	−0.51280*E* 00	0.51141*E* 00	−0.12085*E* 01	0.27408*E* 01

SWP[1, 2, 3, 4]**T** =

−0.10542*E*-00	0.41946*E*-01	0.96067*E*-01	0.18491*E*-01	−0.36920*E*-00	0.19814*E*-00
0.41946*E*-01	−0.86039*E*-01	−0.33173*E*-01	−0.12904*E*-01	0.13387*E*-00	0.38528*E*-01
0.96067*E*-01	−0.33173*E*-01	−0.57265*E* 00	−0.81166*E*-02	0.11853*E*-00	−0.50865*E* 00
0.18491*E*-01	−0.12904*E*-01	−0.81166*E*-02	−0.62275*E*-01	−0.24930*E*-00	0.31848*E*-01
−0.36920*E*-00	0.13387*E*-00	0.11853*E*-00	−0.24930*E*-00	0.47589*E* 01	−0.10810*E* 01
0.19814*E*-00	0.38528*E*-01	−0.50865*E* 00	0.31848*E*-01	−0.10810*E* 01	0.27245*E* 01

SWP[1, 2, 3, 4, 5]**T** =

−0.13407*E*-00	0.52332*E*-01	0.10526*E*-00	−0.84984*E*-03	−0.77581*E*-01	0.11428*E*-00
0.52332*E*-01	−0.89805*E*-01	−0.36507*E*-01	−0.58905*E*-02	0.28131*E*-01	0.68938*E*-01
0.10526*E*-00	−0.36507*E*-01	−0.57560*E* 00	−0.19071*E*-02	0.24908*E*-01	−0.48172*E*-00
−0.84984*E*-03	−0.58905*E*-02	−0.19071*E*-02	−0.75335*E*-01	−0.52386*E*-01	−0.24780*E*-01
−0.77581*E*-01	0.28131*E*-01	0.24908*E*-01	−0.52386*E*-01	−0.21013*E*-00	−0.22715*E*-00
0.11428*E*-00	0.68938*E*-01	−0.48172*E*-00	−0.24780*E*-01	−0.22715*E*-00	0.24790*E* 01

These calculations were done to roughly 16 digit accuracy, and as a result, when RSW[1, 2, 3, 4, 5] was applied to SWP[1, 2, 3, 4, 5], the original **T** was reproduced exactly to the five digits shown in the output.

The output above provides the regression analysis of V_6 on each of the sets V_1 to V_i for $i = 1, 2, 3, 4, 5$. The main point of Cochran's paper was to illustrate the computations required to add V_5 to the predictor based on V_1, V_2, V_3, V_4 and to delete V_5 from the predictor based on V_1, V_2, V_3, V_4, V_5. These computations involve, in the language of this book, the operations SWP[5] applied to SWP[1, 2, 3, 4]**T** and RSW[5] applied to SWP[1, 2, 3, 4, 5]**T**. Note, however, that in Cochran's context it was necessary to assimilate V_5 before the 6×6 matrix SWP[1, 2, 3, 4]**T** was available.

The various simple and joint regression coefficients of V_6 on V_1 produced by this analysis are given by the (1, 6) elements of the above matrices:

$$\begin{aligned} w_{61} &= 0.14787 \\ w_{61(12)} &= 0.12357 \\ w_{61(123)} &= 0.20760 \\ w_{61(1234)} &= 0.19814 \\ w_{61(12345)} &= 0.11428. \end{aligned}$$

It is clear that the weight given to V_1 depends considerably on what other predictor variables are used.

The initial corrected sum of squares of V_6 is shown as the (6, 6) element of **T** to be 3.5520 and is seen to be reduced successively to 3.2453, 3.2009, 2.7408, 2.7245, and 2.4790 by successively adding V_1, V_2, V_3, V_4, and V_5 to the set of fitted variables. The corresponding fractions of residual variance to total variance are

$$1 - r^2_{61} = 3.2453/3.5520 = 0.9137$$
$$1 - r^2_{6(12)} = 3.2009/3.5520 = 0.9012$$
$$1 - r^2_{6(123)} = 2.7408/3.5520 = 0.7716$$
$$1 - r^2_{6(1234)} = 2.7245/3.5520 = 0.7670$$
$$1 - r^2_{6(12345)} = 2.4790/3.5520 = 0.6979.$$

Various partial correlation coefficients may also be deduced, such as

$$1 - r^2_{62.1} = 3.2009/3.2453 = 0.9863$$
$$1 - r^2_{63.12} = 2.7408/3.2009 = 0.8563$$
$$1 - r^2_{64.123} = 2.7245/2.7408 = 0.9941$$
$$1 - r^2_{65.1234} = 2.4790/2.7245 = 0.9099.$$

To pursue the analysis of various correlation coefficients, the matrix **T** is reduced to the corresponding correlation matrix **R** where

R =

0.10000*E* 01	0.39659*E*-00	0.36883*E*-00	0.17640*E*-00	−0.46320*E*-00	0.29387*E*-00
0.39659*E*-00	0.10000*E* 01	0.23181*E*-01	−0.85410*E*-01	0.19259*E*-01	0.21914*E*-00
0.36883*E*-00	0.23181*E*-01	0.10000*E* 01	0.49425*E*-01	−0.13499*E*-00	−0.23762*E*-00
0.17640*E*-00	−0.85410*E*-01	0.49425*E*-01	0.10000*E* 01	−0.46708*E*-00	0.11352*E*-00
−0.46320*E*-00	0.19259*E*-01	−0.13499*E*-00	−0.46708*E*-00	0.10000*E* 01	−0.36560*E*-00
0.29387*E*-00	0.21914*E*-00	−0.23762*E*-00	0.11352*E*-00	−0.36560*E*-00	0.10000*E* 01

The largest correlation coefficients in this array are those relating V_1 with V_2, V_3, and V_5 and those relating V_5 with V_4 and V_6. None of these attain 0.5 in absolute value, however, so that no variable explains as much as 25% of the variance of any other.

The computer then produced SWP$[i_1, i_2, \ldots, i_t]$**R** where $i_1, i_2, \ldots, i_t$ run over all subsets of 1, 2, 3, 4, 5. The (6, 6) elements of these matrices yield $1 - r^2_{6(i_1 i_2 \ldots i_t)}$ for these subsets as shown in Table 8.3.1.

It is now clear that the forward method of variable selection would choose in order V_5, V_3, V_1, V_2, V_4. Also the backward method would drop in succession from the complete set V_4, V_2, V_5, V_3, V_1, i.e., the order of importance given by the backward method is V_1, V_3, V_5, V_2, V_4, which differs from the forward method. If the best single predictor is desired, namely V_5, it is that given by the forward method but not by the backward method. On the other hand, among all ten pairs of predictors, the best pair V_1, V_3 agrees with the pair given by the backward method but not with the pair given by the forward method.

None of this indicates what predictor should be used, but it appears from Table 8.3.1 that very little is to be gained by including more than three, and

Table 8.3.1

$1 - r^2_{61} = 0.91364$	$1 - r^2_{6(2345)} = 0.72534$
$1 - r^2_{62} = 0.95198$	$1 - r^2_{6(1345)} = 0.71282$
$1 - r^2_{63} = 0.94354$	$1 - r^2_{6(1245)} = 0.81142$
$1 - r^2_{64} = 0.98711$	$1 - r^2_{6(1235)} = 0.70021$
$1 - r^2_{65} = 0.86634$	$1 - r^2_{6(1234)} = 0.76705$
$1 - r^2_{6(12)} = 0.90115$	$1 - r^2_{6(345)} = 0.77766$
$1 - r^2_{6(13)} = 0.77507$	$1 - r^2_{6(245)} = 0.81310$
$1 - r^2_{6(14)} = 0.90972$	$1 - r^2_{6(235)} = 0.72777$
$1 - r^2_{6(15)} = 0.84659$	$1 - r^2_{6(234)} = 0.87189$
$1 - r^2_{6(23)} = 0.89304$	$1 - r^2_{6(145)} = 0.84327$
$1 - r^2_{6(24)} = 0.93436$	$1 - r^2_{6(135)} = 0.71604$
$1 - r^2_{6(25)} = 0.81516$	$1 - r^2_{6(134)} = 0.77190$
$1 - r^2_{6(34)} = 0.92781$	$1 - r^2_{6(125)} = 0.81343$
$1 - r^2_{6(35)} = 0.78246$	$1 - r^2_{6(124)} = 0.89424$
$1 - r^2_{6(45)} = 0.86214$	$1 - r^2_{6(123)} = 0.77163$
$1 - r^2_{6(12345)} = 0.69792$	

V_1, V_3, V_5 appears to be the best triple on the scene. Oddly enough, however, V_2, V_3, V_5 is nearly as good as V_1, V_3, V_5. At the present time, the science of variable selection apparently can do no better than this.

8.4 A LEAST SQUARES EXAMPLE ILLUSTRATING THE DELETION OF INDIVIDUALS

Example 8.3. This example will review the original calculations of Gauss (1811) combining 12 observations on the asteroid Pallas to determine six parameters governing its orbit. The example will be described without going into details of the astronomical context in which least squares prediction first arose. The computations for deleting individuals will also be illustrated.

A set of observed quantities, say γ_i for $i = 1, 2, \ldots, 12$, is thought to be expressible as

$$\gamma_i = f_i(\theta_1, \theta_2, \ldots, \theta_6) + l_i.$$

Here l_i is the error of measurement in the observable quantity γ_i, where, if measurement could be perfect, physical theories would predict that γ_i should be a known function f_i of six quantities $\theta_1, \theta_2, \ldots, \theta_6$ whose values are unknown. The concept of measurement error arises here for the very practical reason that no values for $\theta_1, \theta_2, \ldots, \theta_6$ are sufficient to satisfy all 12 equations

$\gamma_i = f_i(\theta_1, \theta_2, \ldots, \theta_6)$ with the observed γ_i. The problem therefore is to combine the 12 observations in order to come as close as possible to the unknown values $\theta_1, \theta_2, \ldots, \theta_6$ despite the known presence of error in the original observations.

The solution proposed by Gauss was to choose $\theta_1, \theta_2, \ldots, \theta_6$ to minimize $\sum_1^{12} [\gamma_i - f_i(\theta_1, \theta_2, \ldots, \theta_6)]^2$. The minimization problem was to be solved by beginning with an initial guess $\theta_1^{(0)}, \theta_2^{(0)}, \ldots, \theta_6^{(0)}$ which is known to be close to the desired answer, perhaps from physical understanding of the parameters. Then the functions f_i were to be approximated linearly by the first term Taylor series approximation

$$f_i(\theta_1, \theta_2, \ldots, \theta_6) = a_i + \sum_{j=1}^{6} (\theta_i - \theta_i^{(0)}) b_{ij},$$

where

$$a_i = f_i(\theta_1^{(0)}, \theta_2^{(0)}, \ldots, \theta_6^{(0)})$$

and

$$b_{ij} = \frac{\partial}{\partial \theta_j} f_i(\theta_1^{(0)}, \theta_2^{(0)}, \ldots, \theta_6^{(0)}).$$

The problem then became to find $\delta\theta_j = \theta_j - \theta_j^{(0)}$ for $j = 1, 2, \ldots, 6$ which minimized

$$\sum_{i=1}^{12} (\gamma_i - a_i - b_{i1}\,\delta\theta_1 - b_{i2}\,\delta\theta_2 - \cdots - b_{i6}\,\delta\theta_6)^2.$$

This is simply the least squares criterion (8.2.18) in a different notation, where $n = 12$ and $p = 7$ and where the role of the $n \times p$ data matrix $\mathbf{X}$ is played by

$$\begin{bmatrix} b_{11} & b_{12} & \cdots & b_{16} & \gamma_1 - a_1 \\ b_{21} & b_{22} & & b_{26} & \gamma_2 - a_2 \\ \cdot & \cdot & & \cdot & \cdot \\ \cdot & \cdot & & \cdot & \cdot \\ \cdot & \cdot & & \cdot & \cdot \\ b_{\overline{12}1} & b_{\overline{12}2} & & b_{\overline{12}6} & \gamma_{\overline{12}} - a_{\overline{12}} \end{bmatrix}.$$

Gauss (1811) gave the above data matrix to be

$\mathbf{X} =$

0.79363	143.66	0.39493	0.95920	−0.18856	0.17387	183.93
−0.02658	46.71	0.02658	−0.20858	0.15946	1.25782	6.81
0.58880	358.12	0.26208	−0.85234	0.14912	0.17775	0.06
0.01318	28.39	−0.01318	−0.07861	0.91704	0.54365	3.09
1.73436	1846.17	−0.54603	−2.05662	−0.18833	−0.17445	0.02
−0.12606	−227.42	0.12606	−0.38939	0.17176	−1.35441	8.98
0.99584	1579.03	0.06456	1.99545	−0.06040	−0.33750	2.31
−0.08089	−67.22	0.08089	−0.09970	−0.46359	1.22803	−2.47
0.65311	1329.09	0.38994	−0.08439	−0.04305	0.34268	−0.01
0.69957	1719.32	0.12913	−1.38787	0.17130	−0.08360	317.73
−0.01315	−43.84	0.01315	0.02929	1.02138	−0.27187	−117.97
−0.00218	38.47	0.00218	−0.18710	0.47301	−1.14371	−38.12

Rows 10, 11, and 12 of Gauss's matrix are shown above as rows 12, 10, and 11 respectively. Gauss dropped his row 10 because he regarded the experiment yielding that observation as suspect. In other words he took his data matrix to be the first 11 rows of **X** shown above. If these first 11 rows are called $\mathbf{X}_{(-)}$, Gauss first calculated $\mathbf{Q}_{(-)} = \mathbf{X}'_{(-)}\mathbf{X}_{(-)}$. He then followed out the first layer of the elimination method of Section 4.3.1 which gave the residual sum of squares 96364.0 and essentially the triangular matrix **B** where $\mathbf{V} = \mathbf{B}\mathbf{V}^*$. By solving back he got the last row of **A**, where $\mathbf{V}^* = \mathbf{A}\mathbf{V}$, which yielded

$$\begin{aligned}
\delta\theta_1 &= -3.06 \\
\delta\theta_2 &= 0.054335 \\
\delta\theta_3 &= 166.44 \\
\delta\theta_4 &= -4.29 \\
\delta\theta_5 &= -34.37 \\
\delta\theta_6 &= -3.15.
\end{aligned}$$

Such was the origin of the basic computing device of Section 4.3.1.

The present analysis was carried out along similar lines, but doing several more steps for illustrative purposes. Twelve additional columns were added to the data matrix **X** corresponding to the indicator variables of the 12 individuals, thus giving the enlarged 12×19 data matrix

$$\mathbf{X}^* = [\mathbf{X}, \mathbf{I}],$$

where **I** denotes the 12×12 identity matrix. From this the 19×19 raw sum inner product matrix

$$\mathbf{Q}^* = \mathbf{X}^{*\prime}\mathbf{X}^*$$

was found, for use as the basis for further calculations. Note that

$$\mathbf{Q}^* = \begin{bmatrix} \mathbf{Q} & \mathbf{X}' \\ \mathbf{X} & \mathbf{I} \end{bmatrix},$$

where $\mathbf{Q} = \mathbf{X}'\mathbf{X}$ is the usual 7×7 raw sum inner product matrix.

The next step was to calculate SWP[1, 2, 3, 4, 5, 6]**Q***. In its upper left 7×7 part, this has SWP[1, 2, 3, 4, 5, 6]**Q** which yields the least squares analysis based on the full sample of twelve individuals. The (7, 7) element gives the residual sum of squares 85850.82 and the elements (7, 1), (7, 2), . . . , (7, 6) give

$$\begin{aligned}
\delta\theta_1 &= -15.46409 \\
\delta\theta_2 &= 0.0539589 \\
\delta\theta_3 &= 216.1136 \\
\delta\theta_4 &= -32.56353 \\
\delta\theta_5 &= -55.26174 \\
\delta\theta_6 &= -2.952751.
\end{aligned}$$

The remaining elements (7, 8), (7, 9), . . . , (7, 19) of row 7 of

$$\mathrm{SWP}[1, 2, 3, 4, 5, 6]\mathbf{Q}^*$$

provide the residuals when the predictor is applied to the 12 individuals, namely

$$\begin{array}{r} 124.4295 \\ 3.8682 \\ -85.7873 \\ 54.3330 \\ -32.6659 \\ -15.1287 \\ -20.8007 \\ -42.8145 \\ -150.0130 \\ 171.8944 \\ -62.0554 \\ -24.0310. \end{array}$$

Note that the observation which Gauss rejected does not appear to have a suspicious residual.

In order to eliminate the twelfth individual from $\mathbf{Q}$, recall from (7.5.2) that SWP[19]$\mathbf{Q}^*$ yields the desired reduced raw sum inner product matrix $\mathbf{Q}_{(-)}$ as its upper left 7×7 part. Consequently the further operation SWP[19] applied to SWP[1, 2, 3, 4, 5, 6]$\mathbf{Q}^*$ yields the least squares analysis based on the first 11 individuals. The resulting residual sum of squares is 85094.14 and the weights are

$$\begin{aligned} \delta\theta_1 &= -15.5884 \\ \delta\theta_2 &= \quad 0.053991 \\ \delta\theta_3 &= \quad 218.4079 \\ \delta\theta_4 &= -33.09147 \\ \delta\theta_5 &= -51.19588 \\ \delta\theta_6 &= \quad -7.698775. \end{aligned}$$

Again the residuals were found to be

$$\begin{array}{r} 125.7156 \\ 9.0136 \\ -86.5398 \\ 53.1740 \\ -32.4062 \\ -22.7582 \\ -21.1797 \\ -35.3474 \\ -149.1134 \\ 169.8026 \\ -67.5134 \\ -31.4876. \end{array}$$

Note that the last element here, which is the (7, 19) element of

$$\mathrm{SWP}[1, 2, 3, 4, 5, 6, 19]\mathbf{Q}^*,$$

is the residual when the predictor based on the first 11 individuals is applied to the twelfth individual.

Since Gauss's calculations produced results different from those given here, both sets of calculations were checked. Gauss's numbers are self-consistent in that the original data matrix produces the raw sum of products matrix except for two small discrepancies. However, much larger errors begin to appear in Gauss's computed values at the first stage of elimination. The change in the outcome of the analysis when the twelfth individual is dropped is not striking.

It is of some interest to examine the residuals for individual i with $i = 1, 2, \ldots, 12$ based on the predictor derived from the 11 individuals excluding individual i. The residual -31.4876 above is the special case $i = 12$. The full column of these residuals may be found directly from $\mathrm{SWP}[1, 2, 3, 4, 5, 6]\mathbf{Q}^*$ by dividing element $(7 + i, 7)$ by element $(7 + i, 7 + i)$ for $i = 1, 2, \ldots, 12$. These are

$$\begin{array}{r} 438.739 \\ 5.340 \\ -138.768 \\ 103.534 \\ -710.193 \\ -24.196 \\ -133.545 \\ -58.661 \\ -265.824 \\ 428.794 \\ -110.159 \\ -31.488. \end{array}$$

Since each of these residuals concerns an individual not included in the associated predictor, its square is an estimate of the squared error expected for predictors based on a sample of size 11. It is strikingly clear that these residuals are much larger than those resulting when the regression hyperplane is fitted directly to the twelve individuals. In fact the sum of squares of these residuals is 1,016,384, which is nearly 12 times the sum of squares of deviations from the fitted regression hyperplane. See the further discussion of these residuals in Chapter 14.

8.5 CORRELATION WITH A SINGLE CATEGORICAL VARIABLE

This section illustrates the use of regression and correlation techniques where the variable V_p to be predicted is a dichotomous variable. For simplicity, V_p will be assumed scaled to take the values zero or one.

In such a situation, the usefulness of a multiple regression analysis might be questioned. In particular, it makes little sense to use a predictor $\hat{V}_p$ taking continuous values to predict V_p taking values zero or one only. Still, a formal analysis leading to a multiple correlation coefficient between V_p and its best linear predictor can shed light on observed data. A correlation coefficient calculated for a pair of variables, one dichotomous and the other continuous, is sometimes called in the psychological literature a *biserial correlation coefficient* (cf. McNemar, 1962).

Consider a sample of $n = n_1 + n_2$ individuals where V_p takes the value zero for n_1 individuals and unity for n_2 individuals. Suppose that $X^{(11)}, X^{(12)}, \ldots, X^{(1n_1)}$ and $X^{(21)}, X^{(22)}, \ldots, X^{(2n_2)}$ denote the sample observations on another variable V where the $X^{(1i)}$ correspond to individuals having the value zero on V_p and the $X^{(2i)}$ correspond to individuals having the value unity on V_p. It is easily seen that the sample corrected sum inner product matrix of V and V_p is given by

$$\left[\begin{array}{c|c} \sum_{i=1}^{n_1}(X^{(1i)} - \bar{X}^{(1)})^2 + \sum_{i=1}^{n_2}(X^{(2i)} - \bar{X}^{(2)})^2 + \dfrac{n_1 n_2}{n}(\bar{X}^{(1)} - \bar{X}^{(2)})^2 & \dfrac{n_1 n_2}{n}(\bar{X}^{(1)} - \bar{X}^{(2)}) \\ \hline \dfrac{n_1 n_2}{n}(\bar{X}^{(1)} - \bar{X}^{(2)}) & \dfrac{n_1 n_2}{n} \end{array}\right], \quad (8.5.1)$$

where

$$\bar{X}^{(1)} = \frac{1}{n_1}\sum_{i=1}^{n_1} X^{(1i)} \quad \text{and} \quad \bar{X}^{(2)} = \frac{1}{n_2}\sum_{i=1}^{n_2} X^{(2i)}.$$

It follows that the point biserial correlation coefficient r between V and V_p may be expressed as

$$r = \frac{(n_1 n_2/n)^{1/2}(\bar{X}^{(1)} - \bar{X}^{(2)})}{[\sum_{i=1}^{n_1}(X^{(1i)} - \bar{X}^{(1)})^2 + \sum_{i=1}^{n_2}(X^{(2i)} - \bar{X}^{(2)})^2 + (n_1 n_2/n)(\bar{X}^{(1)} - \bar{X}^{(2)})^2]^{1/2}}. \quad (8.5.2)$$

The particular form (8.5.2) shows the relation of r to several other quantities familiar to statisticians. In *analysis of variance* terminology the quantity

$$G = \frac{(n_1 n_2/n)(\bar{X}^{(1)} - \bar{X}^{(2)})^2}{\sum_{i=1}^{n_1}(X^{(1i)} - \bar{X}^{(1)})^2 + \sum_{i=1}^{n_2}(X^{(2i)} - \bar{X}^{(2)})^2} \quad (8.5.3)$$

is called a ratio of a *between sample mean square* on 1 degree of freedom to a *pooled within sample sum of squares* on $n - 2$ degrees of freedom. The two samples are of course $X^{(11)}, X^{(12)}, \ldots, X^{(1n_1)}$ and $X^{(21)}, X^{(22)}, \ldots, X^{(2n_2)}$, and

G clearly depends only on their sample means and variances. Statistics equivalent to G are

$$F = \frac{(n_1 n_2/n)(\bar{X}^{(1)} - \bar{X}^{(2)})^2}{[1/(n-2)][\sum_{i=1}^{n_1}(X^{(1i)} - \bar{X}^{(1)})^2 + \sum_{i=1}^{n_2}(X^{(2i)} - \bar{X}^{(2)})^2]} \tag{8.5.4}$$

where the denominator sum of squares has been reduced to a *mean square*, and

$$D = \frac{\bar{X}^{(1)} - \bar{X}^{(2)}}{\{[1/(n-2)][\sum_{i=1}^{n_1}(X^{(1i)} - \bar{X}^{(1)})^2 + \sum_{i=1}^{n_2}(X^{(2i)} - \bar{X}^{(2)})^2]\}^{1/2}} \tag{8.5.5}$$

which represents the ratio of the difference of the sample means to a pooled *root mean square*.

From these definitions it follows easily that

$$\frac{r^2}{1 - r^2} = G = \frac{1}{n-2} F = \frac{n_1 n_2}{n(n-2)} D^2 \tag{8.5.6}$$

so that any one of r^2, G, F, or D^2 determines the other three. Also, r and D have the same sign and so determine each other.

The foregoing quantities were defined for the pair of variables V and V_p where V_p is dichotomous. In particular, they may be defined where V is chosen to be the best linear predictor $\dot{V}_p$ for V_p in terms of $V_1, V_2, \ldots, V_{p-1}$. Note that $\dot{V}_p$ has the property of maximizing each of r^2, G, F, and D^2 among all V in the subspace spanned by $V_1, V_2, \ldots, V_{p-1}$. This maximum D^2 will be discussed further from the viewpoint of two multivariate samples in Section 10.2. The case of a categorical variable with more than two categories will be fully examined in Section 9.4.

Example 8.4 following also illustrates the use of principal component analysis in connection with multiple correlation analysis. The question being asked of the data is essentially: does a certain dichotomous variable exhibit any correlation with a set of sample principal variables?

Example 8.4. The data of this example were collected by Dr. Gene Smith in connection with his studies of the measurement of personality. The 264 individuals were freshman nursing students of whom 219 successfully completed their year while the remaining 45 either chose to leave or were asked to leave during or at the end of their freshman year. Fifteen dropouts were not included in the study since they left either to marry or for health or financial reasons.

Two batteries of personality tests were given to these 264 students before they entered nursing school. These resulted in 15 variables from the Edwards Personal Preference Schedule (Edwards, 1959) and 16 variables representing personality factors (Cattell, Saunders, and Stice, 1957). Two further variables measuring reading and verbal ability were also provided in the data. Suppose that V_1 and V_2 denote the reading and verbal ability variables, that $V_3, V_4, \ldots,$

$V_{\overline{17}}$ denote the Edwards variables, that $V_{\overline{18}}, V_{\overline{19}}, \ldots, V_{\overline{33}}$ denote the Cattel variables, and that $V_{\overline{34}}$ denotes the dichotomous variable where *pass* is represented by a zero score and *fail* is represented by a score of unity.

Since the scales of measurement here have no absolute meaning, it is convenient to work as much as possible in terms of standardized variables, i.e., variables scaled to have unit variances. The corresponding covariances become correlation coefficients. Also, it was decided to remove from consideration all components of these variables which are correlated with V_1 and V_2 in order to escape at least partially the criticism that any correlation between success and personality is due to the common influence of ability on both scores.

Accordingly, the first step was to form the corrected sum inner product matrix of the variables $V_1, V_2, \ldots, V_{\overline{34}}$ which was then standardized to a correlation matrix. This correlation matrix was next subjected to SWP[1, 2] to remove components along V_1 and V_2. The remaining 32×32 inner product matrix was then standardized again to yield the correlation matrix of $V_{3.12}, V_{4.12}, \ldots, V_{\overline{34}.12}$.

The first standardization to a correlation matrix was strictly unnecessary, although it did help to show how the ability variables V_1 and V_2 are correlated with the rest. For example, it appeared that $r^2_{\overline{34}(12)} = 0.0477$, which is small but greater than could reasonably be attributed to sampling fluctuations in a sample of size 264 drawn from a normal population whose corresponding $\rho_{\overline{34}(12)} = 0$. (By chance one would have expected roughly $r^2_{\overline{34}(12)} \approx \frac{2}{263} = 0.0076$. See Section 14.2 for a discussion of the sampling distribution.) On the other hand, the correlations between V_1 or V_2 and the personality measures present much more nearly the aspect of chance fluctuations with the possible exception of the following subtable of correlation coefficients.

	V_5	V_{10}	V_{15}	V_{19}
V_1	−0.185	0.178	−0.189	0.330
V_2	−0.140	0.163	−0.170	0.297

A simple correlation of $\sqrt{1/263} = 0.062$ is a rough guide to the sampling fluctuation expected here. A high correlation with one of V_1 or V_2 is usually accompanied by a high correlation with the other. This is partly a reflection of the initial high correlation $r_{12} = 0.594$, but is also due to the fact that all of these variables measure somewhat similar attributes.

The main part of the analysis started from the 32×32 correlation matrix $V_{3.12}, V_{4.12}, \ldots, V_{\overline{34}.12}$. Denote this matrix by **R**. The pair [**R**, **I**] was subjected to the eigenvalue and eigenvector operations SDG[1, 2, 3, . . . , 15], followed by operations SDG[16, 17, . . . , 31] as defined in (5.4.21) in order to carry out principal component analysis on $V_{3.12}, V_{4.12}, \ldots, V_{17.12}$ and $V_{18.12}, V_{19.12}, \ldots, V_{33.12}$. Denote the outcome of these operations by $[\mathbf{Q}, \mathbf{K}]$.

Then **K** has the form

$$\mathbf{K} = \begin{bmatrix} \mathbf{K}_{11} & \mathbf{0} & \mathbf{0} \\ \mathbf{0} & \mathbf{K}_{22} & \mathbf{0} \\ \mathbf{0} & \mathbf{0} & 1 \end{bmatrix},$$

representing a partition of rows and columns into $15 + 16 + 1$ where the off-diagonal matrices consist entirely of zeros. The rows of $\mathbf{K}_{11}$ express a set of principal variables $U_1, U_2, \ldots, U_{15}$ in terms of $V^*_{3.12}, V^*_{4.12}, \ldots, V^*_{17.12}$ and the rows of $\mathbf{K}_{22}$ express a set of principal variables $W_1, W_2, \ldots, W_{16}$ in terms of $V^*_{18.12}, V^*_{19.12}, \ldots, V^*_{33.12}$ where $V^*_{i.12}$ denotes the standardized $V_{i.12}$.

Q provides the sample corrected sum inner product matrix of $U_1, U_2, \ldots, U_{15}, W_1, W_2, \ldots, W_{16}, V^*_{34.12}$. It partitions into

$$\mathbf{Q} = \begin{bmatrix} \mathbf{Q}_{11} & \mathbf{Q}_{12} & \mathbf{Q}_{13} \\ \mathbf{Q}_{21} & \mathbf{Q}_{22} & \mathbf{Q}_{23} \\ \mathbf{Q}_{31} & \mathbf{Q}_{32} & 1 \end{bmatrix},$$

where $\mathbf{Q}_{11}$ is a diagonal matrix of eigenvalues whose elements:

3.33, 1.86, 1.38, 1.19, 1.09, 0.91, 0.87
0.81, 0.74, 0.62, 0.60, 0.49, 0.48, 0.42, 0.001

are the principal components of variance for a principal component analysis of the reduced Edwards variables $V_{3.12}, V_{4.12}, \ldots, V_{17.12}$. Similarly, $\mathbf{Q}_{22}$ is the diagonal matrix of eigenvalues:

2.93 1.76 1.35 1.22 1.10 1.00 0.88 0.85
0.80 0.74 0.68 0.67 0.59 0.47 0.40 0.32

representing a set of principal components from a principal component analysis of the reduced Cattell variables $V_{18.12}, V_{19.12}, \ldots, V_{33.12}$.

The matrix **Q** was then standardized to provide the correlation matrix of $U_1, U_2, \ldots, U_{15}, W_1, W_2, \ldots, W_{16}, V_{34.12}$. This is a convenient form for inspecting the three off-diagonal blocks of correlation coefficients which interrelate the Edwards variables, the Cattell variables, and the pass-fail variable.

Now the reason for the principal component analysis in the first place was to simplify the inspection of the overly large correlation matrix **R** by restricting consideration to the first few principal variables of each kind. *Visual inspection of the correlation matrix of* $V_1, V_2, \ldots, V_{15}, W_1, W_2, \ldots, W_{16}, V_{34.12}$ *does indeed show a concentration of meaningful-appearing correlations in the restricted* *correlation matrix of* U_1, U_2, U_3, U_4, W_1, W_2, W_3, W_4, $V_{\overline{34}.12}$ *which is reproduced below.*

1.000	0	0	0	0.350	0.363	−0.185	−0.021	−0.155
0	1.000	0	0	0.203	−0.059	0.009	−0.116	0.005
0	0	1.000	0	−0.362	0.216	−0.113	0.102	0.076
0	0	0	1.000	0.113	−0.061	−0.049	−0.030	0.129
0.350	0.203	−0.362	0.113	1.000	0	0	0	−0.171
0.363	−0.059	0.216	−0.061	0	1.000	0	0	−0.091
−0.185	0.009	−0.113	−0.049	0	0	1.000	0	−0.056
−0.021	−0.116	0.102	−0.030	0	0	0	1.000	−0.136
−0.155	0.005	0.076	0.129	−0.171	−0.091	−0.056	−0.136	1

Again it may be remembered that 0.062 is a rough guide for a typical meaningless r value. There do appear to be meaningful relations among the two sets of principal variables. Still, these relationships are weak. The reader should always remember that weak relationships can be clearly demonstrated with large samples even though the relationships have little or no practical value for subsequent prediction. Even weaker are the relations between the pass-fail variable and the personality variables.

The foregoing example has some interest for a statistical theoretician because it demonstrates empirically that nontrivial correlation effects can be concentrated by means of a principal component analysis. In this way, attempts at a better theoretical understanding of principal component analysis may be encouraged.

No attempt has been made to draw conclusions for psychology from the example. In particular, the psychologist usually assigns suggestive names to his variables to give "meaning" to his analysis, and the discussion here does not attempt to penetrate this name-meaning approach to interpretations. The data are disappointing in that so little prediction capability appears to reside in the personality measures. Nor, perhaps, is the small apparent capability any more than might be expected from the leakage of ability measures into intended personality measures.

CHAPTER 9

ONE SAMPLE OF INDIVIDUALS: EXTENSIONS OF MULTIPLE REGRESSION ANALYSIS

9.1 JOINT PREDICTION OF A SET OF VARIABLES

Rather than predict a single variable from a set of predictor variables, it may be required to predict a battery of variables from a common set of predictor variables, the prediction method being based on a sample observed on all of the variables. Each member of the battery may be predicted separately, of course, by a multiple regression analysis, and the methods discussed in this chapter are essentially based on such an approach. Section 9.1 makes some introductory remarks on joint prediction.

Suppose that the predictor variables are denoted by $V_1, V_2, \ldots, V_s$ and that the variables to be predicted are denoted by $V_{s+1}, V_{s+2}, \ldots, V_p$. Suppose that a sample of size n on all p variables yields a $p \times p$ sample covariance matrix $\mathbf{S}$. Then the best linear predictors $\dot{V}_{s+1}, \dot{V}_{s+2}, \ldots, \dot{V}_p$ of $V_{s+1}, V_{s+2}, \ldots, V_p$ in terms of $V_1, V_2, \ldots, V_s$ may be described as the orthogonal projections of $V_{s+1}, V_{s+2}, \ldots, V_p$ into the subspace $\mathscr{E}_1$ spanned by $V_1, V_2, \ldots, V_s$ in Euclidean variable-space $\mathscr{E}$, where the inner product over $\mathscr{E}$ is the sample covariance.

In order to understand fully the extension of multiple regression analysis to the case of $p - s$ predicted variables, it is important to notice the following result. *If $\dot{V}_{s+1}, \dot{V}_{s+2}, \ldots, \dot{V}_p$ are the best linear predictors for $V_{s+1}, V_{s+2}, \ldots, V_p$ each in terms of $V_1, V_2, \ldots, V_s$, then the best linear predictor for $\alpha_{s+1}V_{s+1} + \alpha_{s+2}V_{s+2} + \cdots + \alpha_p V_p$ in terms of $V_1, V_2, \ldots, V_s$ is $\alpha_{s+1}\dot{V}_{s+1} + \alpha_{s+2}\dot{V}_{s+2} + \cdots + \alpha_p\dot{V}_p$ where $\alpha_{s+1}, \alpha_{s+2}, \ldots, \alpha_p$ are arbitrary real numbers.* The proof of this is trivial because the best linear predictors involved are all determined by a linear transformation, namely orthogonal projection into $\mathscr{E}_1$. Every linear transformation has by definition the property that the transform of a linear combination of vectors is the same linear combination of their transforms.

Suppose that the corrected sum inner product matrix $\mathbf{T}$ has been computed.

Then

$$\mathrm{SWP}[1, 2, \ldots, s]\mathbf{T} = \begin{bmatrix} -\mathbf{T}_{11}^{-1} & \mathbf{H}_{12} \\ \mathbf{H}_{21} & \mathbf{T}_{22.1} \end{bmatrix} \tag{9.1.1}$$

provides the multiple regression analyses of each of $V_{s+1}, V_{s+2}, \ldots, V_p$ on $V_1, V_2, \ldots, V_s$. The rows of $\mathbf{H}_{21}$ define the best linear predictors $\dot{V}_{s+1}, \dot{V}_{s+2}, \ldots, \dot{V}_p$ for $V_{s+1}, V_{s+2}, \ldots, V_p$ in terms of $V_1, V_2, \ldots, V_s$. The matrix $\mathbf{T}_{22.1}$ is the corrected sum inner product matrix of $V_t - \dot{V}_t = V_{t.12\ldots s}$ for $t = s + 1, s + 2, \ldots, p$.

In matrix terms, defining $\mathbf{V}_1 = [V_1, V_2, \ldots, V_s]'$, $\mathbf{V}_2 = [V_{s+1}, V_{s+2}, \ldots, V_p]'$ and $\dot{\mathbf{V}}_2 = [\dot{V}_{s+1}, \dot{V}_{s+2}, \ldots, \dot{V}_p]'$, one has

$$\dot{\mathbf{V}}_2 = \mathbf{H}_{21}\mathbf{V}_1, \tag{9.1.2}$$

and $\mathbf{T}_{22.1}$ is the inner product matrix of $\mathbf{V}_2 - \dot{\mathbf{V}}_2$. In addition, from the result italicized above, the best linear predictor of

$$\boldsymbol{\alpha}_2\mathbf{V}_2 = \alpha_{s+1}V_{s+1} + \alpha_{s+2}V_{s+2} + \cdots + \alpha_pV_p \tag{9.1.3}$$

is given by

$$\boldsymbol{\alpha}_2\dot{\mathbf{V}}_2 = (\boldsymbol{\alpha}_2\mathbf{H}_{21})\mathbf{V}_1, \tag{9.1.4}$$

and the corresponding residual sum of squares is $\boldsymbol{\alpha}_2\mathbf{T}_{22.1}\boldsymbol{\alpha}_2'$.

It should be remembered of course that the use of these predictors also requires knowledge of the sample mean vector, where such means are easily computed along with $\mathbf{T}$ from (7.5.4). Indeed the augmented predictors may be computed from $\mathrm{SWP}[1, 2, \ldots, s]\mathbf{Q}_{(+)}$ which includes (9.1.1) as a submatrix.

9.2 CANONICAL CORRELATION ANALYSIS

The analysis of Section 9.1 may be described as the determination of variables in the space $\mathscr{E}_1$ spanned by $\mathbf{V}_1 = [V_1, V_2, \ldots, V_s]'$ which are best linear predictors for variables in the space $\mathscr{E}_2$ spanned by $\mathbf{V}_2 = [V_{s+1}, V_{s+2}, \ldots, V_p]'$. A natural extension is the determination of that variable in $\mathscr{E}_2$ which is "most predictable" in terms of a variable in $\mathscr{E}_1$. The question here actually involves $\mathscr{E}_1$ and $\mathscr{E}_2$ symmetrically in that it seeks that pair of variables, one in $\mathscr{E}_1$ and one in $\mathscr{E}_2$, having maximal sample correlation coefficient. This question leads directly to the method of canonical correlation analysis proposed by Hotelling (1935).

The required theory has already been derived in Section 5.6 in terms of the relationships between a pair of subspaces of a Euclidean space, the subspaces here being $\mathscr{E}_1$ and $\mathscr{E}_2$ in variable-space $\mathscr{E}$ and the inner product being sample covariance. Using the theory of eigenvalues and eigenvectors relating a pair of inner products, one determines special orthogonal bases $\mathbf{W}_1 = [W_1, W_2, \ldots, W_s]'$ for $\mathscr{E}_1$ and $\mathbf{W}_2 = [W_{s+1}, W_{s+2}, \ldots, W_p]'$ for $\mathscr{E}_2$ with the property that

$$\mathrm{cov}\,(W_i, W_j) = 0 \tag{9.2.1}$$

for $i = 1, 2, \ldots, s$ and $j = s + 1, s + 2, \ldots, p$, except when $j = s + i$. In other words, only the pairs (W_i, W_{s+i}) for $i = 1, 2, \ldots, \min(s, p - s)$ may make angles θ_i different from $\pi/2$ among all pairs with one member in $\mathbf{W}_1$ and one member in $\mathbf{W}_2$. The scaling may be chosen and the subscripts arranged so that

$$0 \leq \theta_1 \leq \theta_2 \leq \cdots \leq \theta_{\min(s,p-s)}. \tag{9.2.2}$$

The corresponding correlation coefficients

$$r_i = \cos \theta_i = \operatorname{cor}(W_i, W_{s+i}), \tag{9.2.3}$$

$i = 1, 2, \ldots, \min(s, p - s)$ satisfy

$$1 \geq r_1 \geq r_2 \cdots \geq r_{\min(p,p-s)} \geq 0. \tag{9.2.4}$$

The pair W_i, W_{s+i} will be called *the ith pair of canonical variables* and the corresponding r_i will be called *the ith canonical correlation coefficient*.

It is clear that the pair W_1, W_{s+1} satisfies the original "most predictable" criterion of Hotelling. With this pair fixed, the pair W_2, W_{s+2} is the most predictable pair where W_2 is taken from the subspace of $\mathscr{E}_1$ orthogonal to W_1 and W_{s+2} is taken from the subspace of $\mathscr{E}_2$ orthogonal to W_{s+1}, and so on. The special covariance matrix of the basis $\mathbf{W} = [\mathbf{W}_1, \mathbf{W}_2]'$ implies that the best linear predictor in $\mathscr{E}_1$ for W_{s+i} in $\mathscr{E}_2$ is $[\operatorname{cov}(W_i, W_{s+i})/\operatorname{var}(W_i)]W_i$ and the best linear predictor in $\mathscr{E}_2$ for W_i in $\mathscr{E}_1$ is $[\operatorname{cov}(W_i, W_{s+i})/\operatorname{var}(W_{s+i})]W_{s+i}$ for $i = 1, 2, \ldots, \min[s, p - s]$. More generally, the best linear predictor in $\mathscr{E}_1$ for any variable $\sum_1^{p-s} \beta_{s+j} W_{s+j}$ in $\mathscr{E}_2$ is

$$\sum_{i=1}^{\min(s,p-s)} \beta_{s+i} \frac{\operatorname{cov}(W_i, W_{s+i})}{\operatorname{var}(W_{s+i})} W_i, \tag{9.2.5}$$

and the reader may easily supply the formula reversing the roles of $\mathscr{E}_1$ and $\mathscr{E}_2$. Note that $\mathbf{W}_1$ and $\mathbf{W}_2$ may be chosen to be orthonormal and in this case (9.2.5) takes the simple form

$$\sum_{i=1}^{\min(s,p-s)} \beta_{s+i} r_i W_i. \tag{9.2.6}$$

The canonical correlation coefficients are uniquely determined and the degree of uniqueness of the canonical variables may be deduced from Theorem 5.1.2. In general, with sample data the canonical correlation coefficients will all be distinct and the pairs of canonical variables will therefore be uniquely determined up to scale factors. The other case, which allows for sets of equal r_i, will not be described in detail. Note, however, that the shorter of the two bases $\mathbf{W}_1$ and $\mathbf{W}_2$ has a set of $|2s - p|$ variables at the end which are uncorrelated with all of the other canonical variables of either set and which may be replaced by any orthogonal basis of the subspace which they span.

Canonical correlation analysis has an obvious mathematical appeal; whether or not it is a statistically useful tool is less easily discovered. A similar question was raised when considering principal component analysis, which also involves eigenvalue and eigenvector analysis. The canonical correlation analysis method is less vague than the principal component method in the sense that it is free of an arbitrary choice of a reference inner product, but the question of meaning and usefulness of the artificial canonical variables remains. The hope is that in a many-variable situation the first few canonical variables will prove to be the important ones and thus provide a means for reducing the number of variables under consideration to more easily comprehensible dimensions.

The computations required for canonical correlation analysis afford good illustrations of the SWP, MST, and SDG operators. Consider an initial position given the sample corrected sum inner product matrix

$$\mathbf{T} = \begin{bmatrix} \mathbf{T}_{11} & \mathbf{T}_{12} \\ \mathbf{T}_{21} & \mathbf{T}_{22} \end{bmatrix} \tag{9.2.7}$$

of the basis $\mathbf{V} = [\mathbf{V}_1, \mathbf{V}_2]'$, where the partitions refer as usual to $p = s + (p - s)$.

According to the theory of Section 5.6 the canonical variables $\mathbf{W}_2 = [W_{s+1}, W_{s+2}, \ldots, W_p]'$ are eigenvectors of an inner product π_1 relative to an inner product π_2. The roles of $\mathscr{U}$ and $\mathscr{V}$ in Section 5.6 are played here by $\mathscr{E}_2$ and $\mathscr{E}_1$, respectively. Using the sample corrected sum inner product to make $\mathscr{E}$ Euclidean, the inner product matrix relative to $\mathbf{V}_2$ for π_2 is $\mathbf{T}_{22}$. Since π_1 refers to the inner products among the components of $\mathbf{V}_2$ in $\mathscr{E}_1$, the inner product matrix relative to $\mathbf{V}_2$ for π_1 is $\mathbf{T}_{22} - \mathbf{T}_{22.1}$. The corresponding eigenvalues are interpreted in (5.6.1) as $\cos^2 \theta$, or r^2 in correlation coefficient terms. It is computationally more convenient to deal with $\mathbf{T}_{22.1}$ rather than $\mathbf{T}_{22} - \mathbf{T}_{22.1}$, and thence to find the eigenvalues and eigenvectors of $\pi_2 - \pi_1$ relative to π_2. The eigenvectors are the same, of course, while the eigenvalues $\cos^2 \theta$ or r^2 are replaced by $\sin^2 \theta$ or $1 - r^2$.

The calculations proceed in three steps each of which may be regarded as a computer subroutine:

$$\text{MST}[s + 1, s + 2, \ldots, p][\mathbf{T}, \mathbf{I}] = \left[\begin{bmatrix} \mathbf{T}_{11} & \dot{\mathbf{T}}_{12} \\ \dot{\mathbf{T}}_{21} & \mathbf{I} \end{bmatrix}, \begin{bmatrix} \mathbf{I} & \mathbf{0} \\ \mathbf{0} & \mathbf{K}_{22} \end{bmatrix}\right], \tag{9.2.8}$$

$$\text{SWP}[1, 2, \ldots, s]\begin{bmatrix} \mathbf{T}_{11} & \dot{\mathbf{T}}_{12} \\ \dot{\mathbf{T}}_{21} & \mathbf{I} \end{bmatrix} = \begin{bmatrix} -\mathbf{T}_{11}^{-1} & \mathbf{T}_{11}^{-1}\cdot{}_{12} \\ \dot{\mathbf{T}}_{21}\mathbf{T}_{11}^{-1} & \end{bmatrix}, \tag{9.2.9}$$

and

$$\text{SDG}[s + 1, s + 2, \ldots, p]\left[\begin{bmatrix} -\mathbf{T}_{11}^{-1} & \mathbf{T}_{11}^{-1}\dot{\mathbf{T}}_{12} \\ \dot{\mathbf{T}}_{21}\mathbf{T}_{11}^{-1} & \dot{\mathbf{I}} \end{bmatrix}, \begin{bmatrix} \mathbf{I} & \mathbf{0} \\ \mathbf{0} & \mathbf{K}_{22} \end{bmatrix}\right]$$

$$= \left[\begin{bmatrix} -\mathbf{T}_{11}^{-1} & \mathbf{T}_{11}^{-1}\ddot{\mathbf{T}}_{12} \\ \ddot{\mathbf{T}}_{21}\mathbf{T}_{11}^{-1} & \ddot{\mathbf{I}} \end{bmatrix}, \begin{bmatrix} \mathbf{I} & \mathbf{0} \\ \dot{\mathbf{0}} & \mathbf{C}_{22}\mathbf{K}_{22} \end{bmatrix}\right]. \tag{9.2.10}$$

The step (9.2.8) in effect replaces the basis $\mathbf{V}_2$ of $\mathscr{E}_2$ by the basis $\mathbf{U}_2 = \mathbf{K}_{22}\mathbf{V}_2$ whose π_2 inner product matrix is $\mathbf{I}$. The step (9.2.9) completes the preparation for the eigenvalue analysis by finding the $\pi_2 - \pi_1$ inner product matrix for the basis $\mathbf{U}_2$ which is denoted in (9.2.9) by $\dot{\mathbf{I}} = \mathbf{I} - \dot{\mathbf{T}}_{21}\mathbf{T}_{11}^{-1}\dot{\mathbf{T}}_{12}$. The third computing step (9.2.10) produces the diagonal matrix $\ddot{\mathbf{I}}$ whose diagonal elements are eigenvalues of the form $1 - r_i^2$ where r_i is a canonical correlation coefficient. The eigenvectors $(\mathbf{C}_{22}\mathbf{K}_{22})\mathbf{V}_2$ form a basis of canonical variables $\mathbf{W}_2$ in $\mathscr{E}_2$; a corresponding set of canonical variables in $\mathscr{E}_1$ is given by $(\ddot{\mathbf{T}}_{21}\mathbf{T}_{11}^{-1})\mathbf{V}_1$.

The only assertion here which is not obvious is that concerning the canonical variables in $\mathscr{E}_1$. From (9.2.9) it is clear that $(\dot{\mathbf{T}}_{21}\mathbf{T}_{11}^{-1})\mathbf{V}_1$ provides the best linear predictors for $\mathbf{U}_2$ in terms of $\mathbf{V}_1$, and it is easily checked that the operations (9.2.10) modify $\dot{\mathbf{T}}_{21}\mathbf{T}_{11}^{-1}$ into $\ddot{\mathbf{T}}_{21}\mathbf{T}_{11}^{-1}$ by row operations in such a way that $(\ddot{\mathbf{T}}_{21}\mathbf{T}_{11}^{-1})\mathbf{V}_1$ provides the best linear predictors for $\mathbf{W}_2$ in terms of $\mathbf{V}_1$. But, from (9.2.2), these best linear predictors are simply specially scaled versions of the corresponding canonical variables in $\mathscr{E}_1$, as claimed above.

Some details deserve further explanation. For convenience of notation suppose that the diagonal elements of $\ddot{\mathbf{I}}$ in (9.2.10) are arranged in *increasing* order. If these diagonal elements are denoted by $1 - r_1^2, 1 - r_2^2, \ldots, 1 - r_{p-s}^2$ then $r_1, r_2, \ldots, r_{\min(s,p-s)}$ are the ordered canonical correlation coefficients satisfying (9.2.4). If $s < p - s$, then only the first s of the diagonal elements $1 - r_1^2, 1 - r_2^2, \ldots, 1 - r_{p-s}^2$ correspond to nontrivial canonical correlation coefficients while the remaining $p - 2s$ are simply unity, corresponding to zero correlations. Also, if $s < p - s$ then only the first s elements of $(\ddot{\mathbf{T}}_{21}\mathbf{T}_{11}^{-1})\mathbf{V}_1$ are different from $\emptyset$ and these s non-$\emptyset$ elements define the basis $\mathbf{W}_1$ of canonical variables in $\mathscr{E}_1$. On the other hand, if $s \geq p - s$, there will in general be no unit-valued elements of $\ddot{\mathbf{I}}$, but only the first $p - s$ elements of $\mathbf{W}_1$ will be provided by $(\ddot{\mathbf{T}}_{21}\mathbf{T}_{11}^{-1})\mathbf{V}_1$. The remaining $2s - p$ elements of $\mathbf{W}_1$ may be chosen to form any orthogonal basis of the subspace of $\mathscr{E}_1$ orthogonal to $\mathscr{E}_2$, but they are not provided by the above computations.

It is of interest to understand the choice of scale implied by the given computations. Since the SDG operation modifies the $(\pi_2 - \pi_1)$-orthonormal basis $\mathbf{V}_2$ into another $(\pi_2 - \pi_1)$-orthonormal basis $\mathbf{W}_2$, and since π_2 is the sample corrected sum inner product, it follows that the canonical variables $\mathbf{W}_2 = (\mathbf{C}_{22}\mathbf{K}_{22})\mathbf{V}_2$ are scaled to have unit norm according to the sample corrected sum inner product. The scaling of the corresponding $(\ddot{\mathbf{T}}_{22}\mathbf{T}_{11}^{-1})\mathbf{V}_1$ may be deduced from their interpretation as best linear predictors for $\mathbf{W}_2$. In fact, if the ith element of $(\ddot{\mathbf{T}}_{21}\mathbf{T}_{11}^{-1})\mathbf{V}_1$ were to be rescaled by dividing by r_i, then it too would have unit norm according to the sample corrected sum inner product while in its given form it has norm r_i.

A final observation on the computations is that the roles of $\mathscr{E}_1$ and $\mathscr{E}_2$ may be interchanged. Thus, there is a choice between an s-dimensional or $(p - s)$-dimensional eigenvalue calculation, and for some purposes it may be better to choose the smaller dimension.

9.3 AN EXAMPLE ILLUSTRATING EXPLORATORY USE OF CANONICAL CORRELATION ANALYSIS

Example 9.1. The data analyzed here were supplied by Dr. Gene Smith. They consist of the scores of 221 nursing students on two sets of personality measures. The first set provides the 16 personality variables of Cattell, Saunders, and Stice (1957) which also appeared in Example 8.4, while the second set provides 31 variables devised by Dr. Smith. The purpose of analysis is to try to throw light on the nature and extent of the covariation between the two sets of variables.

The first analysis which comes to mind is to find the $(16 + 31) \times (16 + 31)$ sample correlation matrix $\mathbf{R}$ of the two sets of variables combined. Then the $16 \times 31 = 496$ correlation coefficients relating the two sets of variables may be examined with reference to the name-meanings of the individual variables to see if large correlations appear where expected. For example, variables intended to measure something like extroversion in the different sets should show large correlations. The signs of the correlation coefficients are also subject to interpretation. For example, a variable measuring extroversion should be positively correlated with another variable measuring extroversion but negatively correlated with a variable measuring introversion.

By and large, this type of analysis is extrastatistical and subjective in that it depends on the meaning which the psychologist attributes to his variables. It can be very satisfying to see sets of nontrivial correlation coefficients (e.g. in these data 0.3, 0.4, or occasionally 0.5) appearing in places where they seem to have natural interpretations. On the other hand the initial impact of such correlation coefficients may need re-assessment because they are often partial reflections of one another, i.e., if V_1 and U_1 are correlated, then one may expect V_2 and U_2 to be correlated if V_1 is correlated with V_2 and U_1 with U_2. Thus there remains a need for judging the significance of observed correlations. Strictly speaking, this should mean displaying all the sets of interrelated correlation coefficients which could have any psychologically sensible interpretation, and then trying to determine how many of these sets of possible interpretations are meaningfully supported by the sample data. Even more, there is a need to assess in quantitative terms the strength of those relations which are deemed meaningful.

All this is difficult if not impossible, at least in the current state of the art. What is usually done is to carry out a significance test of the null hypothesis of no correlation whatsoever between the two sets. If this null hypothesis is rejected, then the psychologist will feel that at least the worst did not happen and he will use his own judgment to make as many interpretations as he thinks the data will support. Such interpretations are then used to deepen understanding of what the given psychological measures are providing and to suggest new measuring instruments.

Analyses directly involving the name-meanings of the variables are not discussed in this book, which is not to say that they are unimportant, but only to admit that the science of statistics is not yet able to be of much assistance in that area. Instead, more statistical explorations are carried out which ignore the opportunities and difficulties of psychological interpretation.

The most obvious analysis is simply to find the sample canonical correlation coefficients and corresponding canonical variables. This was done beginning computationally from the 47 × 47 correlation matrix **R** whose direct interpretation was discussed above. Applying the operations (9.2.6), (9.2.7), and

Table 9.1.1

$1 - r_i^2$ AND r_i FOR THE 16 PAIRS OF SAMPLE CANONICAL VARIABLES RELATING THE 16 CATTELL VARIABLES AND THE 31 SMITH VARIABLES

$1 - r_i^2$	r_i
0.4352	0.7515
0.5742	0.6525
0.6547	0.5876
0.7063	0.5420
0.7418	0.5081
0.7728	0.4767
0.7932	0.4547
0.8132	0.4322
0.8237	0.4199
0.8539	0.3822
0.8852	0.3389
0.8996	0.3169
0.9261	0.2719
0.9453	0.2339
0.9489	0.2283
0.9724	0.1662

(9.2.8) to **R** instead of **T** means only that a standardized basis is used in place of the original basis. The canonical correlation coefficients are the same, but the canonical variables are expressed in terms of the standardized variables rather than the original variables. To save space only the set of $1 - r_i^2$ together with r_i and not the coefficients defining the canonical variables are reproduced in Table 9.1.1. Judged as single simple correlation coefficients these sample canonical correlation coefficients appear quite large. It should be remembered, however, that each may also be interpreted as a multiple correlation coefficient relating a canonical variable chosen from one set of variables with the other complete set of variables. A typical meaningless multiple r^2 with 31 variables is 31 times a typical meaningless simple r^2.

An additional analysis was carried out on the same 47 × 47 correlation matrix **R**. To begin, a principal component analysis was carried out on the Cattell and Smith variables separately by computing

$$\text{SDG}[1, 2, \ldots, 16]\text{SDG}[17, 18, \ldots, 47][\mathbf{R}, \mathbf{I}] = \left[\begin{bmatrix} \mathbf{R}_{11}^* & \mathbf{R}_{12}^* \\ \mathbf{R}_{21}^* & \mathbf{R}_{22}^* \end{bmatrix}, \begin{bmatrix} \mathbf{K}_{11}^* & \mathbf{0} \\ \mathbf{0} & \mathbf{K}_{22}^* \end{bmatrix}\right],$$

where $\mathbf{R}_{11}^*$ is the diagonal matrix of principal components for the Cattell variables and $\mathbf{R}_{22}^*$ is the same for the Smith variables. $\mathbf{K}_{11}^*$ expresses the 16 Cattell

Table 9.1.2

PRINCIPAL COMPONENTS OF THE 16 CATTELL VARIABLES AND THE 31 SMITH VARIABLES

Cattell components	Smith components	
3.7618	11.4583	0.1726
2.2444	6.5800	0.1478
1.7615	4.6448	0.1368
1.2207	2.1822	0.1343
1.0256	1.1778	0.1211
0.9461	0.6819	0.1000
0.8869	0.4348	0.0973
0.7499	0.3997	0.0937
0.5944	0.3646	0.0918
0.5379	0.3164	0.0845
0.4991	0.2415	0.0783
0.4475	0.2191	0.0705
0.4249	0.2091	0.0671
0.3638	0.2079	0.0553
0.2945	0.1915	0.0551
0.2410	0.1834	
Total 16.0000	Total 31.0000	

principal variables in terms of the original standardized Cattell variables, and $\mathbf{K}_{22}^*$ does the same for the Smith variables. If, as would normally be the case, the original standardized variables were regarded as having unit *sample variance*, then the sample principal components are also *sample variances* for the corresponding principal variables and the elements of $\mathbf{R}_{12}^*$ are the *sample covariances* between the two sets of principal variables. The two sets of principal components are shown in Table 9.1.2. Note that the Cattell components drop off more slowly than the Smith components. For example, to achieve 95% of the total of 16.0000 requires 14 of the 16 Cattell variables, while to achieve 95% of the total 31.0000 requires only 16 of the 31 Smith variables. This suggests a greater redundancy in the Smith variables than in the Cattell variables.

The next stage of analysis is to reduce the sample covariance matrix of the principal variables to a correlation matrix, i.e., to alter

$$\begin{bmatrix} \mathbf{R}_{11}^{*} & \mathbf{R}_{12}^{*} \\ \mathbf{R}_{21}^{*} & \mathbf{R}_{22}^{*} \end{bmatrix} \quad \text{to} \quad \begin{bmatrix} \mathbf{I} & \mathbf{R}_{12}^{**} \\ \mathbf{R}_{21}^{**} & \mathbf{I} \end{bmatrix}$$

by dividing through each row and column by the square root of its diagonal elements. The 16×31 matrix $\mathbf{R}_{12}^{**}$ provides the set of 496 correlation coefficients between the two sets of principal variables. In accordance with the hope that

Table 9.1.3

THE DISTRIBUTION OF THE 25 CORRELATION COEFFICIENTS AMONG THE FIRST 5 PRINCIPAL VARIABLES OF EACH SET AND OF THE REMAINING 471 CORRELATION COEFFICIENTS AMONG PRINCIPAL VARIABLES. THE EXPECTED FREQUENCIES ARE CALCULATED ACCORDING TO THE $\beta(\frac{1}{2}, \frac{219}{2})$ DISTRIBUTION FOR r^2 (see Section 14.2.)

$\lvert r \rvert$	Group of 471		Group of 25	
	Observed frequency	Null expected frequency	Observed frequency	Null expected frequency
0–0.025	127	136.6	4	7.3
0.025–0.050	126	119.2	5	6.3
0.050–0.075	77	90.9	2	4.8
0.075–0.100	67	60.8	3	3.2
0.100–0.125	34	34.8	0	1.9
0.125–0.150	22	17.4	4	0.9
0.150–0.175	6	7.5	2	0.4
0.175–0.200	9	2.7	1	0.1
0.200+	3	1.1	4	0.1
	471	471.0	25	25.0

only the first few principal variables of each set contain important variation, these correlation coefficients were looked at in two groups, the first group of 25 being the correlation coefficients relating the first 5 principal variables of each kind, and the second group being the remaining $471 = 496 - 25$ correlation coefficients. The two distributions of the absolute values of these correlation coefficients corresponding to the set of 25 and the set of 471 are shown in Table 9.1.3. Two points should be kept in mind when considering Table 9.1.3. The first is that these are correlations among two sets of variables where correlations within each set are all zero. Consequently, no correlation in the table is contaminated by another in the sense of relating intracorrelated pairs of variables. The second point is that although an expected frequency is given for each observed frequency under the hypothesis of no correlation at all between

Cattell and Smith variables, it is obviously not appropriate to compare the observed and expected frequencies by a χ^2 goodness-of-fit test because the observed correlation coefficients are not independently drawn from a population. Still the agreement between observed and expected on the left side is quite striking except for the two most extreme categories. On the right side the last 4 categories considerably exceed their null expectations. On the left side the three values exceeding 0.2 are 0.243 between the first Smith principal variable and the fifteenth Cattell principal variable, 0.227 between the twenty-second Smith and the eleventh Cattell, and 0.205 between the thirty-first Smith and the fifth Cattell. It is difficult to believe that these three correlations mean anything more specific

Table 9.1.4

THE SAMPLE CORRELATION COEFFICIENTS AMONG THE FIRST FIVE PRINCIPAL VARIABLES OF EACH KIND

		Smith principal variables				
		1	2	3	4	5
Cattell principal variables	1	−0.227	−0.175	−0.041	0.017	0.138
	2	−0.296	0.557	0.087	−0.061	0.086
	3	0.140	0.040	−0.170	−0.134	0.021
	4	−0.042	−0.058	0.043	0.176	0.013
	5	0.005	0.029	−0.079	0.360	0.128

than that some small residual tendency for correlation remains after the 25 more promising elements have been removed. The four values exceeding 0.2 on the right are 0.227, 0.296, 0.360, and 0.557 as may be seen from Table 9.1.4.

The fact that the largest value 0.557 relates the second principal variables in each set is striking evidence that variables pulled out by a principal component analysis have a tendency to be good variables for prediction purposes as well. The other large value 0.360 shows that this tendency persists down to the fourth and fifth principal variables.

Next reconsider canonical correlation analysis. If the analysis applied to $\mathbf{R}$ were applied to

$$\begin{bmatrix} \mathbf{I} & \mathbf{R}_{12}^* \\ \mathbf{R}_{21}^* & \mathbf{I} \end{bmatrix}$$

instead, then exactly the same canonical correlation coefficients as those in Table 9.1.1 would result, for these quantities are not dependent on the choice of basis in $\mathscr{E}_1$ or $\mathscr{E}_2$. It is instructive to note how an array like $\mathbf{R}_{12}^*$ which Table 9.1.3 shows to be so close to a null distribution can produce canonical correlations as healthy-appearing as those in Table 9.1.1. This in turn suggests doing the canonical correlation analysis on smaller subsets of principal variables in the hope of

Table 9.1.5

CANONICAL CORRELATION ANALYSES BASED ON TABLE 9.1.4

	$1 - r_i^2$	r_i
First 5 Cattell principal variables versus first 5 Smith principal variables.	0.5699	0.6558
	0.8094	0.4366
	0.8783	0.3489
	0.9658	0.1819
	0.9969	0.0559
First 2 Cattell principal variables versus first 2 Smith principal variables.	0.6028	0.6303
	0.9209	0.2812

getting more meaningful sample canonical correlation coefficients. Two such reduced canonical correlation analyses were done, the first relating the first five principal variables from each set and the second relating the first two principal variables in each set. The results are shown in Table 9.1.5.

9.4 THE CASE OF A SINGLE CLASSIFICATION VARIABLE REPRESENTED BY $V_{s+1}, V_{s+2}, \ldots, V_p$

A *classification variable with $p - s$ classes* is defined by a rule such that each individual is assigned to one of $p - s$ classes. Such a variable could be reduced to a standard real-valued variable by assigning a real value to each of the $p - s$ classes, but information is lost by doing so. A means of retaining all of the sample information is to set up an indicator variable for each of the $p - s$ classes; more specifically, to define V_{s+i} to be a variable taking the value unity for a variable in class i and zero otherwise, for $i = 1, 2, \ldots, p - s$. The discussion of this section follows out special cases of the analyses described earlier in this chapter which arise when such a classification variable is related to s measured variables $V_1, V_2, \ldots, V_s$. The still more special case of $p - s = 2$ was introduced in Section 8.5. It will be seen that the notation and terminology of multivariate analysis of variance is helpful in the present context.

A few remarks about classification variables may help clarity and perspective. A sample of male children of a certain age might be measured on height, weight, and eye color, where eye color is reported in one of five categories. Such a sample belongs to the type considered here where V_1 and V_2 refer to height and weight while V_3, V_4, V_5, V_6, and V_7 denote indicator variables for eye color. If a second categorical variable were adjoined, say hair color classified into four categories, then the pair of classification variables together define a cross classification into $4 \times 5 = 20$ categories, and again the present analyses could be carried out. Note, however, that the standard linear and quadratic analyses are not suggested here for analyzing covariation between such a pair of categorical variables. Nor are cross-classifications explicitly discussed except briefly in Example 10.3.

The hypothetical sample on height, weight, and eye color may be compared with another hypothetical situation providing height and weight for samples of male children of a given age from five different nationalities. The classification in the latter case would normally be conceptualized rather differently: rather than regard nationality as one of many varying characteristics in a unitary population, one would regard the nationality groups as five different populations from which five different samples were available. The line between these two attitudes is not always firmly fixed. The former is adopted in this chapter, but the terminology of analysis of variance developed for the latter attitude will be introduced. Chapter 10 illustrates the separate population attitude, while Chapter 11 illustrates a class of situations where it is appropriate to regard the data as representing a single sample on some variables and several samples on other variables.

Suppose that n_i sample individuals fall in category i for $i = 1, 2, \ldots, p - s$ where $\sum_1^{p-s} n_i = n$. Suppose that the scores on V_r for the n_i individuals in category i are denoted by $X_r^{(i,j)}$ for $j = 1, 2, \ldots, n_i$, $i = 1, 2, \ldots, p - s$, and $r = 1, 2, \ldots, s$. The n sample individuals may be ordered so that the data matrix $\mathbf{X}$ takes the form

$$\mathbf{X} = \begin{bmatrix} X_1^{(1,1)} & \cdots & X_s^{(1,1)} & 1 & 0 & \cdots & 0 \\ \cdot & & \cdot & \cdot & \cdot & & \cdot \\ \cdot & & \cdot & \cdot & \cdot & & \cdot \\ \cdot & & \cdot & \cdot & \cdot & & \cdot \\ X_1^{(1,n_1)} & \cdots & X_s^{(1,n_1)} & 1 & 0 & \cdots & 0 \\ X_1^{(2,1)} & \cdots & X_s^{(2,1)} & 0 & 1 & \cdots & 0 \\ \cdot & & \cdot & \cdot & \cdot & & \cdot \\ \cdot & & \cdot & \cdot & \cdot & & \cdot \\ \cdot & & \cdot & \cdot & \cdot & & \cdot \\ X_1^{(2,n_2)} & \cdots & X_s^{(2,n_2)} & 0 & 1 & \cdots & 0 \\ \cdot & & \cdot & \cdot & \cdot & & \cdot \\ \cdot & & \cdot & \cdot & \cdot & & \cdot \\ \cdot & & \cdot & \cdot & \cdot & & \cdot \\ X_1^{(p-s,n_{p-s})} & \cdots & X_s^{(p-s,n_{p-s})} & 0 & 0 & \cdots & 1 \end{bmatrix}. \tag{9.4.1}$$

The sample means and inner products for $V_1, V_2, \ldots, V_s$ have the general forms given in Section 7.2 while the remaining means and inner products have the special forms

$$
\begin{aligned}
\bar{X}_{s+j} &= n_j/n, \\
(V_i, V_{s+j})_Q &= n_j \bar{X}_i^{(j)}, \\
(V_i, V_{s+j})_T &= n_j(\bar{X}_i^{(j)} - \bar{X}_i), \\
(V_{s+j}, V_{s+k})_Q &= 0, \\
(V_{s+j}, V_{s+k})_T &= -n_j n_k/n, \\
(V_{s+j}, V_{s+j})_Q &= n_j,
\end{aligned}
\tag{9.4.2}
$$

and

$$(V_{s+j}, V_{s+j})_T = n_j(n - n_j)/n,$$

for $i = 1, 2, \ldots, s$, and $j \neq k = 1, 2, \ldots, p - s$, where

$$\bar{X}_i^{(j)} = (1/n_j) \sum_{l=1}^{n_j} X_i^{(j,l)}. \tag{9.4.3}$$

Best linear predictors may be sought either for the V_{s+j} in terms of $V_1, V_2, \ldots, V_s$ or for the V_i in terms of $V_{s+1}, V_{s+2}, \ldots, V_p$. The latter will be explored here. Such multiple regression analyses may be visualized geometrically in the n-dimensional space $\mathcal{N}$ introduced in Section 7.4 where every variable V is represented by a point $P(V)$. The regression analysis of V_i on $V_{s+1}, V_{s+2}, \ldots, V_p$ is clearly related to the orthogonal projection of $P(V_i)$ into the subspace spanned by $P(V_0), P(V_{s+1}), \ldots, P(V_p)$. Usually this subspace would have dimension $p - s + 1$, but here V_0 and $V_{s+1} + V_{s+2} + \cdots + V_p$ are both variables which take the value unity for all individuals; consequently, $P(V_0)$ lies in the subspace spanned by $P(V_{s+1}), P(V_{s+2}), \ldots, P(V_p)$ which has dimension $p - s$. Thus one of the variables $V_0, V_{s+1}, \ldots, V_p$ is redundant.

In computing terms, the desired orthogonal projection is carried out via any $p - s$ of the $p - s + 1$ operations SWP$[s + 1]$, SWP$[s + 2], \ldots$, SWP$[p]$, SWP$[p + 1]$ applied to $\mathbf{Q}_{(+)}$. (The remaining sweeping operation cannot be carried out because there is a zero in the corresponding diagonal position.) By carrying out the first $p - s$ operations one finds that the augmented best linear predictor for V_i is

$$\hat{V}_i = \sum_{j=1}^{p-s} \bar{X}_i^{(j)} V_{s+j} \tag{9.4.4}$$

for $i = 1, 2, \ldots, s$. But of course substitutions may be made by identifying V_0 with $V_{s+1} + \cdots + V_p$ to obtain equivalent expressions.

Similarly the (nonaugmented) best linear predictor may be determined by orthogonal projection of $P_{II}(V_i)$ into the subspace spanned by $P_{II}(V_{s+1})$, $P_{II}(V_{s+2}), \ldots, P_{II}(V_p)$ which has dimension $p - s - 1$ since $P_{II}(V_{s+1} + V_{s+2} + \cdots + V_p) = \emptyset$ in $\mathcal{N}$. The reader may check that the best linear predictor may also be expressed by (9.4.4).

The fitted part of the sample corrected sum norm of V_i may be written

$$(\dot{V}_i, \dot{V}_i)_T = \sum_{j=1}^{p-s} n_j(\bar{X}_i^{(j)} - \bar{X}_i)^2, \tag{9.4.5}$$

and the residual part may be written

$$(V_i - \dot{V}_i, V_i - \dot{V}_i)_T = \sum_{j=1}^{p-s} \sum_{l=1}^{n_j} (X_i^{(j,l)} - \bar{X}_i^{(j)})^2, \tag{9.4.6}$$

so that the decomposition $(V_i, V_i)_T = (\dot{V}_i, \dot{V}_i)_T + (V_i - \dot{V}_i, V_i - \dot{V}_i)_T$ is expressed here by the identity

$$\sum_{j=1}^{p-s} \sum_{l=1}^{n_j} (X_i^{(j,l)} - \bar{X}_i)^2 = \sum_{j=1}^{p-s} n_j(\bar{X}_i^{(j)} - \bar{X}_i)^2 + \sum_{j=1}^{p-s} \sum_{l=1}^{n_j} (X_i^{(j,l)} - \bar{X}_i^{(j)})^2. \tag{9.4.7}$$

More generally, in the spirit of Section 9.1 consider the joint prediction of each of $V_1, V_2, \ldots, V_s$ in terms of $V_{s+1}, V_{s+2}, \ldots, V_p$. The sample corrected sum inner product of $V_1, V_2, \ldots, V_s$ decomposes accordingly into the sum of an inner product associated with the fitted parts of $V_1, V_2, \ldots, V_s$ and an inner product associated with the residual parts of $V_1, V_2, \ldots, V_s$. The (i, h) elements of the matrices of the latter two inner products are respectively

$$(V_i, V_h)_A = \sum_{j=1}^{p-s} n_j(\bar{X}_i^{(j)} - \bar{X}_i)(\bar{X}_h^{(j)} - \bar{X}_h), \tag{9.4.8}$$

and

$$(V_i, V_h)_W = \sum_{j=1}^{p-s} \sum_{l=1}^{n_j} (X_i^{(j,l)} - \bar{X}_i^{(j)})(X_h^{(j,l)} - \bar{X}_h^{(j)}), \tag{9.4.9}$$

where

$$(V_i, V_h)_T = (V_i, V_h)_A + (V_i, V_h)_W \tag{9.4.10}$$

for i and $h = 1, 2, \ldots, s$.

The quantities appearing above are all familiar to users of *analysis of variance* ideas. The particular analysis of variance under consideration is the simple case of *a one-way classification into $p - s$ groups*. Expression (9.4.5) may be called the *among group sum of squares* for V_i while the term (*pooled*) *within group sum of squares* is used for expression (9.4.6). Considering V_1, $V_2, \ldots, V_s$ jointly, rather than just a single V_i, the terminology and concepts of analysis of variance are generalized to *multivariate analysis of variance*. Thus the among group sum of squares is replaced by the *among group sum inner product* defined by (9.4.8) and the *within group sum inner product* defined by (9.4.9) and the analysis of variance decomposition (9.4.7) generalizes to the multivariate analysis of variance decomposition (9.4.10).

Note that knowledge of the analysis of variance decomposition for every variable in the space spanned by $V_1, V_2, \ldots, V_s$ is equivalent to the knowledge of the multivariate analysis of variance decomposition (9.4.10). In other words, multivariate analysis of variance may be described as the determination of the whole complex of univariate analyses of variance for all of the variables of a subspace.

Recall, however, the remark made earlier that the concern of Section 9.4 is with classifications which are more like *bona fide* variables rather than classifications which mark the individuals into separate samples. Since the terminology of analysis of variance is more often used in the latter situation, its uses here should be compared with the uses discussed in Chapters 10 and 11. Here the concern is more with best linear prediction from one subspace to another and with correlation analyses relating the two subspaces.

If the multiple correlation coefficient between V_i and the set $V_{s+1}, V_{s+2}, \ldots, V_p$ is denoted by t_i, then

$$t_i^2 = (V_i, V_i)_A/(V_i, V_i)_T = \sum_{j=1}^{p-s} n_j(\bar{X}_i^{(j)} - \bar{X}_i)^2 \Big/ \sum_{j=1}^{p-s}\sum_{l=1}^{n_j} (X_i^{(j,l)} - \bar{X}_i)^2 \quad (9.4.11)$$

for $i = 1, 2, \ldots, s$. The equivalent ratio

$$H_i = (V_i, V_i)_A/(V_i, V_i)_W = t_i^2/(1 - t_i^2) \quad (9.4.12)$$

is more familiar in analysis of variance contexts. The canonical correlation analysis relating the sets $V_1, V_2, \ldots, V_s$ and $V_{s+1}, V_{s+2}, \ldots, V_p$ produces sets of canonical variables $W_1, W_2, \ldots, W_s$ and $W_{s+1}, W_{s+2}, \ldots, W_p$. Formulas like (9.4.11) and (9.4.12) could also be written for the canonical correlation coefficients r_i and their associated

$$G_i = r_i^2/(1 - r_i^2). \quad (9.4.13)$$

This set of G_i generalizes the single ratio G defined in (8.5.3).

Certain details need to be filled in. Since $P_{II}(V_{s+1}), \ldots, P_{II}(V_p)$ span a subspace of dimension $p - s - 1$, the among group sum inner product is said to have $p - s - 1$ *degrees of freedom*. Similarly, the within group sum inner product is said to have $n - (p - s)$ degrees of freedom. The rank of the among group sum inner product is the dimension of the subspace spanned by the components of $P(V_1), P(V_2), \ldots, P(V_s)$ in the $(p - s - 1)$-dimensional subspace spanned by $P_{II}(V_{s+1}), \ldots, P_{II}(V_p)$, and so this rank is at most min $(s, p - s - 1)$. Similarly, the maximum rank of the within group sum inner product is min $(s, n - p + s)$. These maxima are generally attained with sample data, since precise linear relations among $V_1, V_2, \ldots, V_s$ are rare.

In the general theory of canonical correlation analysis of Section 9.2, the number of nonzero canonical correlation coefficients is at most min $(s, p - s)$. Here, because the among group sum inner product has rank at most min $(s, p - s - 1)$, the number of nonzero canonical correlation coefficients is at most min $(s, p - s - 1)$. Another way to see this is to note that the sample corrected sum inner product of $V_{s+1}, V_{s+2}, \ldots, V_p$ has rank $p - s - 1$ and so is a semidefinite inner product over a $(p - s)$-dimensional space. The last canonical variable in the set $W_{s+1}, W_{s+2}, \ldots, W_p$ has variance zero, i.e., is $V_{s+1} + V_{s+2} + \cdots + V_p$ apart from a scale factor, and meaningful correlation coefficients may be associated only with $W_{s+1}, W_{s+2}, \ldots, W_{p-1}$.

9.5 THE FORWARD METHOD OF SELECTING PREDICTOR VARIABLES

The discussion in Section 8.2 of various methods for selecting a subset of a set of available predictor variables is extended here to cover the selection of a subset of $V_1, V_2, \ldots, V_s$ for use in predicting the set $V_{s+1}, V_{s+2}, \ldots, V_p$. For brevity only the *forward* method will be discussed, but a similar discussion could easily be supplied for the *backward* method or for other variants.

Having selected $V_{i_1}, V_{i_2}, \ldots, V_{i_{t-1}}$ the forward method of Section 8.2 next chooses V_{i_t} to maximize the multiple correlation coefficient between V_p and the selected predictors. When V_p is generalized to $V_{s+1}, V_{s+2}, \ldots, V_p$, there is unfortunately no single multiple correlation coefficient to be maximized. Instead there is such a multiple correlation coefficient between each variable in the subspace spanned by $V_{s+1}, V_{s+2}, \ldots, V_p$ and the set of selected predictors.

If the problem of choosing V_{i_t} is regarded in a coordinate-free way, then the aim is to make the subspace spanned by $V_{i_1}, V_{i_2}, \ldots, V_{i_t}$ as close as possible to the subspace spanned by $V_{s+1}, V_{s+2}, \ldots, V_p$, where "close" is to be measured in terms of the sample covariance inner product. Any set of quantities possessing this degree of invariance is determined by the set of canonical correlation coefficients. These may be denoted by $r_1, r_2, \ldots, r_{p-s}$, some of which may be zero. Thus the problem is reduced to the specification of a criterion $C = C(r_1, r_2, \ldots, r_{p-s})$ to be optimized by the choice of V_{i_t}. Some of the criteria which have been proposed are

$$C_1 = \prod_{i=1}^{p-s} (1 - r_i^2),$$

$$C_2 = \sum_{i=1}^{p-s} r_i^2, \quad \text{and} \quad C_3 = \sum_{i=1}^{p-s} \frac{r_i^2}{1 - r_i^2}. \tag{9.5.1}$$

These criteria may also be used for testing the null hypothesis that the two sets of variables are uncorrelated. Note that large values of C_2 and C_3 are desirable, while small values of C_1 are hoped for. Another criterion sometimes proposed for testing is $C_4 = \max(r_1, r_2, \ldots, r_{p-s}) = r_1$, but this seems less desirable for a selection criterion since it concentrates on a single dimension and ignores possibly important ability to predict in other dimensions. C_4 also has the disadvantage of requiring that the canonical correlations be computed at each stage, while this computation may be circumvented under C_1, C_2, or C_3. In some circumstances, one might abandon the coordinate-free approach and specify a nonnegative quadratic form in the prediction errors to be minimized. Such a quadratic loss would be equivalent to specifying a new basis $U_{s+1}, U_{s+2}, \ldots, U_p$ of the space spanned by $V_{s+1}, V_{s+2}, \ldots, V_p$ and maximizing the sum of the squares of the multiple correlation coefficients of $U_{s+1}, U_{s+2}, \ldots, U_p$ with the space spanned by $V_{i_1}, V_{i_2}, \ldots, V_{i_t}$.

Having decided on a criterion, the selection procedure is defined, except for a rule saying when to stop. Such a stopping rule would be based on the change in C at any stage, i.e., if the selection of a further predictor does not bring about sufficient improvement in C, then the selection procedure is stopped. A measure of what constitutes sufficient improvement may be deduced in a rough and logically imperfect way by a consideration of significance tests.

Having selected a subset of predictors $V_{i_1}, V_{i_2}, \ldots, V_{i_t}$ there are two further reductions which need consideration. The real concern is with the best linear predictors of $V_{s+1}, V_{s+2}, \ldots, V_p$ in terms of $V_{i_1}, V_{i_2}, \ldots, V_{i_t}$ and, if $p - s < t$, these best linear predictors span only a proper subspace of the space spanned by $V_{i_1}, V_{i_2}, \ldots, V_{i_t}$. Consequently one need only retain this subspace. Moreover, within this subspace one may isolate a set of canonical predictors with associated canonical correlation coefficients given by the nonzero subset of $r_1, r_2, \ldots, r_{p-s}$. Again it may be judged, using a tenuous significance testing argument, that only a smaller subset of $r_1, r_2, \ldots, r_{p-s}$ are large enough to represent more than meaningless sampling fluctuations. If so, the space of effective predictors may be further reduced to include only those canonical variables having apparently adequate r. Note that the second stage of reduction here actually includes the first, for a decision to retain all of the canonical variables which correspond to nonzero canonical correlations automatically restricts consideration to the appropriate space of best linear predictors.

To understand the computations required for forward variable selection, it is necessary to have a convenient form for the chosen criterion C and then to find a direct way to compute the revised C when a new variable enters the system. Since the criteria (9.5.1) are symmetric between the two sets $V_{i_1}, V_{i_2}, \ldots, V_{i_t}$ and $V_{s+1}, V_{s+2}, \ldots, V_p$ the following description may be applied with the two sets interchanged. However, the prescription for revising C when a new variable is added is different depending on whether the first or second set is swept. The description here follows the latter path, but the reader may wish to work out the former and compare the two.

Suppose that

$$\mathbf{T} = \begin{bmatrix} \mathbf{T}_{11} & \mathbf{T}_{12} \\ \mathbf{T}_{21} & \mathbf{T}_{22} \end{bmatrix} \tag{9.5.2}$$

denotes the corrected sum inner product matrix of the two sets $V_{i_1}, V_{i_2}, \ldots, V_{i_t}$ and $V_{s+1}, V_{s+2}, \ldots, V_p$. The criteria C_1 and C_2 are, respectively, the product of the eigenvalues of $\mathbf{T}_{11.2} = \mathbf{T}_{11} - \mathbf{T}_{12}\mathbf{T}_{22}^{-1}\mathbf{T}_{21}$ relative to $\mathbf{T}_{11}$ and the sum of the eigenvalues of $\mathbf{T}_{11} - \mathbf{T}_{11.2}$ relative to $\mathbf{T}_{11}$. These quantities are simply expressible when $V_{i_1}, V_{i_2}, \ldots, V_{i_t}$ is replaced by an orthonormal basis $U_1, U_2, \ldots, U_t$ so that the corrected sum inner product matrix of $U_1, U_2, \ldots, U_t, V_{s+1}, V_{s+2}, \ldots, V_p$ has the form

$$\mathbf{T} = \begin{bmatrix} \mathbf{I} & \dot{\mathbf{T}}_{12} \\ \dot{\mathbf{T}}_{21} & \mathbf{T}_{22} \end{bmatrix}. \tag{9.5.3}$$

Then C_1 is the product of the eigenvalues of $\mathbf{I} - \dot{\mathbf{T}}_{12}\mathbf{T}_{22}^{-1}\dot{\mathbf{T}}_{21}$ relative to $\mathbf{I}$, or

$$C_1 = \det(\mathbf{I} - \dot{\mathbf{T}}_{12}\mathbf{T}_{22}^{-1}\dot{\mathbf{T}}_{21}), \tag{9.5.4}$$

and, similarly,

$$C_2 = \operatorname{tr}(\dot{\mathbf{T}}_{12}\mathbf{T}_{22}^{-1}\dot{\mathbf{T}}_{21}) = t - \operatorname{tr}(\mathbf{I} - \dot{\mathbf{T}}_{12}\mathbf{T}_{22}^{-1}\dot{\mathbf{T}}_{21}). \tag{9.5.5}$$

Note that $\dot{\mathbf{T}}$ may be defined from $\mathbf{T}$ using MST$[1, 2, \ldots, t]$, while $\mathbf{I} - \dot{\mathbf{T}}_{12}\mathbf{T}_{22}^{-1}\dot{\mathbf{T}}_{21}$ follows from $\mathbf{T}$ using SWP$[t+1, t+2, \ldots, t+p-s]$. (One of these sweeping operations must be omitted if $V_{s+1}, V_{s+2}, \ldots, V_p$ represent a categorical variable.) Finally $\det(\mathbf{I} - \dot{\mathbf{T}}_{12}\mathbf{T}_{22}^{-1}\dot{\mathbf{T}}_{21})$ is a by-product of the successive sweepings SWP$[1, 2, \ldots, t]$ applied to $\mathbf{I} - \dot{\mathbf{T}}_{12}\mathbf{T}_{22}^{-1}\dot{\mathbf{T}}_{21}$. The criterion C_3 is similar to C_2 except that the eigenvalues being summed are those of $\mathbf{T}_{11} - \mathbf{T}_{11.2}$ relative to $\mathbf{T}_{11.2}$ and different orthogonalizations are important.

Finally, consider the situation when $V_{i_1}, V_{i_2}, \ldots, V_{i_t}$ have been selected and a further $V_{i_{t+1}}$ is contemplated. Suppose that SWP$[t+1, t+2, \ldots, t+p-s]\mathbf{T}$ and SWP$[t+1, t+2, \ldots, t+p-s, 1, 2, \ldots, t]\mathbf{T}$ are both in hand. Suppose that $V_{i_{t+1}}$ is assimilated into the system and that $\mathbf{T}_{(+)}$ denotes the $(t+p-s+1) \times (t+p-s+1)$ extension of $\mathbf{T}$ with $V_{i_{t+1}}$ put into row and column $t+1$. The ASM operator of Section 4.3.3 may be made to produce SWP$[t+2, t+3, \ldots, t+p-s+1]\mathbf{T}_{(+)}$ and SWP$[t+2, t+3, \ldots, t+p-s+1, 1, 2, \ldots, t]\mathbf{T}_{(+)}$. Denoting the $(t+1, t+1)$ elements of these two matrices by A_{t+1} and B_{t+1}, respectively, it is easily checked that B_{t+1}/A_{t+1} is the factor by which C_1 must be multiplied when $V_{i_{t+1}}$ is adjoined. The reader may supply corresponding descriptions for C_2 and C_3, which are somewhat easier. It should be stressed that the forward method requires that these assimilation procedures be tried for all possible choices of $V_{i_{t+1}}$ at each stage. This means that sums of products of each such $V_{i_{t+1}}$ with each of $V_{i_1}, V_{i_2}, \ldots, V_{i_t}, V_{s+1}, V_{s+2}, \ldots, V_p, V_0$ must be found. However, the sums of products for each pair of unselected variables are not required, which can result in considerable saving of computation when the number of unselected variables is large, as in the following example.

9.6 AN EXAMPLE ILLUSTRATING PREDICTION OF A CATEGORICAL VARIABLE AND FORWARD SELECTION OF PREDICTOR VARIABLES

Example 9.2. The following discussion summarizes an analysis of meteorological data by Dr. Robert Miller (1961, 1962). The objective of the analysis was to provide a method of forecasting short term ceiling conditions at an air force base. The specific data refer to McGuire Air Force Base, Wrightstown, New Jersey. The forecasts were to be provided two hours in the future for the categorical variable determined by the five ceiling conditions:

1. Closed: ceiling 0–200 feet.
2. Low instrument: ceiling 200–500 feet.
3. High instrument: ceiling 500–1500 feet.
4. Low open: ceiling 1500–5000 feet.
5. High open: ceiling 5000 feet and up.

Any particular forecast is based on the values of 75 quantities measuring 15 meteorological variables at each of five weather stations at the time of forecasting. The five weather stations consist of McGuire Air Force Base and four surrounding stations at Philadelphia, Newark, Lakehurst Naval Air Station, and Atlantic City. The 15 meteorological variables are:

1. Height of the lowest cloud layer.
2. Height of the second cloud layer.
3. Amount of lowest cloud layer.
4. Amount of second cloud layer.
5. Height of ceiling.
6. Visibility.
7. Three hour change in ceiling height.
8. Three hour change in visibility.
9. Three hour change in pressure.
10. Temperature-dewpoint depression/temperature.
11. East-west wind component.
12. North-south wind component.
13. Three hour change in wind direction.
14. Total cloud cover.
15. Three hour change in temperature.

The past data to be used in setting up the forecasting method consist of 1874 time points falling at consecutive three hour intervals during the winter months of 1954–55 and 1955–56. A further 926 time points from the winter months of 1956–57 were held in reserve for checking the forecasts on independent data. At each of these 1874 + 926 time points the values of 75 variables are given, and the corresponding ceiling category two hours later is also given. In the original data the numbers n_i in ceiling category i for $i = 1, 2, 3, 4, 5$ are 49, 84, 158, 228, 1355. In the independent data the corresponding numbers are 35, 76, 118, 124, 573. Evidently, the flying weather was worse in the winter of 1956–57 than in the average of the two preceding winters.

Miller's basic calculations with the original sample of size 1874 were those described in Section 9.4 and 9.5. Miller used the terminology of multivariate analysis of variance rather than the equivalent approach in terms of artificial variables $V_{s+1}, V_{s+2}, \ldots, V_p$ and his computer programs were written directly rather than in terms of the operators described in this book. The forward method of selection was used, the criterion being C_3 in (9.5.1). Note that

$$C_3 = \sum_{i=1}^{p-s} G_i,$$

using the G measure (9.4.9) in place of the r measure. Miller reports that the first five predictor variables chosen in order are:

1. Height of ceiling at Philadelphia.
2. Height of ceiling at McGuire Air Force Base.
3. East-west component at McGuire Air Force Base.
4. Height of ceiling at Newark.
5. Total cloud cover at Newark.

The corresponding values of C_3 after selecting t predictors for $t = 1, 2, 3, 4, 5$ are 2.369, 2.994, 3.171, 3.318, 3.419. Miller ceased selecting at this point because he judged that the next few variables selected resulted in an insufficient increase in the value of C_3. The basis for this judgment has a tenuous connection with significance testing, but it is doubtful whether the subsequent analysis would have been much altered by the addition of a small number of additional predictors. Miller had found from experience that the inclusion of a large number of predictors is often harmful in that forecasts based on independent data become less accurate.

The next step was to carry out the canonical correlation analysis of the five selected predictors against the artificial variables representing the classification. This results in four nontrivial canonical correlation coefficients r_i and the four corresponding linear combinations of the five selected predictor variables. Miller reports the values of $G_i = r_i^2/(1 - r_i^2)$ to be

$$\begin{aligned} G_1 &= 3.312 \\ G_2 &= 0.087 \\ G_3 &= 0.020 \\ G_4 &= 0.001 \end{aligned}$$

and the corresponding canonical predictors to be

$$\begin{aligned} W_1 &= -7.246V_1 - 6.276V_2 + 1.898V_3 - 3.008V_4 + 1.000V_5 \\ W_2 &= 0.251V_1 - 0.271V_2 - 0.589V_3 + 0.319V_4 + 1.000V_5 \\ W_3 &= -2.353V_1 + 2.664V_2 + 0.980V_3 + 0.971V_4 + 1.000V_5 \\ W_4 &= 7.105V_1 - 10.880V_2 + 4.427V_3 + 7.372V_4 + 1.000V_5, \end{aligned}$$

where V_1, V_2, V_3, V_4, V_5 represent the five selected predictors listed above. Note the scaling of each W_i has been fixed arbitrarily by choosing the coefficient of V_5 to be unity.

The canonical correlation analysis provides four different potential sets of predictors, i.e., W_1 alone *or* W_1 and W_2 *or* W_1, W_2, and W_3 *or* W_1, W_2, W_3, and W_4. Miller again presents a tenuous significance-testing argument suggesting that only W_1 need be taken into account. Later he shows empirically that the best forecasts on the independent data result from the use of three or four canonical predictors.

The analysis was also made to produce the sample mean vectors and sample covariance matrices of the five selected predictors for each of the five subsamples corresponding to the five ceiling categories. From these the sample mean vectors and sample covariances of the four canonical predictors were found, again for each of the five subsamples. Rather than reproduce these numbers, a graphical analysis of the first two canonical variables is reproduced. Suppose that W_1^* and W_2^* denote rescaled versions of W_1 and W_2, chosen to have pooled within sample mean squares of 1 and G_2/G_1, respectively. The corresponding dual two-dimensional individual-space is represented in the following graphs where w_1^* and w_2^* are drawn to appear orthonormal. Figure 9.6.1 shows the mean-centered concentration ellipses of the five subsamples, except that the radii have been rescaled by the factor 1.18, which is the factor required to rescale the ellipse of concentration of a bivariate normal probability distribution so that half of the probability is contained within the ellipse. In other words, it is the factor such that roughly half of the sample points should lie inside the ellipse if the subsample distributions resemble bivariate normal distributions. The subsequent Figs. 9.6.2, 9.6.3, 9.6.4, 9.6.5, and 9.6.6 show the

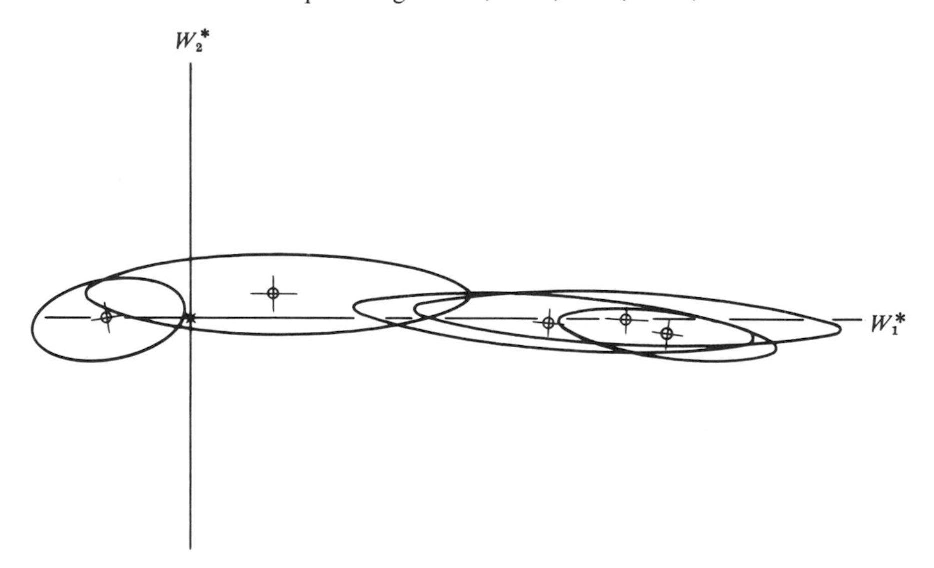

Fig. 9.6.1. Concentration ellipses (after scaling by the factor 1.18) corresponding to the five weather categories, and defined by the canonical variables W_1^*, W_2^* and the original sample of 1874 time points.

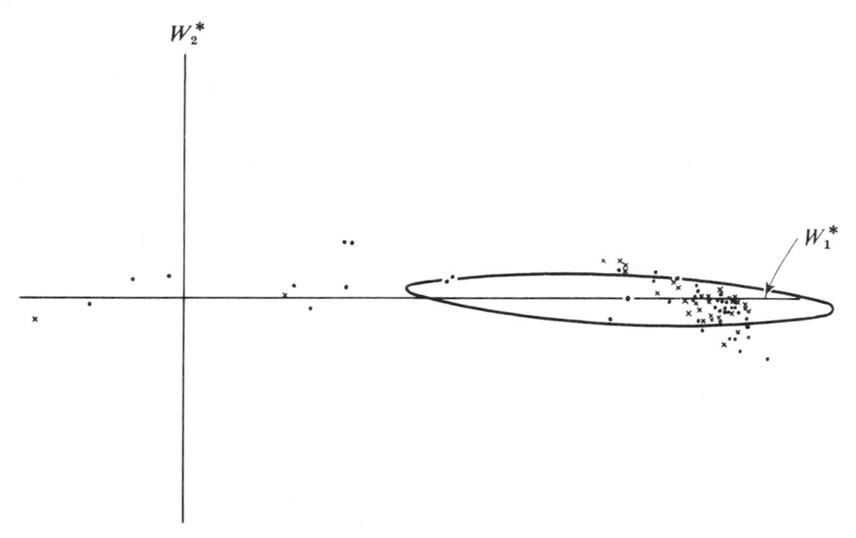

Fig. 9.6.2. Same as Fig. 9.6.1, showing the concentration ellipse of the first weather category only, and showing the original sample points (dots) and independent sample points (crosses) of the first weather category.

actual sample individuals in the five subsamples, including both those in the original data and those in the independent data.

Miller remarks that these pictures show clearly that the subsamples do not follow bivariate normal distributions. He also notes that the two sets of data coincide fairly well except possibly for ceiling category 2, and points out the

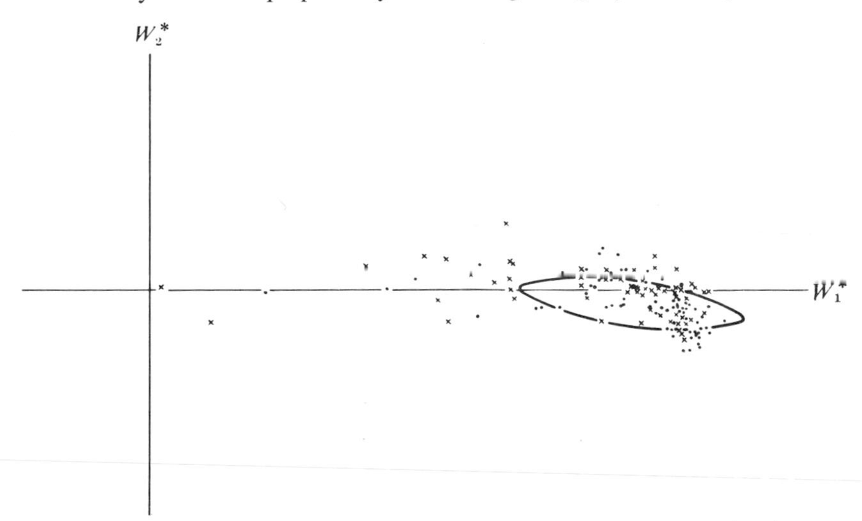

Fig. 9.6.3. Same as Fig. 9.6.2, replacing the first weather category by the second.

double clustering in category 5, apparently due to discreteness in the predictors.

For a detailed discussion of how these preliminary stages of data reduction lead to actual forecasts the reader is referred to Miller's monograph, but the general approach is clear from Fig. 9.6.1. Each time a forecast is desired, the values of the canonical predictors W_1^* W_2^* are computed and a point in the plane of Fig. 9.6.1 is located. One must then decide how probable it is that this point belongs in each of the five subsamples. Roughly speaking this is to be based on

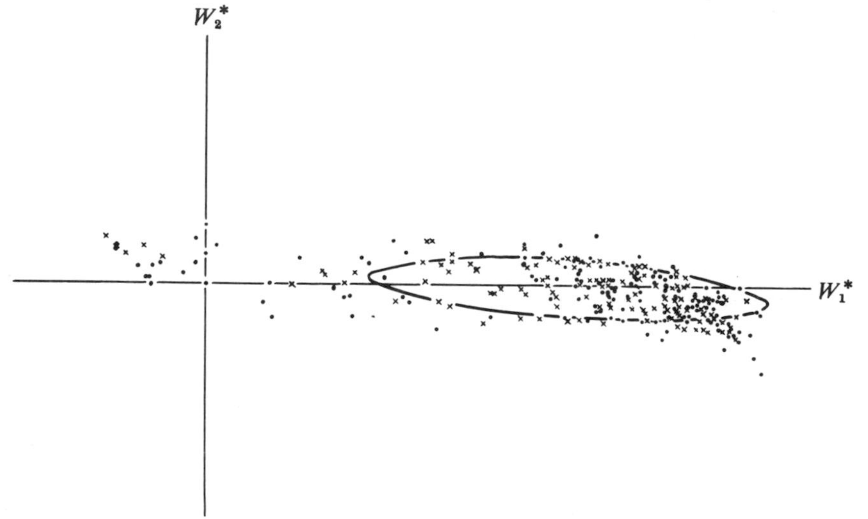

Fig. 9.6.4. Same as Fig. 9.6.2, replacing the first weather category by the third.

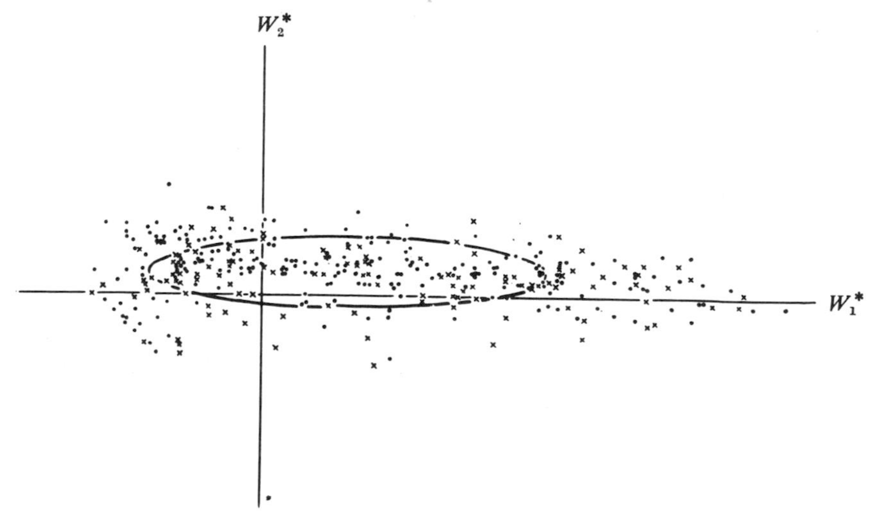

Fig. 9.6.5. Same as Fig. 9.6.2, replacing the first weather category by the fourth.

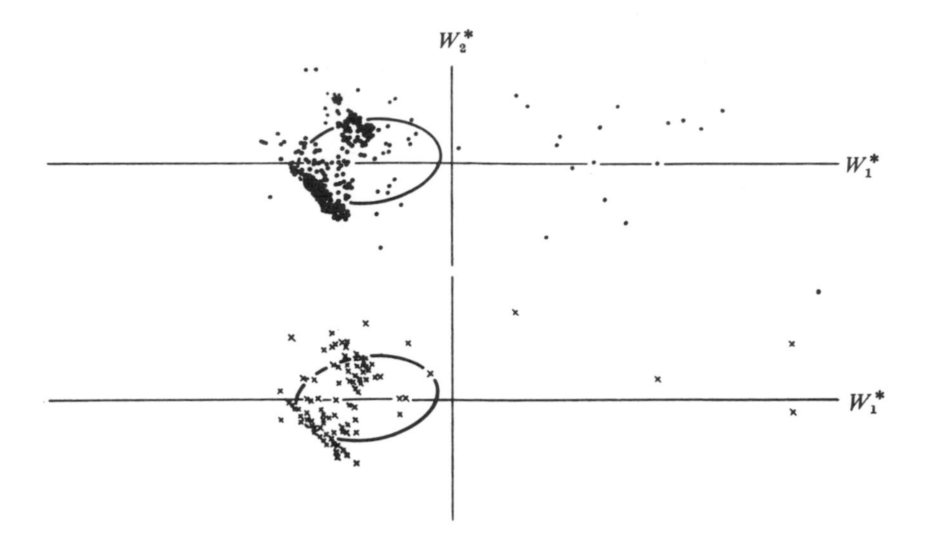

Fig. 9.6.6. Same as Fig. 9.6.2, replacing the first weather category by the fifth, and separating the original and independent data.

distance from subsample means. The scaling of W_1^* and W_2^* to have sample variances 1 and G_2/G_1 was chosen so that the distance measure reflects the relative importance of the canonical variables as measured by G. Miller had some empirical backing for the specific choice of 1 and G_2/G_1, i.e., other choices have produced less accurate forecasts in a variety of examples.

Corresponding to the canonical variables W_1, W_2, W_3, W_4 is another set of canonical variables which are linear combinations of the artificial variables which represent the ceiling categories. These corresponding canonical variables are determined up to scale changes to be the best linear predictors of W_1, W_2, W_3, W_4 in terms of the artificial variables, and the form of these best linear predictors is clear from (9.4.5), i.e., the subsample means of the canonical predictors provide the other set of canonical variables. These subsample means for at least W_1 and W_2 may be seen in Fig. 9.6.1. Drawing a rough curve through these means suggests that the first canonical predictor may be thought of as discriminating between high and low ceilings while the second canonical predictor separates the middle range from the two extremes.

The fact that the sample means in Fig. 9.6.1 do not lie in order on a simple smooth curve may plausibly be regarded as a consequence of sampling variation. Recall that the ceiling categories 1 and 2 have relatively few individuals. This sampling variation is a very complex phenomenon for several reasons. For one, the effect of the procedure for selecting variables on sampling variation is very difficult to understand. In addition, the individuals in these data are successive time points at only three hour intervals. Since weather conditions often change little over such periods, there is a sense in which there are many fewer than the apparent number of sample individuals, and correspondingly greater sampling variation could be expected than for random samples from a population of the same size.

Much as with the psychological examples 8.4 and 9.1, it is tempting to try to interpret the selected predictors and canonical predictors in terms of physical or meteorological theories. For example, the selection of the Philadelphia ceiling and the east-west wind component suggests the importance of looking west for future weather. No direct tie with a physical theory seems possible, however.

CHAPTER 10

TWO OR MORE SAMPLES OF INDIVIDUALS

10.1 INTRODUCTION

A set of k samples on a common set of p variables may be determined by their k data matrices $\mathbf{X}^{(1)}, \mathbf{X}^{(2)}, \ldots, \mathbf{X}^{(k)}$. If the sample sizes are $n_1, n_2, \ldots, n_k$, then the data matrices have dimensions $n_1 \times p, n_2 \times p, \ldots, n_k \times p$, respectively. The ith row of $\mathbf{X}^{(l)}$ representing the ith individual in sample l will be denoted by $\mathbf{X}^{(l,i)}$ for $i = 1, 2, \ldots, n_l$ and $l = 1, 2, \ldots, k$.

Each of these samples yields the basic statistics which were described in Section 7.2 for a single sample, namely

$$\bar{\mathbf{X}}^{(l)} = \sum_{i=1}^{n_l} \mathbf{X}^{(l,i)}/n_l, \tag{10.1.1}$$

$$\mathbf{Q}^{(l)} = \sum_{i=1}^{n_l} \mathbf{X}^{(l,i)\prime}\mathbf{X}^{(l,i)}, \tag{10.1.2}$$

$$\mathbf{T}^{(l)} = \mathbf{Q}^{(l)} - n_l\bar{\mathbf{X}}^{(l)\prime}\bar{\mathbf{X}}^{(l)}, \tag{10.1.3}$$

and

$$\mathbf{S}^{(l)} = \mathbf{T}^{(l)}/(n_l - 1), \tag{10.1.4}$$

for $l = 1, 2, \ldots, k$.

If the k samples are combined to form a single sample of size

$$n = \sum_{l=1}^{k} n_l, \tag{10.1.5}$$

then there is a *total mean* or *grand mean* vector

$$\bar{\mathbf{X}} = \sum_{l=1}^{k}\sum_{j=1}^{n_l} \mathbf{X}^{(l,j)}/n_l \tag{10.1.6}$$

and a corresponding *total sum of products corrected for the grand mean* inner product matrix

$$\mathbf{T} = \sum_{l=1}^{k}\sum_{j=1}^{n_l} (\mathbf{X}^{(l,j)} - \bar{\mathbf{X}})'(\mathbf{X}^{(l,j)} - \bar{\mathbf{X}}), \tag{10.1.7}$$

and thence a *total sample covariance* matrix

$$\mathbf{S} = \mathbf{T}/(n-1). \tag{10.1.8}$$

It is often unnatural to pool k samples into a single sample, and correspondingly the statistics $\bar{\mathbf{X}}$, $\mathbf{T}$, and $\mathbf{S}$ may not have much direct appeal. They do, however, relate closely to the analysis of variance formulation which was introduced in Section 9.4. Thus $\mathbf{T}$ decomposes into

$$\mathbf{T} = \mathbf{T}_A + \mathbf{T}_W, \tag{10.1.9}$$

where

$$\mathbf{T}_A = \sum_{l=1}^{k} n_l(\bar{\mathbf{X}}^{(l)} - \bar{\mathbf{X}})'(\bar{\mathbf{X}}^{(l)} - \bar{\mathbf{X}}) \tag{10.1.10}$$

and

$$\mathbf{T}_W = \sum_{l=1}^{k} \sum_{j=1}^{n_l} (\mathbf{X}^{(l,j)} - \bar{\mathbf{X}}^{(l)})'(\mathbf{X}^{(l,j)} - \bar{\mathbf{X}}^{(l)})$$

$$= \sum_{l=1}^{k} \mathbf{T}^{(l)}. \tag{10.1.11}$$

This is mathematically natural in the sense of representing the inner products of components in special orthogonal subspaces in $\mathcal{N}$ which are defined in terms of the indicator variables of the k groups. The theory was given in Section 9.4, where s was used in place of p and $p - s$ in place of k, and will not be repeated. Here $\mathbf{T}_A$ defines the among group inner product on $k - 1$ degrees of freedom with rank at most $\min(p, k-1)$ while $\mathbf{T}_W$ defines the within group inner product on $n - k$ degrees of freedom with rank at most $\min(p, n-k)$. In the special case $k = 2$, $n\bar{\mathbf{X}} = n_1\bar{\mathbf{X}}^{(1)} + n_2\bar{\mathbf{X}}^{(2)}$ and substitution in (10.1.10) leads to the inner product matrix

$$\mathbf{T}_A = (\bar{\mathbf{X}}^{(1)} - \bar{\mathbf{X}}^{(2)})'(\bar{\mathbf{X}}^{(1)} - \bar{\mathbf{X}}^{(2)})/(1/n_1 + 1/n_2) \tag{10.1.12}$$

with rank unity (or zero if $\bar{\mathbf{X}}^{(1)} = \bar{\mathbf{X}}^{(2)}$).

Analysis of variance considerations also suggest the weighted average

$$\mathbf{S}_W = \mathbf{T}_W/(n-k), \tag{10.1.13}$$

which may be written in the form

$$\mathbf{S}_W = \sum_{l=1}^{k} w_l \mathbf{S}^{(l)} \Big/ \sum_{l=1}^{k} w_l, \tag{10.1.14}$$

where

$$w_l = n_l - 1 \tag{10.1.15}$$

for $l = 1, 2, \ldots, k$. The particular weights (10.1.15) are suggested by the sampling theory of statistical inference for circumstances where it may be assumed that the k populations being sampled have essentially the same covariance inner products.

In general, the grand mean $\bar{\mathbf{X}}$ defined in (10.1.6) or the pooled within sample covariance $\mathbf{S}_W$ defined in (10.1.13) are not directly interesting quantities unless the underlying population means or population covariances, respectively, are common. Both $\bar{\mathbf{X}} = (n_1\bar{\mathbf{X}}^{(1)} + n_2\bar{\mathbf{X}}^{(2)} + \cdots + n_k\bar{\mathbf{X}}^{(k)})/n$ and $\mathbf{S}_W$ weight the contributions from each sample roughly in proportion to sample size. But the variation in sample size may be accidental and irrelevant to the subject of investigation. Equal weightings of $\bar{\mathbf{X}}^{(l)}$ and $\mathbf{S}^{(l)}$ could be interesting, as could be weightings which reflect population sizes. For any set of constants $c_1, c_2, \ldots, c_k$, the weighting $w_l = c_l^2/n_l$ in (10.1.14) would lead to an $\mathbf{S}_W$ appropriate for judging the sampling variation of $(c_1\bar{\mathbf{X}}^{(1)} + c_2\bar{\mathbf{X}}^{(2)} + \cdots + c_k\bar{\mathbf{X}}^{(k)})/(c_1 + c_2 + \cdots + c_k)$.

10.2 TWO-SAMPLE ANALYSIS

Consideration will be given first to the comparison of a pair of sample means $m^{(1)}$ and $m^{(2)}$ and later to the more complex task of describing similarities and differences between a pair of sample covariance inner products. Viewed as two points in individual-space $\mathscr{F}$, with no reference to any coordinate system or to any inner product, the relative positions of $m^{(1)}$ and $m^{(2)}$ cannot be compared in any meaningful way. Consequently an inner product π_d over $\mathscr{F}$, or equivalently its dual inner product π over $\mathscr{E}$, will be assumed. The dual pair π and π_d will be assumed to have full rank unless otherwise stated, but their source need not be specified exactly. They might be sample-determined in various ways, or they might be reference inner products determined apart from the sample data. The initial aim is to study the information provided by $m^{(1)}$, $m^{(2)}$, and π_d.

Two important concepts arise here, namely that of *distance* which was introduced by Mahalanobis (1936) and that of *best linear discriminator* which was independently introduced by Fisher (1936, 1938). The close relations between these concepts, to be explored below, quickly became clear.

The *distance D* between $m^{(1)}$ and $m^{(2)}$ may be defined simply to be

$$D = (m^{(1)} - m^{(2)}, m^{(1)} - m^{(2)})_d^{1/2}, \tag{10.2.1}$$

where $(a, a)_d^{1/2}$ denotes the norm of a under π_d. A more general approach is to define a *distance* $D(\mathscr{W})$ *for every subspace* $\mathscr{W}$ *of variable-space* $\mathscr{E}$, so that D defined by (10.2.1) is the special case $D(\mathscr{E})$. $D(\mathscr{W})$ is defined in the same way as $D(\mathscr{E})$ in terms of the same sample means $m^{(1)}$ and $m^{(2)}$ and the same inner product π_d considered as linear functionals and an inner product over the restricted variable-space $\mathscr{W}$. If $\mathscr{W}$ has dimension unity, then $D(\mathscr{W})$ will also be denoted by $D(W)$ for any W different from $\emptyset$ in $\mathscr{W}$, and in this case (10.2.1) may be written

$$D(W) = |m^{(1)}(W) - m^{(2)}(W)|/(W, W)^{1/2}. \tag{10.2.2}$$

Note that the substitution of αW for W, with $\alpha \neq 0$, does not alter the right side of (10.2.2).

A *best linear discriminator* may be defined to be any variable V in $\mathscr{E}$ with maximum $D(V)$, the idea being that such a variable makes the sample means appear as far apart as any variable can. In fact, as shown in Theorem 10.2, such a variable has as much separating power in the sense of distance as the whole space $\mathscr{E}$ of variables.

Theorem 10.2. *The best linear discriminator V defined by $m^{(1)}$, $m^{(2)}$, and π_d is unique up to a scale factor. The unique one-dimensional subspace of best linear discriminators is the dual space of the orthogonal complement of the one-dimensional subspace of $\mathscr{F}$ spanned by $m^{(1)} - m^{(2)}$. For any best linear discriminator V,*

$$D(V) = D(\mathscr{E}), \tag{10.2.3}$$

and, for any variable U in the subspace of $\mathscr{E}$ orthogonal to V,

$$D(U) = 0. \tag{10.2.4}$$

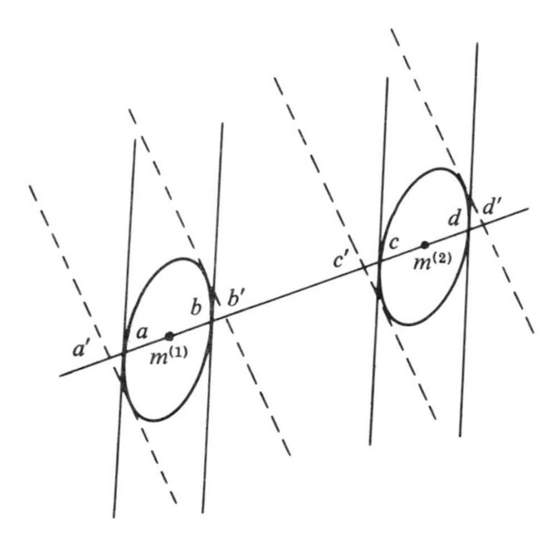

Fig. 10.2.1. Mean-centered concentration ellipses and associated tangent lines ($p = 2$) as described in the text.

The theorem follows simply because there is only a small amount of mathematical structure present, which may be characterized geometrically in individual-space $\mathscr{F}$ as in Fig. 10.2.1, i.e., by the pair of points $m^{(1)}$ and $m^{(2)}$ and the pair of ellipsoids consisting of points at distance unity or less from $m^{(1)}$ and $m^{(2)}$ according to π_d. Define $\mathscr{U}_d$ to be the one-dimensional subspace of $\mathscr{F}$ spanned by $m^{(1)} - m^{(2)}$. Define $\mathscr{V}_d$ to be the orthogonal complement of $\mathscr{U}_d$ in $\mathscr{F}$. Note that the family of parallel $(p - 1)$-dimensional hyperplanes including $\mathscr{V}_d$ also includes the four tangent hyperplanes to the two ellipsoids where the line joining $m^{(1)}$ and $m^{(2)}$ meets these ellipsoids, as illustrated in Fig. 10.2.1. The subspaces $\mathscr{U}$ and $\mathscr{V}$ in $\mathscr{E}$ dual to $\mathscr{U}_d$ and $\mathscr{V}_d$ in $\mathscr{F}$ are those which Theorem 10.2

claims to consist of variables U such that $D(U) = 0$ and of best linear discriminators V such that $D(V) = D(\mathscr{E})$, respectively.

The claim about $\mathscr{U}$ is the more obvious of the two. Each U in $\mathscr{U}$ defines a family of parallel $(p - 1)$-dimensional hyperplanes in $\mathscr{F}$ on which U takes constant values. The duality of $\mathscr{U}$ and $\mathscr{U}_d$ means that the family includes a hyperplane containing the line joining $m^{(1)}$ and $m^{(2)}$. Consequently $m^{(1)}(U) = m^{(2)}(U)$, and, from (10.2.2), $D(U) = 0$.

Consider now any variable W as a candidate for a best linear discriminator. Such a W has a unique expression as $V + U$ with V in $\mathscr{V}$ and U in $\mathscr{U}$. Now $m^{(1)}(W) - m^{(2)}(W) = m^{(1)}(V) - m^{(2)}(V)$ because $m^{(1)}(U) = m^{(2)}(U)$, and $(W, W) \geq (V, V)$ because V and U are orthogonal. Consequently from (10.2.2)

$$D(W) \leq D(V) = D(\mathscr{V}), \tag{10.2.5}$$

which shows that $\mathscr{V}$ is a space of best linear discriminators. Furthermore, the inequality in (10.2.5) is strict unless W belongs to $\mathscr{V}$, so that $\mathscr{V}$ is the unique space of best linear discriminators. Finally, $D(\mathscr{E}) = D(\mathscr{U}) + D(\mathscr{V})$ because $\mathscr{U}$ and $\mathscr{V}$ are orthogonal complements, and $D(\mathscr{U}) = 0$ because $D(U) = 0$ for all U in $\mathscr{U}$, so that $D(V) = D(\mathscr{V}) = D(\mathscr{E})$, as required to complete the proof.

An alternative proof could proceed more directly in terms of the geometry illustrated in Fig. 10.2.1. If the line joining $m^{(1)}$ and $m^{(2)}$ intersects the ellipsoid centered at $m^{(1)}$ in a and b, and the ellipsoid centered at $m^{(2)}$ in c and d, then $D = D(\mathscr{E})$ is the ratio of length of the line segment $m^{(1)}m^{(2)}$ to the length of any of the equal line segments (semi-axes) $m^{(1)}a$, $m^{(1)}b$, $m^{(2)}c$, and $m^{(2)}d$. Any variable W is characterized by the family of parallel $(p - 1)$-dimensional hyperplanes on which it takes constant values, and this family includes four tangents to the two ellipsoids, as illustrated in Fig. 10.2.1. Projection along the family of parallel hyperplanes into the line joining $m^{(1)}$ and $m^{(2)}$ carries individuals having common values on W into a single individual, so that the line becomes a particular representation of the one-dimensional individual-space of W. The two samples still have means $m^{(1)}$ and $m^{(2)}$ after projection, so that $m^{(1)}$ and $m^{(2)}$ represent the sample means in the individual-space of W (and do so for every choice of W). From Theorem 6.6, the shadows $a'b'$ and $c'd'$ cast on the line joining $m^{(1)}$ and $m^{(2)}$ by the projection represent the one-dimensional ellipsoids of points having distance at most unity from $m^{(1)}$ and $m^{(2)}$ according to the inner product dual to the inner product induced by π on the one-dimensional space spanned by W. This means that $D(W)$ is the ratio of lengths of the line segment $m^{(1)}m^{(2)}$ to any of the line segments $m^{(1)}a'$, $m^{(1)}b'$, $m^{(2)}c'$, $m^{(2)}d'$.

The geometric proof of Theorem 10.2 is now obvious. Clearly the ratio $D(W)$ is maximized when $a = a'$, $b = b'$, $c = c'$, $d = d'$, which is achieved by making W that variable V whose corresponding hyperplanes are tangent at a, b, c, and d. Also $D(V) = D(\mathscr{E})$ for such a V. Moreover, the line segment $m^{(1)}a'$ has infinite length when W is any U orthogonal to V, so that $D(U) = 0$ for such U.

Some readers may object that the foregoing discussion does not give simple formulas or computing rules for distances or best linear discriminators. But such concrete descriptions are trivial, and not in themselves very illuminating. If $\mathbf{V}$ and $\mathbf{v}$ are dual bases of $\mathscr{E}$ and $\mathscr{F}$, if $m^{(1)} = \bar{\mathbf{X}}^{(1)}\mathbf{v}$ and $m^{(2)} = \bar{\mathbf{X}}^{(2)}\mathbf{v}$, and if π is represented by $\mathbf{Q}$ relative to $\mathbf{V}$, then

$$D^2 = (\bar{\mathbf{X}}^{(1)} - \bar{\mathbf{X}}^{(2)})\mathbf{Q}^{-1}(\bar{\mathbf{X}}^{(1)} - \bar{\mathbf{X}}^{(2)})', \tag{10.2.6}$$

and

$$V = [(\bar{\mathbf{X}}^{(1)} - \bar{\mathbf{X}}^{(2)})\mathbf{Q}^{-1}]\mathbf{V} \tag{10.2.7}$$

defines a best linear discriminator. The reader should check directly that $D(V)^2 = D^2$ for V defined in (10.2.7), and that this particular choice of V is scaled to have norm D^2. To compute D^2 and V, given $\bar{\mathbf{X}}^{(1)}$, $\bar{\mathbf{X}}^{(2)}$ and $\mathbf{Q}$, a convenient approach is to set up a $(p + 1) \times (p + 1)$ matrix

$$\begin{bmatrix} \mathbf{Q} & (\bar{\mathbf{X}}^{(1)} - \bar{\mathbf{X}}^{(2)})' \\ \bar{\mathbf{X}}_1^{(1)} - \bar{\mathbf{X}}^{(2)} & 0 \end{bmatrix},$$

and to apply SWP$[1, 2, \ldots, p]$. The last row of the result yields $(\bar{\mathbf{X}}^{(1)} - \bar{\mathbf{X}}^{(2)})\mathbf{Q}^{-1}$ and $-D^2$. Moreover, the successive stopping points SWP$[1, 2, \ldots, s]$ along the way for $s = 1, 2, \ldots, p$ provide best linear discriminators and distances for subsets of $\mathbf{V}$, making it possible to see how D increases as variables are successively put into the system.

It may sometimes be useful to produce a full orthogonal basis whose first member is a best linear discriminator and whose remaining members span the orthogonal space $\mathscr{U}$. From Theorem 10.2, such a basis may be characterized as a basis of eigenvectors of the among sample inner product (10.1.12) relative to π. The reader may check that the corresponding eigenvalues are $(1/n_1 + 1/n_2)^{-1}D^2, 0, 0, \ldots, 0$.

Sample-based inner products will now be considered more fully, first as a means of choosing π in the analyses just described, and then as sample properties which merit comparison in their own right.

The most common choice for π is the pooled within sample covariance with inner product matrix $\mathbf{S}_W$. In this case $(1/n_1 + 1/n_2)^{-1}D(W)^2$ is immediately seen from (10.2.2) and (10.1.12) to be the familiar ratio of among sample mean square to pooled within sample mean square (or F statistic) as used in the analysis of variance. The alternative choices for π defined by the inner product matrices $\mathbf{S}_W$, $\mathbf{T}_W$, $\mathbf{S}$, or $\mathbf{T}$ are all closely related. By expressing the data in terms of a basis of eigenvectors of $\mathbf{T}_A$ relative to $\mathbf{S}_W$ it is easily seen that all four choices for π lead to the same best linear discriminators while the corresponding distances D, D', D'', and D''' are related by

$$D^2 = (n_1 + n_2 - 2)D'^2, \tag{10.2.8}$$

$$D''^2 = (n_1 + n_2 - 1)D'''^2, \tag{10.2.9}$$

and

$$D'''^2 = D'^2/[1 + D'^2/(1/n_1 + 1/n_2)]. \tag{10.2.10}$$

The various distances D, D', D'', and D''' are all in the tradition of analysis of variance thinking. If it is presumed that the samples come from populations with essentially different covariance structures, then other distances may be interesting. For example, the use of the individual sample covariances $\mathbf{S}^{(1)}$ and $\mathbf{S}^{(2)}$ determines a pair of *directed distances* $D^{(1)}$ and $D^{(2)}$. The directed distance $D^{(1)}$ measures how far away the mean of sample 2 appears from the center of sample 1 when viewed in relation to the spread of sample 1, and so measures the extent to which $\bar{\mathbf{X}}^{(2)}$ might or might not appear a plausible member of sample 1. A similar observation applies to $D^{(2)}$. Note that $\bar{\mathbf{X}}^{(1)}$ could easily appear a plausible member of sample 2 while $\bar{\mathbf{X}}^{(2)}$ did not appear a plausible member of sample 1, or vice versa. More generally, weightings as in (10.1.14) for various w_l could sometimes be of interest. In particular, for judging the significance of the difference $\bar{\mathbf{X}}^{(1)} - \bar{\mathbf{X}}^{(2)}$ irrespective of the difference in covariance matrices, one would be interested in D_Δ defined from

$$\mathbf{S}_\Delta = \frac{\mathbf{S}^{(1)}/n_1 + \mathbf{S}^{(2)}/n_2}{1/n_1 + 1/n_2}. \qquad (10.2.11)$$

Direct comparison of $\mathbf{S}^{(1)}$ and $\mathbf{S}^{(2)}$ may be approached in several ways. Simple direct comparison of corresponding elements will give first indications. Another possibility would be to examine the eigenvalues and eigenvectors of $\mathbf{S}^{(1)}$ relative to $\mathbf{S}^{(2)}$. Note that these eigenvectors are also orthogonal with respect to any weighted combination of $\mathbf{S}^{(1)}$ and $\mathbf{S}^{(2)}$, such as $\mathbf{S}_W$ and $\mathbf{S}_\Delta$. A third approach relating the apparent differences to $m^{(1)}$ and $m^{(2)}$ is discussed below.

Four possible relative positions and shapes of a pair of mean-centered concentration ellipsoids are illustrated in Fig. 10.2.2, for $p = 2$, as cases a, b, c, d. In case a, $\mathbf{S}^{(1)} = \mathbf{S}^{(2)}$, while in cases b, c, and d increasingly general differences between the two covariance structures appear. The tangent lines to the ellipses in Fig. 10.2.2 represent $(p - 1)$-dimensional hyperplanes in $\mathscr{F}$ on which the corresponding best linear discriminator is constant, while, by the shadow theory of Theorem 6.6, the semi-axes of the ellipsoids along the line joining $m^{(1)}$ and $m^{(2)}$ represent the sample standard deviations when the individual-space of the best linear discriminator is represented as the line joining $m^{(1)}$ and $m^{(2)}$. Case b refers to a situation where the best linear discriminators defined by $\mathbf{S}^{(1)}$ and $\mathbf{S}^{(2)}$ are the same and even have the same standard deviations, while the covariance structures differ in other respects. Under case c, the two best linear discriminators are again the same, but this common best linear discriminator has different sample variances in the two samples, as is shown by the different lengths of the semi-axes of the ellipses. Finally, case d represents a general situation where the sample best linear discriminators defined by $\mathbf{S}^{(1)}$ and $\mathbf{S}^{(2)}$ are different.

Although case d will almost always occur with actual sample data, it is of interest to ascertain how close to situations a, b, or c the data come. Several statistics which may partly serve this purpose will now be defined. Suppose that the origin-centered concentration ellipsoids defined by $\mathbf{S}^{(1)}$, $\mathbf{S}^{(2)}$, and $\mathbf{S}_W$ are denoted by $\pi^{(1)}$, $\pi^{(2)}$, and π_W respectively. Suppose that the line joining ø and $m^{(1)} - m^{(2)}$ cuts these ellipsoids in $s^{(1)}$, $s^{(2)}$, and s_W. Two further points s_1 and s_2 on this line may be defined to be the intersections of the line with the pair of $(p - 1)$-dimensional hyperplanes tangent to $\pi^{(1)}$ and $\pi^{(2)}$ and parallel to the hyperplane which is tangent to π_W at s_W. This situation is pictured in Fig. 10.2.3 for the general case *d*. Note that Fig. 10.2.3 includes the information of the kind given by case *d* of Fig. 10.2.2 along with additional information.

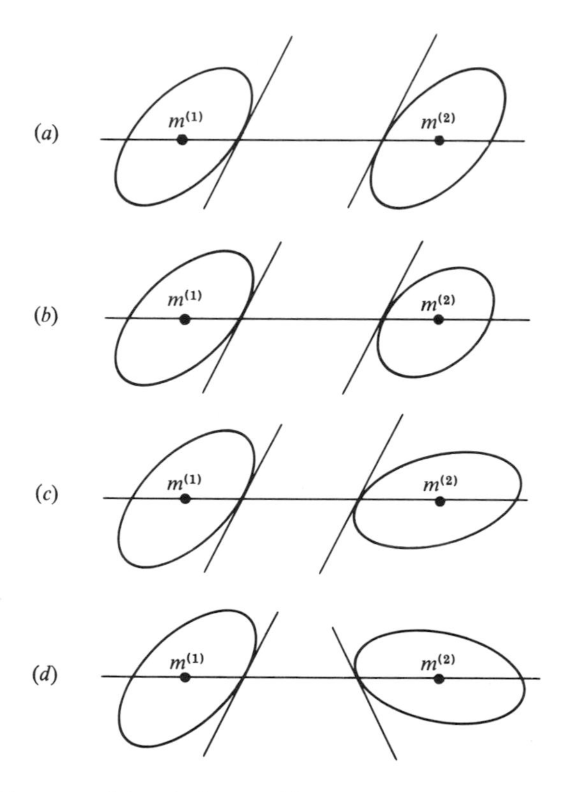

Fig. 10.2.2. Four possible relative positions of a pair of concentration ellipsoids.

Under case *a* described above, the three ellipsoids $\pi^{(1)}$, $\pi^{(2)}$, and π_W are identical, and consequently the five points $s^{(1)}$, $s^{(2)}$, s_W, s_1, and s_2 are likewise identical. Under case *b*, the three ellipsoids are no longer identical, but they still define the same best linear discriminator and assign it the same variance, so that $s^{(1)}$, $s^{(2)}$, s_W, s_1, and s_2 are still the same. Under case *c* ambiguity begins to appear, not in the concept of best linear discriminator which is the same for $\mathbf{S}^{(1)}$, $\mathbf{S}^{(2)}$, and any weighting thereof, but in the variance to be assigned to this best linear discriminator; for $s^{(1)} = s_1$ and $s^{(2)} = s_2$, while the ratio of the lengths of the line segments $øs_1$ and $øs_2$ deviates from unity and is therefore a measure of deviation from case b towards case c. These lengths are proportional to the standard deviations of the common best linear discriminator under $\mathbf{S}^{(1)}$ and $\mathbf{S}^{(2)}$, i.e., proportional to the distance-like quantities D_1 and D_2 expressible as

$$D_i^2 = [(\bar{\mathbf{X}}^{(1)} - \bar{\mathbf{X}}^{(2)})\mathbf{S}_W^{-1}]\mathbf{S}^{(i)}[(\bar{\mathbf{X}}^{(1)} - \bar{\mathbf{X}}^{(2)})\mathbf{S}_W^{-1}]' \tag{10.2.12}$$

for $i = 1, 2$, and a suggested measure is

$$K = (øs_1)^2/(øs_2)^2 = D_1^2/D_2^2. \tag{10.2.13}$$

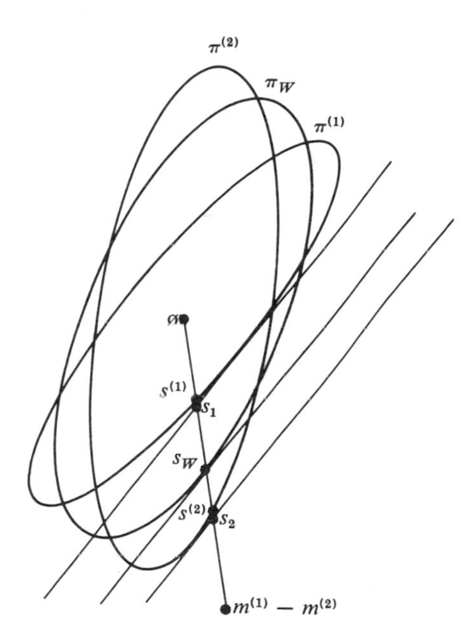

Fig. 10.2.3. Two origin-centered sample concentration ellipses and their associated pooled within sample ellipse, together with a mean difference vector and related points and tangent lines.

The ratio of the lengths of the line segments $øs_1$ and $øs^{(1)}$ is unity when case c holds, but greater than unity under case d, and similarly for $øs_2$ and $øs^{(2)}$. Consequently the ratios $øs_1/øs^{(1)}$ and $øs_2/øs^{(2)}$ may serve to indicate deviations from case c toward case d. By noting that D_1, D_2, and D are directly proportional to the lengths of $øs_1$, $øs_2$, and $øs$, and also that D, $D^{(1)}$, and $D^{(2)}$ are inversely proportional to the lengths of the line segments $øs$, $øs^{(1)}$, and $øs^{(2)}$ one may deduce that

$$K_i = (øs_i)^2/(øs^{(i)})^2 = D^{(i)^2} D_i^2/D^4 \tag{10.2.14}$$

for $i = 1, 2$, thus relating the suggested measures K_1 and K_2 to easily computed distance measures.

10.3 EXAMPLES OF TWO-SAMPLE ANALYSIS

Example 10.1. This example is based on data collected by Tagiuri (1965) in a study of the values of research *scientists* in industry, the managers of scientists in industry called here *research managers*, and *executives* of a more traditional kind. Values are defined quantitatively as the scores obtained on the "Study of values" questionnaire of Allport, Vernon, and Lindzey (1960). Each questionnaire yields six numerical scores intended to measure the relative importance for the individual of *theoretical*, *economic*, *aesthetic*, *social*, *political*, and *religious* values. Each of the individuals in a sample from each of the three categories of individuals filled out the questionnaire in the normal way to reflect their own values. In addition, subsamples of individuals from each category filled out the questionnaire a second time to rate their conception of a typical individual in a different category. In this fashion executives rated a typical research manager, research managers rated both a typical scientist and a typical executive, and scientists rated research managers. Here, only the self-rating scores of 204 scientists and the self-rating scores of 236 research managers will be discussed but see Section 11.3 for further aspects of these data.

The Allport-Vernon-Lindzey questionnaire has the special feature that the six scores yielded by each questionnaire are constrained to have a constant sum of 240 points, implying that an elevated score on one variable is necessarily accompanied by an average depressing effect on the scores arising from the remaining variables. The same phenomenon applies to sample averages. Also, the sample covariance matrix is necessarily of less than full rank because the sum of the variables, having a constant value, necessarily has variance zero. The absence of full rank covariances causes only a minor complication for the standard multivariate analysis to be described, because the variable-space $\mathscr{E}$ may be considered from the beginning to have dimension five instead of six, and the sample covariances do have rank 5. Thus, while it is convenient to display means, variances, and covariances for all six variables, the analyses involving inversion, such as distance and best linear discriminator computations, will be carried out using only the first five variables. The choice of a variable for omission is arbitrary but has no effect on the resulting analyses which are coordinate-free in $\mathscr{E}$ and so may be based on any five linearly independent basis variables.

An examination of the basic linear and quadratic statistics yields much useful information. The mean vector for the self-rating data on the 204 scientists is

$$[51.21, 40.73, 38.11, 34.27, 40.43, 35.26],$$

and for the 236 research managers is

$$[48.97, 43.67, 37.62, 32.14, 42.11, 35.50].$$

The same pair of samples in the same order yielded sample covariance matrices

$$\begin{bmatrix} 47.7 & -1.2 & 5.8 & -7.0 & -3.2 & -42.0 \\ -1.2 & 82.7 & -38.5 & -31.2 & 8.2 & -20.0 \\ 5.8 & -38.5 & 82.1 & 1.7 & -13.8 & -37.3 \\ -7.0 & -31.2 & 1.7 & 54.0 & -14.9 & -2.5 \\ -3.2 & 8.2 & -13.8 & -14.9 & 46.1 & -22.5 \\ -42.0 & -20.0 & -37.3 & -2.5 & -22.5 & 124.4 \end{bmatrix}$$

and

$$\begin{bmatrix} 40.4 & 2.2 & -4.2 & -16.3 & 3.1 & -25.3 \\ 2.2 & 77.5 & -33.0 & -29.8 & 19.9 & -36.8 \\ -4.2 & -33.0 & 80.0 & 7.7 & -20.8 & -29.8 \\ -16.3 & -29.8 & 7.7 & 51.5 & -16.5 & 3.4 \\ 3.1 & 19.9 & -20.8 & -16.5 & 41.0 & -26.8 \\ -25.3 & -36.8 & -29.8 & 3.4 & -26.8 & 115.2 \end{bmatrix}.$$

The standard deviations computed from the two covariance matrices are respectively

$$[6.91, 9.09, 9.06, 7.35, 6.79, 11.15]$$

and

$$[6.36, 8.80, 8.94, 7.18, 6.40, 10.73].$$

Similarly the corresponding correlation matrices are

$$\begin{bmatrix} 1 & -0.019 & 0.093 & -0.138 & -0.068 & -0.546 \\ -0.019 & 1 & -0.468 & -0.467 & 0.133 & -0.197 \\ 0.093 & -0.468 & 1 & 0.026 & -0.224 & -0.369 \\ -0.138 & -0.467 & 0.026 & 1 & -0.299 & -0.031 \\ -0.068 & 0.133 & -0.224 & -0.299 & 1 & -0.281 \\ -0.546 & -0.197 & -0.369 & -0.031 & -0.281 & 1 \end{bmatrix}$$

and

$$\begin{bmatrix} 1 & 0.039 & -0.074 & -0.357 & 0.076 & -0.371 \\ 0.039 & 1 & -0.419 & -0.472 & 0.353 & -0.390 \\ -0.074 & -0.419 & 1 & 0.120 & -0.363 & -0.311 \\ -0.357 & -0.472 & 0.120 & 1 & -0.359 & 0.044 \\ 0.076 & 0.353 & -0.363 & -0.359 & 1 & -0.390 \\ -0.371 & -0.390 & -0.311 & 0.044 & -0.390 & 1 \end{bmatrix}.$$

The questionnaire is designed so that a score of 40 on each value-scale should be roughly typical. Thus both the scientists and research managers show high average scores for theoretical values, with the scientists slightly higher. The other five value scales may be discussed in similar terms. In general the self-rating average scores of the two groups differ from 40 in directions which might have been expected, and differ between groups as might have been expected from *a priori* judgments about the tastes and attitudes of the two sets of subjects.

The various distance quantities defined in Section 10.2 were computed for the chosen pair of samples. The pooled within sample covariance matrix was found to be

$$\mathbf{S}_W = \begin{bmatrix} 43.77 & 0.62 & 0.44 & -12.00 & 0.20 & -33.04 \\ 0.62 & 79.89 & -35.52 & -30.48 & 14.50 & -29.01 \\ 0.44 & -35.52 & 80.09 & 4.91 & -17.53 & -33.31 \\ -12.00 & -30.48 & 4.91 & 52.66 & -15.75 & 0.66 \\ 0.20 & 14.50 & -17.53 & -15.75 & 43.36 & -24.79 \\ -33.04 & -29.01 & -33.31 & 0.66 & -24.79 & 119.48 \end{bmatrix},$$

whose first five rows and columns have inverse

$$\begin{bmatrix} 0.0250 & 0.0030 & 0.0012 & 0.0080 & 0.0023 \\ 0.0030 & 0.0208 & 0.0086 & 0.0122 & 0.0009 \\ 0.0012 & 0.0086 & 0.0171 & 0.0054 & 0.0060 \\ 0.0080 & 0.0122 & 0.0054 & 0.0300 & 0.0090 \\ 0.0023 & 0.0009 & 0.0060 & 0.0090 & 0.0284 \end{bmatrix}.$$

The vector of mean differences is

$$[2.24, \ -2.94, \ -0.49, \ 2.13, \ -1.69, \ -0.24],$$

whose first five elements multiplied by the above 5×5 inverse covariance matrix yielded the standard best linear discriminator

$$0.06092V_1 + 0.02575V_2 + 0.01285V_3 - 0.03339V_4 + 0.02338V_5.$$

Equivalent expressions omitting a different V_i may be obtained by dropping a different row and column from the matrix inversion. Multiplying the first five elements of the mean difference vector by the vector of best linear discriminator coefficients yielded

$$D^2 = 0.318 \qquad \text{or} \qquad D = 0.564.$$

Thus the sample means on the best linear discriminator differ by 0.564 standard deviations where standard deviation is defined in terms of the pooled within sample covariance structure.

An alternative distance analysis is provided by

$$\mathbf{S}_\Delta = \begin{bmatrix} 44.30 & 0.37 & 1.17 & -11.33 & -0.26 & -34.26 \\ 0.37 & 80.28 & -35.92 & -30.59 & 13.64 & -27.79 \\ 1.17 & -35.92 & 81.15 & 4.47 & -17.02 & -33.85 \\ -11.33 & -30.59 & 4.47 & 52.84 & -15.63 & 0.23 \\ -0.26 & 13.64 & -17.02 & -15.63 & 43.74 & -24.48 \\ -34.26 & -27.79 & -33.85 & 0.23 & -24.48 & 120.15 \end{bmatrix}$$

in place of $\mathbf{S}_W$. (See 10.2.11.) The resulting best linear discriminator is

$$0.0593V_1 - 0.02679V_2 - 0.01352V_3 + 0.03142V_4 - 0.02393V_5$$

and the related distance is

$$D_\Delta^2 = 0.312 \qquad \text{or} \qquad D_\Delta = 0.559.$$

The smallness of the difference between D and D_Δ results from similarity of the two sample sizes as well as the similarity of the two sample covariance matrices.

Distances were also computed using the individual sample covariances, giving

$$D^{(1)2} = 0.286 \qquad \text{or} \qquad D^{(1)} = 0.535,$$

and

$$D^{(2)2} = 0.367 \qquad \text{or} \qquad D^{(2)} = 0.606.$$

The range from $D^{(1)}$ to $D^{(2)}$ indicates the possible range of distances resulting from different weightings of the two sample covariance matrices.

The covariance structures of the two samples are at first sight quite similar. For another look at the differences inherent in the two covariance matrices, the statistics (10.2.14) and (10.2.15) were computed. From (10.2.12)

$$D_1^2 - 0.379 \qquad \text{or} \qquad D_1 = 0.616,$$

and

$$D_2^2 = 0.286 \qquad \text{or} \qquad D_2 = 0.535.$$

Thus the ratio (10.2.13) is

$$K = (\o s_1/\o s_2)^2 - 1.325,$$

which says that the ratio of variances of the sample best linear discriminator is considerably larger than that for the original variables. Likewise the ratios (10.2.14) are

$$K_1 = (\o s_1/\o s^{(1)})^2 = 1.072,$$

and

$$K_2 = (\o s_2/\o s^{(2)})^2 = 1.048,$$

which exceed their minimum values of unity by small but significant amounts. (See Section 14.3.)

Example 10.2. The data given in this example, kindly provided by H. D. Sylwestrowicz of CIBA, are of a very common type in pharmaceutical experimentation. Many sets of such data are typically collected in routine animal experiments with drugs. The particular set considered here in isolation provides 9 measurements on each of 19 animals. The 9 variables are all measurements of renal blood pressure, but taken at intervals of half an hour over four hours. These variables will be denoted by $V_1, V_2, \ldots, V_9$ in order of time. Before the experiment, the animals had been divided randomly into two groups of sizes 12 and 7. The first group was a *control* group to which no drug was given, while the second or *treated* group received a specific drug treatment after the first of the 9 measurements had been taken. Thus differential effects between treated and control groups should not appear in V_1 but may appear in $V_2, V_3, \ldots, V_9$.

In the language of randomized experiments V_1 is usually called a *covariate*. The handling of such covariates will be discussed in some detail in Chapter 11, and the reader may wish to review this example in the light of the later discussion.

An important difference between Examples 10.1 and 10.2 is that the samples are very small in the present case. Consequently the sample means and sample covariances must be regarded with extreme caution as indicators of population means and covariances. This is especially true of the covariance structures: an unknown population covariance when $p = 9$ is determined by 36 functionally independent quantities and it is a dubious venture to attempt to estimate so many quantities from samples of sizes 7 or 12. The following analysis concentrates accordingly on mean differences.

The computations of Example 10.1, which were not described in detail, relied on straightforward subroutines for matrix addition, multiplication, and inversion. The computations of Example 10.2 rely on the SWP operator and are more efficient and informative. The original 19×9 data matrix was roughly centered about zero by subtracting 100.0 from each element to reduce the rounding error entering at the first sweeping operation which corrects for the grand mean. Two further columns were then added to the data matrix, representing dummy variables V_{10} taking the values zero in the control group and unity in the treated group, and V_{11} always taking the value unity. (Any three constants would serve as well.)

The resulting data matrix $\mathbf{Y}$ is reproduced below along with $\mathrm{SWP}[11, 10]\mathbf{Y}'\mathbf{Y}$ and $-\mathrm{SWP}[1, 2, \ldots, 9, 11, 10]\mathbf{Y}'\mathbf{Y}$.

$$\mathbf{Y} = \begin{bmatrix}
17 & 27 & 17 & 17 & 25 & 25 & 25 & 15 & 17 & 0 & 1 \\
5 & 5 & 2 & 2 & 5 & 10 & 10 & 12 & 12 & 0 & 1 \\
20 & 20 & 20 & 20 & 18 & 17 & 17 & 17 & 15 & 0 & 1 \\
8 & 17 & 8 & 15 & 25 & 25 & 25 & 25 & 27 & 0 & 1 \\
22 & 22 & 20 & 20 & 15 & 12 & 18 & 13 & 12 & 0 & 1 \\
13 & 17 & 17 & 12 & 17 & 17 & 17 & 17 & 7 & 0 & 1 \\
35 & 23 & 25 & 23 & 28 & 27 & 42 & 42 & 30 & 0 & 1 \\
45 & 43 & 37 & 33 & 35 & 35 & 33 & 32 & 30 & 0 & 1 \\
2 & 5 & 2 & -5 & -7 & -10 & -8 & -8 & -18 & 0 & 1 \\
33 & 37 & 22 & 28 & 32 & 30 & 30 & 27 & 28 & 0 & 1 \\
25 & 35 & 22 & 28 & 28 & 30 & 28 & 25 & 22 & 0 & 1 \\
32 & 47 & 48 & 47 & 47 & 47 & 47 & 48 & 47 & 0 & 1 \\
45 & -2 & 2 & 0 & -5 & -5 & -10 & -10 & -12 & 1 & 1 \\
-3 & -27 & -30 & -33 & -35 & -35 & -33 & -33 & -33 & 1 & 1 \\
32 & 17 & 12 & 12 & 7 & 2 & 2 & 7 & 7 & 1 & 1 \\
30 & -2 & -10 & -12 & -12 & -12 & -12 & -13 & -13 & 1 & 1 \\
13 & -20 & -22 & -22 & -23 & -27 & -27 & -28 & -28 & 1 & 1 \\
20 & 18 & 2 & -13 & -18 & -18 & -22 & -22 & -23 & 1 & 1 \\
22 & 18 & 8 & -8 & -10 & -8 & -7 & -2 & 0 & 1 & 1
\end{bmatrix}$$

$$\text{SWP}[11, 10]\mathbf{Y}'\mathbf{Y} =$$

$$\begin{bmatrix}
3318.3453 & 2618.4048 & 2697.1429 & 2810.2858 & 2667.9048 & 2605.1548 & 2566.5239 & 2561.7262 & 2543.4406 & 1.2976 & 21.4167 \\
2618.4048 & 4095.0954 & 3450.8572 & 3158.7144 & 3017.0954 & 3021.5954 & 2784.4764 & 2869.0239 & 3114.3096 & -24.5476 & 24.8333 \\
2697.1429 & 3450.8572 & 3409.7144 & 3126.4286 & 2893.8572 & 2858.8572 & 2757.2859 & 2925.7144 & 2984.2858 & -25.4286 & 20.0000 \\
2810.2858 & 3158.7144 & 3126.4286 & 3350.8573 & 3197.7145 & 3115.7145 & 2981.5716 & 3082.4287 & 3277.5716 & -30.8571 & 20.0000 \\
2667.9048 & 3017.0953 & 2893.8572 & 3197.7145 & 3282.0955 & 3237.0954 & 3117.4764 & 3188.5240 & 3430.8097 & -36.0476 & 22.3333 \\
2605.1548 & 3021.5954 & 2858.8572 & 3115.7144 & 3237.0953 & 3282.3454 & 3120.4763 & 3208.7739 & 3484.0596 & -36.7976 & 22.0833 \\
2566.5239 & 2784.4763 & 2757.2858 & 2981.5716 & 3117.4764 & 3120.4763 & 3242.3812 & 3350.6192 & 3502.0477 & -39.2381 & 23.6667 \\
2561.7262 & 2869.0239 & 2925.7144 & 3082.4287 & 3188.5240 & 3208.7740 & 3350.6193 & 3620.6311 & 3718.2025 & -36.5119 & 22.0833 \\
2543.4405 & 3114.3096 & 2984.2858 & 3277.5716 & 3430.8097 & 3483.0596 & 3502.0479 & 3718.2025 & 4088.6310 & -33.6548 & 19.0833 \\
1.2976 & -24.5476 & -25.4286 & -30.8571 & -36.0476 & -36.7976 & -39.2381 & -36.5119 & -33.6548 & -0.2262 & 0.0833 \\
21.4167 & 24.8333 & 20.0000 & 20.0000 & 22.3333 & 22.0833 & 23.6667 & 22.0833 & 19.0833 & 0.0833 & -0.0833
\end{bmatrix}$$

$$-\text{SWP}[1, 2, \ldots, 9, 11, 10]\mathbf{Y}'\mathbf{Y} =$$

$$\begin{bmatrix}
0.0015 & 0.0001 & -0.0001 & -0.0015 & 0.0012 & -0.0011 & -0.0017 & 0.0001 & 0.0015 & -0.0552 & 0.0026 \\
0.0001 & 0.0025 & -0.0033 & 0.0016 & -0.0013 & -0.0003 & -0.0003 & 0.0024 & -0.0014 & -0.0028 & -0.0136 \\
-0.0001 & -0.0033 & 0.0072 & -0.0059 & 0.0050 & -0.0017 & 0.0006 & -0.0048 & 0.0032 & -0.0085 & 0.0162 \\
-0.0015 & 0.0016 & -0.0059 & 0.0127 & -0.0140 & 0.0054 & 0.0034 & 0.0019 & -0.0036 & 0.0560 & -0.0030 \\
0.0012 & -0.0013 & 0.0050 & -0.0140 & 0.0294 & -0.0168 & -0.0079 & 0.0004 & 0.0039 & -0.0636 & 0.0051 \\
-0.0011 & -0.0003 & -0.0017 & 0.0054 & -0.0168 & 0.0176 & 0.0009 & 0.0017 & -0.0053 & 0.0756 & -0.0112 \\
-0.0017 & -0.0003 & 0.0006 & 0.0034 & -0.0079 & 0.0009 & 0.0151 & -0.0086 & -0.0012 & 0.1040 & -0.0265 \\
0.0001 & 0.0024 & -0.0048 & 0.0019 & 0.0004 & 0.0017 & -0.0086 & 0.0127 & -0.0058 & -0.0005 & -0.0146 \\
0.0015 & -0.0014 & 0.0032 & -0.0036 & 0.0039 & -0.0053 & -0.0012 & -0.0058 & 0.0085 & -0.0937 & 0.0359 \\
-0.0552 & -0.0028 & -0.0085 & 0.0560 & -0.0636 & 0.0756 & 0.1040 & -0.0005 & -0.0937 & 3.1399 & -0.6940 \\
0.0026 & -0.0136 & 0.0162 & -0.0030 & 0.0051 & -0.0112 & -0.0265 & -0.0146 & 0.0359 & -0.6940 & 0.4998
\end{bmatrix}$$

The first 9 rows and columns provide $\mathbf{T}_W$ for the original $V_1, V_2, \ldots, V_9$ of SWP[11, 10]$\mathbf{Y}'\mathbf{Y}$. The first 9 elements of row 10 provide $\bar{\mathbf{X}}^{(2)} - \bar{\mathbf{X}}^{(1)}$ and the (10, 10) element is $-(1/n_1 + 1/n_2) = -\frac{1}{12} - \frac{1}{7} = -0.2262$. The stage is now set for distance and best linear discriminator analyses based on the inner product $\mathbf{T}_W$. The same best linear discriminators are valid for $\mathbf{S}_W$ while distances according to $\mathbf{T}_W$ should be multiplied by the degrees of freedom $n_1 + n_2 - 2 = 17$ to provide the more natural distances according to $\mathbf{S}_W$.

After applying SWP[1, 2, . . . , 9] and changing signs, the first 9 elements of row 10 provide the sample best linear discriminator while the (10, 10) element is

Table 10.3.1

	Coefficient of								
s	V_1	V_2	V_3	V_4	V_5	V_6	V_7	V_8	V_9
2	−10.3	12.6							
3	−18.6	−5.4	27.6						
4	−28.9	−7.0	4.7	35.6					
5	−29.5	−12.3	16.3	−1.5	33.3				
6	−29.5	−12.8	15.4	2.0	19.4	11.9			
7	−30.5	−8.3	8.0	11.9	1.9	3.4	20.4		
8	−38.9	−18.7	27.2	16.3	−20.5	17.6	90.3	−64.6	
9	−55.2	−2.8	−8.5	56.0	−63.6	75.6	104.0	−0.5	−93.7

$0.2262 + D^2$. Thus, the D^2 defined by $\mathbf{T}_W$ is 2.9137 or the more usual D^2 defined by $\mathbf{S}_W$ is 49.533.

Of course, it costs little along the way to look successively at SWP[1], SWP[1, 2], . . . , SWP[1, 2, . . . , 8] which provide the same analyses for the subsets V_1, $[V_1, V_2], \ldots, [V_1, V_2, \ldots, V_8]$. The weights for the best linear discriminators based on $V_1, V_2, \ldots, V_s$ are summarized in Table 10.3.1, after scaling by the arbitrary factor of 100.

In a similar fashion the successive values of D^2 for the spaces spanned by $V_1, [V_1, V_2], \ldots, [V_1, V_2, \ldots, V_9]$ are easily found, as shown in Table 10.3.2.

Many other decompositions of D^2 are possible. For example, each of the 9! orders of applying SWP[1], SWP[2], . . . , SWP[9] leads to a different decomposition. The given order following time is perhaps the most natural in the present context, since each successive contribution to D^2 may be regarded as a treatment effect associated with the corresponding increase of observation time. Note that the distance associated with V_1 is small, which is consistent with V_1 being a covariate. The large contributions to D^2 associated with V_8 and V_9 are rather surprising, and will be discussed later.

For comparative purposes, and to continue an empirical investigation of principal component analysis, a decomposition of D^2 based on principal

Table 10.3.2

s	$D(V_1, V_2, \ldots, V_s)^2$	$D(V_1, \ldots, V_s)^2 - D(V_1, \ldots, V_{s-1})^2$
1	0.009	0.009
2	5.488	5.479
3	10.097	4.609
4	18.434	8.337
5	22.198	3.764
6	22.380	0.182
7	23.893	1.513
8	31.992	8.099
9	49.534	17.542

variables was also computed. The principal component analysis used the total sample mean-corrected inner product matrix relative to the identity matrix as a reference inner product matrix. The computations proceeded as above, except that the operations SWP[11], SWP[10] were replaced by SWP[11], SDG[1, 2, . . . , 9], SWP[10]. The decomposition of D^2 related to the principal variables $V_1, V_2, \ldots, V_9$ is displayed in Table 10.3.3.

The contributions to D^2 do appear somewhat earlier in this table than in the preceding table, but the large contribution from U_6 appears suspicious. Incidentally, the principal components of variance or, more properly, the principal components of the total sum inner product corrected for the grand mean are 65164.9, 3186.9, 1398.6, 446.0, 344.7, 190.5, 76.5, 39.5, and 21.7 which show a very rapid drop-off.

One further decomposition of D^2 was computed, based essentially on the idea of fitting polynomials of increasing order in time, i.e., linear, quadratic,

Table 10.3.3

s	$D(U_1, U_2, \ldots, U_s)^2$	$D(U_1, U_2, \ldots, U_s)^2$ $D(U_1, \ldots, U_{s-1})^2$
1	5.532	5.532
2	15.511	9.979
3	17.964	2.453
4	25.305	7.341
5	29.059	3.754
6	43.388	14.329
7	43.692	0.304
8	44.216	0.524
9	49.534	5.318

cubic, etc. The variables $V_1, V_2, \ldots, V_9$ were first replaced by $V_1, V_2 - V_1, V_3 - V_2, \ldots, V_9 - V_8$ and the 8 differences were replaced by

$$\begin{bmatrix} W_2 \\ W_3 \\ \cdot \\ \cdot \\ \cdot \\ W_9 \end{bmatrix} = \mathbf{K} \begin{bmatrix} V_2 - V_1 \\ V_3 - V_2 \\ \cdot \\ \cdot \\ \cdot \\ V_9 - V_8 \end{bmatrix},$$

where **K** is an orthogonal matrix whose rows are successively constant, linear, quadratic, etc. The matrix **K** was computed by starting from

$$\begin{bmatrix} 1 & 1 & 1 \ldots 1 \\ 1 & 2 & 3 \ldots 8 \\ 1^2 & 2^2 & 3^2 \ldots 8^2 \\ \cdot & & \\ \cdot & & \\ \cdot & & \\ 1^7 & 2^7 & 3^7 \ldots 8^7 \end{bmatrix},$$

successively orthogonalizing its rows, and finally reducing them to unit length. These rows of **K** are sometimes called *orthogonal polynomials.* The raw sum inner product matrix for $V_1, V_2, \ldots, V_{11}$ was successively transformed into that for $V_1, V_2 - V_1, \ldots, V_9 - V_8, V_{10}, V_{11}$ and then that for $V_1, W_2, W_3, \ldots, W_9, V_{10}, V_{11}$. From there, the computations proceeded as in the original analysis of $V_1, V_2, \ldots, V_9$, i.e., SWP[11], SWP[10], SWP[1], SWP[2], . . . , SWP[9] were successively applied. The resulting decomposition of D^2 is given in Table 10.3.4.

The sampling distributions of the various sample statistics computed above are discussed in Section 14.3, on the assumption of random samples from

Table 10.3.4

s	$D(V_1, W_2, \ldots, W_s)^2$	$D(V_1, W_2, \ldots, W_s)^2 - D(V_1, W_2, \ldots, W_{s-1})^2$
1	0.009	0.009
2	9.549	9.540
3	23.105	13.556
4	40.973	17.869
5	41.648	0.675
6	42.928	1.280
7	45.308	2.380
8	46.551	1.243
9	49.533	2.912

multivariate normal populations. These distributions make possible certain postdictive inference procedures which provide uncertain information about the parameters of the normal population. In particular, significance tests are applied in Section 14.3 to the three sequences of increments of D^2 values given in Tables 10.3.2, 10.3.3, and 10.3.4.

In connection with sampling theory considerations, it is sometimes argued that the stepwise procedures illustrated above should be applied in an order which takes first those variables which may be assumed to have zero population differences in their means. Thus, in the principal variable analysis one might think of reversing the order of the sweeping operations, while in the polynomial fitting analysis one might retain the initial time variable in first position while reversing the order of the rest to deal first with higher order effects. The argument for these reversals is that the variables with zero population differences act as covariates and so increase the sensitivity of tests and estimation procedures reflecting on the variables which really matter. A counter-argument is that it can never really be known that higher order population differences are not present, and their presence tends to bias the tests relating to the important variables in an unknown way. A second counter-argument is that the use of covariates consumes degrees of freedom available for covariance estimation and thereby decreases the sensitivity of the tests. The second counter-argument is quite important with these data, since the samples are very small. The reader with adequate computing facilities may wish to carry out the analyses using the alternative orders, including the significance tests based on the decomposition of D^2, for indications of a loss of sensitivity to important effects.

Polynomial fitting has a considerable literature of its own, and many variations of the above techniques have been suggested. For example, Rao (1965) has proposed applications of the orthogonal polynomials of one higher degree to the original 9 variables, instead of the application as above to the 8 time-difference variables. The latter was preferred here on the belief that the time-difference variables are more likely to be roughly uncorrelated with constant variance than are the original variables; for sampling theory considerations suggest that optimal fitting without the use of covariates is provided by orthogonal polynomials when the basic variables are uncorrelated with constant variance (in the population). Potthoff and Roy (1964) describe formally the correct set of polynomials to use in the presence of arbitrary population covariance structure. Rao (1965) also presents methods appropriate to the (artificial?) assumption that each animal corresponds to a random polynomial of given degree, while all observations are subject to independent errors of measurement with zero means and constant variance.

10.4 ANALYSIS OF MORE THAN TWO SAMPLES

The two sample theory of Section 10.2 suggests generalizations of many kinds, some of which are explained here. The emphasis will be put on the comparison of means. Techniques for comparing more than two sample means at once will be described, but the development of techniques for simultaneous comparison of more than two sample covariances will not be attempted.

A set of k sample means $m^{(1)}, m^{(2)}, \ldots, m^{(k)}$ in $\mathscr{F}$ may be considered in two ways, first without regard for any inner product and second in relation to an inner product π_d over $\mathscr{F}$. The first of these approaches will not be pursued in detail except for one comment. If $k - 1 \leq p$, then any set of k points not lying in a hyperplane of dimension $k - 2$ is affinely like any other such set, for two such sets are related by a wide sense linear transformation. On the other hand, if $k - 1 > p$, then the k points necessarily lie in a hyperplane of dimension less than $k - 1$ and so begin to have a distinctive pattern independent of any inner product. To take an extreme example, if $p = 1$ and $k \geq 3$, then the k mean points on a line do form a meaningful pattern. Such patterns are less easy to view in an affine way when $p > 1$ and are difficult to view at all when $p > 3$. No general analysis of these patterns is attempted here.

Henceforth it will be assumed that a set of k means is to be viewed in relation to an inner product π_d over $\mathscr{F}$. Later, the choice of π_d from k sample data will be discussed briefly. Having π_d one has distances defined between each of $k(k - 1)/2$ pairs of means and also a best linear discriminator for each pair of samples. The subspace of variable-space $\mathscr{E}$ spanned by this set of $k(k - 1)/2$ best linear discriminators will be called the *space of best linear discriminators among the k means.* This space is a natural generalization of the one-dimensional space of best linear discriminators defined when $k = 2$, and its properties are set out in the following generalization of Theorem 10.2.

Theorem 10.4. *The space $\mathscr{V}$ of best linear discriminators among $m^{(1)}$, $m^{(2)}, \ldots, m^{(k)}$ determined by the rank p inner product π_d over $\mathscr{F}$ is the dual space of the orthogonal complement of the subspace of $\mathscr{F}$ spanned by the differences among $m^{(1)}, m^{(2)}, \ldots, m^{(k)}$. If W is any variable in $\mathscr{E}$ and V is the orthogonal projection of W into $\mathscr{V}$, then*

$$D_{ij}(W) \leq D_{ij}(V) \tag{10.4.1}$$

for i and $j = 1, 2, \ldots, k$, where D_{ij} denotes distance between $m^{(i)}$ and $m^{(j)}$ as defined in Section 10.2.

Theorem 10.4 gives first a characterization of $\mathscr{V}$ and second the basic property (10.4.1) which shows that only variables inside $\mathscr{V}$ need be considered for discrimination, at least in the sense that for any variable outside $\mathscr{V}$ there is another inside $\mathscr{V}$ yielding greater distances uniformly over all pairs of samples.

The proof of Theorem 10.4 requires only minor extensions of the theory of Section 10.2. The best linear discriminator V_{ij} between the pair of samples i and j defines a one-dimensional subspace $\mathscr{V}_{ij}$ whose dual is a $(p - 1)$-dimensional subspace $\mathscr{V}_{ijd}$ in $\mathscr{F}$ orthogonal to the one-dimensional subspace $\mathscr{U}_{ijd}$ spanned by $m^{(i)} - m^{(j)}$. $\mathscr{V}$ is the direct sum of the $\mathscr{V}_{ij}$, so that $\mathscr{V}_d$ is the intersection of the $\mathscr{V}_{ijd}$ and the orthogonal complement $\mathscr{U}_d$ of $\mathscr{V}_d$ is the direct sum of the $\mathscr{U}_{ijd}$, as required for the first part of Theorem 10.4. The second part of the theorem is a consequence of the fact that the sample means are identical on the subspace $\mathscr{U}$ orthogonal to $\mathscr{V}$, so that W and its orthogonal projection V into $\mathscr{V}$ have identical mean differences. In terms of the expression (10.2.2) for distance, both $D_{ij}(W)$ and $D_{ij}(V)$ have the same numerators while $(V, V) \leq (W, W)$, and (10.4.1) follows.

The dimension f of the space $\mathscr{V}$ of best linear discriminators is the same as the dimension of $\mathscr{U}_d$ or $m^{(1)} + \mathscr{U}_d$, the latter being the smallest hyperplane containing $m^{(1)}, m^{(2)}, \ldots, m^{(k)}$. Clearly $f \leq \min(k-1, p)$. In general $f = p$ if $k - 1 \geq p$, and in this case $\mathscr{V} = \mathscr{E}$ so that no reduction occurs, i.e., the concept of a space of best linear discriminators contributes nothing. If $k - 1 < p$, however, a simplification does result from the concept of $\mathscr{V}$.

The notion of distance does not generalize so unambiguously as the notion of best linear discriminator. Consider first generalized distance for a single variable V, the aim being to define a measure reflecting separation among all k means which reduces to $D(V)$ when $k = 2$. If the k mean values of V are denoted by $\bar{X}^{(1)}, \bar{X}^{(2)}, \ldots, \bar{X}^{(k)}$, then any nonnegative quadratic form in the differences $\bar{X}^{(i)} - \bar{X}^{(j)}$ might be chosen as a measure of these differences, examples being $\sum_1^k n_i(\bar{X}^{(i)} - \bar{X})^2$ where $\bar{X} = \sum_1^k n_i\bar{X}^{(i)}/n$, or $\sum_1^k (\bar{X}^{(i)} - \bar{X}_G)^2$ where $\bar{X}_G = \sum_1^k \bar{X}^{(i)}/k$. But other choices are possible. If a particular *contrast* $\sum_1^k a_i\bar{X}^{(i)}$ with $\sum_1^k a_i = 0$ were the main source of interest, then $(\sum_1^k a_i\bar{X}^{(i)})^2$ would be a suitable distance measure. Or, more generally, a weighted linear combination of several such squared contrasts could be of interest. Any such quadratic form may be taken as a generalization of $D(V)^2$ for a given V. It would be preferable, however, to divide by (V, V) so that the generalized measure would share with $D(V)^2$ the property of having a common value over the one-dimensional subspace $\mathscr{V}$ spanned by V.

Given such a generalized $D(V) = D(\mathscr{V})$, the next step is to extend the definition to a corresponding generalization of $D(\mathscr{V})$ where $\mathscr{V}$ has dimension greater than unity. The straightforward extension of the above quadratic form concept is an inner product concept. For example, $\sum_1^k n_i(X^{(i)} - \bar{X})^2$ generalizes to the inner product defined by $\mathbf{T}_A = \sum_1^k n_i(\bar{\mathbf{X}}^{(i)} - \bar{\mathbf{X}})'(\bar{\mathbf{X}}^{(i)} - \bar{\mathbf{X}})$. "Division" of this inner product by π is generalized to the eigenvector and eigenvalue structure of the quadratic form inner product relative to π. Thus the generalized $D(V)^2$ extends to a set of eigenvalues which are themselves generalized $D(V)^2$ for a set of eigenvectors.

Sometimes a single best linear discriminator might be sought, or a single generalized distance measure. The first of these could be taken to be the eigenvector corresponding to the largest generalized distance eigenvalue. Any such eigenvector must be in the space $\mathscr{V}$ of best linear discriminators defined above, as, indeed, must any set of such eigenvectors, from (10.4.1). Similarly, a single function of the generalized distance eigenvalues could be chosen as a single generalized distance, for example, the sum of the eigenvalues. Note, however, that no single discriminator or single distance measure can tell the whole story. Indeed, there is a very strong flavor of arbitrariness about all of the analyses described in this section, since so many choices are open. Only a few guidelines can be given.

The example of Section 10.5 uses $\mathbf{T}_W$ or $\mathbf{S}_W$ to define the inner product π. The generalized distance inner product is the familiar analysis of variance choice $\mathbf{T}_A$, but several decompositions of $\mathbf{T}_A$ are considered as well.

Eigenvector and eigenvalue analyses of the kind described above are often called *multiple discriminant analyses*. The eigenvectors determine variables in the space of best linear discriminators which are often called *discriminants*.

10.5 AN EXAMPLE WITH SIX SAMPLES CROSS-CLASSIFIED INTO TWO SEXES AND THREE RACES

Example 10.3. The data of this example are based on 276 human skulls assembled and measured by Prof. W. W. Howells. The individuals were classified at the start into 6 groups as in Table 10.5.1.

Table 10.5.1

THE DISTRIBUTION OF SKULLS BY RACE AND SEX FOR EXAMPLE 10.3

	Male	Female	Total
Japanese	56	35	91
Ainu	57	55	112
Australian	38	35	73
Total	151	125	276

The Japanese and Ainus represent racial groups now living in Japan, the Ainus being descendents of one or more of the tribes which occupied the Japanese islands before the arrival of the long-dominant Japanese. The Australian racial group represents the darkskinned aboriginals who predated European immigration. It was conjectured that the present analysis might demonstrate affinities between the Australian and Ainu groups and thus support a hypothesis of a common source in prehistoric times, as has sometimes been suggested. In fact, however, the analysis indicates closer relations between the Japanese and the Ainus than between either of these and the Australians.

The analysis is based on 21 variables representing physical dimensions considered to encompass much of the important variation in human skulls, i.e., based on expert opinion of what it is that makes skulls look different. The technical definitions of these 21 variables are omitted from the present discussion, as are any interpretations of the data based on the names and meanings of the variables. A few of the values making up the 276 × 21 data matrix could not be measured directly because of incomplete skulls. These were filled in according to a professional guess as to what the complete skull would have been like. Other analyses of these data have been reported by Howells (1966).

Several analyses were carried out, only one of which is reported here. Originally, six racial groups were used, including three African groups. The latter set were later dropped since they had been measured by a different

Table 10.5.2

ARTIFICIAL VARIABLES FOR EXAMPLE 10.3

	V_0	S	R_1	R_2	I_1	I_2
Japanese male	1	−1	−1	−1	1	1
Ainu male	1	−1	1	0	−1	0
Australian male	1	−1	0	1	0	−1
Japanese female	1	1	−1	−1	−1	−1
Ainu female	1	1	1	0	1	0
Australian female	1	1	0	1	0	1

investigator and there was some evidence that investigator biases were confounded with actual physical differences between the two sets of races. Also, the analyses were done both on the original measurements and on their logarithms, but only the former is reported here because the latter is virtually indistinguishable in its outcome.

Most of the following discussion is concerned with the technical details of the version of multiple discriminant analysis which was carried out. As usual, artificial variables were used to build group identifications into the data matrix. These were chosen in a special way in order that the five degrees of freedom for among group variation could be easily decomposed into a single degree of freedom for sex differences, two degrees of freedom for race differences, and two degrees of freedom for race by sex interaction. This type of decomposition is familiar to the user of a two-way "row by column" analysis of variance, except that it is carried out here for 21 variables and all of their linear combinations. Also, there is a confounding difficulty due to unequal sample sizes.

Six artificial variables were added to the original 21. These variables take the same values on all the individuals of a given group, and their values on the six groups are shown in Table 10.5.2. The symbols S, R_1, R_2, I_1, and I_2 may be regarded as abbreviations for *sex dummy*, *first race dummy*, *second race dummy*, *first interaction dummy*, and *second interaction dummy*, respectively. These variables take the place of the indicator variables of the six groups used in the original discussion of multivariate analysis of variance in Section 9.4. For the purpose of ordinary six sample multiple discriminant analysis the above set of six dummy variables is equivalent to the choice of V_0 together with any five of the six group indicator variables; the basic requirement is that both sets include V_0 and span the same six-dimensional subspace. But the present set is much more convenient for computing a decomposition into sex, race, and race by sex interaction components.

The selected dummy variables have the property that, had the sample sizes been equal, the four subspaces spanned in $\mathcal{N}$ by the representatives of V_0, S, $[R_1, R_2]$, $[I_1, I_2]$ would have been orthogonal. The difficulty caused by the lack of balanced sample sizes is not computational only but also conceptual, for it is no longer clear how to break the six-dimensional subspace of $\mathcal{N}$ spanned by the dummy variables into a direct sum of four orthogonal subspaces labelled for grand mean, sex differences, race differences, and race by sex interactions. Various decompositions are possible depending on different orders of applying successive orthogonalization to the dummy variables. For example, suppose that V_0, S', $[R_1', R_2']$, $[I_1', I_2']$ represent the set V_0, S, $[R_1, R_2]$, $[I_1, I_2]$ after successive orthogonalization in the stated order, according to the sample raw sum inner product. Then the subspaces of $\mathcal{N}$ spanned by the representatives of V_0, S', $[R_1', R_2']$ and $[I_1', I_2']$ are orthogonal and could be labelled for grand mean, sex differences, race differences, and race by sex interactions, respectively. On the other hand, if the orthogonalization is carried out in the order V_0, $[R_1, R_2]$, S, $[I_1, I_2]$, then the resulting V_0, $[R_1'', R_2'']$, S'', $[I_1', I_2']$ define alternative candidates for the orthogonal subspaces to be associated with race differences and sex differences.

Several other orders of orthogonalization each beginning with V_0 are possible, but the orders selected above are perhaps most natural on the grounds that simpler main effects should be hypothesized before more complicated interaction effects. In any case, only the selected pair of orders is carried along in this example to illustrate the fact of confounding of sex main effects and race main effects. The dilemma posed by such *confounding* may be clarified as follows.

The sex differences measured by components along S' in $\mathcal{N}$ are free of any constant addition to all of the data on a given variable, but they are not free of additions which are constant only for a given race. On the other hand, components along S'' are unaffected by systematic race differences. The difficulty with S'' is that, when sample sizes are unequal, valid sex differences necessarily contribute apparent race differences so that the use of S'' in place of S' eliminates valid as well as spurious sex differences.

The possible extent of this type of confounding may be judged by looking at the angles among the dummy variables in $\mathcal{N}$. It is assumed by convention that V_0 components should be removed first. The cosines of the angles among the components of S, R_1, R_2, I_1, I_2 are given by the total sample correlation matrix

$$\begin{bmatrix} 1.0000 & 0.0894 & 0.0773 & 0.0970 & 0.0773 \\ 0.0894 & 1.0000 & 0.5101 & -0.1213 & -0.1213 \\ 0.0773 & 0.5101 & 1.0000 & -0.1090 & -0.1402 \\ 0.0970 & -0.1213 & -0.1090 & 1.0000 & 0.4953 \\ 0.0773 & -0.1213 & -0.1402 & 0.4953 & 1.0000 \end{bmatrix}$$

which was obtained as part of the output of the computations to be described shortly. The square of the multiple correlation coefficient between S and $[R_1, R_2]$ is 0.0083, the fraction of the squared components associated with sex difference which could conceivably be falsely eliminated when S' is replaced by S''. By such reasoning it is clear that confounding effects are necessarily rather slight between the major sources of variation associated with sex and race. Nevertheless, the computations were performed assigning the doubtful race and sex components in both ways.

Multiple discriminant analysis was carried out with the pooled within sample covariance inner product playing the role of π in Section 10.4 and with seven different choices of a numerator inner product reflecting differences among the sample means. The numerator inner products were in each case the inner products of the sample representation in a subspace of $\mathcal{N}$ of the data vectors of 21 observed variables, the seven subspaces of $\mathcal{N}$ being those spanned by S', $[R_1', R_2']$, $[R_1'', R_2'']$, S'', $[S', R_1', R_2']$, $[I_1', I_2']$, and $[S', R_1', R_2', I_1', I_2']$. These analyses produced one eigenvector or discriminant variable for each dimension, i.e., $1 + 2 + 2 + 1 + 3 + 2 + 5 = 16$ variables altogether. Of course, all of these variables lie in a single five-dimensional space of best linear discriminants, and therefore must exhibit substantial correlations which will be displayed shortly.

The computing steps were as follows. Basic linear and quadratic statistics were computed for the total sample of 276 using a program which gave a vector of means, a vector of standard deviations, and a correlation matrix for the 26 variables consisting of S, R_1, R_2, I_1, I_2 and the 21 original variables. A more convenient starting point would appear to be simply the total sum of products matrix corrected for the grand mean, but the analysis can be carried out in terms of a rescaled basis and the correlation matrix described above is in fact a total sum of products matrix corrected for the grand mean for a basis in which each of the original elements is divided by $\sqrt{275}$ times its standard deviation. To compensate for the nuisance of an additional transformation, the scaling provides an array of numbers more alike in order of magnitude and hence easier to scan by eye.

Subsequent steps were based on the correlation matrix (*cum* total sum of products matrix corrected for the grand mean) as follows. First the operation SWP[1, 2, 3, 4, 5] removed components along S, R_1, R_2, I_1, I_2 so that the lower right 21×21 part represented a pooled within sample sum inner product for the rescaled variables, i.e., the inner product which plays the role of π in Section 10.4 and which will be called here the *denominator inner product*. Recall that π produces the same discriminant variables as does the pooled within sample covariance which differs only by a scale factor.

Secondly, the operator MST[6, 7, . . . , 26] was applied to the output of the first step. The second input matrix of the MST operator was a diagonal matrix whose elements were the scale factors ($\sqrt{275}$ standard deviation)$^{-1}$ which express the scaled basis in terms of the original basis of variables. The MST operator effects a transformation of the first input matrix so that it refers to a basis whose last 21 elements are orthonormal with respect to the denominator inner product; achieving the orthonormal basis is always a preliminary to an eigenvector calculation. The first output matrix of the MST operator is denoted here by $\mathbf{Q}$. The 21×21 part of the second MST output matrix expresses the orthonormal basis in terms of the original 21 measured variables.

The next step is to find the $\mathbf{T}_A$ matrix and its various decompositions which are called here numerator inner product matrices. These are all expressed in terms of the basis produced by the MST operator. They are found by RSW operations, which add back to $\mathbf{Q}$ various removed components, followed by subtractions to isolate these added back components. Specifically

RSW[4, 5]**Q**,
RSW[4, 5, 2, 3]**Q**,
RSW[4, 5, 1]**Q**, and
RSW[4, 5, 1, 2, 3]**Q**

were found, and thence

RSW[4, 5, 1, 2, 3]**Q** − RSW[4, 5, 2, 3]**Q**,
RSW[4, 5, 2, 3]**Q** − RSW[4, 5]**Q**,
RSW[4, 5, 1, 2, 3]**Q** − RSW[4, 5, 1]**Q**,
RSW[4, 5, 1]**Q** − RSW[4, 5]**Q**,
RSW[4, 5, 1, 2, 3]**Q** − RSW[4, 5]**Q**,
RSW[4, 5]**Q** − **Q**, and
RSW[4, 5, 1, 2, 3]**Q** − **Q**,

which provided, respectively, the numerator inner product matrices relative to the orthonormal basis, associated with

Sex, unadjusted for race,
Race, adjusted for sex,
Race, unadjusted for sex,
Sex, adjusted for race,
Sex and race together,
Race by sex interaction, adjusted for sex and race, and
Race, sex, and race by sex interaction all together.

The SDG operator was applied to the 21×21 parts of each of these numerator inner product matrices yielding the following nonzero eigenvalues:

2.4184,
2.6015, 0.7714,
2.6258, 0.7396,
2.4260,
2.8627, 2.1958, 0.7328,
0.1570, 0.0671, and
2.9037, 2.2021, 0.7476, 0.1017, 0.0605.

Some interpretations of these eigenvalues will be reported in Section 14.3.

The second input matrix for each of these SDG operations was the second output matrix of the MST operation. Thus the second output matrix of each SDG operation produces eigenvectors expressed as linear combinations of the original 21 variables. Since these eigenvectors have unit norms according to the pooled within sample sum inner product, they were multiplied by $\sqrt{270}$ so they finally had unit variances according to the pooled within sample covariance inner product. Altogether, 7 sets of eigenvectors were found, including 16 discriminant variables.

The eigenvectors were then applied to the 276×21 data matrix to produce the 276×16 data matrix of the 16 discriminants. The pooled within sample covariance matrix for the 16 discriminants, as directly computed from the 276×16 data matrix, is shown in Table 10.5.3.

Since Table 10.5.3 was computed as a sample covariance matrix, the fact that the diagonal elements are very close to unity serves as a check on the intended normalization of the discriminant variables. Likewise the zero covariances within the blocks of 1, 2, 2, 1, 3, 2, 5 variables in order are checks on these theoretically intended zero covariances.

Very high correlations may be observed in positions (6, 1), (4, 2), (5, 3), indicating that the two approaches to sex and race discriminants produced almost identical results. Other high correlations may be observed in places where they make sense. For example, discriminants 1, 2, 3, 11, 12 provide one basis of the five-dimensional space of best linear discriminators while discriminants 12, 13, 14, 15, 16 provide another. The elements of the first basis have direct relations to sex (1), race (2 and 3), and interaction (11 and 12), but the first basis is not orthonormal. The second basis is the one provided by the straightforward analysis described in Section 10.4 and this second basis is orthonormal. The correlation matrix above shows a rough pairing of these discriminators in the orders 1, 2, 3, 11, 12, and 13, 12, 14, 15, 16 but a better matching of 1 and 2 could be provided by a pair of linear combinations of 12 and 13. Thus it appears that the general discriminators 12 through 16 could reasonably be labelled for race, sex, and interaction effects, but that sharper delineations of these effects are provided by the decomposition analyses.

Table 10.5.3

1.000	−.131	.183	−.166	−.029	.998	−.675	.773	.084	.174	.017	−.657	.749	.086	−.003	−.002
−.131	1.000	.000	.999	.004	−.092	.819	.573	.014	−.519	−.122	.832	.554	.005	.026	.003
.183	.000	1.000	−.001	−.988	.233	−.143	.228	−.963	.246	−.272	−.195	.228	−.961	−.043	.026
−.166	.999	−.001	1.000	−.000	−.127	.839	.545	.006	−.521	−.123	.851	.525	−.004	.025	.003
−.029	.004	−.988	−.000	1.000	−.079	.058	−.100	.993	−.235	.276	.100	−.098	.992	.044	−.026
.998	−.092	.233	−.127	−.079	1.000	−.646	.762	.035	.166	−.002	−.628	.777	.038	−.004	−.000
−.675	.819	−.143	.839	.058	−.646	1.000	.000	−.000	.495	−.090	.999	−.023	−.009	.022	.002
.733	.573	.228	.545	−.100	.762	.000	1.000	.000	−.192	−.091	.023	1.000	−.004	.011	.003
.084	.014	−.963	.006	.993	.035	−.000	.000	1.000	−.227	.274	.008	.003	.999	.044	−.026
.174	−.519	.246	−.521	−.235	.166	−.495	−.192	−.227	1.000	−.000	−.520	−.190	−.258	.792	−.007
.017	−.122	−.272	−.123	.276	−.002	−.090	−.091	.274	−.000	1.000	−.092	−.091	.299	.024	.945
−.657	.832	−.195	.851	.100	−.628	.999	.023	.008	−.520	−.092	1.000	.000	.000	.000	.000
.749	.554	.228	.525	−.098	.777	−.023	1.000	.003	−.190	−.091	.000	1.000	.000	.000	.000
.086	.005	−.961	−.004	.992	.038	−.009	−.004	.999	−.258	.299	.000	.000	1.000	.000	.000
−.003	.026	−.043	.025	.044	−.004	.022	.011	.044	.792	.024	.000	.000	.000	1.000	.000
−.002	.003	.026	.003	−.026	−.000	.002	.003	−.026	−.007	.945	.000	.000	.000	.000	1.000

Three sets of two-dimensional plots were prepared to give pictures of the variation within and among samples for three pairs of discriminant variables 1 and 2, 2 and 3, and 7 and 8. The first pair of these sets together covers the sex and race main effect discriminators while the third set refers to the interaction discriminators. In each of the three sets, a set of 6 scatterplots show the individual skulls within each sample and also the sample concentration ellipse (Figs. 10.5.2–7, 10.5.9–14, and 10.5.16–21). A seventh plot shows all 6 ellipses of concentration (Fig. 10.5.1, 10.5.8, and 10.5.15).

Table 10.5.4

ACTUAL AND EXPECTED FREQUENCIES WITHIN CONCENTRATION ELLIPSES. THE FIRST THREE NUMBERS DENOTE ACTUAL FREQUENCIES FOR THE DISCRIMINANT PAIRS (1, 2), (2, 3), AND (7, 8). THE FOURTH NUMBER DENOTES AN APPROXIMATE EXPECTED FREQUENCY UNDER NORMALITY. THE BRACKETED NUMBER IS AN APPROPRIATE SAMPLING STANDARD DEVIATION.

	Male	Female
Japanese	22 23 20 22.03 (3.66)	15 12 19 13.77 (2.89)
Ainu	26 25 22 22.43 (3.69)	16 18 21 21.64 (3.62)
Australian	17 15 14 14.95 (3.01)	15 16 15 13.77 (2.89)

The 18 scatterplots each present to the eye much the same appearance as a sample of random drawings from a bivariate normal distribution. The distributions roughly follow the shape of the concentration ellipses without definite clusters or patterns of a nonelliptical sort. A brief analysis was done which indicates that the distributions do not have "heavy tails," i.e., do not have too much weight far from the means relative to the bivariate normal distribution. The proportion of a bivariate normal distribution contained within its concentration ellipse is the probability that a $\chi^2(2, 1)$ random variable is less than unity or $1 - e^{-1/2} = 0.39347$. The expected numbers of sample individuals within their sample concentration ellipses should under normality be roughly 0.39347 times the sample sizes, as shown in Table 10.5.4 along with the observed numbers.

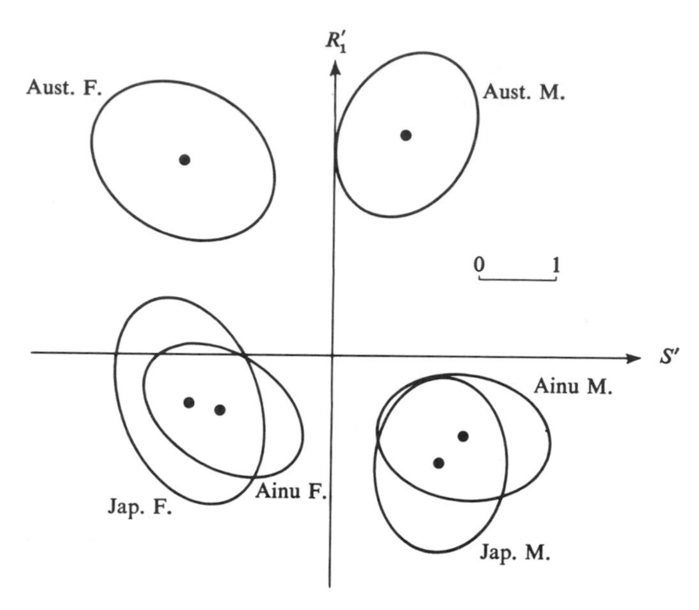

Fig. 10.5.1. Mean-centered sample concentration ellipses for a sex discriminant and first race discriminant. The pooled within sample concentration ellipse is a unit circle in the scale shown.

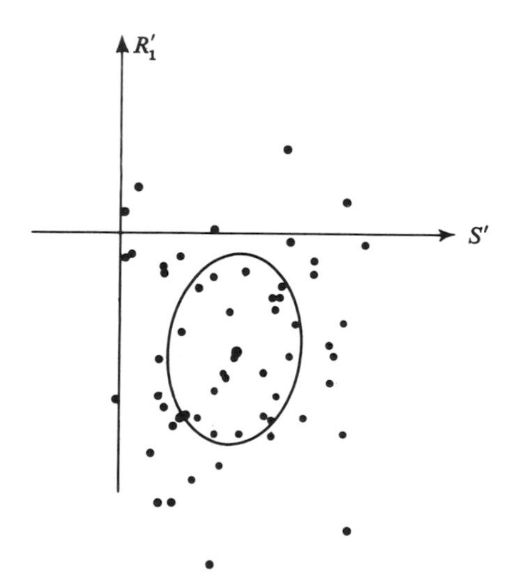

Fig. 10.5.2. The scatterplot of the Japanese male sample corresponding to the ellipse shown in Fig. 10.5.1.

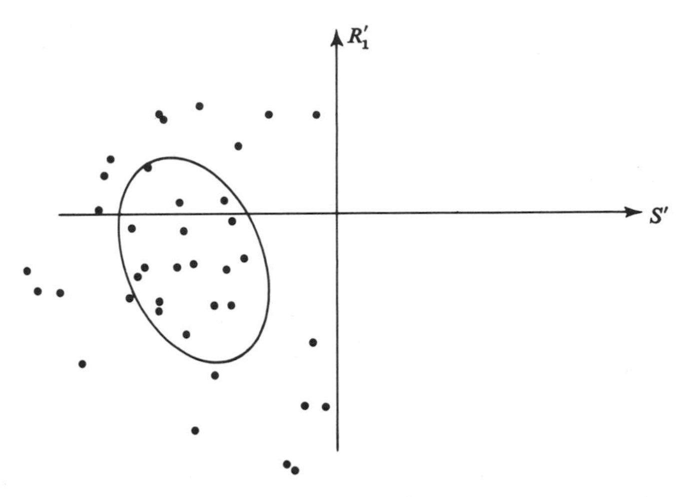

Fig. 10.5.3. The scatterplot of the Japanese female sample corresponding to the ellipse shown in Fig. 10.5.1.

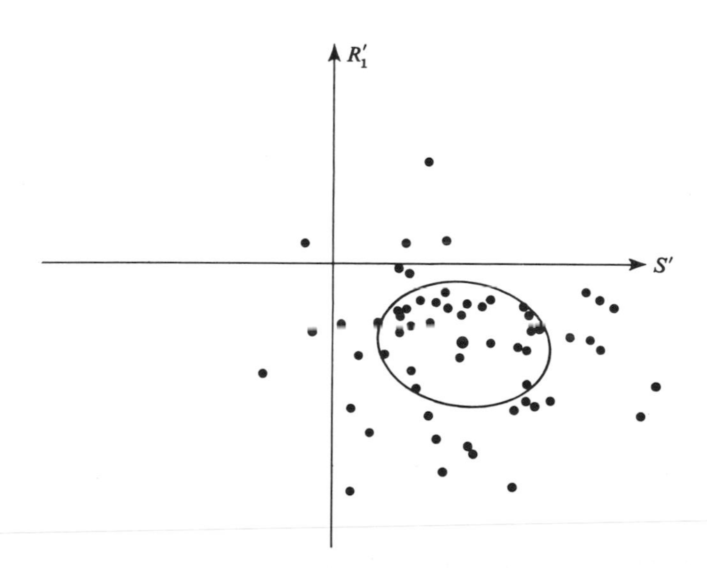

Fig. 10.5.4. The scatterplot of the Ainu male sample corresponding to the ellipse shown in Fig. 10.5.1.

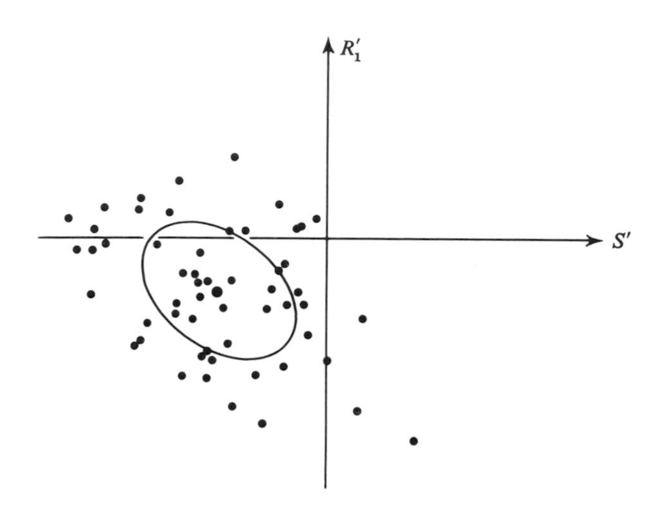

Fig. 10.5.5. The scatterplot of the Ainu female sample corresponding to the ellipse shown in Fig. 10.5.1.

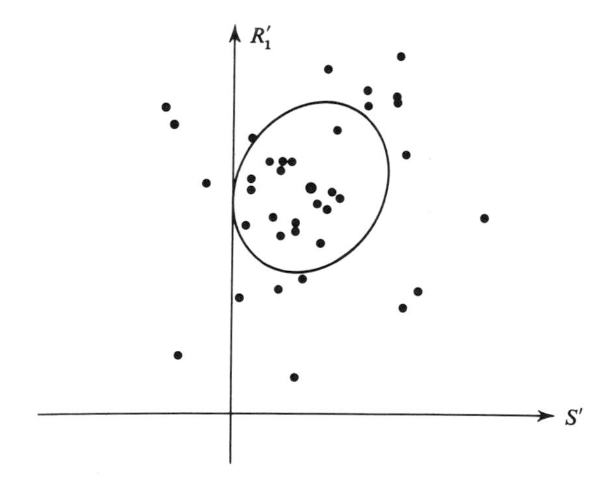

Fig. 10.5.6. The scatterplot of the Australian male sample corresponding to the ellipse shown in Fig. 10.5.1.

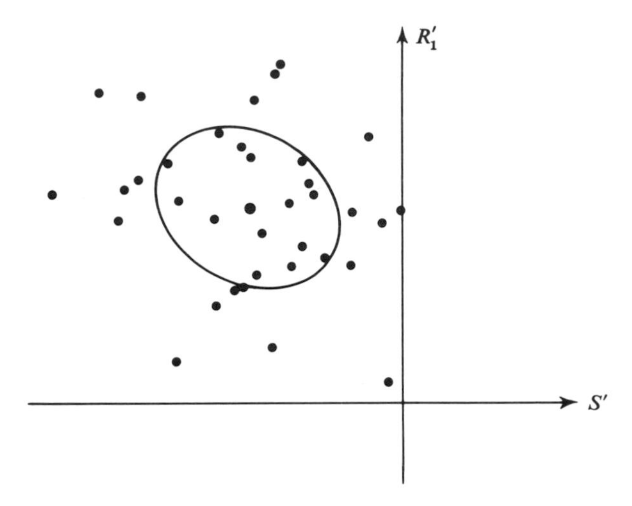

Fig. 10.5.7. The scatterplot of the Australian female sample corresponding to the ellipse shown in Fig. 10.5.1.

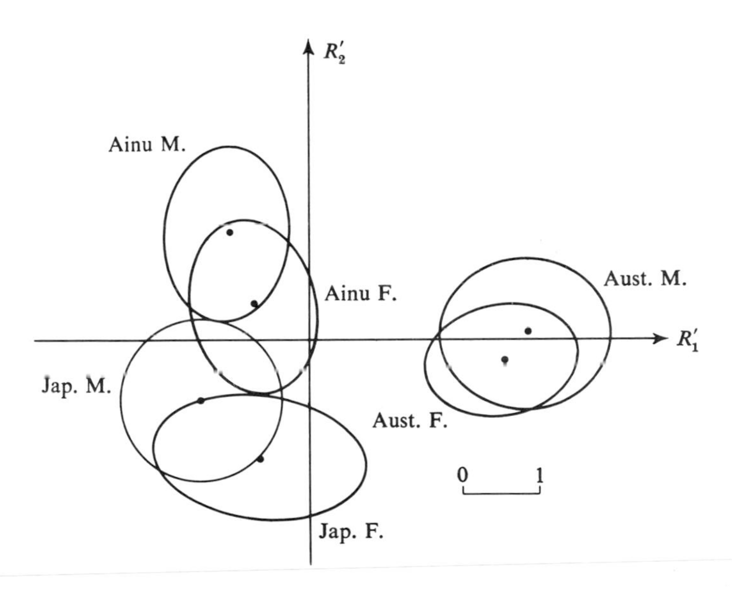

Fig. 10.5.8. Mean-centered sample concentration ellipses for a pair of race discriminants. The pooled within sample concentration ellipse is a unit circle in the scale shown.

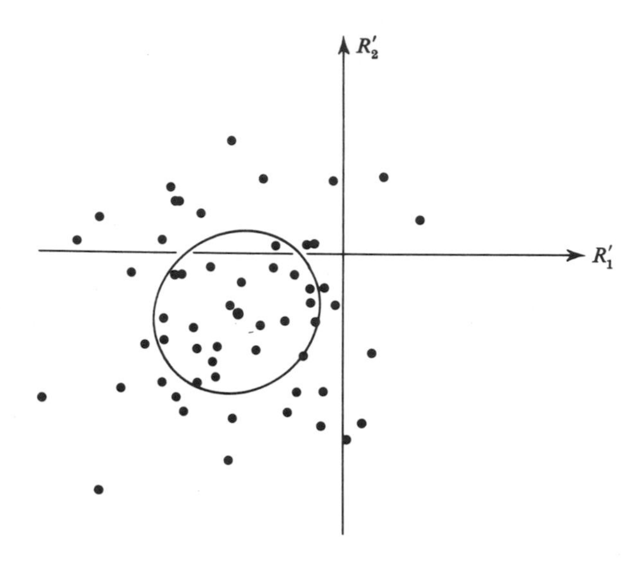

Fig. 10.5.9. The scatterplot of the Japanese male sample corresponding to the ellipse shown in Fig. 10.5.8.

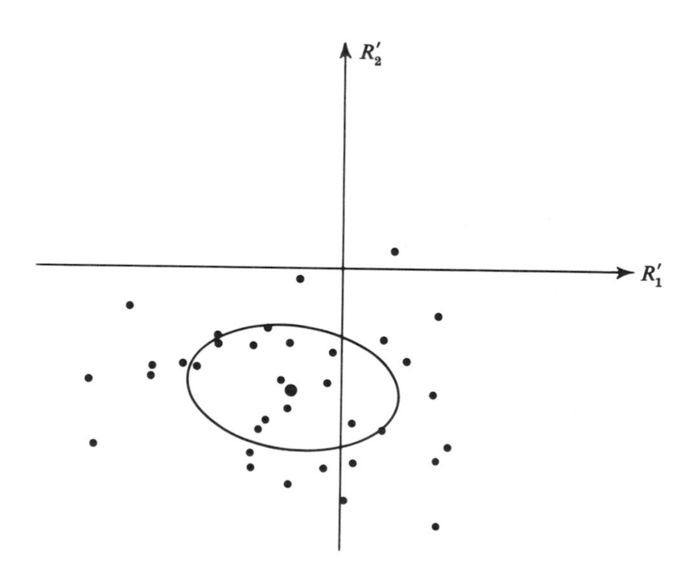

Fig. 10.5.10. The scatterplot of the Japanese female sample corresponding to the ellipse shown in Fig. 10.5.8.

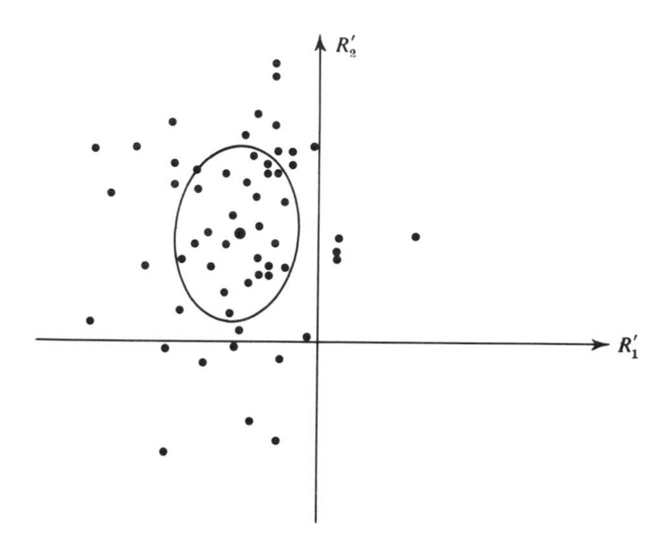

Fig. 10.5.11. The scatterplot of the Ainu male sample corresponding to the ellipse shown in Fig. 10.5.8.

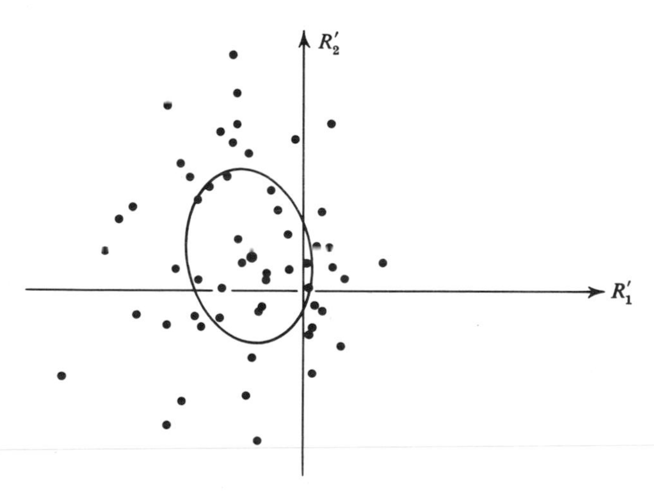

Fig. 10.5.12. The scatterplot of the Ainu female sample corresponding to the ellipse shown in Fig. 10.5.8.

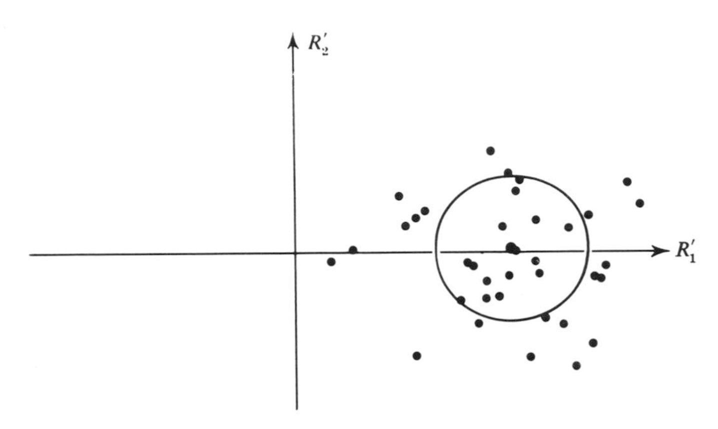

Fig. 10.5.13. The scatterplot of the Australian male sample corresponding to the ellipse shown in Fig. 10.5.8.

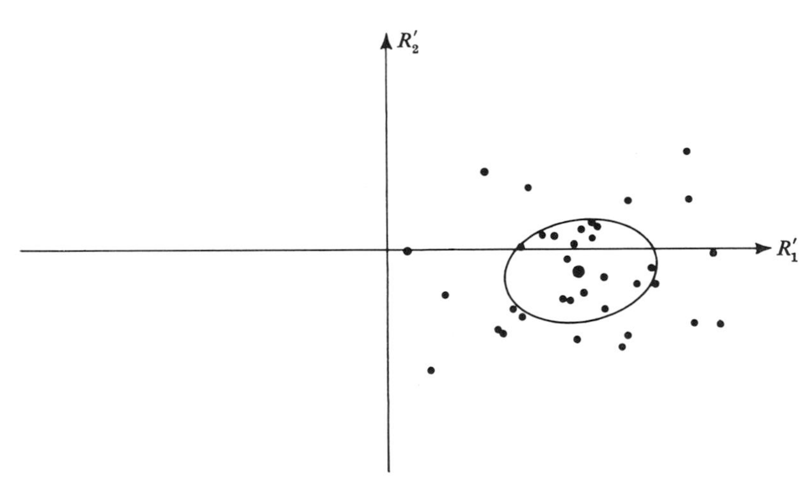

Fig. 10.5.14. The scatterplot of the Australian female sample corresponding to the ellipse shown in Fig. 10.5.8.

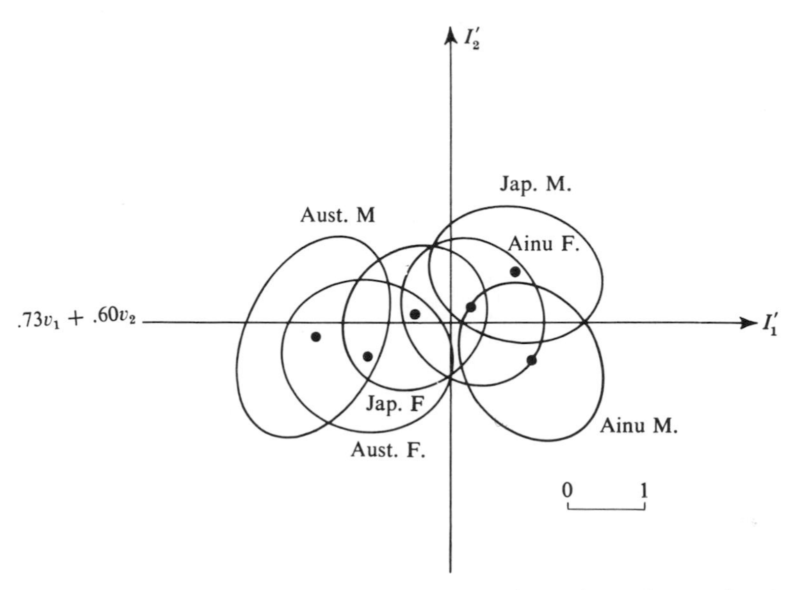

Fig. 10.5.15. Mean-centered sample concentration ellipses for a pair of sex by race interaction discriminants. The pooled within sample concentration ellipse is a unit circle in the scale shown.

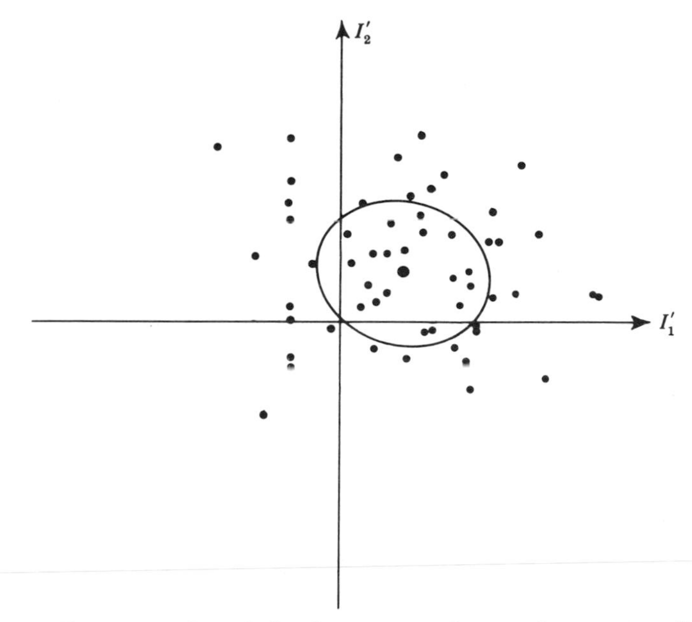

Fig. 10.5.16. The scatterplot of the Japanese male sample corresponding to the ellipse shown in Fig. 10.5.15.

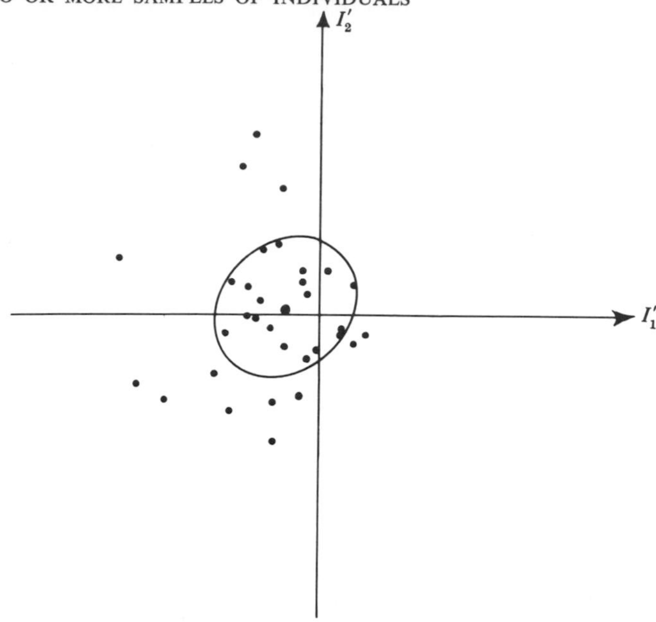

Fig. 10.5.17. The scatterplot of the Japanese female sample corresponding to the ellipse shown in Fig. 10.5.15.

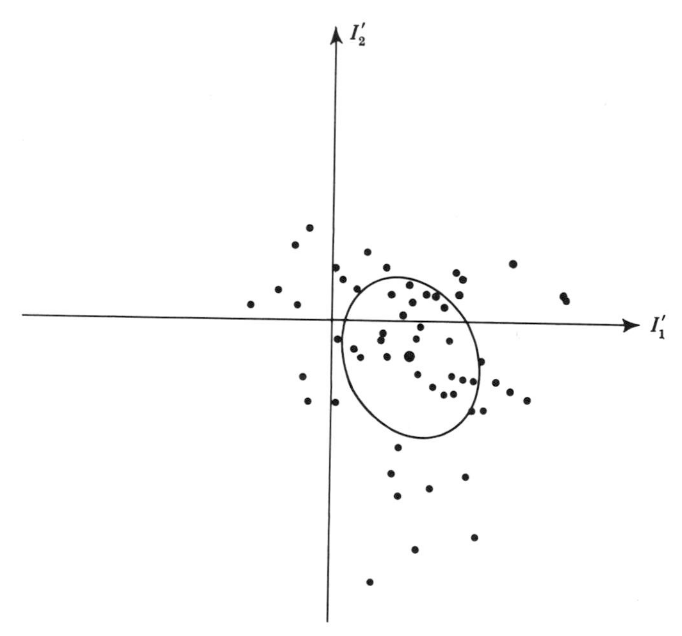

Fig. 10.5.18. The scatterplot of the Ainu male sample corresponding to the ellipse shown in Fig. 10.5.15.

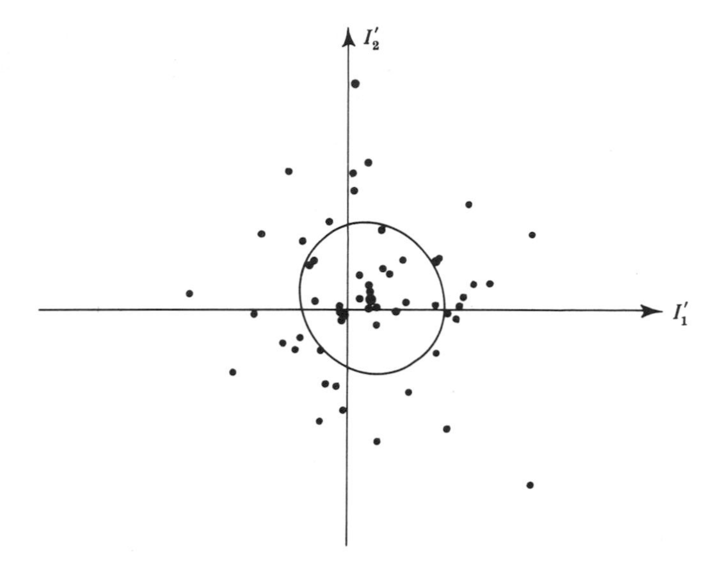

Fig. 10.5.19. The scatterplot of the Ainu female sample corresponding to the ellipse shown in Fig. 10.5.15.

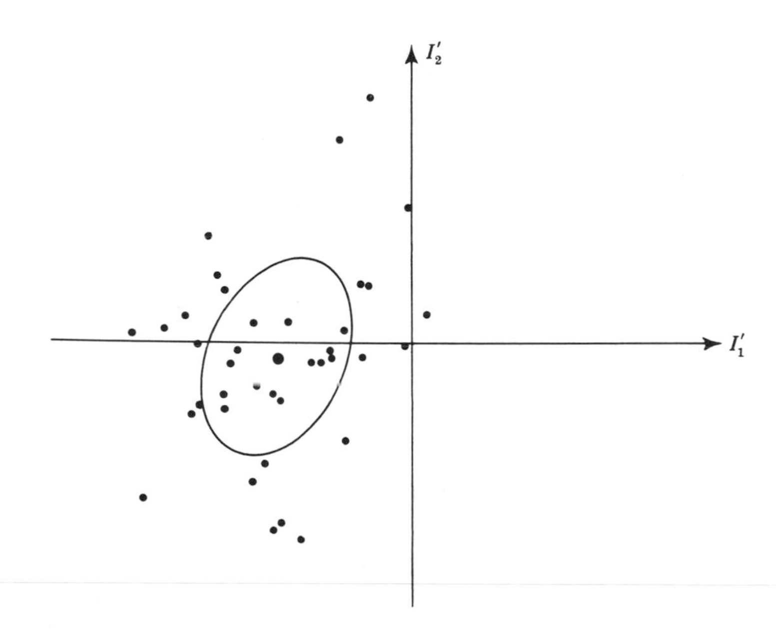

Fig. 10.5.20. The scatterplot of the Australian male sample corresponding to the ellipse shown in Fig. 10.5.15.

There are no serious discrepancies; the overall observed fraction within ellipses is $\frac{331}{828} = 0.400$ which is quite close to 0.393. Unnormally heavy tails would have shown up in expanded concentration ellipses without much effect in the center of the distribution, and one would have expected an increased observed fraction within the ellipses.

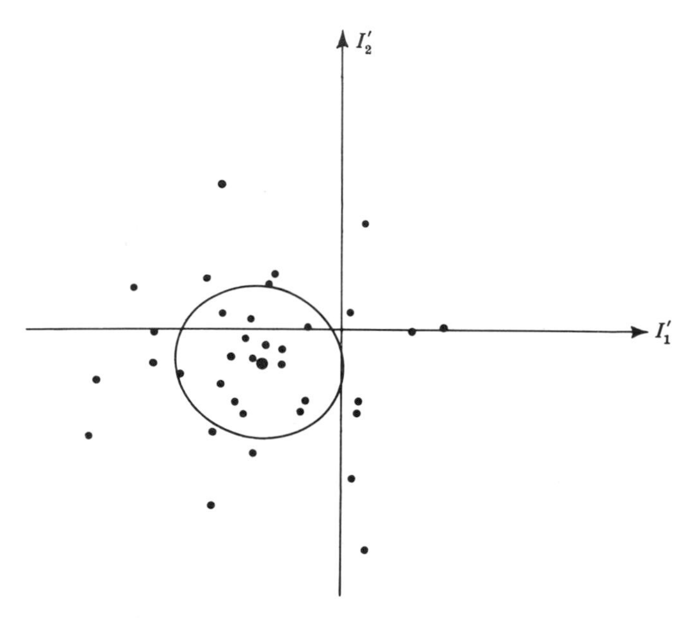

Fig. 10.5.21. The scatterplot of the Australian female sample corresponding to the ellipse shown in Fig. 10.5.15.

Attention is now directed to the sample differences visible in Figs. 10.5.1, 10.5.8, and 10.5.15. An average of the six ellipses shown on each figure is the concentration ellipse determined by the pooled within sample covariance. Thus on Figs. 10.5.8 and 10.5.15 an average is provided by a unit circle while on Fig. 10.5.1 the average corresponds to unit variances and a covariance of −0.131. The deviations of the individual sample ellipses from their averages appear minor and roughly consistent with sampling variation about a common population ellipse.

The differences among the sample means provide more obvious and interesting patterns. Significance tests are applied in Section 14.3 which leave no doubt that the apparent sex differences shown in Fig. 10.5.1 and the apparent race differences shown in Figs. 10.5.1 and 10.5.8 are inconsistent with sampling variation based on samples from normal populations with zero race and sex differences, respectively. On the other hand, interaction differences associated with the variables pictured in Fig. 10.5.15 are not significant. It is apparent also that Figs. 10.5.1 and 10.5.8 are more likely to be overestimating the population, sex, and race differences than to be underestimating them, and some rough approaches to the correction of such biases are given in Section 14.3.

It is a property of these analyses that a discriminator chosen to discriminate well for one type of difference among populations need not have zero discriminating power against other types of differences *even when the dummy variables corresponding to the two types of differences are orthogonal.* For example, in Fig. 10.5.8 it is seen that the R_2' discriminator also shows a consistent sex difference. This property is a corollary of nonzero correlation between the sets of discriminators. For example, any variable uncorrelated with a sex discriminator must have zero mean differences on sex while any other variable does have a mean difference on sex.

Figure 10.5.8 suggests that the Ainus are somewhat closer to the Japanese than to the Australians and, moreover, are in no sense intermediate between the Japanese and Australians.

10.6 SMALL SAMPLES ON MANY VARIABLES

The distance and best linear discriminator analyses described in Sections 10.2 and 10.4 have assumed a rank p inner product π over $\mathscr{E}$. If π had been semi-definite, its dual π_d would have been a partial inner product defined over a subspace $\mathscr{V}$ of $\mathscr{F}$. Consequently, the distance D between a pair of means $m^{(1)} - m^{(2)}$ could not in general have been defined from (10.2.1). At the same time, the ratio (10.2.2) would have been either infinite or undefined for variables W in the subspace $\mathscr{U}$ of $\mathscr{E}$ over which $(W, W) = 0$, and the definition of best linear discriminator would have become meaningless.

An exception to these disasters arises when $m^{(1)} - m^{(2)}$ belongs to $\mathscr{V}$, for (10.2.1) again becomes meaningful. A meaningful definition of a best linear discriminator can then also be given, although such a best linear discriminator is unique only up to differences lying in the subspace $\mathscr{U}$ of $\mathscr{E}$. The exceptional case can arise in an artificial way, as in Example 10.1, where certain variables are redundant in the sense that their values for *every* sample individual are expressible as linear combinations of the values on the remaining variables. Barring such artificial relations among variables, with actual sample means it would almost never happen that $m^{(1)} - m^{(2)}$ would belong to $\mathscr{V}$. The purpose of this section is to draw attention to a pair of simple expedients which are available in the nonexceptional cases.

If π and π_d are sample-based covariance and concentration inner products of the various types described earlier in this chapter, the common cause of insufficient rank is insufficient sample size. The sample covariance of a p-variate sample of size n is necessarily semi-definite, in general of rank $n - 1$ when $n - 1 < p$. More generally, a linear weighting of sample covariances from k p-variate samples of sizes $n_1, n_2, \ldots, n_k$ is necessarily semi-definite, in general of rank $\sum_1^k (n_i - 1)$, when $\sum_1^k (n_i - 1) < p$. In these circumstances, the analyses of Sections 10.2 and 10.4 *using sample based inner products* become impossible. The following discussion concerns tentative ways to bypass this difficulty.

It is always possible to examine variables one at a time, or to examine them in small sets to which satisfactory multivariate methods apply. Such an approach leaves one with no easy method of forming a combined impression from the separate analyses, and sometimes a series of differences in sample means can be misleading if, due to unsuspected correlations, these differences are largely reflections and repetitions of a single phenomenon. Another approach is to use a few index variables constructed from the original variables via *a priori* weightings. In effect this asks the scientist who originally proposed the high-dimensional variable-space to give up the idea that statistical analysis *per se* can extract information from many variables and that he should condense his set of variables before coming to the statistician.

The author has proposed two methods for attempting to digest a large set of variables simultaneously (Dempster, 1960; 1963b). The aim of these methods is to be relatively free of the hard-to-assess covariation. Both methods rely on an initial reference inner product π. The first method simply suggests looking at the distance between sample means relative to π with the additional wrinkle that a scale factor for π is estimated from the data. This method would be comparable to the earlier methods of this chapter if π could be chosen proportional to a population covariance inner product. Its effectiveness in practice depends on faith in a feasible choice of π being reasonably effective. The second method is based on a faith in principal component analysis as a device for reducing the dimension of variable-space in such a way that important information is not lost. This is a considerable assumption when samples are small.

Current theories of statistical inference are not yet equipped to understand what can be learned from small samples on many variables. The author believes that such understanding, when it comes, will not be encouraging and that data collectors should not have high hopes from such data. The following example is indicative of the type of frustration that may result.

Example 10.4. The body of data considered here consists of 62 biochemical variables measured on each of 12 human subjects of whom four were alcoholics and eight were controls. The data were collected by Roger J. Williams *et al.* (1950) in a shot-gun attempt to find some biochemical differences between alcoholics and normal people. Of the 62 variables, 54 are chemical concentrations from samples of blood serum, urine, and saliva taken under controlled circumstances, five are taste threshholds, and three are phagocytic indices.

In these data, most of the individual variables have values which overlap considerably from one sample to the other, but a few show separation which would be judged significant by simple tests. The methods described above were tried out to see whether plausible methods of judging overall significance would tap hidden aspects of the data and would thereby render a clear judgment of significance. The answer on these data is negative.

An inner product π over the 62-dimensional variable-space was constructed by scaling the original variables so that they had a roughly similar scale of variation, and then choosing the scaled variables to be orthonormal according to π. It will be assumed here that the 12×62 data matrix $\mathbf{X}$ has been scaled to represent the orthonormal variables.

The first method of analysis is basically concerned with the squared length

$$(\bar{\mathbf{X}}^{(1)} - \bar{\mathbf{X}}^{(2)})(\bar{\mathbf{X}}^{(1)} - \bar{\mathbf{X}}^{(2)})'$$

which should be regarded as the squared norm according to π_d of the mean difference vector. This norm will be corrected to express it in a scale comparable to the variation in the samples.

To derive the scale factor, consider the data first as represented by 62 vectors in the 12-dimensional Euclidean space $\mathscr{N}$. As usual in analysis of variance, the orthonormal basis $\mathscr{N}$ corresponding to the original 12 sample individuals may be altered to an orthonormal basis whose first vector corresponds to the grand mean, whose second vector corresponds to the difference of sample means, and whose remaining vectors representing within sample variation are chosen in any way to complete the basis. Next consider the data plotted as 11 vectors $\mathbf{Z}^{(2)}, \mathbf{Z}^{(3)}, \ldots, \mathbf{Z}^{(12)}$ in individual-space $\mathscr{I}$, where $\mathbf{Z}^{(i)}$ for $i = 1, 2, \ldots, 12$ denote the rows of the data matrix $\mathbf{Z}$ expressed in terms of the new basis in $\mathscr{N}$.

Now

$$\mathbf{Z}^{(2)} = \pm \frac{\bar{\mathbf{X}}^{(1)} - \bar{\mathbf{X}}^{(2)}}{(\frac{1}{4} + \frac{1}{8})^{1/2}} \tag{10.6.1}$$

represents the differences between sample means, while $\mathbf{Z}^{(3)}, \mathbf{Z}^{(4)}, \ldots, \mathbf{Z}^{(12)}$ are comparable vectors measuring within sample variation. The quantity

$$\frac{1}{10} \sum_{j=3}^{12} \mathbf{Z}^{(j)} \mathbf{Z}^{(j)\prime}$$

estimates a factor which makes π comparable to within sample variation. Finally, the quantity

$$\dot{D}^2 = \frac{(\bar{\mathbf{X}}^{(1)} - \bar{\mathbf{X}}^{(2)})(\bar{\mathbf{X}}^{(1)} - \bar{\mathbf{X}}^{(2)})'}{\frac{1}{10} \sum_{j=3}^{12} \mathbf{Z}^{(j)} \mathbf{Z}^{(j)\prime}} \tag{10.6.2}$$

is suggested as a distance measure, roughly similar in intent to D^2 of Section 10.2.

The derivation makes use of a special basis in $\mathscr{N}$, but the reader may easily check that the denominator of (10.6.2) is $\operatorname{tr} \mathbf{S}$ where $\mathbf{S}$ is the pooled within sample covariance matrix relative to any basis orthonormal with respect to π. Thus

$$\dot{D}^2 = (\bar{\mathbf{X}}^{(1)} - \bar{\mathbf{X}}^{(2)})(\bar{\mathbf{X}}^{(1)} - \bar{\mathbf{X}}^{(2)})'/\mathrm{tr}\,\mathbf{S}. \tag{10.6.3}$$

To compute $\dot{D}^2$ one needs only the vector of mean differences and the pooled within sample covariance matrix $\mathbf{S}$ both computed from the scaled data matrix $\mathbf{X}$.

The result in the example was found to be

$$\dot{D}^2 = 3.685.$$

This value lies at roughly the 0.90 quantile of its normal theory null distribution (see Dempster, 1958; 1960) so should not be regarded as inconsistent with the hypotheses that populations of alcoholics and controls underlying the samples do not differ in their distributions on the 62 variables.

The second method of analysis begins with a reduction to a set of principal variables. The same reference inner product π was used, and the total sample sum inner product corrected for the grand mean was used to represent sample variation. An alternative choice would have been to represent the sample variation in terms of the pooled within sample covariance. The latter choice would have been more appropriate in the presence of clearly meaningful mean differences between the samples. The former was chosen here for technical reasons, to facilitate a program of stepwise significance testing (see Dempster, 1963a; 1963b).

The computations were carried out as follows. The scaled data matrix $\mathbf{X}$ was replaced by $\mathbf{Y}$ in which each element had its grand mean subtracted. The principal component analysis is defined in terms of the eigenvalues of the 62×62 matrix $\mathbf{Y}'\mathbf{Y}$ which, like $\mathbf{Y}$, has rank 11. In view of Theorem 6.5, the 11 nonzero eigenvalues of $\mathbf{Y}'\mathbf{Y}$ may also be found as the 11 nonzero eigenvalues of $\mathbf{YY}'$ where $\mathbf{YY}'$ is a more manageable matrix of dimensions 12×12 only. Also, according to Theorem 6.5, the eigenvectors of $\mathbf{YY}'$ provide the data matrix on the resulting principal variables. The computations were done by finding $\mathbf{YY}'$ and thence its 11 nonzero eigenvalues and eigenvectors. The result is shown in Table 10.6.1.

The principal variables are shifted in this analysis so that their grand means are zero. Consequently their sample mean differences may be computed as $\frac{3}{8}$ of the sums of the four alcoholic scores. Also the principal variables are scaled to be orthonormal according to the total sum inner product (corrected or not corrected for the grand mean), so that distances D'''^2 in the sense of Section 10.2 are very easily computed as the sums of squares of mean differences. Finally, the more usual D^2 relative to the pooled within sample covariance may be computed from (10.2.8) and (10.2.10). These distances are shown in Table 10.6.2 for subsets of the principal variables.

Table 10.6.1

Principal variable		1	2	3	4	5	6	7	8	9	10	11
Eigenvalues		159.[illegible]244	113.4557	83.4787	71.8194	65.1554	53.0508	43.0775	35.0866	29.5223	23.1098	10.3909
Alcoholic scores	1	.3995	.2505	.2552	.1988	.1644	.2078	.6103	.0390	.1729	.2704	.2060
	2	−.1970	−.0382	.5664	−.4960	−.0199	.0642	.1855	−.0799	−.4117	−.3059	−.0349
	3	.3277	−.1524	−.2095	−.0069	−.0938	−.6052	.1797	−.4787	.0970	−.3113	−.0155
	4	.2105	−.7613	−.1389	−.1612	−.1188	.4261	−.0875	.0399	.1246	.0859	.1397
Control scores	5	.0537	.2816	−.4066	.0295	−.0129	.2951	−.1367	−.4082	−.5704	.2615	−.0443
	6	−.2344	−.1063	.2893	.1471	−.3960	−.3854	−.1404	−.0104	−.0023	.6220	.0840
	7	.2268	−.0516	.3032	.6281	.0101	.0701	−.3401	.1650	−.1586	−.3090	−.3277
	8	−.3296	.0392	−.4109	.0748	−.3483	.0241	.4480	.4337	−.0154	−.1607	−.3097
	9	−.3339	−.2162	−.1369	.1184	.7928	−.1972	.0284	.0856	−.0555	.0686	.0805
	10	−.4058	.2356	.0569	.0514	−.0490	.3180	−.1618	−.4105	.5946	−.1951	.0101
	11	.0391	.2831	−.1338	−.0937	−.1019	−.1070	−.3011	.3788	−.0344	−.2470	.6954
	12	.2934	.2360	−.0343	−.4902	.1731	−.1105	−.2842	.2455	.2591	.2206	−.4838

Table 10.6.2

Principal variables included	D'''^2	D^2
1	0.0772	0.97
1, 2	0.1463	2.40
1, 2, 3	0.1779	3.38
1, 2, 3, 4	0.2083	4.69
1, 2, 3, 4, 5	0.2090	4.71
1, 2, 3, . . . , 6	0.2102	4.78
1, 2, 3, . . . , 7	0.4311	22.32
1, 2, 3, . . . , 8	0.3534	61.40
1, 2, 3, . . . , 9	0.3535	61.52
1, 2, 3, . . . , 10	0.3630	113.6
1, 2, 3, . . . , 11	0.3753	∞

The values of D^2 in Table 10.6.2 are quite meaningless as estimates of population distances. Indeed the tests of the successive increments in D^2 as described in Section 14.3 show that only the jump from 22.32 to 61.40 is beyond its 0.95 quantile assuming identical normal samples. Furthermore it is only slightly beyond at 0.96, and such a result among 10 tests is not surprising. It thus appears that the principal component analysis did not succeed in isolating variables which point to a difference between alcoholics and normal people.

CHAPTER 11

RANDOMIZED EXPERIMENTATION, MISSING VALUES, AND COVARIATES

11.1 GENERAL DISCUSSION

The type of data considered in Sections 11.1 and 11.2 has features of a single sample and features of several samples, simultaneously. It is supposed here that the individuals of a single sample are divided at random into several subsamples to which are applied different treatments whose effects are under investigation. One set of variables is measured before any treatments are applied, and on these variables the data may be regarded as a single sample. Another set of variables is measured after the treatments have been applied, and, since these variables are in general affected differently by the different treatments, the groups of individuals receiving different treatments should be regarded as different samples in relation to the post-treatment set of variables. The term *covariate* is commonly used for a variable in the set of variables measured before treatment, while the term *response variable* is used for a variable in the post-treatment set.

The importance of the set of covariates is that they can often be used to increase the accuracy with which the population means of response variables may be estimated from the samples in the different treatment groups. This idea may of course be given a precise analysis in terms of a precise theory of statistical inference as in Section 14.3, but the discussion of this section is more informal.

Suppose that the covariates are denoted by $V_1, V_2, \ldots, V_r$ and the response variables by $V_{r+1}, V_{r+2}, \ldots, V_p$. Then, in terms of an appropriate covariance inner product, each V_{r+i} may be split into a best linear predictor in terms of $V_1, V_2, \ldots, V_r$ and a residual variable, i.e., in symbols

$$V_{r+i} = \hat{V}_{r+i} + (V_{r+i} - \hat{V}_{r+i}) \qquad (11.1.1)$$

for $i = 1, 2, \ldots, p - r$, where

$$\hat{V}_{r+i} = b_{\overline{r+i}\,1} V_1 + b_{\overline{r+i}\,2} V_2 + \cdots + b_{\overline{r+i}\,r} V_r. \qquad (11.1.2)$$

The separate treatment groups may be regarded as randomly drawn from separate populations whose means are the same for the first term in (11.1.1) but different for the second term. Consequently, to estimate the population mean of V_{r+i} for a specified treatment group, one may estimate the population mean of the first term in (11.1.1) using the sample mean of the whole sample, then estimate the population mean of the second term in (11.1.1) using only the sample with the specified treatment, and, finally, add the estimates for the two terms. To express the estimation scheme in formulas, suppose that the treatment groups are indexed by t running over $t = 1, 2, \ldots, k$ so that the k sample notation of Chapter 10 may be adopted. Denoting the estimate of the population mean for variable V_{r+i} in treatment group t by $\hat{\mu}^{(t)}_{r+i}$, the above prescription for finding $\hat{\mu}^{(t)}_{r+i}$ may be written

$$\hat{\mu}^{(t)}_{r+i} = [b_{\overline{r+i}\,1}\bar{X}_1 + \cdots + b_{\overline{r+i}\,r}\bar{X}_r] + [\bar{X}^{(t)}_{\overline{r+i}} - b_{\overline{r+i}\,1}\bar{X}^{(t)}_1 - \cdots - b_{\overline{r+i}\,r}\bar{X}^{(t)}_r] \quad (11.1.3)$$

or

$$\hat{\mu}^{(t)}_{r+i} = \bar{X}^{(t)}_{r+i} - [b_{\overline{r+i}\,1}(\bar{X}^{(t)}_1 - \bar{X}_1) + b_{\overline{r+i}\,2}(\bar{X}^{(t)}_2 - \bar{X}_2) + \cdots + b_{\overline{r+i}\,r}(\bar{X}^{(t)}_r - \bar{X}_r)], \quad (11.1.4)$$

for $i = 1, 2, \ldots, p - r$.

The idea here is to capitalize as much as possible on the reduction of sampling error which accompanies increased sample size. This is accomplished by estimating from the whole sample a component of V_{r+i} with maximal variance, leaving a component with minimal variance to be estimated from the smaller sample receiving a specific treatment. Note that the second term in (11.1.4) just estimates zero whatever the choice of $b_{\overline{r+i}\,1}, b_{\overline{r+i}\,2}, \ldots, b_{\overline{r+i}\,r}$. Consider the relative performances of the estimator $\bar{X}^{(t)}_{r+i}$ which corresponds to dropping the correction term in (11.1.4) and the estimator $\hat{\mu}^{(t)}_{r+i}$ which uses the regression coefficients defining the best linear predictor. The gain from using $\hat{\mu}^{(t)}_{r+i}$ depends on the ratio of the (population) residual and fitted variances of the best linear predictor. If the fitted variance is zero, then $\hat{\mu}^{(t)}_{r+i} = \bar{X}^{(t)}_{r+i}$ and there is no gain. On the other hand, if the residual variance is zero, the second term in (11.1.3) is zero and the estimate is based entirely on the whole sample.

The covariance inner product used to define the best linear predictor involved in $\hat{\mu}^{(t)}_{r+i}$ should ideally be the population covariance associated with the tth treatment group. When this inner product is unknown, as is usually the case, several delicate problems are posed. Since the estimated coefficients $b_{\overline{r+i}\,j}$ in (11.1.3) are necessarily beset by sampling errors it is not clear that $\hat{\mu}^{(t)}_{r+i}$ is better than simply $\bar{X}^{(t)}_{r+i}$. Or it might be better than either of these to use guessed population regression coefficients or regression coefficients estimated from previous experience rather than those estimated from small samples. Moreover, if regression coefficients are to be estimated from a sample, it may or may not be wise to pretend that the k treatment groups have common population covariance inner products so that the pooled within sample covariance can be used in estimation, for the population covariances may be sufficiently different that separate estimation pays off. These issues come under the general question of how many parameters is it wise to fit with limited data, a sore spot in all statistical analyses where the samples are small. See Examples 11.1, 11.2, and 11.3 following for brief discussions in specific contexts.

Consider next the question: what is the proper definition of a sample best linear discriminator in the presence of covariates? Attention has been drawn by Cochran (1964) to two different answers to this question. (See also Cochran and Bliss, 1948.) The easiest answer is to view the data as illustrating the k sample situation treated in Chapter 10 and to define best linear discriminators as in that chapter. It can be argued, however, that this is wasteful of sample information, much as the use of $\bar{X}^{(t)}_{r+i}$ is wasteful relative to the use of $\hat{\mu}^{(t)}_{r+i}$. The best linear discriminators defined in Chapter 10 look among the linear combinations of *all* of $V_1, V_2, \ldots, V_p$ for those which maximize differences among the sample means in a special sense. To the extent that the sample means of $V_1, V_2, \ldots, V_r$ in the k treatment groups differ due to sampling fluctuations, these covariates will influence the best linear discriminators in a spurious way. The remedy is simply to replace the different sample means on $V_1, V_2, \ldots, V_r$ by a common grand mean.

The effect of the remedy is to produce an analysis which may be described as follows. Suppose that π and π_d denote the pair of dual inner products over $\mathscr{E}$ and $\mathscr{F}$ as used in Chapter 10 to define best linear discriminators. Suppose also that the best linear predictors used in (11.1.1) are defined with respect to π. *Then one need only look for best linear discriminators in the* $(p - r)$*-dimensional subspace of* $\mathscr{E}$ *spanned by the residual variables*

$$V_{r+i} - \hat{V}_{r+i} = V_{r+i} - b_{\overline{r+i}\,1}V_1 - b_{\overline{r+i}\,2}V_2 - \cdots - b_{\overline{r+i}\,r}V_r, \quad (11.1.5)$$

for $i = 1, 2, \ldots, p - r$. To check this assertion, consider a pair of variables

$$\sum_{j=1}^{p} \alpha_j V_j \qquad \text{and} \qquad \sum_{i=1}^{p-r} \alpha_{r+i}(V_{r+i} - \hat{V}_{r+i}). \quad (11.1.6)$$

If the first of these were contemplated as a best linear discriminator, it could be immediately rejected in favor of the second, which is of the restricted type. The reasoning here is that assuming the k groups to have the same means on $V_1, V_2, \ldots, V_r$, the pair of variables in (11.1.6) have identical mean differences among the k samples, while, by the properties of best linear predictors, the norm of the second variable in (11.1.6) is at least as small as the norm of the first variable. Consequently, the criterion D_{ij} as in (10.4.1) can only be reduced when the second variable replaces the first.

In practice, π must usually be estimated from sample data. In the following discussion it will be supposed that a common population covariance may be postulated to underlie the k treatment groups and therefore that the pooled within sample covariance is a reasonable choice for π. Of course, both of these suppositions have weaknesses. It may become apparent after analysis that the k treatment groups have quite different population covariance matrices, and then, as discussed in Chapter 10, it may be desirable to carry out the best linear discriminator analysis using a different weighting of the individual sample covariance inner products. Such re-analyses are not illustrated in this chapter. The second supposition was that the pooled within sample covariance inner product is sensible, assuming common population covariances. It could be argued that the total sample covariance is more appropriate for the covariates. However, the issue here is of small importance, nor does there necessarily exist an unambiguously appropriate way to mix the total sample covariance and the pooled within sample covariance.

(1, 1)	(1, 2)	(1, 3)	}Dummy variables
(2, 1)	(2, 2)	(2, 3)	}Covariates
(3, 1)	(3, 2)	(3, 3)	}Response variables

Fig. 11.1.1. Schematic diagram of the basic computing matrix for analyses with covariates.

The computations for a best linear discriminator analysis with covariates and with pooled sample covariance for π may be sketched as follows. A raw cross-products matrix should be created for variables of three types: response variables, covariates, and dummy variables including V_0. A matrix of this type may be viewed as in Fig. 11.1.1.

Sweeping on V_0 produces among other things the grand means used in (11.1.3) or (11.1.4), and sweeping on a set of k dummy variables, representing k dimensions in $\mathcal{N}$ spanned by the sample means, produces the sample means for the k treatment groups. Sweeping on both the dummy variables and the covariates produces in the (2, 3) position the regression coefficients required for (11.1.3) or (11.1.4) and (11.1.5). The same swept matrix produces in the (3, 3) position the pooled within sample sum inner product matrix for the residuals (11.1.5). Consequently, the best linear discriminators are found as the eigenvectors of this (3, 3) matrix relative to the (3, 3) matrix found after the further step of reverse sweeping the covariates. In practice, before carrying out the reverse sweeping of the covariates, one should apply an MST operator to the indices corresponding to the block of response variables, thus establishing an orthonormal basis for one of the inner products entering the eigenvalue analysis. The details of such a computation are illustrated in Example 11.2.

Up to this point, the use of covariates has been regarded as a technical device to improve the sensitivity of various comparisons. The section concludes with brief remarks on the potential use of covariates for predicting or deciding which treatment should be assigned to an individual. For example, in medicine such a use of covariates would be a mathematical device for improving diagnosis and prescription of treatment, where the diagnosis step remains hidden in the mathematical "black box." Surprisingly enough, the usefulness of covariates in this regard actually requires differences in covariance inner products among the treatment groups.

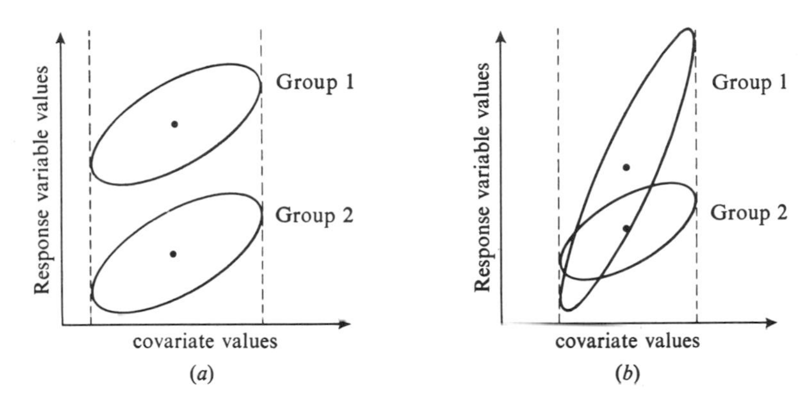

Fig. 11.1.2. Mean-centered concentration ellipses for a pair of hypothetical treatment groups: case *a* with common covariance, case *b* with different covariances.

It is sufficient for present purposes to consider a situation with two treatments, one response variable, and one covariate. Consider two possibilities as illustrated in Fig. 11.1.2 which shows mean-centered concentration ellipses in $\mathscr{F}$ for a pair of hypothetical treatment groups. Case *a* assumes that the covariance inner products are the same, while case *b* assumes they are different. In both cases the mean and variance of the covariate are shown as being the same for the two groups. In case *a* of Fig. 11.1.2, the treatment difference consists, as far as the basic linear and quadratic statistics show, of a vertical shift. The treatment difference appears to be same regardless of whether the covariate takes high or low values. In case *b*, however, it appears that the treatment difference changes markedly as the value assigned to the covariate changes. For example, if the situation were as pictured in case *b* of Fig. 11.1.2, and if a high value of the response variable were desirable, then it would be desirable to assign an individual with a high or medium score on the covariate to treatment group 1 and to assign an individual with a low score on the covariate to treatment group 2. The further development of the theory and practice of such a use of covariates is not pursued in this book.

11.2 EXAMPLES

Example 11.1. The first example reported here is a very small one to make clear the basic ideas before becoming involved in the computational complexity associated with a larger example. The data were used by Cochran (1964) to illustrate the two ways of defining a best linear discriminator that were discussed above. The sample consisted of $n = 108$ leprosy patients who were assigned at random to two treatment groups. The first group ($n_1 = 53$) received a drug D and the second group ($n_2 = 55$) received an ineffective placebo P which was actually a mild vitamin pill. A total bacteriological score taken over six fixed sites on the body was recorded for each patient at each of two times, namely, before treatment and after a period of daily treatments. The first score determines a covariate, say U, and the second score determines a response variable, say V. Thus, in the general notation of Section 11.1, $r = 1$ and $p = 2$. A high score on U or V indicates the presence of many leprosy bacilli.

The mean vectors for $[U, V]$ were reported to be

$$[10.6226, 7.2075] \quad \text{and} \quad [11.2364, 9.8909]$$

for groups D and P, respectively. The inner product matrices for the sum of products corrected for the grand mean were reported to be

$$\begin{bmatrix} 1314.5 & 1130.2 \\ 1130.2 & 1728.7 \end{bmatrix} \quad \text{and} \quad \begin{bmatrix} 1851.9 & 1605.4 \\ 1605.4 & 2665.3 \end{bmatrix}$$

again for $[U, V]$ and treatment groups D and P, respectively.

Cochran's analysis was based on (*i*) the difference of the above mean vectors (P less D)

$$[0.6138, 2.6834],$$

which leads to the between sample inner product matrix

$$[0.6138, 2.6834]'[0.6138, 2.6834]/(\tfrac{1}{53} + \tfrac{1}{55}) = \begin{bmatrix} 10.1 & 44.4 \\ 44.4 & 194.4 \end{bmatrix}$$

having a single degree of freedom, and (*ii*) the pooled within sample sum of products matrix

$$\begin{bmatrix} 3166.4 & 2735.6 \\ 2735.6 & 4394.0 \end{bmatrix}$$

on 106 degrees of freedom, which is found by summing the contributions from each sample reported above.

The reader may wish to follow Cochran and pursue the analysis in terms of U and V. A slightly richer variant of the analysis is produced by noting that, in the present context,

$$W = V - U$$

is a natural alternative choice of response variable, measuring as it does the change in bacteriological score associated with treatment. The following analysis uses therefore the pair $[U, W]$ regarded as [covariate, response variable]. The mean vectors for $[U, W]$ are easily computed from above to be

$$[10.6226, -3.4151] \quad \text{and} \quad [11.2364, -1.3455]$$

for D and P, respectively. Similarly, the sample corrected sum inner product matrices in $[U, W]$ terms are

$$\begin{bmatrix} 1314.5 & -184.3 \\ -184.3 & 782.8 \end{bmatrix} \quad \text{and} \quad \begin{bmatrix} 1851.9 & -246.5 \\ -246.5 & 1306.4 \end{bmatrix},$$

which yield after division by 52 and 54 the sample covariance matrices

$$\begin{bmatrix} 25.279 & -3.544 \\ -3.544 & 15.054 \end{bmatrix} \quad \text{and} \quad \begin{bmatrix} 34.294 & -4.565 \\ -4.565 & 24.193 \end{bmatrix}$$

for D and P, respectively.

The above statistics indicate that the P group was initially slightly worse than the D group on the bacteriological score, a difference which would be assigned, *a priori* at least, to sampling fluctuations associated with the randomization design of the experiment. Both groups improved during treatment, the D group substantially more than the P group. These improvements may be ascribed to a combination of sampling fluctuations and treatment effects. The sample covariance matrices indicate that the P group was initially more variable than the D group, again presumably a sampling fluctuation, and the change associated with treatment was likewise more variable in the P group, due to some combination of sampling and treatment effects. The sample correlation coefficients from the two samples are -0.182 and -0.158 which are remarkably small. The relations between these sample statistics on the one hand and hypothetical population values on the other hand may be explained via the tool of significance testing. In particular, it could be shown (cf. Section 14.2) that the sample correlation coefficients -0.182 and -0.158 do not differ significantly from zero in the ordinary normal sampling theory sense. This finding rather undercuts the use of the covariate in connection with these data, a point which will be reviewed later.

To illustrate the statistics defined in Section 11.1, a convenient starting place is the pooled within sample covariance matrix of (U, W) which is easily computed to be

$$\begin{bmatrix} 29.872 & -4.064 \\ -4.064 & 19.709 \end{bmatrix}.$$

Sweeping on the first row and column yields

$$\begin{bmatrix} -0.033476 & -0.13605 \\ -0.13605 & 19.156 \end{bmatrix}.$$

It follows that, according to the pooled within sample covariance, the variables

U and $W + 0.13605U$ are uncorrelated with variances 29.872 and 19.156. More completely, the pair $[U, W + 0.13605U]$ has mean difference vector

$$[0.6138, 2.1531]$$

and pooled within sample covariance matrix

$$\begin{bmatrix} 29.872 & 0 \\ 0 & 19.156 \end{bmatrix}.$$

In the present situation there are three fairly natural definitions of a best linear discriminator between the two groups. The first two are those contrasted by Cochran. First, one may ignore the fact that the 0.6138 really estimates zero and compute a best linear discriminator as in Section 10.2. Applying (10.2.7) to the basis $[U, W + 0.13605U]$ yields

$$(0.6138/29.872)U + (2.1531/19.156)(W + 0.13605U),$$

or, rescaling,

$$W + 0.13605U + (0.6138/29.872)(19.156/2.1531)U = W + 0.31886U.$$

The D^2 associated with this best linear discriminator is

$$0.6138^2/29.872 + 2.1531^2/19.156 = 0.0126 + 0.2420 = 0.2546.$$

Second, it may be assumed that the mean difference in U should be zero, in which case the discriminator is simply the residual

$$W + 0.13605U,$$

whose associated D^2 is

$$2.1531^2/19.156 = 0.2420.$$

The third method is suggested by the idea that the regression coefficient 0.13605 really estimates zero which would imply that the best linear discriminator should be

$$W,$$

with associated D^2

$$2.0696^2/19.709 = 0.2173.$$

Replacing W by $V - U$, the three discriminators above may be expressed as

$$V - 0.68114U,$$

$$V - 0.86395U,$$

and

$$V - U.$$

There are three corresponding ways to estimate the population mean of V in the two treatment groups. The first way ignores the fact that the data are a single sample and simply uses the original sample means

$$7.2075 \quad \text{for } D, \qquad \text{and} \qquad 9.8909 \quad \text{for } P.$$

The second way uses the full sample to estimate means for U and the separate sample means for $V - 0.86395U$. This is the general method of using the covariate described in Section 11.1. It yields estimated means

$$7.2075 - 0.86395(10.6226 - 10.9352) = 7.4784 \quad \text{for } D,$$

and

$$9.8909 - 0.86395(11.2364 - 10.9352) = 9.6307 \quad \text{for } P.$$

The third method is to guess that the regression coefficient of V on U is actually unity, which gives estimated means

$$7.2075 - 1 \cdot (10.6226 - 10.9352) = 7.5201 \quad \text{for } D,$$

and

$$9.8909 - 1 \cdot (11.2364 - 10.9352) = 9.5897 \quad \text{for } P.$$

In each of these sets of three methods, namely for estimating a best linear discriminator and for estimating means for V, the first method appears the least defensible, since there is clearly covariation present between V and U and some effort should be made to take advantage of it. The choice between the second and third methods amounts to a choice between the estimated value 0.86395 and a guessed value 1.0 for the regression coefficient of V on U. Insofar as the estimated value does not differ significantly from the guessed value it may be judged preferable to use the latter. Note that in terms of the analysis using U and $W = V - U$, this amounts to ignoring covariance effects. Always remember, however, that the failure of an estimated sample value to differ significantly from a hypothesized population value is not positive confirmation of the correctness of the latter.

To conclude, consider the question of the difference between the two treatments. The various D^2 measures computed above are small, indicating a shift of slightly less than half a standard deviation in the sample means. Judged by the standard significance test, they may be regarded as real, in the sense that the differences could reasonably be expected to hold up in a larger random sample of patients from the same population.

Example 11.2. This example analyzes data from a small but well-defined population of young depressed female patients from the New Jersey State Hospital System. The data were provided by J. R. Wittenborn; see Wittenborn *et al.* (1964) for a similar analysis of these data. Patients qualifying for the study were given an intensive pretreatment program of testing, observation, and rating upon entering the hospital. They were also assigned at random to one of three treatment groups. The first and second groups of sizes 28 and 31 received a

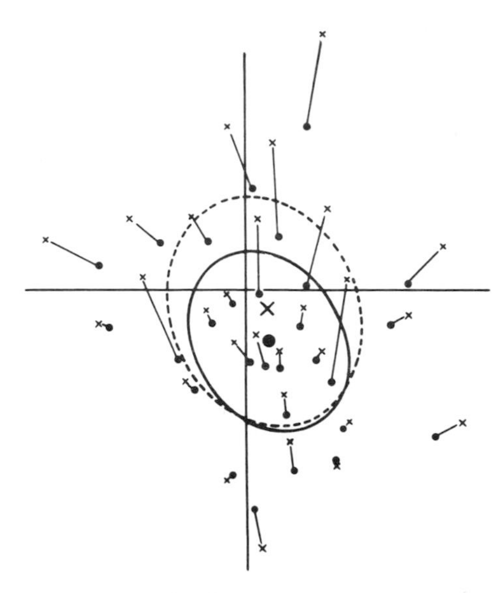

Fig. 11.2.1. The dots represent the first treatment group plotted in the individual-space of the two discriminants computed in Example 11.2. The solid ellipse is the corresponding sample mean-centered concentration ellipse. The crosses represent the jackknifed sample individuals, whose sample mean-centered ellipse is shown as a dotted curve.

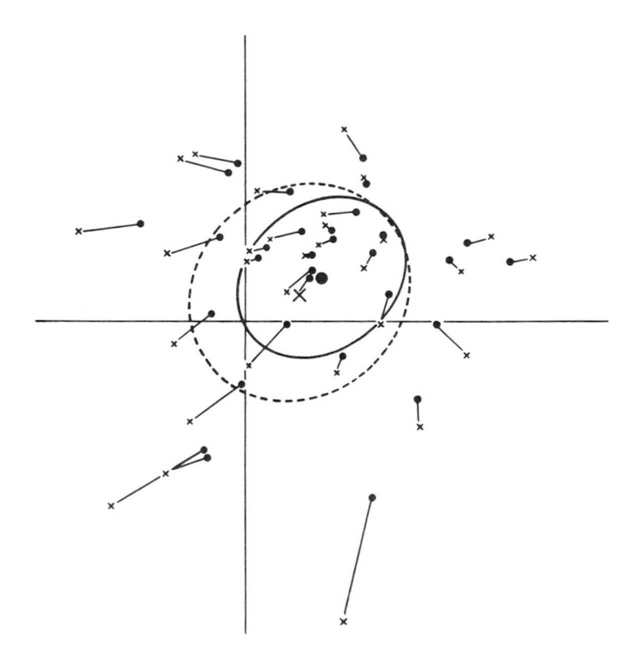

Fig. 11.2.2. As in Fig. 11.2.1 for the second treatment group.

placebo and a drug treatment, respectively, on a double-blind basis, while the third group of size 25 received electric shock treatment.

A set of five covariates and ten response variables was used in the present analysis. The covariates consisted of three "factor" scores culled from a social worker's analysis of the patient's home life and of two physician's ratings on scales relating to manic state and paranoid schizophrenia. The response variables reflected pretreatment–post-treatment changes on a set of scales, and thus have covariates already built into them.

The objective of the present analysis is to summarize these data in a way which shows up the differences in treatment effects. The main analysis is a multiple discriminant analysis using the device discussed in Section 11.1 of equating the different sample means on the covariates. A subsequent *jackknife* analysis was performed to learn something about the biases in the original analysis.

The first step in the main analysis was to find the total sum of products matrix corrected for the grand mean for a set of 17 variables consisting of two artificial variables indicating sample differences, five covariates, and ten response variables. As described in Section 11.1, the analysis proceeded by sweeping on the artificial variables and covariates, multistandardizing the 10×10 residual response variable matrix, reverse sweeping on the artificial variables, and finally applying SDG[8, 9, . . . , 17] to find ten eigenvalues and ten eigenvectors of dimensions 1×10 each.

By choosing the second input matrix of the SDG to be the second output matrix of the MST, whose input matrix in turn was **I**, the 1×10 eigenvectors were made to relate to the original basis of ten response variables. The discriminators were found by replacing these response variables $V_8, V_9, \ldots, V_{17}$ by their residuals $V_8 - b_{83}V_3 - b_{84}V_4 - \cdots - b_{87}V_7$, etc., where the regression coefficients were taken from the output of the first sweeping operation above, and finally applying the 1×10 eigenvectors to get 1×15 discriminant variables involving the covariates and the response variables.

The eigenvalues are 1.4470, 1.2246, 1.0000, 1.0000, . . . , 1.0000. Only two of these reflect differences among the means of the three samples; the rest are unity showing that the reverse sweeping operation did not add anything to the norms of the eight corresponding discriminators, as should indeed be so. The sample values for the first two discriminant variables and all 84 individuals were computed. They are plotted on Figs. 11.2.1, 11.2.2, and 11.2.3 for the three samples separately, together with their mean-centered concentration ellipses. The three concentration ellipses are drawn together on Fig. 11.2.4.

The plots just described are good summaries of how the response variable means appear to shift with treatment differences. An important question, however, to ask is: how would these pictures look if the sample discriminant variables were applied to a new sample of patients instead of to the original sample? In qualititive terms, the answer is clearly that one should not expect

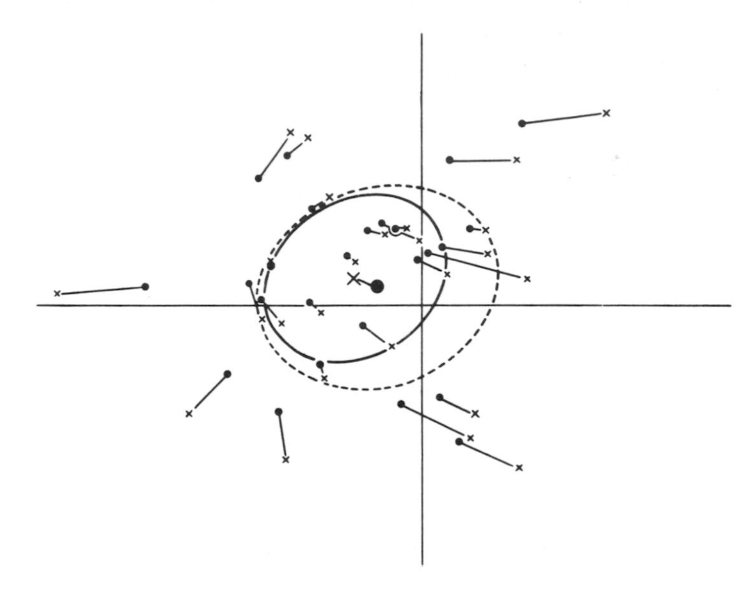

Fig. 11.2.3. As in Fig. 11.2.1 for the third treatment group.

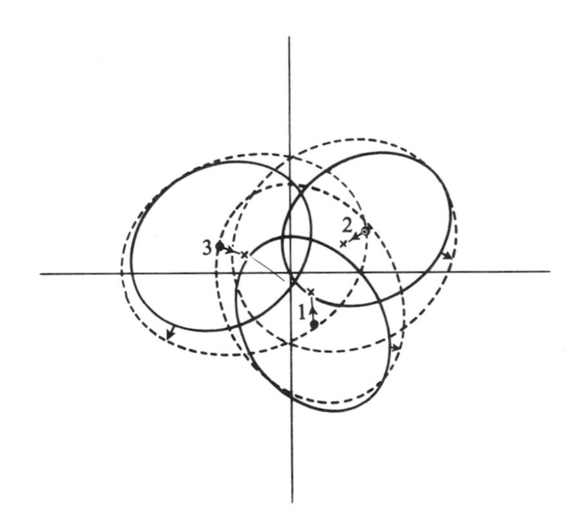

Fig. 11.2.4. The superimposed concentration ellipses from Figs. 11.2.1, 11.2.2, and 11.2.3.

the sample differences to appear so great. To justify this answer, consider first the limiting but often plausible hypothesis of samples drawn from identical underlying populations, i.e., the hypothesis of no treatment effects. There will certainly be apparent mean differences among samples, and multiple discriminant analysis actually picks out the variables whose apparent sample differences are largest in a specified sense. The smaller the sample sizes, and the larger the set of variables, the greater would be the spurious apparent differences shown up in the sample best linear discriminators. Naturally, in a future sample, the differences could not be expected to hold up. More generally, some of the apparent differences do reflect population differences and some reflect sampling variation. Only the latter are subject to exaggerating biases. The remainder of this example illustrates one method of attempting to distinguish the two types of difference.

The following analysis belongs to a set of techniques which are called jackknife methods (see Mosteller and Tukey, 1968). The common idea of these techniques is to perform analyses repeatedly, dropping a subset of the sample at each analysis. In the present example, the main analysis was carried out 84 times, each time omitting one of the sample individuals. In this way, each sample individual may be regarded as a future sample individual for the analysis based on the remaining 83, thus giving a direct answer to the question posed at the beginning of the preceding paragraph.

At first sight, the computational burden of 84 similar analyses might seem intolerable, but there are two mitigating factors. One large computing task is the original matrix multiplication of the data matrix by its transpose to yield raw sums of products. This need only be done once, and then corrected by subtraction for each removal of an individual. The largest computing task is that of finding eigenvalues and eigenvectors. Here one may capitalize on the facts that (*i*) dropping a single individual affects the analysis only slightly, and that (*ii*) the computation of eigenvalues and eigenvectors proceeds by successive approximations. Having done the analysis once, it is possible to start close to the correct answer for each of the subsequent analyses. In practice the input data for the jackknife analysis was taken to be the sample data on the five covariates and the ten discriminants from the main analysis, thus achieving the desired closeness to the eigenvectors. The choice of input variables is legitimate because the main analysis is invariant under any linear transformation of the 15-dimensional variable-space which sends the five-dimensional covariate-space into itself.

The position of each individual on the discriminant variables computed from the remaining 83 is shown overlaid on Figs. 11.2.1, 11.2.2, and 11.2.3. The scatter of these new points is also represented by concentration ellipses on these figures, and on Fig. 11.2.4.

The conclusions to be drawn from these pictures are that the pattern of means and concentrations from the first analysis is reproduced in the corrected analysis, but that the means are closer together while the spreads are somewhat enlarged. The apparent distances among sample means are sharply reduced. The author believes that the pictures provided by the second analysis are roughly speaking as good as any indicators of treatment effects yet devised.

The fact that the pattern of the first analysis is not destroyed in the second is heuristic evidence that the pattern does reflect population differences. A similar indication is given by the normal sampling theory significance test based on Wilks's Λ. Λ is computed from the eigenvalues in the main analysis to be $[1.4470 \times 1.2246]^{-1} = 0.5643$. More generally, a Wilks Λ statistic may be computed from all 15 variables, namely $\Lambda = 0.8782$, and a Wilks Λ statistic may be computed from the five covariates alone, namely $\Lambda_1 = 0.4956$. The ratio $\Lambda_{2.1} = \Lambda/\Lambda_1 = 0.5643$ is the Wilks Λ statistic for the response variables after adjustment for the covariates. The values 0.8782 and 0.4956 were computed in separate analyses not described here, and the agreement between the two values and 0.5643 serves as a check on the computations. Definitions and distributions for Λ and its decomposition are given in Section 13.7. Assuming zero population differences on the covariates, or more accurately assuming random samples from common normal populations, the distribution of Λ_1 is the $\Lambda(83, 2, 5)$ distribution discussed in Section 13.7, whence $\frac{77}{5}(1 - \Lambda_1^{1/2})/\Lambda_1^{1/2} = 1.034$ may be placed on the $F(10, 154)$ distribution and judged not significant. On the other hand, $\Lambda_{2.1}$ has the $\Lambda(78, 2, 10)$ distribution, assuming identical normal populations on all variables, whence $\frac{67}{10}(1 - \Lambda_{2.1}^{1/2})/\Lambda_{2.1}^{1/2} = 2.23$ may be placed on the $F(20, 134)$ distribution and judged significant.

11.3 MISSING VALUES: A SIMPLE CASE

Most multivariate data matrices which arise in statistical practice have a scattering of missing values. If there are not too many, and if they do not form a systematic pattern, one may fill in estimated values to obtain a complete matrix for analysis. For example, in Example 10.3 expert opinion was used while in Example 11.2 total sample means were inserted in a few places. Also in Example 11.2, a few individuals with fragmentary data were dropped from the analysis. It is not possible to justify such *ad hoc* procedures except through an initial belief or calculation that a resulting analysis is unlikely to differ substantially from that which would have been produced by a complete data matrix.

Example 11.3 illustrates the use of a special analysis tailored to a special pattern of missing values. The data consist of a sample of n individuals measured on $V_1, V_2, \ldots, V_s$ with a subsample of n_1 individuals measured on a larger set of variables $V_1, V_2, \ldots, V_s, \ldots, V_p$. This is perhaps the simplest case of a systematic pattern of missing values, but its analysis illustrates a general principle—namely that covariance adjustments may often improve the raw estimate of a population mean given by a subsample mean. Here the covariates are used to increase the accuracy of estimates of the population means of

$V_{s+1}, V_{s+2}, \ldots, V_p$. Other patterns may be treated in a similar fashion. More complicated analyses may also be essayed for random or irregular patterns of missing values, based perhaps on the principle of maximum likelihood, but these are beyond the scope of this volume. All of these analyses assume that the pattern of missing values may be regarded as random with respect to individuals, i.e., not distinguishable on the basis of observable characteristics. For example, if a sample of eighteen year old American males were to exclude those over six feet tall, then the following approach to estimating the population mean height of eighteen year old American males would be clearly invalid, as would be mean estimates for variables correlated with height for which height was used as a covariate.

The data considered here consist of $\mathbf{X}^{(1)} = [\mathbf{X}_1^{(1)}, \mathbf{X}_2^{(1)}]$ defining a first sample of size n_1 on $\mathbf{V}_1 = [V_1, V_2, \ldots, V_s]'$ and $\mathbf{V}_2 = [V_{s+1}, V_{s+2}, \ldots, V_p]'$ together with $\mathbf{X}_2^{(1)}$ defining a second sample of size $n_2 = n - n_1$ on $\mathbf{V}_1 = [V_1, V_2, \ldots, V_s]'$ alone. Viewing the two samples as a single sample of size n, it is clear how to define the sample mean vector $\bar{\mathbf{X}}_1$ of V_1, namely by summing the n rows of $\mathbf{X}_1^{(1)}$ and $\mathbf{X}_1^{(2)}$ and dividing by n. But it is not at all clear how to define a sample mean vector for $\mathbf{V}_2$. One might think that $\bar{\mathbf{X}}_2^{(1)}$ calculated in the usual way from the subsample of size n was the obvious choice, but in fact this is just one member of a very large class of possible choices.

Consider any basis $\mathbf{U} = \mathbf{KV}$ such that

$$\begin{bmatrix}\mathbf{U}_1\\ \mathbf{U}_2\end{bmatrix} = \begin{bmatrix}\mathbf{K}_{11} & \mathbf{0}\\ \mathbf{K}_{21} & \mathbf{K}_{22}\end{bmatrix}\begin{bmatrix}\mathbf{V}_1\\ \mathbf{V}_2\end{bmatrix} \tag{11.3.1}$$

and denote the inverse relation by $\mathbf{V} = \mathbf{HU}$ where $\mathbf{H} = \mathbf{K}^{-1}$, $\mathbf{H}_{11} = \mathbf{K}_{11}^{-1}$, $\mathbf{H}_{22} = \mathbf{K}_{22}^{-1}$, $\mathbf{H}_{21}\mathbf{K}_{11} + \mathbf{H}_{22}\mathbf{K}_{21} = \mathbf{0}$, and $\mathbf{H}_{12} = \mathbf{0}$. $\mathbf{U}$ shares with $\mathbf{V}$ the property that the full sample $\mathbf{Y}_1 = \mathbf{X}_1\mathbf{K}_{11}'$ is given on $\mathbf{U}_1$ while only the subsample $\mathbf{Y}_2^{(1)} = \mathbf{X}_1^{(1)}\mathbf{K}_{21}' + \mathbf{X}_2^{(1)}\mathbf{K}_{22}'$ is given on $\mathbf{U}_2$. Moreover this sample information on $\mathbf{U}$ is equivalent to the original sample information on $\mathbf{V}$. If the sample mean of $\mathbf{U}$ were defined in the obvious way to be $[\bar{\mathbf{Y}}_1, \bar{\mathbf{Y}}_2^{(1)}]$, then the corresponding sample mean of $\mathbf{V}$ is

$$[\bar{\mathbf{Y}}_1\mathbf{H}_{11}', \bar{\mathbf{Y}}_1\mathbf{H}_{21}' + \bar{\mathbf{Y}}_2^{(1)}\mathbf{H}_{22}'] = [\bar{\mathbf{X}}_1, \bar{\mathbf{X}}_2^{(1)} - (\bar{\mathbf{X}}_1^{(1)} - \bar{\mathbf{X}}_1)\mathbf{L}] \tag{11.3.2}$$

where

$$\mathbf{L} = \mathbf{K}_{11}'\mathbf{H}_{21}' = -\mathbf{K}_{21}'\mathbf{H}_{22}'. \tag{11.3.3}$$

Note that $\mathbf{L}$ may be *any* $s \times (p - s)$ matrix, since one may choose

$$\mathbf{K} = \begin{bmatrix}\mathbf{I} & \mathbf{0}\\ -\mathbf{L}' & \mathbf{I}\end{bmatrix}. \tag{11.3.4}$$

Thus, if a coordinate-free attitude is taken towards variable-space, then a choice of $\mathbf{L}$ becomes necessary.

The obvious data-based choice of $\mathbf{L}$ is given by the matrix $\mathbf{H}_{12}^{(1)}$ which specifies sample best linear predictors of $\mathbf{V}_2$ in terms of $\mathbf{V}_1$, based on the subsample of size n_1. The two parts $\bar{\mathbf{X}}_2^{(1)} - \bar{\mathbf{X}}_1^{(1)}\mathbf{L}$ and $\bar{\mathbf{X}}_1\mathbf{L}$ of the second element of (11.3.2) estimate means of $\mathbf{V}_2 - \mathbf{L}'\mathbf{V}_1$ and $\mathbf{L}'\mathbf{V}_1$ from partial and full samples, respectively, and the choice $\mathbf{L} = \mathbf{H}_{12}^{(1)}$ makes this division in such a way as to estimate from the full sample a piece with the largest apparent sample variance. This is the same idea which underlay the use of covariates in Section 11.1.

A similar principle may be followed in covariance estimation. The full sample covariance estimate $\mathbf{S}_{11}$ may be used for $\mathbf{V}_1$, while the naive choice for the remainder of the sample covariance matrix would be $\mathbf{S}_{12}^{(1)}$ and $\mathbf{S}_{22}^{(1)}$ based on the subsample of size n_1. Alternatively, an estimated covariance matrix for $[\mathbf{V}_1, \mathbf{V}_2 - \mathbf{L}'\mathbf{V}_1]$ would be

$$\begin{bmatrix} \mathbf{S}_{11} & \mathbf{S}_{12}^{(1)} - \mathbf{S}_{11}^{(1)}\mathbf{L} \\ \mathbf{S}_{21}^{(1)} - \mathbf{L}'\mathbf{S}_{11}^{(1)} & \mathbf{S}_{22}^{(1)} - \mathbf{L}'\mathbf{S}_{12}^{(1)} - \mathbf{S}_{21}^{(1)}\mathbf{L} + \mathbf{L}'\mathbf{S}_{11}^{(1)}\mathbf{L} \end{bmatrix}, \tag{11.3.5}$$

leading to the estimated covariance matrix

$$\begin{bmatrix} \mathbf{S}_{11} & \mathbf{S}_{12}^{(1)} - (\mathbf{S}_{11}^{(1)} - \mathbf{S}_{11})\mathbf{L} \\ \mathbf{S}_{21}^{(1)} - \mathbf{L}'(\mathbf{S}_{11}^{(1)} - \mathbf{S}_{11}) & \mathbf{S}_{22}^{(1)} - \mathbf{L}'(\mathbf{S}_{11}^{(1)} - \mathbf{S}_{11})\mathbf{L} \end{bmatrix}. \tag{11.3.6}$$

Again the choice $\mathbf{L} = \mathbf{H}_{12}^{(1)}$ is indicated, in order that the piece of $\mathbf{\Sigma}_{22}$ estimated from the full sample should be *apparently* maximized.

The analyses just described using $\mathbf{L} = \mathbf{H}_{12}^{(1)}$ are very close to those produced by the principle of maximum likelihood as described by Anderson (1957). The change lies only in the fact that the factor $1/(n-1)$ in (7.2.5) must be replaced by $1/n$ in defining $\mathbf{S}$. Similarly, the factor $1/n_1$ replaces $1/(n_1 - 1)$ in defining $\mathbf{S}^{(1)}$. This does not affect estimation of the mean, and makes a very small difference in the estimate of covariance.

Sampling theory for the various estimates of the mean is given in Section 14.1.

Example 11.3. Further aspects of the Tagiuri data of Example 10.1 are analyzed here. Of the 204 scientists who rated themselves using the Allport-Vernon-Lindzey "Study of values" questionnaire, a subsample of 47 also rated a typical research manager. Denoting the self-rating scores by $V_1^*, V_2^*, \ldots, V_6^*$ and the other-rating scores by $V_7^*, V_8^*, \ldots, V_{12}^*$, one has an example of the type of data described in the text with $n_1 = 47$, $n = 204$, and $s = p - s = 6$. It is more convenient, however, to change to a slightly different formulation in which the "normal" score of 40 is subtracted from each actual score and the other-rating scores are replaced by the differences between corresponding other-rating and self-rating scores. In symbols, the variables adopted here are

$$V_i = V_i^* - 40 \qquad \text{and} \qquad V_{6+i} = V_{6+i}^* - V_i^*$$

for $i = 1, 2, \ldots, 6$.

The sample mean vector from the full sample is

$$\bar{\mathbf{X}}_1 = [11.21, 0.73, -1.89, -5.73, 0.43, -4.74],$$

while the reduced sample yielded

$$\bar{\mathbf{X}}_1^{(1)} = [9.53, 1.19, -1.85, -4.96, -1.15, -2.77]$$

and

$$\bar{\mathbf{X}}_2^{(1)} = [-1.32, 10.26, -6.60, -3.87, 10.85, -9.32].$$

The message from $\bar{\mathbf{X}}_2^{(1)}$ is that the scientists think that a typical manager puts more of his value-currency in political and economic pockets and compensates by putting less in religious, aesthetic, social, and theoretical pockets (in decreasing order of importance).

The purpose of this section is to illustrate the alternatives to $\bar{\mathbf{X}}_2^{(1)}$ as indicators of the self- vs. other- comparison. For example, one might compute the sample mean of the reduced sample on the other-rating scores (subtracting 40 from each), namely

$$[8.21, 11.45, -8.45, -8.83, 9.70, -12.09],$$

and subtract $\bar{\mathbf{X}}_1$ to get

$$[-3.00, 10.72, -6.56, -3.10, 9.27, -7.35]$$

as an alternative to $\bar{\mathbf{X}}_2^{(1)}$. This amounts to choosing $\mathbf{L}' = -\mathbf{I}$ in (11.3.4). The data-based choice $\mathbf{L} = \mathbf{H}_{12}^{(1)}$ yields

$$[-2.09, 10.91, -6.54, -3.73, 9.89, -8.45].$$

It appears that the differences produced by different choices of $\mathbf{L}$ do not substantially alter the interpretation of the result, but they are large enough that one should be concerned about making a good choice.

The sample covariance matrix of $V_1, V_2, \ldots, V_6$ based on the full sample of size 204 is

$$\mathbf{S}_{11} = \begin{bmatrix} 47.45 & -1.21 & 5.76 & -6.98 & -3.17 & -41.84 \\ -1.21 & 82.31 & -38.28 & -31.09 & 8.19 & -19.92 \\ 5.76 & -38.28 & 81.74 & 1.65 & -13.72 & -37.16 \\ -6.98 & -31.09 & 1.65 & 53.69 & -14.79 & -2.48 \\ -3.17 & 8.19 & -13.72 & -14.79 & 45.88 & -22.40 \\ -41.84 & -19.92 & -37.16 & -2.48 & -22.40 & 123.80 \end{bmatrix}.$$

Note here that the factor $\frac{1}{204}$ was applied to the mean-corrected sample sum inner product rather than the factor $\frac{1}{203}$ generally used in this book. This gives the maximum likelihood estimate of a population covariance matrix assuming a random sample from a normal population of size 204. Similarly, one finds

$$\mathbf{S}_{21}^{(1)} = \begin{bmatrix} -28.30 & 21.03 & -15.11 & -4.68 & 15.93 & 11.13 \\ 8.25 & -59.67 & 11.75 & 29.34 & -9.42 & 19.74 \\ -5.06 & 27.39 & -57.61 & 6.02 & 8.13 & 21.13 \\ -9.14 & 20.22 & 7.13 & -25.69 & 16.07 & -8.60 \\ 11.04 & -4.15 & 4.53 & 10.72 & -39.02 & 16.89 \\ 23.20 & -4.83 & 49.31 & -15.71 & 8.31 & -60.29 \end{bmatrix}$$

and

$$\mathbf{S}_{22}^{(1)} = \begin{bmatrix} 51.62 & -18.32 & 10.47 & 2.15 & -18.98 & -26.93 \\ -18.32 & 96.96 & -33.55 & -41.63 & 39.27 & -42.73 \\ 10.47 & -33.55 & 69.60 & -5.14 & -24.32 & -17.06 \\ 2.15 & -41.63 & -5.14 & 42.37 & -29.09 & 31.34 \\ -18.98 & 39.27 & -24.32 & -29.09 & 76.13 & -43.00 \\ -26.93 & -42.73 & -17.06 & 31.34 & -43.00 & 98.39 \end{bmatrix}$$

where the divisor $\frac{1}{47}$ has been used in place of $\frac{1}{46}$.

From (11.3.6) using maximum likelihood estimates one gets

$$\hat{\mathbf{S}}_{21} = \begin{bmatrix} -30.63 & 2.45 & -0.55 & -8.72 & 9.10 & 28.35 \\ 13.84 & -60.15 & 34.80 & 24.30 & -9.55 & -3.23 \\ -7.87 & 21.71 & -59.05 & -2.32 & 12.27 & 35.26 \\ -2.35 & 29.17 & -1.52 & -28.18 & 10.72 & -7.83 \\ 14.88 & -13.63 & 16.65 & 14.21 & -42.09 & 9.98 \\ 12.14 & 20.46 & 9.67 & 0.72 & 19.55 & -62.53 \end{bmatrix}$$

and

$$\hat{\mathbf{S}}_{22} = \begin{bmatrix} 53.53 & -14.76 & 7.92 & 1.09 & -17.46 & -30.31 \\ -14.76 & 96.56 & -39.14 & -41.97 & 42.35 & -43.04 \\ 7.92 & -39.14 & 69.83 & 0.81 & -30.11 & -9.30 \\ 1.09 & -41.97 & 0.81 & 41.89 & -28.59 & 26.77 \\ -17.46 & 42.35 & -30.11 & -28.59 & 78.86 & -45.05 \\ -30.31 & -43.04 & -9.30 & 26.77 & -45.05 & 100.93 \end{bmatrix},$$

which differ only slightly from the simple-minded estimates.

PART 4

NORMAL SAMPLING THEORY AND STATISTICAL INFERENCE

CHAPTER 12

THE FAMILY OF NORMAL DISTRIBUTIONS

12.1 INTRODUCTION

The family of *normal distributions*, as the term is used here, includes both distributions along a line and distributions in a space of more than one dimension. A more complete description for a distribution of the latter type is *multivariate normal*. These distributions arise in many ways in statistical theory, for example, as approximate sampling distributions or as approximate posterior distributions in the large sample theory of statistical inference. It was in the latter context that the general form of the multivariate normal distribution first appeared (implicitly at least) in Gauss (1809). The term *Gaussian distribution* is interchangeable with normal distribution. In this book normal distributions serve primarily as a family of idealized populations. A multivariate population of size N is defined by N points in its associated individual-space $\mathscr{F}$, and the population is clearly equivalent mathematically to a simple discrete probability measure which assigns probability $1/N$ to each of the population individuals. A multivariate normal distribution is also a probability measure over a space $\mathscr{F}$, and, while it is not of the simple discrete type which defines a finite population, it may be regarded as a limit of such distributions as $N \to \infty$. In this way a multivariate normal distribution may be regarded as a mathematical model for a population.

As commonly used, the term distribution signifies more than just a probability measure over a space $\mathscr{F}$. It is generally taken to be the distribution of a set of random quantities whose values $X_1, X_2, \ldots, X_p$ are coordinates for a point of $\mathscr{F}$. A distribution makes contact with the outside world through the meaning which is attached to these quantities. For example, if the distribution is viewed as an infinite population then the set of random quantities is in correspondence with the set of variables associated with the population, and the random values $X_1, X_2, \ldots, X_p$ provide a random sample of size one from the population. This example is sufficiently suggestive and fundamental that the notation $V_1, V_2, \ldots, V_p$ will be used in this chapter for a basis set of random quantities, but the reader should keep clearly in mind that these V_i are quantities and not variables (cf. Sections 1.2 and 1.4).

The distribution of a set of random quantities $V_1, V_2, \ldots, V_p$ may be partially described by its mean values (or first moments)

$$\mu_i = E(X_i) \tag{12.1.1}$$

for $i = 1, 2, \ldots, p$ and by its covariances (or second moments about the mean)

$$\sigma_{ij} = E([X_i - \mu_i][X_j - \mu_j]) \tag{12.1.2}$$

for i and $j = 1, 2, \ldots, p$. It is assumed here that the integrals defining these moments are finite. When the distribution is viewed as a population, the means μ_i and the covariances σ_{ij} become the population means and population covariances in the sense that, if population means and covariances are computed from a population of size N as though it were a sample of size N, and if the finite population distribution converges to a general infinite population distribution, then the means and covariances of the finite population converge to (12.1.1) and (12.1.2). Since the methods of data analysis in this book are all based on sample means and sample covariances, it follows that the population analogues about which inferences are desired are similarly based on the moments (12.1.1) and (12.1.2). The family of normal distributions fits neatly into this picture because there is exactly one member of the family for each possible set of first and second moments.

The reader is assumed to have a working knowledge of the mathematics of probability distributions such as might be found in a first course in mathematical statistics. Some basic facts about one-dimensional normal distributions, gamma distributions, beta distributions, and relations among them are included in Section 12.5 but will be used throughout this chapter. The remainder of Section 12.1 is devoted to the build-up of coordinate-free ways of dealing with distributions over a p-dimensional space $\mathscr{F}$.

A set of p quantities $V_1, V_2, \ldots, V_p$ defines a p-dimensional vector space of quantities of the form $\sum_1^p \alpha_i V_i$. This space will be called here *quantity-space* and denoted by $\mathscr{E}$, while its dual space will be called *outcome-space* and denoted by $\mathscr{F}$. These spaces will appear in several ways related to a p-variate sample of size n. First, the quantities $V_1, V_2, \ldots, V_p$ may represent the quantities defined by a corresponding set of variables and a particular sample individual. Or, replacing p by n, the quantities $V_1, V_2, \ldots, V_n$ may represent the quantities defined by a fixed variable paired with each of the n sample individuals. Or, replacing p by np, all pairings of the p variables and n individuals may be used. The first of these three ways is perhaps the most natural for the reader to keep in mind, as a working model in which $V_1, V_2, \ldots, V_p$ represent a sample of size one from some population. In this case quantity-space and outcome-space are isomorphic respectively to variable-space and individual-space, and the notation $\mathscr{E}$ and $\mathscr{F}$ used throughout the book for the latter pair is borrowed here for the former pair.

Suppose next that the quantities $V_1, V_2, \ldots, V_p$ are assigned a probability distribution and so become random quantities. Just as each V_i is associated with a random value X_i, it is natural to regard the quantity-space $\mathscr{E}$ of random quantities as being associated with a *random outcome* $x \in \mathscr{F}$. A random outcome is simply an outcome in a p-dimensional outcome-space $\mathscr{F}$ with an associated probability distribution over $\mathscr{F}$. This concept of a random outcome x provides a coordinate-free language for discussing distributions over $\mathscr{F}$. Denoting by $\mathbf{V} = [V_1, V_2, \ldots, V_p]'$ the given basis of $\mathscr{E}$ and by $\mathbf{v} = [v_1, v_2, \ldots, v_p]'$ the dual basis of $\mathscr{F}$, one may formally set

$$x = \mathbf{X}\mathbf{v}, \tag{12.1.3}$$

where $\mathbf{X} = [X_1, X_2, \ldots, X_p]$ is the vector of random values associated with $\mathbf{V}$. The means and covariances defined in (12.1.1) and (12.1.2) may also be regarded as coordinate-free concepts closely analogous to sample means and sample covariances. Specifically, if $\boldsymbol{\mu}$ is the $1 \times m$ vector whose ith element is μ_i and $\boldsymbol{\Sigma}$ is the $p \times p$ matrix whose (i, j) element is σ_{ij}, then

$$\mu = E(x) = \boldsymbol{\mu}\mathbf{v} \tag{12.1.4}$$

defines the *mean outcome* in $\mathscr{F}$, and $\boldsymbol{\Sigma}$ defines the *covariance inner product* Σ over $\mathscr{E}$, when $\boldsymbol{\Sigma}$ is viewed as an inner product matrix relative to the basis $\mathbf{V}$. By going back to the basic linearity property of the expectation operator together with the fact that a nonnegative random value has a nonnegative expected value, the reader should check that Σ is in fact a definite or semi-definite inner product. The dual inner product Σ_d over $\mathscr{F}$ will be called the *concentration inner product* of the distribution over $\mathscr{F}$. Just as a sample mean and sample concentration can be represented geometrically by the sample mean-centered concentration ellipsoid in individual-space $\mathscr{F}$, the mean μ and concentration Σ_d of a random outcome x can be represented geometrically by its *mean-centered concentration ellipsoid*, i.e., by the set of points in outcome-space $\mathscr{F}$ lying at most unit distance from μ according to Σ_d.

The family of normal distributions which will be defined in this chapter forms a special class of distributions of a random outcome x such that each member of the family is uniquely determined by its mean μ and covariance Σ. These distributions all belong to a wider family of distributions which will be called *spherical* with respect to a specified inner product. Spherical distributions are defined and analyzed in Section 12.2, thus leading easily to the special case of normal distributions in Section 12.3.

12.2 SPHERICALLY DISTRIBUTED RANDOM OUTCOMES

Suppose that a quantity-space $\mathscr{E}$ and its dual outcome-space $\mathscr{F}$ are a pair of ordinary p-dimensional Euclidean spaces. A random outcome x in $\mathscr{F}$ will be called *spherically distributed about the origin* in $\mathscr{F}$ provided that $y = \mathbf{G}x$

has the same distribution as x for every orthogonal linear transformation G which carries $\mathscr{F}$ into itself and leaves the origin fixed. It is implicit in this definition that the distribution of y is the distribution induced from the distribution of x by the mapping G. Specifically, for any Borel set $A \subset \mathscr{F}$, $\Pr\{y \in A\}$ is defined to be $\Pr\{x \in \mathsf{G}^{-1}A\}$ where $\mathsf{G}^{-1}A$ is the set of points in $\mathscr{F}$ which map under G into some point of A. The term *spherical* is used because such distributions are invariant under all linear transformations which carry an origin-centered sphere into itself.

Several extensions of the definition and terminology are required. The random outcome x will be called spherically distributed about the point μ in $\mathscr{F}$ provided that $x - \mu$ is spherically distributed about the origin. Sometimes several different inner products over $\mathscr{F}$ may be in the picture, in which case it is necessary to expand the term *spherically distributed* to *spherically distributed with respect to the inner product* π_d where π_d is the appropriate inner product over $\mathscr{F}$. Finally, the whole theory may be extended to define spherical distributions where π_d is a partial inner product, i.e., where the dual inner product π over $\mathscr{E}$ has rank less than p. This extension is described in detail at the end of Section 12.2.

In view of the foregoing definitions it is to be expected that coordinate-dependent discussions will be simplest in terms of an orthonormal basis. Suppose that $\mathbf{V}$ denotes the original basis of $\mathscr{E}$ and $\mathbf{v}$ denotes the dual of $\mathbf{V}$ in $\mathscr{F}$. Suppose that $\mathbf{X}$ and $\boldsymbol{\mu}$ denote the coordinates of x and μ relative to $\mathbf{v}$, and that $\mathbf{U}$ and $\mathbf{u}$ are a pair of dual orthonormal bases of $\mathscr{E}$ and $\mathscr{F}$ and $\mathbf{Y}$ denotes the coordinates of $x - \mu$ relative to $\mathbf{u}$, i.e.,

$$x - \mu = (\mathbf{X} - \boldsymbol{\mu})\mathbf{v} = \mathbf{Y}\mathbf{u}. \tag{12.2.1}$$

Then there exists a pair of inverse matrices $\mathbf{D}$ and $\mathbf{C} = \mathbf{D}^{-1}$ such that $\mathbf{V} = \mathbf{D}\mathbf{U}$, $\mathbf{U} = \mathbf{C}\mathbf{V}$, $\mathbf{v} = \mathbf{C}'\mathbf{u}$, and $\mathbf{u} = \mathbf{D}'\mathbf{v}$. Consequently,

$$\mathbf{X} - \boldsymbol{\mu} = \mathbf{Y}\mathbf{D}' \tag{12.2.2}$$

and

$$\mathbf{Y} = (\mathbf{X} - \boldsymbol{\mu})\mathbf{C}'. \tag{12.2.3}$$

In terms of $\mathbf{u}$ coordinates, it is clear that *x is spherically distributed about μ if and only if $\mathbf{Y}\mathbf{G}'$ has the same distribution as $\mathbf{Y}$ for every $p \times p$ orthogonal matrix $\mathbf{G}$.*

The most obvious properties of a spherically distributed random outcome x concern its mean and covariance. Since the origin is the only point left invariant by every orthogonal linear transformation, and since the mean of an invariant distribution is itself invariant, the mean of an origin-centered spherical distribution must be the origin. More generally, it follows that the mean of a spherical distribution centered at μ must be μ. Similarly, the origin-centered concentration ellipsoid of a spherical distribution must remain invariant under every orthogonal linear transformation, and the only such ellipsoids are spheres.

Thus it follows that Σ_d is a scaled version of π_d and that Σ is a scaled version of π, where π and π_d denote the given pair of dual inner products of the Euclidean spaces $\mathscr{E}$ and $\mathscr{F}$. These results are summarized in Theorem 12.2.1.

Theorem 12.2.1. *Any random outcome x which is spherically distributed about μ with respect to π_d, and which possesses first and second moments, must have mean μ and covariance $\lambda\pi$ for some scale factor $\lambda > 0$.*

All spherical distributions share the simple structure described in Theorem 12.2.2 which is an immediate consequence of the following two lemmas.

Lemma 12.2.1. *For any random outcome x which is spherically distributed about μ, and for any real number S such that the conditional distribution of x given $(x - \mu, x - \mu)_d = S^2$ is defined, this conditional distribution is itself spherical about μ.*

Note that the norm of $x - \mu$ under π_d is a random value denoted here by $(x - \mu, x - \mu)_d^{1/2}$. In proving this lemma one may take μ to be the origin, for the general case follows from the special case after a translation. The random outcome x has the same distribution as any orthogonal linear transform $y = \mathsf{G}x$, and hence the conditional distribution of x given that $(x, x)_d = S^2$ is the same as the conditional distribution of y given that $(y, y)_d = S^2$. But $(x, x)_d = (y, y)_d$ by the defining property of orthogonal linear transformations, and hence the conditional distribution of x given $(x, x)_d = S^2$ is the same as the conditional distribution of y given $(x, x)_d = S^2$, as was required to prove.

Lemma 12.2.2. *There is exactly one spherical distribution about μ which assigns probability 1 to the surface of the sphere $(x - \mu, x - \mu)_d = S^2$.*

This lemma will later be generalized in Lemma 13.3.2 which in turn will be related to a more general theory of invariant distributions. A rigorous proof is not attempted here, but it is important to have a heuristic understanding of the distribution in question and of why it is unique. Viewed geometrically as a volume measure instead of a probability measure, this distribution is essentially equivalent to the concept of $(p - 1)$-dimensional volume in the surface of a p-dimensional sphere, i.e., the probability of any region on the surface of the sphere is taken to be its volume, where volume is scaled to have total unity. Thus the special case $p = 2$ relating to length on a circle and $p = 3$ relating to area on the surface of a sphere may easily be visualized. The concept of volume in these special cases may be expressed in terms of integrals of differential elements of volume and these differential elements of volume extend naturally to general p. Furthermore the differential elements are locally like ordinary $(p - 1)$-dimensional Euclidean volume, and so are easily seen to be invariant under any orthogonal linear transformation. Finally, since there is an orthogonal transformation which carries any one point on the sphere into any other point, one need only define the volume element at any one point and it is *uniquely* determined at every other point because of its invariance under orthogonal transformation. Thus volume through its probability analogue gives the unique invariant distribution over the surface of the sphere.

Combining Lemmas 12.2.1 and 12.2.2 it is clear that the conditional distribution of $x - \mu$ given $(x - \mu, x - \mu)_d = S^2$ is the unique spherical distribution over the surface of the sphere with center at the origin and radius S. Theorem 12.2.2 follows immediately because the conditional distribution of $x - \mu$ given $(x - \mu, x - \mu)_d = S^2$ implies that the conditional distribution of y is as given in the theorem whatever the value of S^2.

Theorem 12.2.2. *If the random outcome x is spherically distributed about μ, then the squared distance $(x - \mu, x - \mu)_d$ from μ to x is distributed independently of the random outcome*

$$y = (x - \mu, x - \mu)_d^{-1/2}(x - \mu) \tag{12.2.4}$$

which is spherically distributed over the surface of the unit sphere with center at the origin. Thus, to specify uniquely the distribution of x, only μ and the distribution of $(x - \mu, x - \mu)_d$ need be specified.

In geometric terms, the random outcome y may be said to define the *direction* of the random vector $x - \mu$, so that Theorem 12.2.2 isolates two independent aspects of the randomness of x under the geometrically appealing headings of direction and length of $x - \mu$. The latter distribution may be chosen arbitrarily, whereas direction, together with any function of direction alone, has a uniquely determined distribution. The final theorem of this section concerns a special function of direction, namely the angle between the random vector $x - \mu$ and a fixed r-dimensional hyperplane. Since a simple proof of this theorem appears to require the use of normal distributions, the proof is postponed to Section 12.3.

Theorem 12.2.3. *Suppose that $\mathscr{V}$ is an r-dimensional subspace of the p-dimensional space $\mathscr{F}$ of possible outcomes. Suppose that θ denotes the angle between $\mathscr{V}$ and $x - \mu$ where x is spherically distributed about the center μ. Then* $\cos^2 \theta$ *has the $\beta(r/2, (p - r)/2)$ distribution and is independent of $(x - \mu, x - \mu)_d$.*

The theory of Section 12.2 has so far assumed that the given inner product π has full rank p. This assumption will now be relaxed. If π has rank q, then its dual π_d is a partial inner product defined over a q-dimensional subspace $\mathscr{U}$ in $\mathscr{F}$. Since the properties of Euclidean geometry in $\mathscr{U}$ translate to define such properties in all hyperplanes parallel to $\mathscr{U}$, it is possible to define a spherical distribution for a random outcome restricted to such a hyperplane. Consequently a random outcome x will be called *spherically distributed with respect to π_d about the center μ* if x is restricted to lie with probability one in the hyperplane $\mu + \mathscr{U}$, and $x - \mu$ is spherically distributed about the origin in $\mathscr{U}$ with respect to the full rank inner product defined over $\mathscr{U}$.

The relations (12.2.1), (12.2.2), and (12.2.3) extend directly to the rank q situation. One need only define $\mathbf{u}$ to be any $q \times 1$ orthonormal basis of $\mathscr{U}$, $\mathbf{D}$ to be the $p \times q$ rank q matrix relating $\mathbf{u} = \mathbf{D}'\mathbf{v}$, and $\mathbf{C}$ to be any pseudoinverse of $\mathbf{D}$. Then (12.2.1) and (12.2.2) follow as before and (12.2.3) follows from (12.2.2) because $\mathbf{CD} = \mathbf{I}$. The matrix $\mathbf{D}$ was discussed in Section 6.6 using slightly different notation, namely $\mathbf{D}_1$ for $\mathbf{D}$ and f for q. It was shown there that $\mathbf{Q} = \mathbf{DD}'$ where $\mathbf{Q}$ is the inner product matrix of π relative to the basis $\mathbf{V}$. The computation of a particular instance of $\mathbf{D}$ from $\mathbf{Q}$ was also discussed, showing how $\mathbf{D}$ was computed from the appropriate columns of $\mathbf{B}$. In Section 4.4 a method of finding $\mathbf{A}$ pseudoinverse to $\mathbf{B}$ was described. Again the appropriate *rows* of $\mathbf{A}$ may be rescaled to produce the rows of a pseudoinverse $\mathbf{C}$ of $\mathbf{D}$.

In the sequel two inner product matrices $\mathbf{Q}$ and $\mathbf{\Sigma}$ may be under consideration at the same time. The notation $\mathbf{D}$ and $\mathbf{C}$ will be used as above relative to $\mathbf{Q}$, i.e., $\mathbf{DD}' = \mathbf{Q}$ and $\mathbf{C}$ is pseudoinverse to $\mathbf{D}$. The notation $\mathbf{\Delta}$ and $\mathbf{\Gamma}$ will be used relative to $\mathbf{\Sigma}$, i.e., $\mathbf{\Delta\Delta}' = \mathbf{\Sigma}$ and $\mathbf{\Gamma}$ is pseudoinverse to $\mathbf{\Delta}$.

12.3 THE NORMAL DISTRIBUTION WITH GIVEN MEAN AND COVARIANCE

The aim here is to define a family of distributions over a p-dimensional outcome-space $\mathscr{F}$, each member of the family being uniquely determined by its mean vector μ in $\mathscr{F}$ and its covariance inner product Σ over the quantity-space $\mathscr{E}$ dual to $\mathscr{F}$. The normal distribution determined by μ and Σ will be labeled $N(\mu, \Sigma)$. These distributions will be called *normal* distributions for brevity, although the longer terms *multinormal* or *multivariate normal* are more descriptive of the p-dimensional character of the distributions.

The mathematical attractiveness of normal distributions is largely due to two striking properties, either of which implies the other and either of which may be used to define the $N(\mu, \Sigma)$ distribution with given μ and Σ. The basic fact which supports the theory is Lemma 12.5.7 in Section 12.5, which asserts that if a set of independent $N(0, 1)$ random values is transformed by an orthogonal matrix, the result is again a set of independent $N(0, 1)$ random values.

Now suppose that $\mathbf{u}$ is a $q \times 1$ basis of a q-dimensional subspace $\mathscr{U}$ of a p-dimensional outcome-space $\mathscr{F}$. Suppose further that a partial inner product Σ_d over $\mathscr{F}$ and its dual Σ over $\mathscr{E}$ are defined by regarding $\mathbf{u}$ to be orthonormal in $\mathscr{U}$. Consider the random outcome

$$x = \mu + \mathbf{Yu} \tag{12.3.1}$$

in $\mathscr{F}$.

Definition 1. *The random outcome x in $\mathscr{F}$ is said to have the $N(\mu, \Sigma)$ distribution provided that it has the same distribution as x in* (12.3.1) *where the elements $Y_1, Y_2, \ldots, Y_q$ of $\mathbf{Y}$ are independent $N(0, 1)$ random values and $\mathbf{u}$ is related to Σ as specified above.*

Lemma 12.5.7 assures that Definition 1 determines the same distribution for x regardless of the choice of the orthonormal basis $\mathbf{u}$ of $\mathscr{U}$. Note that the random outcome x is restricted to lie in the hyperplane $\mu + \mathscr{U}$ and the $N(\mu, \Sigma)$ distribution should be regarded as a distribution of probability over the possible outcomes in $\mu + \mathscr{U}$. Of course, Σ is most often taken to have full rank p and then any outcome x in $\mathscr{F}$ is allowed.

Definition 2. *The random outcome x in $\mathscr{F}$ is said to have the $N(\mu, \Sigma)$ distribution provided that* (i) *x is spherically distributed about μ relative to the inner product Σ_d in $\mathscr{F}$ dual to Σ in $\mathscr{E}$, and* (ii) $(x - \mu, x - \mu)_d$ *has the* $\chi^2(q, 1)$ *distribution where* $q = \text{rank } \Sigma$.

The equivalence of the two definitions is easily proved. Definition 1 together with Lemma 12.5.7 implies the property (i) in Definition 2. Also, the fact that $\mathbf{u}$ in (12.3.1) is orthonormal implies that $(x - \mu, x - \mu)_d = \mathbf{YY}' = Y_1^2 + Y_2^2 + \cdots + Y_q^2$ which clearly has the $\chi^2(q, 1)$ distribution under Definition 1. Thus property (ii) in Definition 2 is satisfied. Conversely, from Theorem 12.2.2, the properties (i) and (ii) in Definition 2 do in fact uniquely define the distribution of x which, since Definition 1 satisfies the properties of Definition 2, can only be the same distribution as specified in Definition 1.

Definition 2 stresses the spherical nature of normal distributions while Definition 1 stresses the independence of individual components in orthogonal directions. It has been shown (see Lukacs, 1956) that normal distributions are the only distributions which possess both of these properties. Definition 1 will be of more immediate use, but much use will be made in Chapter 13 of the spherical property of normal random outcomes.

A generalized version of the basic property used in Definition 1 is given by the following theorem.

Theorem 12.3.1. *If $\mathscr{U}_1, \mathscr{U}_2, \ldots, \mathscr{U}_t$ are mutually orthogonal subspaces spanning the subspace $\mathscr{U}$ of $\mathscr{F}$ over which Σ_d is defined, and if x has the $N(\mu, \Sigma)$ distribution, then the components of x along each of the subspaces $\mathscr{U}_1, \mathscr{U}_2, \ldots, \mathscr{U}_t$ are independent and normally distributed.*

The components of x in these subspaces are well-defined with probability 1 since x lies in $\mathscr{U}$ with probability 1. To prove the theorem, one need only set up an orthonormal basis $\mathbf{u}$ of $\mathscr{U}$ such that $\mathscr{U}_1, \mathscr{U}_2, \ldots, \mathscr{U}_t$ are spanned by subsets of the elements of $\mathbf{u}$. Then the independence of the coordinates of x relative to $\mathbf{u}$ implies the independence of the components in $\mathscr{U}_1, \mathscr{U}_2, \ldots, \mathscr{U}_t$ which depend on disjoint subsets of the independent coordinates. The normality of the components follows from Definition 1.

A proof will now be given for Theorem 12.2.3. Since the result concerns only the direction of a spherical random outcome which is common to all spherical distributions, it need only be proved for one spherical distribution to be proved for all. In particular, the result may be proved for the $N(\mu, \pi)$

distribution. Consider a basis $\mathbf{u}$ of $\mathscr{F}$ orthonormal with respect to π_d. Suppose that the first r elements of $\mathbf{u}$ are chosen to span $\mathscr{V}$ in Theorem 12.2.3. Then, if x is written $\mu + \mathbf{Yu}$,

$$\cos^2 \theta = \sum_{i=1}^{r} Y_i^2 \Big/ \sum_{i=1}^{p} Y_i^2, \tag{12.3.2}$$

where $Y_1, Y_2, \ldots, Y_p$ are independent $N(0, 1)$ random values. Lemma 12.5.6 together with (12.3.2) implies that $\cos^2 \theta$ has the $\beta(r/2, (p - r)/2)$ distribution, as required.

The notation $N(\mu, \Sigma)$ is intended to be read *normal distribution with mean* μ *and covariance* Σ, but a justification of this terminology is needed. From Theorem 12.2.1 and Definition 2 it follows that the $N(\mu, \Sigma)$ distribution has mean μ and covariance $\lambda\Sigma$, so it remains only to show that $\lambda = 1$. The representation (12.3.1) with $\mathbf{u}$ orthonormal according to Σ_d assures that the quantities with values $Y_1, Y_2, \ldots, Y_q$ are orthonormal according to Σ. It follows that the covariance matrix of these quantities must be $\lambda\mathbf{I}$. But since $Y_1, Y_2, \ldots, Y_q$ are independent $N(0, 1)$ their covariance matrix is clearly $\mathbf{I}$, so that $\lambda = 1$.

The specification of the distribution of a random outcome x in $\mathscr{F}$ is equivalent to the specification of the joint distribution of the $1 \times p$ vector of random values $\mathbf{X}$ which consists of the coordinates of x relative to any basis $\mathbf{v}$ of $\mathscr{F}$. Thus to assert that x has the $N(\mu, \Sigma)$ distribution is to assert that $\mathbf{X}$ has a uniquely defined distribution, which may be denoted by $N(\boldsymbol{\mu}, \boldsymbol{\Sigma})$ where $\boldsymbol{\mu}$ denotes the $1 \times p$ vector of coordinates of μ relative to $\mathbf{v}$, and $\boldsymbol{\Sigma}$ denotes the $p \times p$ covariance matrix of the basis $\mathbf{V}$ of $\mathscr{E}$ dual to $\mathbf{v}$ in $\mathscr{F}$. The notation $N(\boldsymbol{\mu}, \boldsymbol{\Sigma})$ should be read *the normal distribution with mean vector* $\boldsymbol{\mu}$ *and covariance matrix* $\boldsymbol{\Sigma}$. When $p = 1$ the distribution $N(\boldsymbol{\mu}, \boldsymbol{\Sigma})$ specializes to the $N(\mu, \sigma^2)$ distribution as defined in Section 12.5. Another special case of interest is the $N(\mathbf{0}, \mathbf{I})$ distribution of a $1 \times q$ vector $\mathbf{Y}$ of random outcomes. Clearly $\mathbf{Y}$ has the $N(\mathbf{0}, \mathbf{I})$ distribution if and only if the elements of $\mathbf{Y}$ are independent $N(0, 1)$ random values. This distribution of $\mathbf{Y}$ may be called the *q-dimensional unit normal distribution with zero mean.*

Having the family of $N(\mu, \Sigma)$ distributions in hand, it is easy to define the *family of (central) multivariate t distributions* $t(\mu, \Sigma, n)$, which includes the $N(\mu, \Sigma)$ family as the limiting case when $n \to \infty$. A random outcome will be said to have the $t(\mu, \Sigma, n)$ distribution if it has the same distribution as $\mu + s^{-1}x$ where x and s^2 are independent with $N(\varnothing, \Sigma)$ and $\chi^2(n, 1/n)$ distributions. The $t(\mu, \Sigma, n)$ distribution is clearly spherical about μ with respect to Σ_d and is alternatively characterized by this property together with the fact that the square of the Σ_d-norm of $t - \mu$ has the $G(q, n, n)$ distribution, where $q =$ rank Σ. The coordinate-free definition of $t(\mu, \Sigma, n)$ carries with it an obvious coordinate-dependent definition of a $t(\boldsymbol{\mu}, \boldsymbol{\Sigma}, n)$ family. These distributions were introduced by Dunnett and Sobel (1954, 1955). Note that the definitions given here generalize the definition of the one-dimensional $t(\mu, \sigma^2, n)$ family given in Section 12.5. It is less clear how to generalize the one-dimensional noncentral t distributions. See Section 13.6 for a brief discussion.

Probability density functions for the $N(\boldsymbol{\mu}, \boldsymbol{\Sigma})$ and $t(\boldsymbol{\mu}, \boldsymbol{\Sigma}, n)$ families are defined when $\boldsymbol{\Sigma}$ has full rank and are displayed in Exercises 12.6.1 and 12.6.2.

12.4 BASIC PROPERTIES OF THE $N(\boldsymbol{\mu}, \boldsymbol{\Sigma})$ DISTRIBUTION

In practice a statistician may be asked to perform various operations with a $1 \times p$ vector $\mathbf{X}$ of random values which is regarded as having the $N(\boldsymbol{\mu}, \boldsymbol{\Sigma})$ distribution. It is of interest, therefore, to make explicit some of the properties of the normal distribution *in its general coordinate-dependent form.* The basic result of this section is Theorem 12.4.1 which is followed by several other theorems on linear transformation, independence, and conditioning.

Theorem 12.4.1. *Suppose that* $\mathbf{X}$ *has the* $N(\boldsymbol{\mu}, \boldsymbol{\Sigma})$ *distribution where* $\mathbf{X}$ *and* $\boldsymbol{\mu}$ *have dimensions* $1 \times p$ *and* $\boldsymbol{\Sigma}$ *is a* $p \times p$ *positive definite, or semi-definite, symmetric matrix of rank* $q \leq p$. *Suppose that* $\boldsymbol{\Delta}$ *is any* $p \times q$ *matrix such that* $\boldsymbol{\Sigma} = \boldsymbol{\Delta}\boldsymbol{\Delta}'$ *and suppose that* $\boldsymbol{\Gamma}$ *is a pseudoinverse of* $\boldsymbol{\Delta}$. *Then* $\mathbf{Y} = (\mathbf{X} - \boldsymbol{\mu})\boldsymbol{\Gamma}'$ *has the* $N(\mathbf{0}, \mathbf{I})$ *distribution where* $\mathbf{Y}$, $\mathbf{0}$, *and* $\mathbf{I}$ *have dimensions* $1 \times q$, $1 \times q$, *and* $q \times q$, *respectively. Furthermore,* $\mathbf{X}$ *may be recovered from* $\mathbf{Y}$ *with probability 1 using* $\mathbf{X} = \boldsymbol{\mu} + \mathbf{Y}\boldsymbol{\Delta}'$.

The proof requires little more than setting up a coordinate-free statement. Consider a pair of dual spaces $\mathscr{E}$ and $\mathscr{F}$ of dimension p, with a pair of dual bases $\mathbf{V}$ and $\mathbf{v}$. Define $x = \mathbf{X}\mathbf{v}$, $\mu = \boldsymbol{\mu}\mathbf{v}$, and Σ to be the inner product over $\mathscr{E}$ defined by $\boldsymbol{\Sigma}$ relative to $\mathbf{V}$. Then x has the $N(\mu, \Sigma)$ distribution. From the equivalence of (6.6.1) and (6.6.2) it follows that the formulas (12.2.1), (12.2.2), and (12.2.3) hold in the revised notation where $\boldsymbol{\Sigma}$, $\boldsymbol{\Delta}$, and $\boldsymbol{\Gamma}$ replace $\mathbf{Q}$, $\mathbf{D}$, and $\mathbf{C}$. In the special case of the normal distribution this means that $\mathbf{Y}$ has the $N(\mathbf{0}, \mathbf{I})$ distribution.

Computations for finding instances of $\boldsymbol{\Delta}$ and $\boldsymbol{\Gamma}$ from $\boldsymbol{\Sigma}$ were outlined in Section 12.2 where this notation was introduced. The importance of these calculations in the present context is that they afford the means of simulating $\mathbf{X}$ from simulated $\mathbf{Y}$. In other words, an appropriate computer program or a table of random normal deviates such as Rand (1955) may be used to create simulated values $Y_1, Y_2, \ldots, Y_q$ determining $\mathbf{Y}$. Given $\boldsymbol{\mu}$ and $\boldsymbol{\Sigma}$ one computes $\boldsymbol{\Delta}$ and then $\mathbf{X} = \boldsymbol{\mu} + \mathbf{Y}\boldsymbol{\Delta}'$ to complete the simulation of $\mathbf{X}$.

An obvious corollary of Theorem 12.4.1 asserts that, *if* $\boldsymbol{\mu}$ *is a fixed* $1 \times p$ *vector and* $\boldsymbol{\Delta}$ *is a fixed* $p \times q$ *matrix of rank* q, *and if* $\mathbf{Y}$ *is a random* $1 \times q$ *vector having the* $N(\mathbf{0}, \mathbf{I})$ *distribution, then* $\mathbf{X} = \boldsymbol{\mu} + \mathbf{Y}\boldsymbol{\Delta}'$ *has the* $N(\boldsymbol{\mu}, \boldsymbol{\Delta}\boldsymbol{\Delta}')$ *distribution.* Theorem 12.4.2 below is a generalization of the corollary. A first stage of generalization results from noting that $\boldsymbol{\Delta}$ need not have $p \geq q$ and need not have rank $r = \min(p, q)$. The linear transformation $\mathbf{Y} \to \mathbf{Y}\boldsymbol{\Delta}'$ has a range space of dimension r and may be carried out in two steps. The first step $\mathbf{Y} \to \mathbf{Y}\mathbf{G}$

represents the projection into the range space, where $\mathbf{G}$ is a $q \times r$ matrix satisfying $\mathbf{G}'\mathbf{G} = \mathbf{I}$. The second step $\mathbf{YG} \to \mathbf{YG\Delta}^{*\prime} = \mathbf{Y\Delta}'$ represents the full rank linear transformation within the range space. The original form of the lemma applies with $\mathbf{YG}$ and $\mathbf{\Delta}^*$ in place of $\mathbf{Y}$ and $\mathbf{G}$ and gives the first generalization of the corollary because $\mathbf{\Delta}^*\mathbf{\Delta}^{*\prime} = \mathbf{\Delta}^*\mathbf{G}'\mathbf{G\Delta}^{*\prime} = \mathbf{\Delta\Delta}'$. A second stage of generalization of the corollary follows immediately from applying Theorem 12.4.1 to $\mathbf{X}$ and applying the once-generalized corollary to $(\mathbf{H} + \boldsymbol{\mu}\mathbf{K}') + \mathbf{Y}(\mathbf{\Delta}'\mathbf{K}')$:

Theorem 12.4.2. *Suppose that the $1 \times p$ random value vector $\mathbf{X}$ has the $N(\boldsymbol{\mu}, \boldsymbol{\Sigma})$ distribution. Then, for any fixed matrices $\mathbf{H}$ and $\mathbf{K}$ of dimensions $1 \times n$ and $n \times p$, the $1 \times n$ random value vector $\mathbf{Z} = \mathbf{H} + \mathbf{XK}'$ has the $N(\mathbf{H} + \boldsymbol{\mu}\mathbf{K}', \mathbf{K\Sigma K}')$ distribution.*

A special case of Theorem 12.4.2 asserts that *any marginal distribution of an $N(\boldsymbol{\mu}, \boldsymbol{\Sigma})$ distribution is also normal.* To see this, set $\mathbf{H} = \mathbf{0}$ for some $n < p$ and choose $\mathbf{K}$ to be a subset of n of the p rows of the $p \times p$ identity $\mathbf{I}$.

The remaining theory of this section concerns independence and conditioning. Theorem 12.4.3 which follows asserts that zero covariance among normally distributed stochastic quantities implies independence, a fact already noted in Section 12.3.

Theorem 12.4.3. *Suppose that $\mathbf{X}$ has the $N(\boldsymbol{\mu}, \boldsymbol{\Sigma})$ distribution. Suppose that the partition $p = r + (p - r)$ leads to*

$$\mathbf{X} = [\mathbf{X}_1, \mathbf{X}_2],\ \boldsymbol{\mu} = [\boldsymbol{\mu}_1, \boldsymbol{\mu}_2] \tag{12.4.1}$$

and

$$\boldsymbol{\Sigma} = \begin{bmatrix} \boldsymbol{\Sigma}_{11} & \mathbf{0} \\ \mathbf{0} & \boldsymbol{\Sigma}_{22} \end{bmatrix}, \tag{12.4.2}$$

i.e., that $\mathbf{X}_1$ and $\mathbf{X}_2$ are uncorrelated. Then $\mathbf{X}_1$ and $\mathbf{X}_2$ are independent with $N(\boldsymbol{\mu}_1, \boldsymbol{\Sigma}_{11})$ and $N(\boldsymbol{\mu}_2, \boldsymbol{\Sigma}_{22})$ distributions.

Theorem 12.4.3 generalizes to provide the conditional distribution of $\mathbf{X}_2$ given $\mathbf{X}_1 = \mathbf{x}_1$ in the case $\boldsymbol{\Sigma}_{12} \neq \mathbf{0}$. Surprisingly enough Theorem 12.4.3 itself provides the generalization using only elementary reasoning.

Theorem 12.4.4. *Suppose that $\mathbf{X}$ has the $N(\boldsymbol{\mu}, \boldsymbol{\Sigma})$ distribution. Suppose that $\boldsymbol{\Xi}_{21}$ satisfies*

$$\boldsymbol{\Sigma}_{21} - \boldsymbol{\Xi}_{21}\boldsymbol{\Sigma}_{11} = \mathbf{0} \tag{12.4.3}$$

and that $\boldsymbol{\Sigma}_{22.1}$ is defined by

$$\boldsymbol{\Sigma}_{22.1} = \boldsymbol{\Sigma}_{22} - \boldsymbol{\Xi}_{21}\boldsymbol{\Sigma}_{12}. \tag{12.4.4}$$

Suppose that $\mathbf{x}_1$ lies in the hyperplane to which the $N(\boldsymbol{\mu}_1, \boldsymbol{\Sigma}_{11})$ distribution restricts $\mathbf{X}_1$ with probability 1. Then the conditional distribution of $\mathbf{X}_2$ given $\mathbf{X}_1 = \mathbf{x}_1$ is $N(\boldsymbol{\mu}_2 - \boldsymbol{\Xi}_{21}[\boldsymbol{\mu}_1 - \mathbf{x}_1], \boldsymbol{\Sigma}_{22.1})$.

The proof requires noting that from (12.4.3) and (12.4.4) the covariance matrix of $[\mathbf{X}_1, \mathbf{X}_2 - \boldsymbol{\Xi}_{21}\mathbf{X}_1]$ is

$$\begin{bmatrix} \boldsymbol{\Sigma}_{11} & \mathbf{0} \\ \mathbf{0} & \boldsymbol{\Sigma}_{22.1} \end{bmatrix},$$

so that $\mathbf{X}_1$ and $\mathbf{X}_2 - \boldsymbol{\Xi}_{21}\mathbf{X}_1$ are independent with $N(\boldsymbol{\mu}_1, \boldsymbol{\Sigma}_{11})$ and $N(\boldsymbol{\mu}_2 - \boldsymbol{\Xi}_{21}\boldsymbol{\mu}_1, \boldsymbol{\Sigma}_{22.1})$ distributions. Because of this independence, the conditional distribution of $\mathbf{X}_2 - \boldsymbol{\Xi}_{21}\mathbf{X}_1$ given $\mathbf{X}_1 = \mathbf{x}_1$ is simply $N(\boldsymbol{\mu}_2 - \boldsymbol{\Xi}_{21}\boldsymbol{\mu}_1, \boldsymbol{\Sigma}_{22.1})$. But given $\mathbf{X}_1 = \mathbf{x}_1$ the values $\mathbf{X}_2 - \boldsymbol{\Xi}_{21}\mathbf{x}_1$ and $\mathbf{X}_2 - \boldsymbol{\Xi}_{21}\mathbf{X}_1$ are the same so that $\mathbf{X}_2 - \boldsymbol{\Xi}_{21}\mathbf{x}_1$ has the conditional distribution $N(\boldsymbol{\mu}_2 - \boldsymbol{\Xi}_{21}\boldsymbol{\mu}_1, \boldsymbol{\Sigma}_{22.1})$ or $\mathbf{X}_2$ has the conditional distribution $N(\boldsymbol{\mu}_2 - \boldsymbol{\Xi}_{21}[\boldsymbol{\mu}_1 - \mathbf{x}_1], \boldsymbol{\Sigma}_{22.1})$, as required.

Note that the symbol $\boldsymbol{\Xi}_{21}$ is being used relative to $\boldsymbol{\Sigma}$ as $\mathbf{H}_{21}$ has been generally used relative to $\mathbf{Q}$. If $\boldsymbol{\Sigma}_{11}$ has rank r, then $\boldsymbol{\Xi}_{21} = \boldsymbol{\Sigma}_{21}\boldsymbol{\Sigma}_{11}^{-1}$ and Theorem 12.4.4 can be stated more simply: *if* $\mathbf{X}$ *has the* $N(\boldsymbol{\mu}, \boldsymbol{\Sigma})$ *distribution, then the conditional distribution of* $\mathbf{X}_2$ *given* $\mathbf{X}_1 = \mathbf{x}_1$ *is*

$$N(\boldsymbol{\mu}_2 - \boldsymbol{\Sigma}_{21}\boldsymbol{\Sigma}_{11}^{-1}[\boldsymbol{\mu}_1 - \mathbf{x}_1], \boldsymbol{\Sigma}_{22} - \boldsymbol{\Sigma}_{21}\boldsymbol{\Sigma}_{11}^{-1}\boldsymbol{\Sigma}_{12}).$$

The general version does not determine $\boldsymbol{\Xi}_{21}$ uniquely although $\boldsymbol{\Xi}_{21}[\boldsymbol{\mu}_1 - \mathbf{x}_1]$ and $\boldsymbol{\Sigma}_{22.1}$ are uniquely determined. The mathematics of the general case is laid out in Exercises 4.4.3, 4.4.4, and 4.4.5 for the interested reader. There, of course, $\boldsymbol{\Sigma}$ and $\boldsymbol{\Xi}_{21}$ are represented by $\mathbf{Q}$ and $\mathbf{H}_{21}$. Note especially that one method of computing $\boldsymbol{\Xi}_{21}$ and $\boldsymbol{\Sigma}_{22.1}$ in the general case is almost identical with the full rank case: simply carry out as many as possible of the operations SWP[1], SWP[2], . . . , SWP[r] on $\boldsymbol{\Sigma}$ omitting those where the corresponding diagonal element is zero.

12.5 STANDARD DISTRIBUTION THEORY

Some useful and well-known properties of distributions which recur frequently in multivariate normal sampling theory are collected in this section. These distributions belong to the three related families of normal, beta, and gamma distributions, and often serve as building blocks for more complicated distributions in the sense that complicated random quantities may often be expressed as functions of independent random quantities having such distributions.

A random value X is said to have *the* $N(0, 1)$ *distribution* or to be $N(0, 1)$ *distributed* if it has the probability density function (p.d.f.)

$$\frac{1}{\sqrt{2\pi}} \exp\left(-\tfrac{1}{2}x^2\right) \tag{12.5.1}$$

for $-\infty < x < \infty$. More generally, a random value Y is said to have the $N(\mu, \sigma^2)$ distribution if $X = (Y - \mu)/\sigma$ has the $N(0, 1)$ distribution. The symbols $N(\mu, \sigma^2)$ should be read *normal with mean* μ *and variance* σ^2 and should be regarded not as a particular mathematical function but simply as a label or name for a specified distribution. It is shown in many textbooks that, if X is $N(0, 1)$ distributed, then $E(X) = 0$ and $E(X^2) = 1$, i.e., that X has mean zero and variance unity. It follows that Y with the $N(\mu, \sigma^2)$ distribution must have mean μ and variance σ^2, thereby justifying the name $N(\mu, \sigma^2)$. The family of normal distributions on the real line is thus defined to be a two-parameter family of distributions, with one member of the family associated with each possible choice of a mean and variance.

A random value X is said to have the *gamma distribution with shape parameter* α *and scale parameter unity* if X has the p.d.f.

$$\frac{1}{\Gamma(\alpha)} x^{\alpha-1}e^{-x} \tag{12.5.2}$$

for $0 < x < \infty$ and $0 < \alpha < \infty$. Here $\Gamma(\alpha)$ denotes the gamma function defined by

$$\Gamma(\alpha) = \int_0^\infty x^{\alpha-1}e^{-x}\,dx. \tag{12.5.3}$$

See also (3.5.7). The distribution determined by (12.5.2) will be denoted by the label $\gamma(\alpha, 1)$. From the relations $E(X^r) = \Gamma(\alpha + r)/\Gamma(\alpha)$ and $\Gamma(y + 1) = y\Gamma(y)$ for all $y > 0$, one can deduce that

$$E(X^r) = \alpha(\alpha + 1) \cdots (\alpha + r - 1), \tag{12.5.4}$$

and hence that the mean and variance of the $\gamma(\alpha, 1)$ distribution are both α. More generally, a random value Y is said to have *the* $\gamma(\alpha, \theta)$ *distribution with shape parameter* $\alpha > 0$ *and scale parameter* $\theta > 0$ if $X = Y/\theta$ has the $\gamma(\alpha, 1)$ distribution. The reader may easily generalize (12.5.2) and (12.5.4).

A random value X is said to have the *beta distribution with parameters* μ *and* ν if X has the p.d.f.

$$\frac{1}{B(\mu, \nu)} x^{\mu-1}(1 - x)^{\nu-1} \quad \text{for} \quad \begin{array}{l} 0 \le x \le 1 \\ 0 < \mu < \infty \\ 0 < \nu < \infty, \end{array} \tag{12.5.5}$$

where $B(\mu, \nu)$ denotes the beta function

$$B(\mu, \nu) = \int_0^1 x^{\mu-1}(1 - x)^{\nu-1}\,dx. \tag{12.5.6}$$

This distribution will be denoted by the label $\beta(\mu, \nu)$.

A basic relationship between the beta and gamma families follows.

Lemma 12.5.1. *Suppose that* X_1, X_2 *and* X_3, Y *are related pairs of random values satisfying*

$$X_3 = X_1 + X_2 \quad \text{and} \quad Y = X_1/(X_1 + X_2), \tag{12.5.7}$$

or, equivalently,

$$X_1 = YX_3 \quad \text{and} \quad X_2 = (1 - Y)X_3. \tag{12.5.8}$$

Then X_1 and X_2 are independently distributed according to $\gamma(\alpha_1, \theta)$ and $\gamma(\alpha_2, \theta)$ distributions if and only if X_3 and Y are independently distributed according to $\gamma(\alpha_1 + \alpha_2, \theta)$ and $\beta(\alpha_1, \alpha_2)$ distributions.

The proof may be carried out by directly computing the joint probability density function of X_3 and Y from that of X_1 and X_2, and vice versa, and is omitted here. One need only give the proof for the case $\theta = 1$, since the general result follows from the special case by appropriately scaling the random values concerned.

Note the fact that $X_1 + X_2$ has a gamma distribution whose shape parameter is the sum of the shape parameters of X_1 and X_2. By induction it follows that if $X_1, X_2, \ldots, X_m$ are independent with $\gamma(\alpha_1, \theta), \gamma(\alpha_2, \theta), \ldots, \gamma(\alpha_m, \theta)$ distributions, then $X_1 + X_2 + \cdots + X_m$ has the $\gamma(\alpha_1 + \alpha_2 + \cdots + \alpha_m, \theta)$ distribution. More generally, induction yields:

Lemma 12.5.2. $X_1/(X_1 + X_2)$, $(X_1 + X_2)/(X_1 + X_2 + X_3)$, $(X_1 + X_2 + X_3)/(X_1 + X_2 + X_3 + X_4), \ldots, (X_1 + X_2 + \cdots + X_{m-1})/(X_1 + X_2 + \cdots + X_m)$ and $X_1 + X_2 + \cdots + X_m$ *are independent with* $\beta(\alpha_1, \alpha_2), \beta(\alpha_1 + \alpha_2, \alpha_3), \ldots,$ $\beta(\alpha_1 + \alpha_2 + \cdots + \alpha_{m-1}, \alpha_m)$ *and* $\gamma(\alpha_1 + \alpha_2 + \cdots + \alpha_m, \theta)$ *distributions if and only if* $X_1, X_2, \ldots, X_m$ *are independent with* $\gamma(\alpha_1, \theta), \gamma(\alpha_2, \theta), \ldots,$ $\gamma(\alpha_m, \theta)$ *distributions.*

Random values with beta and gamma distributions appear in normal sampling theory because of the simple relationship given in Lemma 12.5.3 whose demonstration is left to the reader.

Lemma 12.5.3. *If X has the $N(0, 1)$ distribution, then X^2 has the $\gamma(\frac{1}{2}, 2)$ distribution. Consequently, if $X_1, X_2, \ldots, X_q$ are independent random values each having a $N(0, 1)$ distribution, then $X_1^2 + X_2^2 + \cdots + X_q^2$ has the $\gamma(q/2, 2)$ distribution.*

Statisticians are accustomed to calling the distribution $\gamma(q/2, 2)$ for integral q the *chi-square distributions on q degrees of freedom.* More generally, it is appropriate to call the $\gamma(q/2, 2\theta)$ distribution the *chi-square distribution* on q *degrees of freedom with scale parameter* θ, and to label it $\chi^2(q, \theta)$.

The following generalization of Lemma 12.5.3 is an immediate consequence of Lemmas 12.5.2 and 12.5.3.

Lemma 12.5.4. *If $Y_1, Y_2, \ldots, Y_q$ are independent and each has the $N(0, \sigma^2)$ distribution, then $Y_1^2 + Y_2^2 + \cdots + Y_q^2$ has the $\chi^2(q, \sigma^2)$ distribution and is independent of any set of functions of the ratios among $Y_1^2, Y_2^2, \ldots, Y_q^2$. The distribution of such ratios is in turn free of the value of σ^2.*

A random value Y will be said to have the *G distribution on r and s degrees of freedom and scale parameter* θ, labelled $G(r, s, \theta)$, provided that Y has the same distribution as $\theta R/S$ where R and S are independent with $\chi^2(r, 1)$ and $\chi^2(s, 1)$ distributions. More commonly, $(R/r)/(S/s)$ is said to have the *F distribution on r and s degrees of freedom*, labelled $F(r, s)$. Clearly, the $F(r, s)$ distribution is just the $G(r, s, s/r)$ distribution. The G modification is introduced here to reduce the proliferation of coefficients like $1/r$ and $1/s$ in later formulas. The G or F families are easily transformed into beta families, as indicated below, and the theory relating beta and gamma random values as in Lemmas 12.5.1 and 12.5.2 may be translated into theory relating G (or F) and χ^2 random values. The reader is asked to prove the following two lemmas which define and illustrate the translation.

Lemma 12.5.5. *If*

$$U = (r/s)V = W/(1 - W), \tag{12.5.9}$$

then the three assertions

i) *U has the $G(r, s, 1)$ distribution,*
ii) *V has the $F(r, s)$ distribution, and*
iii) *W has the $\beta(r/2, s/2)$ distribution*

are equivalent.

Another familiar consequence of the foregoing lemmas and definitions is:

Lemma 12.5.6. *If $Y_1, Y_2, \ldots, Y_q$ are independent with the $N(0, \sigma^2)$ distribution, then $(Y_1^2 + Y_2^2 + \cdots + Y_r^2)/(Y_{r+1}^2 + \cdots + Y_q^2)$ and $Y_1^2 + Y_2^2 + \cdots + Y_q^2$ are independent with $G(r, q - r, 1)$ and $\chi^2(q, \sigma^2)$ distributions.*

Definition 1 of normal distributions over a p-dimensional outcome-space $\mathscr{F}$ as given in Section 12.3 is free of the choice of the orthonormal basis $\mathbf{u}$ because of the following fundamental property of sets of independent normal random values on the line.

Lemma 12.5.7. *Suppose that $\mathbf{Y} = [Y_1, Y_2, \ldots, Y_q]$ consists of q independent $N(0, 1)$ distributed random values, and suppose that $\mathbf{X} = [X_1, X_2, \ldots, X_q]$ is given by*

$$\mathbf{X} = \mathbf{YG} \tag{12.5.10}$$

for some fixed $q \times q$ matrix $\mathbf{G}$. Then $X_1, X_2, \ldots, X_q$ have the same distribution as $Y_1, Y_2, \ldots, Y_q$ if and only if $\mathbf{G}$ is an orthogonal matrix.

The necessity of the condition that $\mathbf{G}$ be orthogonal is clear because the covariance matrix of $\mathbf{Y}$ is $\mathbf{I}$ and from (12.5.10) the covariance matrix of $\mathbf{X}$ is $\mathbf{G'IG}$ which coincides with $\mathbf{I}$ only if $\mathbf{G}$ is orthogonal. The sufficiency of the orthogonality of $\mathbf{G}$ may be checked directly by computing the joint probability density function of $X_1, X_2, \ldots, X_q$ from that of $Y_1, Y_2, \ldots, Y_q$. The p.d.f. of $Y_1, Y_2, \ldots, Y_q$ is given by

$$\prod_{i=1}^{q} \left(\frac{1}{2\pi}\right)^{1/2} \exp\left(-\tfrac{1}{2}y_i^2\right) = \left(\frac{1}{2\pi}\right)^{q/2} \exp\left(-\tfrac{1}{2}\mathbf{y}\mathbf{y}'\right), \tag{12.5.11}$$

and the p.d.f. of $X_1, X_2, \ldots, X_q$ is found by substituting in (12.5.11) the expression for $\mathbf{y}$ in terms of $\mathbf{x} = \mathbf{y}\mathbf{G}$ and multiplying by the Jacobian of $\mathbf{y}$ with respect to $\mathbf{x}$ which is $|\det \mathbf{G}'| = 1$. The resulting p.d.f. of $X_1, X_2, \ldots, X_q$ is

$$\left(\frac{1}{2\pi}\right)^{q/2} \exp\left(-\tfrac{1}{2}\mathbf{x}\mathbf{G}'\mathbf{G}\mathbf{x}'\right) |\det \mathbf{G}'| = \left(\frac{1}{2\pi}\right)^{q/2} \exp\left(-\tfrac{1}{2}\mathbf{x}\mathbf{x}'\right), \tag{12.5.12}$$

as required.

Noncentral χ^2 and noncentral G distributions frequently appear in normal sampling theory. The family $\chi^2(q, \theta)$ may be generalized to the three parameter family of *noncentral* χ^2 *distributions* $\chi^2(q, \theta, \tau^2)$ from which the original family is recovered by setting $\tau = 0$. A random value Q is said to have the $\chi^2(q, \theta, \tau^2)$ distribution if it has the same distribution as $\theta[(Y_1 + \tau)^2 + Y_2^2 + \cdots + Y_q^2]$ where $Y_1, Y_2, \ldots, Y_q$ are independent $N(0, 1)$ random values.

Lemma 12.5.8. *If* $Y_1, Y_2, \ldots, Y_q$ *are independent* $N(0, 1)$ *random values, then* $\theta[(Y_1 + \tau_1)^2 + (Y_2 + \tau_2)^2 + \cdots + (Y_q + \tau_q)^2]$ *has the* $\chi^2(q, \theta, \tau^2)$ *distribution where* $\tau^2 = \tau_1^2 + \tau_2^2 + \cdots + \tau_q^2$.

This lemma gives a common representation in which noncentral χ^2 distributions occur. It is interesting that the distribution depends on $\tau_1, \tau_2, \ldots, \tau_q$ only through their sum of squares. The lemma follows immediately from Lemma 12.5.7, choosing the first column of $\mathbf{G}$ to be proportional to $[\tau_1, \tau_2, \ldots, \tau_q]$.

Similarly, one may define noncentral and doubly noncentral G distributions. Q will be said to have *the noncentral G distribution* $G(r, s, \theta, \tau^2)$ if it has the same distribution as $\theta R/S$ where R and S are independent with $\chi^2(r, 1, \tau^2)$ and $\chi^2(s, 1)$ distributions. The *doubly noncentral G distribution* $G(r, s, \theta, \tau^2, \sigma^2)$ is defined in the same way, except that S has the $\chi^2(s, 1, \sigma^2)$ distribution.

Finally,

$$T = \mu + s^{-1}X \tag{12.5.13}$$

will be said to have *the t distribution* $t(\mu, \sigma^2, n, \nu)$ if X and s^2 are independent with $N(\nu, \sigma^2)$ and $\chi^2(n, 1/n)$ distributions. If $\nu = 0$ this may be called the *central t distribution* $t(\mu, \sigma^2, n)$. In general ν is called a noncentrality parameter. The limit of the $t(\mu, \sigma^2, n, \nu)$ distribution as $n \to \infty$ is the $N(\mu + \nu, \sigma^2)$ distribution, as is clear from (12.5.13) because s tends to unity in probability as $n \to \infty$. In particular, the $N(\mu, \sigma^2)$ family is a limiting case of the $t(\mu, \sigma^2, n)$ family as $n \to \infty$.

12.6 EXERCISES

12.1.1 Show that the definition (12.1.4) of the expectation of a random outcome x does not depend on the particular choice of the basis $\mathbf{v}$ in $\mathscr{F}$. Similarly, show that the covariance Σ associated with x has a coordinate-free definition.

12.1.2 Show that $E(\mu + x) = \mu + E(x)$ for any random outcome x and fixed outcome μ in $\mathscr{F}$. Show also that $E(K(x)) = K(E(x))$ where $K(\ldots)$ denotes a linear transformation of $\mathscr{F}$ into itself.

12.1.3 A finite population of size N measured on p variables may be represented by points $a_1, a_2, \ldots, a_N$ in a p-dimensional individual-space $\mathscr{F}$. The same $\mathscr{F}$ may also be regarded as the outcome-space for a random outcome x whose distribution is determined by the assertion

$$\Pr\{x = a_j\} = 1/N$$

for $j = 1, 2, \ldots, N$. Viewed as a sample, the individuals $a_1, a_2, \ldots, a_N$ have a sample mean $\bar{a}$ and a sample covariance S, while the random outcome x has mean μ and covariance Σ. Show that $\bar{a} = \mu$ and $S = [n/(n-1)]\Sigma$.

12.2.1 Show that the set of random values $\mathbf{Y}$ appearing in (12.2.1) and (12.2.3) has mean vector $\mathbf{0}$ and covariance matrix $\lambda\mathbf{I}$ for some $\lambda \geq 0$.

12.2.2 Show that the orthogonal projection x^* of a spherically distributed random outcome x into a subspace of outcome-space yields a random outcome spherically distributed in that subspace. What is the relation of the distribution of $(x^*, x^*)_d$ to the distribution of $(x, x)_d$? [*Hint:* express $(x^*, x^*)_d$ as $(x, x)_d \cos^2 \theta$.]

12.2.3 Consider a p-dimensional random outcome x which is spherically distributed with respect to a given inner product. Show that the conditional distribution of x, given that x lies in a subspace of outcome-space, is spherical in that subspace with respect to the given inner product.

12.2.4 State Lemmas 12.2.1 and 12.2.2 in terms of random coordinates instead of random outcomes, where the random coordinates are taken with respect to an orthonormal basis of $\mathscr{F}$.

12.2.5 Suppose that the random outcome x is spherically distributed over the surface of the sphere with center the origin and radius S. Suppose that X_1 is any random coordinate of x relative to an element of an orthonormal basis. Using Theorem 12.2.3 find the probability density function of X_1. Deduce the variance of X_1, and thence deduce λ in Theorem 12.2.1 for this distribution.

12.2.6 Suppose that x is spherically distributed about the origin in $\mathscr{F}$ and that X denotes the orthogonal projection of x into the subspace spanned by the fixed unit vector u in $\mathscr{F}$. Show that the distribution of the random value X is symmetric about 0. Show that X has the same distribution as the product $JK^{1/2}L^{1/2}$ of three independent random values where $J = \pm 1$ with probability $\frac{1}{2}$, K has the $\beta(\frac{1}{2}, (p-1)/2)$ distribution, and L has the distribution of $(x, x)_d$. Show conversely that the distribution of X uniquely determines the distribution of $(x, x)_d$ and therefore of x.

12.3.1 Suppose that P_m denotes the probability that a p-dimensional random outcome x with the $N(\mu, \Sigma)$ distribution lies within the concentration ellipsoid of the distribution. How would you check the assertions that $P_1 = 0.6827$, $P_2 = 0.3935$, $P_3 = 0.0902$, $P_4 = 0.0144$, $P_5 = 0.0018$, $P_6 = 0.0002$?

12.3.2 Suppose that the $1 \times p$ random vector $\mathbf{X}$ has the $N(\boldsymbol{\mu}, \boldsymbol{\Sigma})$ distribution where $\boldsymbol{\Sigma}$ has full rank p. Show $(\mathbf{X} - \boldsymbol{\mu})\boldsymbol{\Sigma}^{-1}(\mathbf{X} - \boldsymbol{\mu})'$ has the $\chi^2(p, 1)$ distribution or, more generally, that $(\mathbf{X} - \boldsymbol{\nu})\boldsymbol{\Sigma}^{-1}(\mathbf{X} - \boldsymbol{\nu})'$ has the $\chi^2(p, 1, \tau^2)$ distribution where $\tau^2 = (\boldsymbol{\mu} - \boldsymbol{\nu})\boldsymbol{\Sigma}^{-1}(\boldsymbol{\mu} - \boldsymbol{\nu})'$. Still more generally, allowing $\boldsymbol{\Sigma}$ to have any rank $q \leq p$, show that the nonzero eigenvalue of $(\mathbf{X} - \boldsymbol{\nu})'(\mathbf{X} - \boldsymbol{\nu})$ relative to $\boldsymbol{\Sigma}$ has the $\chi^2(q, 1, \tau^2)$ distribution where τ^2 is the nonzero eigenvalue of $(\boldsymbol{\mu} - \boldsymbol{\nu})'(\boldsymbol{\mu} - \boldsymbol{\nu})$ relative to $\boldsymbol{\Sigma}$.

12.3.3 Suppose that the $1 \times p$ random vector $\mathbf{X}$ has the $N(\boldsymbol{\mu}, \boldsymbol{\Sigma})$ distribution where $\boldsymbol{\Sigma}$ has rank q, and that

$$Q = \mathbf{X}\mathbf{X}' = \operatorname{tr} \mathbf{X}'\mathbf{X}.$$

Show that Q may be expressed in the form

$$Q = \omega_1^2(Y_1 + \nu_1)^2 + \omega_2^2(Y_2 + \nu_2)^2 + \cdots + \omega_q^2(Y_q + \nu_q)^2,$$

where $Y_1, Y_2, \ldots, Y_q$ are independent $N(0, 1)$ random values. Find the mean and variance of Q. [*Hint:* $\omega_1^2, \omega_2^2, \ldots, \omega_q^2$ are the eigenvalues of $\boldsymbol{\Sigma}$.]

12.3.4 The distribution in Exercise 12.3.3 is often called the general distribution of a quadratic form in normal variables. Show that $\mathbf{X}\boldsymbol{\Omega}\mathbf{X}'$ has a distribution of this type where $\boldsymbol{\Omega}$ is any $p \times p$ positive semi-definite inner product matrix and $\mathbf{X}$ has the $N(\boldsymbol{\mu}, \boldsymbol{\Sigma})$ distribution.

12.3.5 The $t(\mu, \Sigma, n)$ distribution has covariance $\lambda\Sigma$ where $\lambda \neq 1$. Find λ as a function of n.

12.3.6 The $t(0, 1, 1, 0)$ distribution on the line is often called the *standard Cauchy distribution.* It has the well known property that, if T_1 and T_2 are independent with this distribution, then $a_1T_1 + a_2T_2$ has the same distribution as $(|a_1| + |a_2|)T_3$ where T_3 again has the standard Cauchy distribution. Show that the result generalizes immediately to the multivariate $t(\emptyset, \Sigma, 1)$ distribution. [*Hint:* the linear combination is spherically distributed and a spherical distribution is uniquely determined by the marginal distributions of its projection into any line.]

12.4.1 Suppose that the 1×4 random vector $\mathbf{X}$ has the $N(\mathbf{0}, \boldsymbol{\Sigma})$ distribution where

$$\boldsymbol{\Sigma} = \begin{bmatrix} 4 & 6 & 2 & 4 \\ 6 & 9 & 3 & 6 \\ 2 & 3 & 5 & 4 \\ 4 & 6 & 4 & 6 \end{bmatrix}.$$

Find an explicit matrix $\boldsymbol{\Delta}$ such that $\mathbf{X} = \mathbf{Y}\boldsymbol{\Delta}'$ where $\mathbf{Y}$ has a unit normal distribution. Find an explicit pseudoinverse $\boldsymbol{\Gamma}$ of $\boldsymbol{\Delta}$ such that $\mathbf{Y} = \mathbf{X}\boldsymbol{\Gamma}'$. What is the conditional distribution of $\mathbf{X}_2 = [X_3, X_4]$ given $X_1 = 2$ and $X_2 = 3$?

12.4.2 Suppose that an outcome space $\mathscr{F}$ is spanned by complementary subspaces $\mathscr{F}_1$ and $\mathscr{F}_2$. Suppose that x_i is normally distributed in $\mathscr{F}_i$ for $i = 1, 2$ and that x_1 and x_2 are independent. Show, conversely to Theorem 12.4.3, that $x = x_1 + x_2$ is normally distributed in $\mathscr{F}$ and that coordinates of x relative to a basis of $\mathscr{F}_1$ are uncorrelated with coordinates of x relative to a basis of $\mathscr{F}_2$.

12.4.3 Suppose that x_1 and x_2 are independent random outcomes drawn from the same space $\mathscr{F}$, and that x_i has the $N(\mu_i, \Sigma_i)$ distribution for $i = 1, 2$. Show that $x_1 + x_2$ has the $N(\mu_1 + \mu_2, \Sigma_1 + \Sigma_2)$ distribution.

12.4.4 Generalize Theorem 12.4.3 to the case of k sets of random values with zero covariances between members of different sets. What is the corresponding generalization of Exercises 12.4.2 and 12.4.3?

12.4.5 State Theorem 12.4.4 in coordinate-free terms.

12.4.6 Generalize Theorems 12.4.1 and 12.4.2 to the $t(\boldsymbol{\mu}, \boldsymbol{\Sigma}, n)$ family.

12.4.7 Suppose that $\mathbf{X}$ has the $N(\mathbf{0}, \mathbf{I})$ distribution and partitions into $\mathbf{X} = [\mathbf{X}_1, \mathbf{X}_2]$ consisting of r and $p - r$ components, so that $\mathbf{X}_1$ and $\mathbf{X}_2$ are independent with $N(\mathbf{0}_1, \mathbf{I}_1)$ and $N(\mathbf{0}_2, \mathbf{I}_2)$ distributions. Suppose that s^2 is independent of $\mathbf{X}$ and has the $\chi^2(n, 1/n)$ distribution, and that $\mathbf{T} = [\mathbf{T}_1, \mathbf{T}_2] = (1/s)\mathbf{X}$, so that $\mathbf{T}$ has the $t(\mathbf{0}, \mathbf{I}, n)$ distribution. Given that $\mathbf{T}_1 = \mathbf{t}_1$, show that the conditional distribution of $\mathbf{T}_2$ is $t(\mathbf{0}_2, [(\mathbf{t}_1\mathbf{t}_1' + n)/(n + r)]\mathbf{I}_2, n + r)$. [*Hint:* Set $s^{*2} = (ns^2 + \mathbf{X}_1\mathbf{X}_1')/(n + r)$, so that $\mathbf{X}_2$, $\mathbf{T}_1$ and s^{*2} are independent with $N(\mathbf{0}_2, \mathbf{I}_2)$, $t(\mathbf{0}_1, \mathbf{I}_1, n)$, and $\chi^2(n + r, 1/(n + r))$ distributions. The conditional distribution of $(1/s^*)\mathbf{X}_2$ given that $\mathbf{T}_1 = \mathbf{t}_1$ is therefore $t(\mathbf{0}_2, \mathbf{I}_2, n + r)$. But under the condition $\mathbf{T}_1 = \mathbf{t}_1$, $(s^*/s)^2 = (\mathbf{t}_1\mathbf{t}_1' + n)/(n + r)$, and the desired result follows.]

12.4.8 Use the result of Exercise 12.4.6 to write down the generalizations of Theorems 12.4.3 and 12.4.4 from the special case of normal distributions to the general case of t distributions.

12.5.1 Deduce from (12.5.1) that the $N(\mu, \sigma^2)$ distribution has the p.d.f.

$$\frac{1}{\sqrt{2\pi}\,\sigma} \exp\left(-\frac{1}{2}\left(\frac{x - \mu}{\sigma}\right)^2\right) \quad \text{for} \quad -\infty < x < \infty. \tag{12.6.1}$$

12.5.2 Prove Lemma 12.5.1 and at the same time deduce that

$$B(\mu, \nu) = \Gamma(\mu)\Gamma(\nu)/\Gamma(\mu + \nu) \quad \text{for} \quad \mu > 0 \quad \text{and} \quad \nu > 0. \tag{12.6.2}$$

12.5.3 Suppose that X has the $\beta(\mu, \nu)$ distribution. Show that

$$E(X^r(1 - X)^s) = B(\mu + r, \nu + s)/B(\mu, \nu). \tag{12.6.3}$$

Deduce simple formulas for the mean and variance of X.

12.5.4 Suppose that $U_1, U_2, \ldots, U_{m-1}$ are independent with $\beta(\alpha_1, \alpha_2)$, $\beta(\alpha_1 + \alpha_2, \alpha_3), \ldots, \beta(\alpha_1 + \alpha_2 + \cdots + \alpha_{m-1}, \alpha_m)$ distributions. Show that $U_1U_2 \cdots U_{m-1}$ has the $\beta(\alpha_1, \alpha_2 + \alpha_3 + \cdots + \alpha_m)$ distribution.

12.5.5 Prove Lemma 12.5.3.

12.5.6 Prove Lemma 12.5.5.

12.5.7 Suppose that $X_1, X_2, \ldots, X_{20}$ represent 20 entries in a table of "random normal deviates," i.e., alleged values of a set of 20 independent $N(0, 1)$ random quantities. What distributions are simulated by $P = X_1^2 + X_2^2 + \cdots + X_{10}^2$, $Q = (X_{11}^2 + \cdots + X_{15}^2)/(X_{11}^2 + \cdots + X_{20}^2)$, $R = PQ$, and $S = Q/(1 - Q)$?

12.5.8 Show that the $\chi^2(r, \theta)$ distribution has the p.d.f.

$$Kx^{r/2-1} \exp(-x/2\theta) \tag{12.6.4}$$

for $0 < x < \infty$, where

$$K^{-1} = 2^{r/2}\theta^{r/2}\Gamma(r/2). \tag{12.6.5}$$

12.5.9 Show that the p.d.f. of the $\chi^2(1, 1, \tau^2)$ distribution may be written

$$Kx^{-1/2} \exp(-\tfrac{1}{2}x)[\exp(x^{1/2}\tau) + \exp(-x^{1/2}\tau)]. \tag{12.6.6}$$

for $0 < x < \infty$, where

$$K^{-1} = 2^{3/2}\pi^{1/2} \exp(\tfrac{1}{2}\tau^2). \tag{12.6.7}$$

Deduce that the p.d.f. of the $\chi^2(q, 1, \tau^2)$ distribution may be written

$$K \exp(-\tfrac{1}{2}x)\int_0^x (x-y)^{(q-1)/2-1}y^{-1/2}[\exp(y^{1/2}\tau) + \exp(-y^{1/2}\tau)]\,dy \tag{12.6.8}$$

for $0 < x < \infty$, where

$$K^{-1} = 2^{q/2+1}\pi^{1/2} \exp(\tfrac{1}{2}\tau^2). \tag{12.6.9}$$

12.5.10 Using the identity

$$\Gamma(\tfrac{1}{2})\Gamma(2r+1) = 2^{2r}\Gamma(r+\tfrac{1}{2})\Gamma(r+1) \tag{12.6.10}$$

show that an alternative form for (12.6.6) is the Poisson mixture

$$\sum_{r=0}^{\infty}\left[\frac{1}{2^{r+1/2}\Gamma(r+\frac{1}{2})}\,x^{r-1/2}\exp(-\tfrac{1}{2}x)\right]\frac{\lambda^r}{r!}\,e^{-\lambda}, \tag{12.6.11}$$

where

$$\lambda = \tfrac{1}{2}\tau^2. \tag{12.6.12}$$

Extend this to show that an alternative to (12.6.8) is

$$\sum_{r=0}^{\infty}\left[\frac{1}{2^{r+(q/2)}\Gamma(r+q/2)}\,x^{r+q/2-1}\exp(-\tfrac{1}{2}x)\right]\frac{\lambda^r}{r!}\,e^{-\lambda}. \tag{12.6.13}$$

12.5.11 Show that the p.d.f. of the $G(r, s, 1)$ distribution is

$$\frac{1}{B(r/2, s/2)}\,\frac{x^{r/2-1}}{(1+x)^{(r+s)/2}} \tag{12.6.14}$$

for $0 < x < \infty$.

12.5.12 Since the $\chi^2(q, 1, \tau^2)$ distribution is a Poisson mixture of $\chi^2(q+2r, 1, \tau^2)$ distributions for $r = 0, 1, 2, \ldots$, the $G(r, s, 1, \tau^2, \sigma^2)$ is a double Poisson mixture of $G(r+2m, s+2n, 1)$ distributions of $m = 0, 1, 2, \ldots$ and $n = 0, 1, 2, \ldots$ Use this remark together with (12.6.13) and (12.6.14) to write an expression for the p.d.f. of the $G(r, s, 1, \tau^2, \sigma^2)$ distribution.

12.5.13 Show that the p.d.f. of the $t(0, 1, n, 0)$ distribution is

$$\frac{1}{\sqrt{n}B(\frac{1}{2}, n/2)}\,\frac{1}{(1+x^2/n)^{(n+1)/2}} \tag{12.6.15}$$

for $-\infty < x < \infty$.

12.5.14 Show that the limiting form of the $G(r, s, 1/s, \tau^2, \sigma^2)$ distribution as $s \to \infty$ is the $\chi^2(r, 1, \tau^2)$ distribution.

12.5.15 Suppose that T has the $t(0, \sigma^2, n, \tau)$ distribution. Show that T^2 has the $G(1, n, n, \sigma^2, \tau^2)$ distribution, but that the two distributions are not equivalent because the $t(0, \sigma^2, n, \tau)$ distribution is symmetric if and only if $\tau = 0$.

12.6.1 Show that the $N(\boldsymbol{\mu}, \boldsymbol{\Sigma})$ distribution has the p.d.f.

$$K \exp\left(-\tfrac{1}{2}(\mathbf{x} - \boldsymbol{\mu})\boldsymbol{\Sigma}^{-1}(\mathbf{x} - \boldsymbol{\mu})'\right), \tag{12.6.16}$$

where

$$K = (2\pi)^{-p/2}(\det \boldsymbol{\Sigma})^{-1/2} \tag{12.6.17}$$

provided $\boldsymbol{\Sigma}^{-1}$ exists.

12.6.2 Show that the $t(\boldsymbol{\mu}, \boldsymbol{\Sigma}, n)$ distribution has the p.d.f.

$$K(1 + (\mathbf{x} - \boldsymbol{\mu})\boldsymbol{\Sigma}^{-1}(\mathbf{x} - \boldsymbol{\mu})'/n)^{-(p+n)/2}, \tag{12.6.18}$$

where

$$K = (n\pi)^{-p/2}(\det \boldsymbol{\Sigma})^{-1/2}\Gamma([p + n]/2)\Gamma(n/2) \tag{12.6.19}$$

provided $\boldsymbol{\Sigma}^{-1}$ exists (cf. Dunnett and Sobel, 1954).

CHAPTER 13

ELEMENTS OF MULTIVARIATE NORMAL SAMPLING THEORY

13.1 INTRODUCTION

This chapter studies the basic mathematical theory of sampling from a multivariate normal population. The emphasis is on the construction and understanding of sampling distributions. Applications of the theory are collected in Chapter 14.

A random sample from an origin-centered normal population (Section 13.2) viewed as p vectors in n-space carries information of two kinds called here *configuration* and *orientation* (Section 13.3). The sampling distribution of configuration is commonly called a Wishart distribution. Characterizations are given for Wishart distributions (Section 13.4) and for spherical distributions of orientation (Section 13.5). Wishart distributions are closely related to multivariate t distributions (Section 13.6) and to generalized beta and G distributions (Section 13.7).

In the literature of mathematical statistics a heavy emphasis has been placed on obtaining probability density functions of sample statistics. By contrast, the approach here is to present as much as possible of the theory using geometric arguments that express sample statistics in terms of independent quantities with simple distributions. Some brief remarks on the associated theory of probability density functions conclude this chapter.

Some of the more difficult sampling distributions may be studied asymptotically in large samples. Very little of such asymptotic theory is developed in this book, but some indications of its applicability will be given in Chapter 14.

13.2 SAMPLING AN ORIGIN-CENTERED NORMAL POPULATION

The essentials of multivariate normal sampling theory are best understood by concentrating first on a random sample from an origin-centered normal population. Such a sample may be represented by n points $a_1, a_2, \ldots, a_n$ in the individual-space $\mathscr{F}$ dual to a given variable-space $\mathscr{E}$. These points become a random sample of the desired kind if the a_i are regarded as independent random outcomes each having the $N(\varnothing, \Sigma)$ distribution over an outcome-space isomorphic to $\mathscr{F}$.

The origin-centered theory may be applied more widely through the simple device of subtracting means. For example, if $\dot{a}_1, \dot{a}_2, \ldots, \dot{a}_n$ denote a random sample from an $N(\mu, \Sigma)$ population, then $\dot{a}_1 - \mu, \dot{a}_2 - \mu, \ldots, \dot{a}_n - \mu$ represent a random sample from an $N(\varnothing, \Sigma)$ population. As will be seen, however, there is a more powerful way to extend the range of the special theory, namely to represent the sample as a set of random outcomes in the n-dimensional space $\mathscr{N}$ and to apply the theory in subspaces of $\mathscr{N}$.

If the sample is represented analytically as in Chapter 7 by an $n \times p$ matrix $\mathbf{X}$, then the sample individuals are represented by

$$a_i = \mathbf{X}^{(i)}\mathbf{v} \tag{13.2.1}$$

for $i = 1, 2, \ldots, n$, where $\mathbf{X}^{(i)}$ denotes row i of $\mathbf{X}$ and $\mathbf{v}$ denotes the dual of a given basis $\mathbf{V}$ of variable-space $\mathscr{E}$. The alternative is to view the sample as equivalent to p points

$$x_j = \mathbf{X}_j'\mathbf{N} \tag{13.2.2}$$

for $j = 1, 2, \ldots, p$, where $\mathbf{X}_j$ is column j of $\mathbf{X}$, and $\mathbf{N}$ is an orthonormal basis of the Euclidean space $\mathscr{N}$.

The concepts of configuration and orientation, around which the following sections are organized, are properties of the vectors $x_1, x_2, \ldots, x_p$ in $\mathscr{N}$. By the *configuration* of $x_1, x_2, \ldots, x_p$ is meant the information included in the norms of these vectors and in the angles among them. The standard analytic representation of the configuration is the inner product matrix of $x_1, x_2, \ldots, x_p$ in $\mathscr{N}$, namely

$$\mathbf{Q} = \mathbf{X}'\mathbf{X}. \tag{13.2.3}$$

The term *orientation* is used rather loosely to describe the information required to specify $x_1, x_2, \ldots, x_p$ after $\mathbf{Q}$ is already specified. More precise representations of orientation will be given in Sections 13.3 and 13.5, but the geometric idea should be clear here. The idea is that orientation refers to the positioning in $\mathscr{N}$ of a set of vectors which can only be rotated or reflected as a fixed geometric unit with a given configuration. Note that the concepts of configuration and orientation have coordinate-free geometric interpretations in $\mathscr{N}$, but the representation $x_1, x_2, \ldots, x_p$ is not coordinate-free in $\mathscr{E}$ since $x_1, x_2, \ldots, x_p$ are in one-one correspondence with the basis variables $V_1, V_2, \ldots, V_p$ in $\mathscr{E}$.

One apparent drawback to the representation of the sample using $x_1, x_2, \ldots, x_p$ is that the x_j are not independent, except under special choices of Σ which make $V_1, V_2, \ldots, V_p$ uncorrelated. The difficulty is eased by the following theory which shows how to replace $x_1, x_2, \ldots, x_p$ by an equivalent set of linear combinations of themselves which are independent and indeed identically normally distributed.

According to Theorem 12.4.1, each $\mathbf{X}^{(i)}$ may be expressed as $\mathbf{X}^{(i)} = \mathbf{Y}^{(i)}\boldsymbol{\Delta}'$ where $\mathbf{Y}^{(i)}$ has the q-dimensional $N(\mathbf{0}, \mathbf{I})$ distribution. Since $\mathbf{X}^{(1)}, \mathbf{X}^{(2)}, \ldots, \mathbf{X}^{(n)}$ are independent and $\mathbf{Y}^{(i)} = \mathbf{X}^{(i)}\boldsymbol{\Gamma}'$ for $i = 1, 2, \ldots, n$, it follows that $\mathbf{Y}^{(1)}$, $\mathbf{Y}^{(2)}, \ldots, \mathbf{Y}^{(n)}$ are independent and consequently that

$$\mathbf{X} = \mathbf{Y}\boldsymbol{\Delta}', \tag{13.2.4}$$

where

$$\mathbf{Y} = \begin{bmatrix} \mathbf{Y}^{(1)} \\ \mathbf{Y}^{(2)} \\ \cdot \\ \cdot \\ \cdot \\ \mathbf{Y}^{(n)} \end{bmatrix} \tag{13.2.5}$$

is an $n \times q$ matrix of random values whose elements are each independent with the $N(0, 1)$ distribution.

The following theorem is a direct translation of the preceding paragraph and requires no further proof.

Theorem 13.2.1. *Suppose that* $\mathbf{X}$ *and* $\mathbf{Y}$ *are random matrices with distributions as defined above and satisfying* (13.2.4). *Suppose that* $x_1, x_2, \ldots, x_p$ *are jointly distributed random outcomes in* $\mathcal{N}$ *as defined in* (13.2.2) *and that*

$$y_j = \mathbf{Y}_j'\mathbf{N} \qquad \text{for} \qquad j = 1, 2, \ldots, q, \tag{13.2.6}$$

where $\mathbf{Y}_1, \mathbf{Y}_2, \ldots, \mathbf{Y}_q$ *denote the columns of* $\mathbf{Y}$. *Suppose that the origin in* $\mathcal{N}$ *is denoted by* $\emptyset$ *and that the dual of the inner product over* $\mathcal{N}$ *defined by the orthonormal basis* $\mathbf{N}$ *is denoted by* I. *Then*

$$[x_1, x_2, \ldots, x_p] = [y_1, y_2, \ldots, y_p]\boldsymbol{\Delta}', \tag{13.2.7}$$

where $y_1, y_2, \ldots, y_q$ *are independently distributed random outcomes each having the* $N(\emptyset, I)$ *distribution, and may be found from* $x_1, x_2, \ldots, x_p$ *using the relation*

$$[y_1, y_2, \ldots, y_q] = [x_1, x_2, \ldots, x_p]\boldsymbol{\Gamma}'. \tag{13.2.8}$$

This result is the key to the approach to multivariate normal sampling theory through $\mathcal{N}$. It shows how Definition 1 and Definition 2 of Section 12.3 may be applied in $\mathcal{N}$, as well as in $\mathcal{F}$, in a relevant way. The following result generalizes Theorem 12.3.1 and shows how the main property of Definition 1 applies to sampling theory viewed through $\mathcal{N}$.

Theorem 13.2.2. *Suppose that* $\mathcal{N}_{A_i}$ *for* $i = 1, 2, \ldots, r$ *are mutually orthogonal subspaces of* $\mathcal{N}$ *whose direct sum is* $\mathcal{N}$. *For any outcome* z *in* $\mathcal{N}$ *suppose that* $z^{(A_i)}$ *denotes the orthogonal projection of* z *into* $\mathcal{N}_{A_i}$. *Suppose* *that I_{A_i} denotes the dual of the inner product over $\mathcal{N}_{A_i}$ implied by the dual of I over $\mathcal{N}$. Then the result* (13.2.7) *may be generalized to*

$$[x_1^{(A_i)}, x_2^{(A_i)}, \ldots, x_p^{(A_i)}] = [y_1^{(A_i)}, y_2^{(A_i)}, \ldots, y_q^{(A_i)}]\mathbf{\Delta}' \qquad (13.2.9)$$

for $i = 1, 2, \ldots, r$, where the r different lines of (13.2.9) *are independent. Furthermore, for a given i, $y_1^{(A_i)}, y_2^{(A_i)}, \ldots, y_q^{(A_i)}$ are independent and each has the $N(\emptyset, I_{A_i})$ distribution.*

In other words the components of the original n-dimensional sample outcomes lying in an n_{A_i}-dimensional subspace are distributed precisely like the original sample except that the sample size n is replaced by n_{A_i}; i.e., just as (13.2.7) implies that $x_1, x_2, \ldots, x_p$ represent a sample of size n from the $N(\mathbf{0}, \mathbf{\Delta\Delta}')$ distribution, (13.2.9) does the same with n replaced by the dimension n_{A_i} of $\mathcal{N}_{A_i}$.

The proof of Theorem 13.2.2 comes from applying Definition 1 of Section 12.3 to each of $y_1, y_2, \ldots, y_q$ where the role of the basis $\mathbf{u}$ is played by any orthonormal basis of $\mathcal{N}$ whose elements always lie within some $\mathcal{N}_{A_i}$. The distribution and independence of $y_t^{(A_1)}, y_t^{(A_2)}, \ldots, y_t^{(A_r)}$ follow from Definition 1. The independence of these sequences for different t follows because the y_t which determine the sequences are independent. Finally, (13.2.9) follows from (13.2.7) because the orthogonal projection $z \rightarrow z^{(A_i)}$ is a linear transformation.

The relevance of Theorem 13.2.2 to statistical methods of data analysis should be clear from Sections 7.4 and 9.4 where the relationship of standard methods to orthogonal subspaces of $\mathcal{N}$ was described.

This section concludes by discussing the dimension of the subspace spanned by $x_1, x_2, \ldots, x_p$ in $\mathcal{N}$. It is clear from (13.2.7) that this subspace has dimension at most q where q is the rank of the covariance Σ of the normal distribution being sampled. Now assuming that $y_1, y_2, \ldots, y_r$ span a subspace of dimension $r < n$, it is known that $\cos^2 \theta$ has the $\beta(r/2, (n - r)2)$ distribution where θ is the angle between y_{r+1} and the subspace spanned by $y_1, y_2, \ldots, y_r$. Consequently $\theta = 0$ with probability zero, so that $y_1, y_2, \ldots, y_{r+1}$ span a subspace of dimension $r + 1$ with probability 1. It follows by induction that $y_1, y_2, \ldots, y_q$ and consequently $x_1, x_2, \ldots, x_p$ span a subspace of $\mathcal{N}$ of dimension $\min(q, n)$ with probability 1.

13.3 THE DECOMPOSITION INTO RANDOM CONFIGURATION AND RANDOM ORIENTATION

If the $n \times p$ data matrix $\mathbf{X}$ denotes a random sample of size n from the $N(\mathbf{0}, \mathbf{\Sigma})$ distribution, then $\mathbf{Q}$ as defined in (13.2.3) is said to have the $W(n, \mathbf{\Sigma})$ distribution or *Wishart distribution with n degrees of freedom and parameters* $\mathbf{\Sigma}$. See Wishart (1928, 1948). Important properties of the family of Wishart distributions are collected in Section 13.4. In this section, $\mathbf{Q}$ is regarded as specifying the configuration of the set of random outcomes $x_1, x_2, \ldots, x_p$ which represent the sample in $\mathcal{N}$, and the chief aim is to define the conditional distribution of $x_1, x_2, \ldots, x_p$ given $\mathbf{Q}$. Having this, one may regard the distribution of the sample as being decomposed into two natural pieces, one of which specifies the marginal Wishart distribution of $\mathbf{Q}$, depending on $\mathbf{\Sigma}$, while the other specifies the conditional distribution of orientation given configuration, depending, as will be seen, only on $\mathbf{Q}$. This decomposition is due to James (1954).

The theory required here is a straightforward generalization of the theory of Section 12.2. In place of a single spherically distributed random outcome, the generalization considers a set of jointly distributed random outcomes each in the same space. In the present context the space is naturally taken to be the n-dimensional Euclidean space $\mathcal{N}$. A set of jointly distributed random outcomes $x_1, x_2, \ldots, x_p$ in $\mathcal{N}$ will be called *spherically* distributed about the origin in $\mathcal{N}$ provided that $x_1, x_2, \ldots, x_p$ have the same joint distribution as $\mathsf{G}x_1, \mathsf{G}x_2, \ldots, \mathsf{G}x_p$ for every orthogonal linear transformation G of $\mathcal{N}$ into itself which leaves the origin $\emptyset$ fixed. If $x_1, x_2, \ldots, x_p$ represent a sample from an origin-centered normal population, then the relation (13.2.7) transforms into

$$[\mathsf{G}x_1, \mathsf{G}x_2, \ldots, \mathsf{G}x_p] = [\mathsf{G}y_1, \mathsf{G}y_2, \ldots, \mathsf{G}y_q]\mathbf{\Delta}'. \tag{13.3.1}$$

Since $y_1, y_2, \ldots, y_q$ are independent $N(\emptyset, I)$ random outcomes, $\mathsf{G}y_1, \mathsf{G}y_2, \ldots, \mathsf{G}y_q$ are also, and a comparison of (13.2.7) with (13.3.1) shows that $x_1, x_2, \ldots, x_p$ have a joint distribution which is spherical in the sense just defined.

The following theory shows that the conditional distribution of *any* spherically distributed $x_1, x_2, \ldots, x_p$ given their configuration $\mathbf{Q}$ is the same, so that the joint distribution is uniquely specified by specifying the distribution of a nonnegative definite symmetric matrix $\mathbf{Q}$. The normal sample is thus completely characterized in the class of spherically distributed $x_1, x_2, \ldots, x_p$ by giving $\mathbf{Q}$ the $W(n, \mathbf{\Sigma})$ distribution. The theory is developed by pursuing a straightforward generalization of Lemmas 12.2.1 and 12.2.2 and Theorem 12.2.2.

Lemma 13.3.1. *If the random outcomes $x_1, x_2, \ldots, x_p$ have a joint distribution which is spherical about the origin in $\mathcal{N}$, then the conditional joint distribution of $x_1, x_2, \ldots, x_p$ given their configuration matrix $\mathbf{Q}$ is also spherical about the origin in $\mathcal{N}$.*

The proof is like that of the special case. By assumption the conditional distribution of $[\mathsf{G}x_1, \mathsf{G}x_2, \ldots, \mathsf{G}x_p]$ given the configuration of $[\mathsf{G}x_1, \mathsf{G}x_2, \ldots, \mathsf{G}x_p]$ is the same as the conditional distribution of $[x_1, x_2, \ldots, x_p]$ given the configuration of $[x_1, x_2, \ldots, x_p]$. But, since G is orthogonal, $[x_1, x_2, \ldots, x_p]$ and $[\mathsf{G}x_1, \mathsf{G}x_2, \ldots, \mathsf{G}x_p]$ have the same configuration with inner product matrix $\mathbf{Q}$. Thus the conditional distribution of $[\mathsf{G}x_1, \mathsf{G}x_2, \ldots, \mathsf{G}x_p]$ given $\mathbf{Q}$ is the same as the conditional distribution of $[x_1, x_2, \ldots, x_p]$ given $\mathbf{Q}$, as was to be proved.

Lemma 13.3.2. *If the jointly distributed random outcomes $x_1, x_2, \ldots, x_p$ are spherically distributed about the origin in $\mathcal{N}$ and have a fixed configuration inner product matrix* $\mathbf{Q}$, *then the joint distribution of $x_1, x_2, \ldots, x_p$ is uniquely determined.*

As in the case of Lemma 12.2.2, a heuristic proof from first principles will be given. First, however, it deserves mention that the lemma is merely a very special case of a general theory of invariant measures. The set of orthogonal transformations G of $\mathcal{N}$ into itself forms a group $\mathfrak{G}$ which is a compact topological group. The transformation group $\mathfrak{G}$ operates not only on points of $\mathcal{N}$ but also on sets of points such as $x_1, x_2, \ldots, x_p$. The collection of sets $[x_1, x_2, \ldots, x_p]$ with a given configuration is sometimes called as *Stiefel manifold.* Since $\mathsf{G} \in \mathfrak{G}$ carries $[x_1, x_2, \ldots, x_p]$ into $[\mathsf{G}x_1, \mathsf{G}x_2, \ldots, \mathsf{G}x_p]$ having the same configuration, $\mathfrak{G}$ operates as a transformation group on the given Stiefel manifold. Moreover $\mathfrak{G}$ operates transitively on the Stiefel manifold, since any two sets $[x_1, x_2, \ldots, x_p]$ and $[z_1, z_2, \ldots, z_p]$ with the same configuration are related by some $\mathsf{G} \in \mathfrak{G}$. James (1954) quotes the following theorem: *If $\mathfrak{X}$ is a topological space and $\mathfrak{G}$ is a transitive compact topological group of transformations of $\mathfrak{X}$ onto itself such that HX is a continuous function of H and X into $\mathfrak{X}$, then there exists a unique probability measure μ on $\mathfrak{X}$ invariant under $\mathfrak{G}$.* This theorem yields Lemma 13.3.2 as a special case. See Nachbin (1965) for a development of the general theory of invariant measures.

Whereas the general theorem gives no clue as to what the invariant distribution is, the first step of the following heuristic proof is to explain exactly what it is. To reduce details to a minimum it is convenient to replace $x_1, x_2, \ldots, x_p$ by an equivalent set of linear combinations of themselves which are orthonormal. If $\mathbf{Q}$ has rank q, then a fixed $q \times p$ matrix $\mathbf{C}$ may be found such that

$$[y_1, y_2, \ldots, y_q] = [x_1, x_2, \ldots, x_p]\mathbf{C}' \tag{13.3.2}$$

has the orthonormal configuration. Conversely, since $x_1, x_2, \ldots, x_p$ span a q-dimensional subspace which is none other than the subspace spanned by $y_1, y_2, \ldots, y_q$, there exists a $p \times q$ matrix $\mathbf{D}$ which is pseudoinverse to $\mathbf{C}$ and such that

$$[x_1, x_2, \ldots, x_p] = [y_1, y_2, \ldots, y_q]\mathbf{D}'. \tag{13.3.3}$$

From (13.3.2) the assumed spherical distribution for $[x_1, x_2, \ldots, x_p]$ implies a spherical distribution for $[y_1, y_2, \ldots, y_q]$. From (13.3.3), one need only describe the unique spherical distribution of $[y_1, y_2, \ldots, y_q]$ with a fixed orthonormal configuration, and the general case with configuration inner product matrix $\mathbf{Q} = \mathbf{DD}'$ is covered.

The spherical distribution of the orthonormal set $[y_1, y_2, \ldots, y_q]$ may be characterized by specifying the distribution of y_1 and then specifying the conditional distribution of y_{s+1} given $y_1, y_2, \ldots, y_s$ for $s = 1, 2, \ldots, q - 1$. Lemma 12.2.2 provides the distribution of y_1, namely the spherical distribution over the origin-centered unit sphere in $\mathcal{N}$. Given $y_1, y_2, \ldots, y_s$ it is known that y_{s+1} must be in the $(n - s)$-dimensional subspace of $\mathcal{N}$ orthogonal to $y_1, y_2, \ldots, y_s$ and the spherical symmetry again suggests giving y_{s+1} the spherical distribution over the unit sphere in its $(n - s)$-dimensional range space. The distribution specified in this way is obviously invariant under $\mathfrak{G}$, since its definition is the same regardless of how $\mathcal{N}$ is initially rotated. The uniqueness follows from the general theory, but is heuristically clear as in Lemma 12.2.2. The idea is that any little element of probability for any $y_1, y_2, \ldots, y_s$ transforms because of the transitivity of $\mathfrak{G}$ into the element at any other $y_1, y_2, \ldots, y_s$ so that the probability density everywhere is uniquely determined and constant.

The generalization of Theorem 12.2.2 follows immediately.

Theorem 13.3.1. *Suppose that $x_1, x_2, \ldots, x_p$ are random outcomes whose joint distribution is spherical about the origin in $\mathcal{N}$. Then the conditional distribution of $x_1, x_2, \ldots, x_p$ given the configuration* $\mathbf{Q}$ *defined in* (13.2.3) *is the unique spherical distribution of a set of vectors with a fixed configuration. Suppose further that* $\mathbf{Q}$ *has rank q with probability 1 and that for each such* $\mathbf{Q}$ *a pair of matrices* $\mathbf{C}$ *and* $\mathbf{D}$ *is defined and used to define $y_1, y_2, \ldots, y_q$ as in* (13.3.2) *and* (13.3.3). *Then $y_1, y_2, \ldots, y_q$ have the unique spherical distribution of an orthonormal set and are independent of* $\mathbf{Q}$.

Theorem 13.3.1 gives one reason why it simplifies matters to represent the spherical distribution of $x_1, x_2, \ldots, x_p$ with given configuration in terms of an orthonormal set $y_1, y_2, \ldots, y_q$. Another reason is that the analytic representation of such an orthonormal set is especially simple. Specifically

$$\begin{bmatrix} y_1 \\ y_2 \\ \cdot \\ \cdot \\ \cdot \\ y_q \end{bmatrix} = \mathbf{GN}, \tag{13.3.4}$$

where $\mathbf{G}$ is a $q \times n$ matrix with orthonormal rows, i.e., satisfying $\mathbf{GG}' = \mathbf{I}$. The unique spherical distribution of $y_1, y_2, \ldots, y_q$ implies a unique distribution for the qn random values defining $\mathbf{G}$. In particular $\mathbf{G}$ is a random orthogonal matrix with a uniquely specified distribution when q reaches its maximum value of n.

A specific choice of $\mathbf{G}$ in terms of an $n \times p$ sample data matrix $\mathbf{X}$ is the following. Consider first the common situation where $n \geq p$ and $\mathbf{X}$ has rank p. Define $y_1, y_2, \ldots, y_p$ to be the orthonormal set produced by successively orthogonalizing $x_1, x_2, \ldots, x_p$. Analytically this means producing the triangularization of $\mathbf{X}'$ defined in Exercise 4.3.3, i.e., representing $\mathbf{X}'$ in the form

$$\mathbf{X}' = \mathbf{DG}. \tag{13.3.5}$$

This $\mathbf{G}$ is a specific choice of $\mathbf{G}$ as in (13.3.4) and *may be viewed as a specific analytic representation of orientation.* On the other hand, $\mathbf{D}$ may be described as *the* lower triangular matrix such that the configuration matrix $\mathbf{Q}$ of $x_1, x_2, \ldots, x_p$ is given by $\mathbf{Q} = \mathbf{DD}'$. Since $\mathbf{Q}$ uniquely determines $\mathbf{D}$, one *may regard* $\mathbf{D}$ *as a specific analytic representation of configuration.* Thus the triangularization (13.3.5) is a natural analytic representation of the decomposition of the sample into configuration and orientation. The result extends to the less common situation where $n < p$ and $\mathbf{X}$ has rank n, except that only the first n stages of triangularization can be carried out, stopping with a full orthogonal matrix $\mathbf{G}$.

Formula (13.3.5) suggests a convenient way to a simulate at the same time both a random matrix $\mathbf{Q}$ having the $W(n, \mathbf{\Sigma})$ distribution and a matrix $\mathbf{G}$ having the spherical distribution of an orthonormal set. The steps are (*i*) start with an $n \times q$ matrix $\mathbf{Y}$ of independent $N(0, 1)$ random values, (*ii*) compute $\mathbf{X}$ from (13.2.4), (*iii*) carry out the triangularization (13.3.5) as described in Exercise 4.3.3, and (*iv*) compute $\mathbf{Q} = \mathbf{DD}'$. If only $\mathbf{G}$ is required, one might as well take $\mathbf{\Sigma} = \mathbf{I}$ so that $\mathbf{X} = \mathbf{Y}$ and step (*ii*) may be omitted. If only $\mathbf{Q}$ is required, step (*iii*) may be omitted and (*iv*) replaced by $\mathbf{Q} = \mathbf{X}'\mathbf{X}$. It can be shown, however, that there is no computational saving in the last procedure. In Section 13.4 two more efficient ways to simulate $\mathbf{Q}$ will be described.

13.4 PROPERTIES AND CHARACTERIZATIONS OF WISHART DISTRIBUTIONS

Recall the definition of $W(n, \mathbf{\Sigma})$ given in Section 13.3. The notation does not explicitly show the parameter p which is the dimension both of the $p \times p$ parameter matrix $\mathbf{\Sigma}$ and of a $p \times p$ random matrix $\mathbf{Q}$ which has the $W(n, \mathbf{\Sigma})$ distribution. Also, $\mathbf{\Sigma}$ may be any definite or semi-definite inner product matrix, having therefore any rank $q \leq p$. A random matrix $\mathbf{Q}$ with the $W(n, \mathbf{\Sigma})$ distribution is also a definite or semi-definite inner product matrix, which, from the last paragraph of Section 13.2, has rank min (q, n) with probability 1. The special case $p = q = 1$ provides the family of chi-square distributions $\chi^2(n, \sigma^2)$ defined in Section 12.5. There is a natural extension of the family $W(n, \mathbf{\Sigma})$ to a family of noncentral Wishart distributions $W(n, \mathbf{\Sigma}, \boldsymbol{\tau})$ which generalizes the noncentral chi-square family $\chi^2(n, \sigma^2, \tau^2)$ of Section 12.5. The more general family $W(n, \mathbf{\Sigma}, \boldsymbol{\tau})$ is discussed briefly in Exercises 13.4.11 and 13.7.13.

Like the $N(\mu, \Sigma)$ distributions, the Wishart distributions could have been defined from the beginning in a coordinate-free way. Specifically, $W(n, \Sigma)$ may be defined to be the distribution of a random inner product π generated as the sample raw sum inner product of a random sample of size n from the $N(\varnothing, \Sigma)$ population. The reader may be helped here by visualizing π as a random ellipsoid in $\mathscr{E}$ or, alternatively, a random dual ellipsoid π_d in $\mathscr{F}$.

Under the coordinate-free approach, $\mathbf{Q}$ would be said to have the $W(n, \mathbf{\Sigma})$ distribution if $\mathbf{Q}$ and $\mathbf{\Sigma}$ are respectively inner product matrices of π and Σ where π has the $W(n, \Sigma)$ distribution. Obviously the original and new definitions of $W(n, \mathbf{\Sigma})$ are equivalent. The existence of the coordinate-free approach is conceptually important. It implies that if π is restricted to a subspace of $\mathscr{E}$ then the restricted inner product is also Wishart distributed; or, if $\mathscr{F}$ is embedded in a larger space $\mathscr{F}^*$, then the partial inner product defined over $\mathscr{F}^*$ by the dual of π has a dual which is Wishart distributed. And of course, the matrix representations of π in terms of any coordinate system in $\mathscr{E}$ are all Wishart distributed.

These coordinate-free properties of Wishart distributions are expressed analytically in the following theorem.

Theorem 13.4.1. *If* $\mathbf{Q}$ *has the* $W(n, \mathbf{\Sigma})$ *distribution, then* $\mathbf{KQK}'$ *has the* $W(n, \mathbf{K\Sigma K}')$ *distribution, where* $\mathbf{K}$ *is any fixed* $r \times p$ *matrix and the dimensions of* $\mathbf{Q}$ *and* $\mathbf{\Sigma}$ *are* $p \times p$.

Note that $r < p$, $r = p$, and $r > p$ are all allowed, and no restriction is placed on the rank of $\mathbf{K}$. To prove Theorem 13.4.1 directly from the original definition of $W(n, \mathbf{\Sigma})$, one need only note that if $\mathbf{Q}$ is generated as $\mathbf{X}'\mathbf{X}$ from an $n \times p$ data matrix $\mathbf{X}$ representing a random sample of size n from the $N(\mathbf{0}, \mathbf{\Sigma})$ distribution, then, from Theorem 12.4.1, $\mathbf{XK}'$ represents a random sample of size n from the $N(\mathbf{0}, \mathbf{K\Sigma K}')$ distribution, so that $\mathbf{KX}'\mathbf{XK}'$ has the $W(n, \mathbf{K\Sigma K}')$ distribution, as required. This proof illustrates an important principle which is much used in the sequel, namely that a theorem concerning Wishart matrices is proved in general as soon as it is proved for any particular representation of the Wishart matrices in terms of normal samples.

The following theorem cuts deeply into the structure of a $W(n, \mathbf{\Sigma})$ distribution. The theory here was essentially given in a pioneering work of Bartlett (1933). The various ways of breaking $\mathbf{Q}$ into different but equivalent forms are sometimes called Bartlett decompositions. To simplify the presentation it will be assumed that $\mathbf{\Sigma}$ has full rank. As always in normal sampling theory, if $\mathbf{\Sigma}$ has rank $q < p$, one may throw away basic variables in $\mathscr{E}$ until a basis of q variables with a full rank inner product matrix is found, for the information in the rejected variables is redundant. In principle, therefore, it is a straightforward matter to extend Theorem 13.4.2 to cases where $\mathbf{\Sigma}$ has rank $q < p$.

Theorem 13.4.2. *Suppose that* $\mathbf{Q}$ *has the* $W(n, \mathbf{\Sigma})$ *distribution where* $\mathbf{Q}$ *and* $\mathbf{\Sigma}$ *have dimensions* $p \times p$ *and* $\mathbf{\Sigma}$ *has rank* p. *Suppose for* $1 \leq s \leq \min(p, n)$ *that*

$$\mathrm{SWP}[1, 2, \ldots, s]\mathbf{Q} = \begin{bmatrix} -\mathbf{Q}_{11}^{-1} & \mathbf{H}_{12} \\ \mathbf{H}_{21} & \mathbf{Q}_{22.1} \end{bmatrix} \tag{13.4.1}$$

and

$$\mathrm{SWP}[1, 2, \ldots, s]\mathbf{\Sigma} = \begin{bmatrix} -\mathbf{\Sigma}_{11}^{-1} & \mathbf{\Xi}_{12} \\ \mathbf{\Xi}_{21} & \mathbf{\Sigma}_{22.1} \end{bmatrix}, \tag{13.4.2}$$

where the partitions refer to $p = s + (p - s)$. *Then*

i) $\mathbf{Q}_{11}$ *has the* $W(n, \mathbf{\Sigma}_{11})$ *distribution,*

ii) $\mathbf{Q}_{22.1}$ *has the* $W(n - s, \mathbf{\Sigma}_{22.1})$ *distribution and is independent of* $\mathbf{Q}_{11}$,

iii) $\mathbf{Q}_{22.1}$ *and* $\mathbf{H}_{12}$ *are independent according to their joint conditional distribution given* $\mathbf{Q}_{11}$, *and*

iv) *the conditional distribution of* $\mathbf{H}_{12}$ *given* $\mathbf{Q}_{11}$ *may be specified as follows: if* $\mathbf{C}_{11}$ *is any* $s \times s$ *matrix such that* $\mathbf{C}_{11}'\mathbf{C}_{11} = \mathbf{Q}_{11}^{-1}$ *and* $\mathbf{\Delta}_{22}$ *is any* $(p - s) \times (p - s)$ *matrix such that* $\mathbf{\Delta}_{22}\mathbf{\Delta}_{22}' = \mathbf{\Sigma}_{22.1}$, *then* $\mathbf{H}_{12} - \mathbf{\Xi}_{12}$ *has the same distribution as* $\mathbf{C}_{11}'\mathbf{Z}\mathbf{\Delta}_{22}'$ *where* $\mathbf{Z}$ *is an* $s \times (p - s)$ *random matrix whose elements are independent random values each having an* $N(0, 1)$ *distribution.*

Part (i) follows immediately from the definition of the Wishart family of distributions replacing $\mathbf{X}$ by the first s rows of $\mathbf{X}$.

The remainder of the proof will be carried out using the realization of $\mathbf{Q}$ as the configuration matrix of the set of vectors $x_1, x_2, \ldots, x_p$ representing a sample from $N(\mathbf{0}, \mathbf{\Sigma})$ in $\mathcal{N}$. Suppose that $\mathcal{N}_A$ denotes the s-dimensional subspace of $\mathcal{N}$ spanned by $x_1, x_2, \ldots, x_s$ and that $\mathcal{N}_B$ denotes the $(n - s)$-dimensional orthogonal complement of $\mathcal{N}_A$ in $\mathcal{N}$. The properties (ii), (iii), and (iv) in the theorem will be proved to hold conditional on fixed $x_1, x_2, \ldots, x_s$ rather than conditional on fixed $\mathbf{Q}_{11}$. Note that to fix $x_1, x_2, \ldots, x_s$ is to fix not only their configuration matrix $\mathbf{Q}_{11}$ but also their orientation in the subspace $\mathcal{N}_A$. Since it turns out that the conditional distributions in (ii), (iii), and (iv) given $x_1, x_2, \ldots, x_s$ depend only on the configuration and not on the orientation, it follows that averaging over the distribution of orientation given the configuration has no effect, i.e., the conditional distributions in (ii), (iii), and (iv) given $\mathbf{Q}_{11}$ are the same as those given $x_1, x_2, \ldots, x_s$.

From Theorem 12.4.4 it follows that the conditional distribution of

$$[w_{s+1}, w_{s+2}, \ldots, w_p] = [x_{s+1}, x_{s+2}, \ldots, x_p] - [x_1, x_2, \ldots, x_s]\mathbf{\Xi}_{12} \quad (13.4.3)$$

given $x_1, x_2, \ldots, x_s$ is the same as that of the representation in $\mathcal{N}$ of a sample of size n from the $N(\mathbf{0}, \mathbf{\Sigma}_{22.1})$ distribution. From Theorem 13.2.2 the components of $w_{s+1}, w_{s+2}, \ldots, w_p$ in $\mathcal{N}_A$ and $\mathcal{N}_B$ are independently distributed like samples of sizes s and $n - s$ from the $N(\mathbf{0}, \mathbf{\Sigma}_{22.1})$ distribution. The components in $\mathcal{N}_A$ may be written

$$[w_{s+1}^{(A)}, w_{s+2}^{(A)}, \ldots, w_p^{(A)}] = [x_{s+1}^{(A)}, x_{s+2}^{(A)}, \ldots, x_p^{(A)}] - [x_1, x_2, \ldots, x_s]\mathbf{\Xi}_{12}, \quad (13.4.4)$$

since $x_1, x_2, \ldots, x_s$ already lie in $\mathcal{N}_A$. Similarly

$$[w_{s+1}^{(B)}, w_{s+2}^{(B)}, \ldots, w_p^{(B)}] = [x_{s+1}^{(B)}, x_{s+2}^{(B)}, \ldots, x_p^{(B)}], \quad (13.4.5)$$

since $x_1, x_2, \ldots, x_s$ are orthogonal to $\mathcal{N}_B$. From the properties of the sweep operator in relation to successive orthogonalization, $\mathbf{Q}_{22.1}$ represents the configuration inner product matrix of the components of $x_{s+1}, x_{s+2}, \ldots, x_p$ orthogonal to $x_1, x_2, \ldots, x_s$ or, from (13.4.5), $\mathbf{Q}_{22.1}$ is simply the configuration inner product matrix of $[w_{s+1}^{(B)}, w_{s+2}^{(B)}, \ldots, w_p^{(B)}]$. Since the conditional distribution of $[w_{s+1}^{(B)}, w_{s+2}^{(B)}, \ldots, w_p^{(B)}]$ given $x_1, x_2, \ldots, x_s$ is that of a sample of size $n - s$ from the $N(\mathbf{0}, \mathbf{\Sigma}_{22.1})$ distribution, $\mathbf{Q}_{22.1}$ must have the $W(n - s, \mathbf{\Sigma}_{22.1})$ distribution, again conditional on fixed $x_1, x_2, \ldots, x_s$. Since this conditional distribution does not depend on $x_1, x_2, \ldots, x_s$, it follows that $\mathbf{Q}_{22.1}$ is independent of $x_1, x_2, \ldots, x_s$ and therefore of $\mathbf{Q}_{11}$, as was required to prove in (ii).

It will next be shown that $\mathbf{H}_{12}$ is determined solely by $[w_{s+1}^{(A)}, w_{s+2}^{(A)}, \ldots, w_p^{(A)}]$, always assuming $x_1, x_2, \ldots, x_s$ fixed, which from the independence of (13.4.5) and (13.4.6) will imply part (iii) of the theorem. Actually, this is trivial because $\mathbf{H}_{12}$ simply expresses $[x_{s+1}^{(A)}, x_{s+2}^{(A)}, \ldots, x_p^{(A)}]$ in terms of the basis $[x_1, x_2, \ldots, x_s]$ of $\mathcal{N}_A$, i.e.,

$$[x_{s+1}^{(A)}, x_{s+2}^{(A)}, \ldots, x_p^{(A)}] = [x_1, x_2, \ldots, x_s]\mathbf{H}_{12}. \tag{13.4.6}$$

Since $x_1, x_2, \ldots, x_s$ are regarded as fixed, knowledge of (13.4.4) implies knowledge of the coordinate vectors $\mathbf{H}_{12}$ in (13.4.6), as required.

To prove part (iv) note from (13.4.4) and (13.4.6) that

$$[w_{s+1}^{(A)}, w_{s+2}^{(A)}, \ldots, w_p^{(A)}] = [x_1, x_2, \ldots, x_s](\mathbf{H}_{12} - \mathbf{\Xi}_{12}). \tag{13.4.7}$$

Since this represents a sample of size s from the $N(\mathbf{0}, \mathbf{\Sigma}_{22.1})$ distribution it follows that

$$[w_{s+1}^{(A)}, w_{s+2}^{(A)}, \ldots, w_p^{(A)}]\mathbf{\Delta}_{22}^{\prime -1} = [x_1, x_2, \ldots, x_s](\mathbf{H}_{12} - \mathbf{\Xi}_{12})\mathbf{\Delta}_{22}^{\prime -1} \tag{13.4.8}$$

represents a sample of size s from the $N(\mathbf{0}, \mathbf{I})$ distribution provided that $\mathbf{\Delta}_{22}\mathbf{\Delta}_{22}' = \mathbf{\Sigma}_{22.1}$. Similarly, if $\mathbf{C}_{11}'\mathbf{C}_{11} = \mathbf{Q}_{11}^{-1}$, then $[u_1, u_2, \ldots, u_s] = [x_1, x_2, \ldots, x_s]\mathbf{C}_{11}'$ is an orthonormal basis of $\mathcal{N}_A$ and (13.4.8) may be written

$$[w_{s+1}^{(A)}, w_{s+2}^{(A)}, \ldots, w_p^{(A)}] = [u_1, u_2, \ldots, u_s]\mathbf{C}_{11}^{\prime -1}(\mathbf{H}_{12} - \mathbf{\Xi}_{12})\mathbf{\Delta}_{22}^{\prime -1}. \tag{13.4.9}$$

But, if a sample of size s from the $N(\mathbf{0}, \mathbf{I})$ distribution is expressed in terms of an orthonormal basis $\mathcal{N}_A$ as in (13.4.9), then the coordinates $\mathbf{C}_{11}^{\prime -1}(\mathbf{H}_{12} - \mathbf{\Xi}_{12})\mathbf{\Delta}_{22}^{\prime -1}$ must consist of $s \times (p - s)$ independent random values each with the $N(0, 1)$ distribution. This completes the proof of Theorem 13.4.2.

For each s on $1 \leq s \leq \min(p - 1, n)$, Theorem 13.4.2 provides a characterization of the distribution of SWP$[1, 2, \ldots, s]\mathbf{Q}$. Since SWP$[1, 2, \ldots, s]\mathbf{Q}$ provides information equivalent to $\mathbf{Q}$, Theorem 13.4.2 in effect provides characterizations of the $W(n, \mathbf{\Sigma})$ distribution as well. A sequence of stepwise applications of Theorem 13.4.2 leads to a collection of further characterizations given below as Corollaries 13.4.1, 13.4.2, 13.4.3, and 13.4.4. A pair of procedures for simulating $\mathbf{Q}$ will be given along with these characterizations. It will be assumed henceforth that $n \geq p$. The modifications for $n < p$ are left to the interested reader, the essential point being that $\mathbf{Q}_{22.1} = \mathbf{0}$ in (13.4.1) if $s = n < p$, so that the various constructions must end at this point by constructing $\mathbf{H}_{21}$ as indicated in Theorem 13.4.2.

The notation of Section 4.2 will be followed. Thus $\mathbf{Q}$ has four characterizations flowing from $\mathbf{Q} = \mathbf{BTB}'$, $\mathbf{Q}^{-1} = \mathbf{A}'\mathbf{T}^{-1}\mathbf{A}$, $\mathbf{Q} = \mathbf{DD}'$, and $\mathbf{Q}^{-1} = \mathbf{C}'\mathbf{C}$, where $\mathbf{A}$, $\mathbf{B}$, $\mathbf{C}$, and $\mathbf{D}$ are lower triangular matrices and $\mathbf{T}$ is a diagonal matrix. The (1, 1) element of $\mathbf{T}$ is the (1, 1) element q_{11} of $\mathbf{Q}$ and the $(s+1, s+1)$ element $q_{\overline{s+1}\,\overline{s+1}.12\ldots s}$ of SWP$[1, 2, \ldots, s]\mathbf{Q}$ is the (1, 1) element of $\mathbf{Q}_{22.1}$ in (13.4.1). The diagonal elements of $\mathbf{A}$ and $\mathbf{B}$ are all unity while those of $\mathbf{D}$ and $\mathbf{C}$ are the square roots of those of $\mathbf{T}$ and $\mathbf{T}^{-1}$, respectively. In general, subscripted small letters denote elements of matrices; for example, a_{ij} is the (i, j) element of $\mathbf{A}$. When $\mathbf{Q}$ is replaced by $\mathbf{\Sigma}$, Greek letters are used in general. Thus the analogues of $q_{11}, q_{22.1}, \ldots, q_{pp.12\ldots\overline{p-1}}$ are denoted by $\sigma_{11}, \sigma_{22.1}, \ldots, \sigma_{pp.12\ldots\overline{p-1}}$. The analogues of $\mathbf{C}$ and $\mathbf{D}$ are $\mathbf{\Gamma}$ and $\mathbf{\Delta}$, of a_{ij} and b_{ij} are α_{ij} and β_{ij}, and so on.

Perhaps the most direct way to simulate $\mathbf{Q}$ is to construct the sequence of matrices $\mathbf{Q}_{22.1}$ for $s = p - 1, p - 2, \ldots, 1, 0$ where the final member of this sequence is $\mathbf{Q}$. The first member of the sequence is simply $q_{pp.12\ldots\overline{p-1}}$ which, from the application of Theorem 13.4.2 with $s = p - 1$, has the $\chi^2(n - p + 1, \sigma_{pp.12\ldots\overline{p-1}})$ distribution and is easily simulated from $n - p + 1$ independent $N(0, 1)$ random values. Having $\mathbf{Q}_{22.1}$ for general s, one may construct the $\mathbf{Q}_{22.1}$ corresponding to $s - 1$ in two stages, first finding the last column of $\mathbf{H}_{21}$ and the (s, s) element of $-\mathbf{Q}_{11}^{-1}$ in (13.4.1), and second carrying out the RSW$[s]$ operation on the bottom right $(p - s + 1) \times (p - s + 1)$ part of (13.4.1). From Theorem 13.4.2, the last column of $\mathbf{H}_{21}$ may be constructed as the last column of $\mathbf{\Xi}_{21}$ plus $q_{ss.12\ldots\overline{s-1}}^{-1/2}\mathbf{\Delta}_{22}\mathbf{Z}$ where $\mathbf{Z}$ is a $(p - s) \times 1$ vector of independent $N(0, 1)$ random values, while the (s, s) element of $-\mathbf{Q}_{11}^{-1}$ is simply $-q_{ss.12\ldots\overline{s-1}}^{-1}$ where $q_{ss.12\ldots\overline{s-1}}$ has the $\chi^2(n - s + 1, \sigma_{ss.12\ldots\overline{s-1}})$ distribution. In carrying out this simulation in a computer one would naturally carry along the matrices (13.4.2) for $s = p - 1, p - 2, \ldots, 1$ at the corresponding stages of simulation of $\mathbf{Q}_{22.1}$. Note that this would provide the required last column of $\mathbf{\Xi}_{21}$ and would also allow one to build up the required $\mathbf{\Delta}_{22}$, since column s of $\mathbf{\Delta}$ is given by

$$[\delta_{\overline{s+1}\,s}, \delta_{\overline{s+2}\,s}, \ldots, \delta_{ps}]' = \sigma_{ss.12\ldots\overline{s-1}}^{1/2}[\beta_{\overline{s+1}\,s}, \beta_{\overline{s+2}\,s}, \ldots, \beta_{ps}]', \quad (13.4.10)$$

where $[\beta_{\overline{s+1}\,s}, \beta_{\overline{s+2}\,s}, \ldots, \beta_{ps}]'$ denotes the last column of $\mathbf{\Xi}_{21}$.

The general stage of the simulation just described produces the last column of $\mathbf{H}_{21}$ which is also the subdiagonal part of column s of $\mathbf{B}$. This leads to

Corollary 13.4.1. *Suppose that the hypotheses of Theorem 13.4.2 hold with $n \geq p$ and suppose that $\mathbf{Q}$ is represented as above by $\mathbf{B}$ and $\mathbf{T}$. Then the elements $q_{11}, q_{22.1}, \ldots, q_{pp.12\ldots\overline{p-1}}$ of $\mathbf{T}$ are independent with $\chi^2(n, \sigma_{11})$, $\chi^2(n - 1, \sigma_{22.1}), \ldots, \chi^2(n - p + 1, \sigma_{pp.12\ldots\overline{p-1}})$ distributions. Also, the columns of $\mathbf{B}$ are independent and the conditional distribution of $[b_{\overline{s+1}\,s}, b_{\overline{s+2}\,s}, \ldots, b_{ps}]$ given $q_{ss.12\ldots\overline{s-1}}$ is normal with mean $[\beta_{\overline{s+1}\,s}, \beta_{\overline{s+2}\,s}, \ldots, \beta_{ps}]$ and covariance matrix $q_{ss.12\ldots\overline{s-1}}^{-1}\mathbf{\Sigma}_{22.1}$.*

In view of the analogue of (13.4.1) with $\mathbf{\Sigma}$ replaced by $\mathbf{Q}$, Corollary 13.4.1 may be restated in terms of $\mathbf{D}$ and $\mathbf{\Delta}$.

Corollary 13.4.2. *Suppose that the hypotheses of Theorem 13.4.2 holds with $n \geq p$, and suppose that $\mathbf{Q}$ is characterized as above by $\mathbf{D}$. Then $d_{11}^2, d_{22}^2, \ldots, d_{pp}^2$ are independent with $\chi^2(n, \delta_{11}^2), \chi^2(n-1, \delta_{22}^2), \ldots, \chi^2(n-p+1, \delta_{pp}^2)$ distributions. Also, the columns of $\mathbf{D}$ are independent, and the conditional distribution of $[d_{\overline{s+1}\,s}, d_{\overline{s+2}\,s}, \ldots, d_{ps}]$ given d_{ss} is normal with mean $[\delta_{\overline{s+1}\,s}, \delta_{\overline{s+2}\,s}, \ldots, \delta_{ps}]$ and covariance matrix $(\delta_{ss}/d_{ss})\mathbf{\Delta}_{22}\mathbf{\Delta}_{22}'$.*

There is an alternative natural scheme for simulating $\mathbf{Q}$, also suggested by Theorem 13.4.2. Actually this will produce $\mathbf{Q}^{-1}$ directly, from which $\mathbf{Q}$ must be computed. The idea is to simulate the sequence $-\mathbf{Q}_{11}^{-1}$ for $s = 1, 2, \ldots, p$. For $s = 1$, this is just $-q_{11}^{-1}$ where q_{11} has the $\chi^2(n, \sigma_{11})$ distribution. Having $-\mathbf{Q}_{11}^{-1}$ for general s, one may use Theorem 13.4.2 to create the upper left $(s+1) \times (s+1)$ part of (13.4.1). Then SWP$[s+1]$ may be applied to upstage $-\mathbf{Q}_{11}^{-1}$. The $(s+1, s+1)$ element of (13.4.1) is simply $q_{\overline{s+1}\,\overline{s+1}.12\ldots s}$ which has the $\chi^2(n-s, \sigma_{\overline{s+1}\,\overline{s+1}.12\ldots s})$ distribution, while the first row of $\mathbf{H}_{21}$ is $-(a_{\overline{s+1}\,1}, a_{\overline{s+1}\,2}, \ldots, a_{\overline{s+1}\,s})$ which may be simulated as $-(\alpha_{\overline{s+1}\,1}, a_{\overline{s+1}\,2}, \ldots, \alpha_{\overline{s+1}\,s})$ plus $\mathbf{Z}\mathbf{C}_{11}\sigma^{1/2}_{\overline{s+1}\,\overline{s+1}.12\ldots s}$ where $\mathbf{Z}$ is a $1 \times s$ vector of independent $N(0, 1)$ random values. Note that

$$[c_{\overline{s+1}\,1}, c_{\overline{s+1}\,2}, \ldots, c_{\overline{s+1}\,s}] = q^{-1/2}_{\overline{s+1}\,\overline{s+1}.12\ldots s}[a_{\overline{s+1}\,1}, a_{\overline{s+1}\,2}, \ldots, a_{\overline{s+1}\,s}], \quad (13.4.11)$$

which shows how to build up $\mathbf{C}_{11}$ along with the stages of finding $\mathbf{Q}_{11}^{-1}$.

This second simulation relies on theory which essentially gives the conditional distribution of each row of $\mathbf{A}$ or $\mathbf{C}$ given the preceding row. Thus, analogues to Corollaries 13.4.1 and 13.4.2 are:

Corollary 13.4.3. *Suppose that the hypotheses of Theorem 13.4.2 hold with $n \geq p$. Suppose that $\mathbf{Q}$ is represented in terms of $\mathbf{A}$ and $\mathbf{T}$ as described above. Then the distribution of $\mathbf{T}$ is as given in Corollary 13.4.1. The conditional distribution of $[a_{\overline{s+1}\,1}, a_{\overline{s+1}\,2}, \ldots, a_{\overline{s+1}\,s}]$ given the first s rows of $\mathbf{A}$ and the first s elements of $\mathbf{T}$ is normal with mean $[\alpha_{\overline{s+1}\,1}, \alpha_{\overline{s+1}\,2}, \ldots, \alpha_{\overline{s+1}\,s}]$ and covariance matrix $\sigma_{\overline{s+1}\,\overline{s+1}.12\ldots s}\mathbf{Q}_{11}^{-1}$.*

Corollary 13.4.4. *Suppose that the hypotheses of Theorem 13.4.2 hold with $n \geq p$. Suppose that $\mathbf{Q}$ is represented in terms of $\mathbf{C}$ as above. Then $c_{11}^{-2}, c_{22}^{-2}, \ldots, c_{pp}^{-2}$ are independent with $\chi^2(n, \gamma_{11}^{-1}), \chi^2(n-1, \gamma_{22}^{-1}), \ldots, \chi^2(n-p+1, \gamma_{pp}^{-1})$ distributions. Also the conditional distribution of $[c_{\overline{s+1}\,1}, c_{\overline{s+1}\,2}, \ldots, c_{\overline{s+1}\,s}]$ given the first s rows of $\mathbf{C}$ is normal with mean $[\gamma_{\overline{s+1}\,1}, \gamma_{\overline{s+1}\,2}, \ldots, \gamma_{\overline{s+1}\,s}]$ and covariance matrix $(\sigma_{\overline{s+1}\,\overline{s+1}.12\ldots s}/q_{\overline{s+1}\,\overline{s+1}.12\ldots s})\mathbf{C}_{11}'\mathbf{C}_{11}$.*

It is worth remarking as a separate corollary that, since

$$\frac{\det \mathbf{Q}}{\det \mathbf{\Sigma}} = \frac{q_{11}}{\sigma_{11}} \cdot \frac{q_{22.1}}{\sigma_{22.1}} \cdot \ldots \cdot \frac{q_{pp.12\ldots\overline{p-1}}}{\sigma_{pp.12\ldots\overline{p-1}}}, \quad (13.4.12)$$

the distribution of det $\mathbf{Q}$ is easily characterized. This quantity is closely related to the generalized variance defined in (7.6.2). Its distribution was first characterized by Wilks (1932).

Corollary 13.4.5. *Suppose that* $\mathbf{Q}$ *has the* $W(n, \mathbf{\Sigma})$ *distribution where* $\mathbf{\Sigma}$ *is nonsingular with rank p and* $n \geq p$. *Then* det $\mathbf{Q}$/det $\mathbf{\Sigma}$ *has the same distribution as the product of p independent random values with* $\chi^2(n, 1), \chi^2(n-1, 1), \ldots, \chi^2(n-p+1, 1)$ *distributions.*

Theorem 13.4.2 may be interpreted in a coordinate-free way in the pair of dual spaces $\mathscr{E}$ and $\mathscr{F}$ with their corresponding pair of dual bases $\mathbf{V}$ and $\mathbf{v}$. The subsets $V_1, V_2, \ldots, V_r$ and $V_{r+1}, V_{r+2}, \ldots, V_p$ of the basis $\mathbf{V}$ in $\mathscr{E}$ should be regarded as any pair of complementary subspaces $\mathscr{V}_1$ and $\mathscr{V}_2$ of $\mathscr{E}$. Inner products over $\mathscr{E}$, $\mathscr{V}_1$, and $\mathscr{V}_2$ may be represented by their ellipsoids. Thus $\mathbf{Q}_{11}$ and $\mathbf{\Sigma}_{11}$ are represented by the intersections with $\mathscr{V}_1$ of the ellipsoids representing $\mathbf{Q}$ and $\mathbf{\Sigma}$, respectively. Similarly $\mathbf{Q}_{22.1}$ and $\mathbf{\Sigma}_{22.1}$ are represented by the shadows cast in $\mathscr{V}_2$ by projection along hyperplanes parallel to $\mathscr{V}_1$ of the ellipsoids representing $\mathbf{Q}$ and $\mathbf{\Sigma}$, respectively. Thus, the two random ellipsoids in $\mathscr{V}_1$ and $\mathscr{V}_2$ determined in this way are independent with known distributions. Dually $\mathbf{Q}$ and $\mathbf{\Sigma}$ may be represented by their concentration ellipsoids in $\mathscr{F}$; $\mathbf{Q}_{11}$ and $\mathbf{\Sigma}_{11}$ are represented by shadows in the r-dimensional subspace $\mathscr{V}_{2d}$ dual to $\mathscr{V}_2$; and $\mathbf{Q}_{22.1}$ and $\mathbf{\Sigma}_{22.1}$ are represented by the intersections of the complete concentration ellipsoids with the $(p-r)$-dimensional subspace $\mathscr{V}_{1d}$ dual to $\mathscr{V}_1$. Again there is a pair of random ellipsoids, one in an r-dimensional subspace and one in a $(p-r)$-dimensional subspace, which are independently distributed according to known distributions.

To help in visualizing the foregoing general theory, a pair of simple consequences will be quoted along with their geometric interpretations. *First, if* $\mathbf{Q}$ *has the* $W(n, \mathbf{\Sigma})$ *distribution and if* $\mathbf{L}$ *is any* $1 \times p$ *matrix, then* $\mathbf{LQL}'/\mathbf{L\Sigma L}'$ *has the* $\chi^2(n, 1)$ *distribution.* This ratio has a simple geometric interpretation as the ratio of the squared radii of two ellipsoids in $\mathscr{E}$ along a general common axis, as illustrated in Fig. 13.4.1. A companion result asserts that *if* $\mathbf{Q}$ *has the* $W(n, \mathbf{\Sigma})$ *distribution with nonsingular* $\mathbf{\Sigma}$ *of rank p and* $n \geq p$, *and if* $\mathbf{J}$ *is any* $p \times 1$ *matrix, then* $\mathbf{J}'\mathbf{\Sigma}^{-1}\mathbf{J}/\mathbf{J}'\mathbf{Q}^{-1}\mathbf{J}$ *has the* $\chi^2(n-p+1, 1)$ *distribution.* The particular case $\mathbf{J}' = [0, 0, \ldots, 0, 1]$ of this ratio reduces to $q_{pp.12\ldots\overline{p-1}}/\sigma_{pp.12\ldots\overline{p-1}}$ and therefore is known to have the stated distribution. The general case follows from the coordinate-free nature of the Wishart distribution, i.e., it is the same result in terms of a general coordinate system in $\mathscr{F}$. Again, the ratio $\mathbf{J}'\mathbf{\Sigma}^{-1}\mathbf{J}/\mathbf{J}'\mathbf{Q}^{-1}\mathbf{J}$ is a ratio of squared radii of two ellipsoids along a common axis, where the ellipsoids are concentration ellipsoids in $\mathscr{F}$ as illustrated in Fig. 13.4.2.

Theorem 13.4.2 and its consequences are closely tied to the idea of successive orthogonalization. It is also of interest to understand how to characterize the distribution of π in terms of its eigenvalues and eigenvectors relative to Σ, where

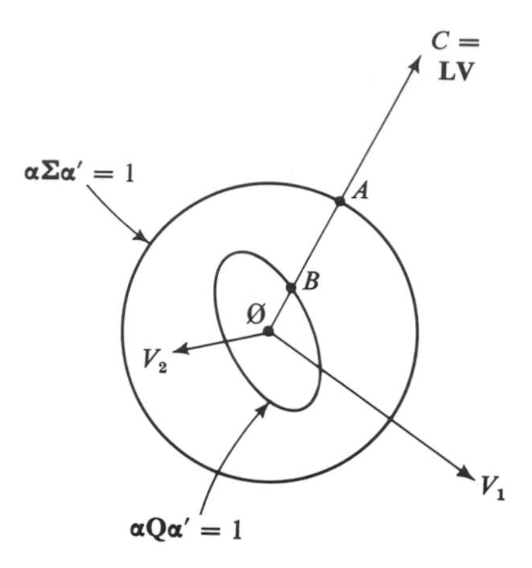

Fig. 13.4.1. Two-dimensional variable-space $\mathscr{E}$ in which $(ØC/ØB)^2 = \mathbf{LQL}'$ and $(ØC/ØA)^2 = \mathbf{L\Sigma L}'$ so that $(ØA/ØB)^2 = \mathbf{LQL}'/\mathbf{L\Sigma L}'$.

π is a $W(n, \Sigma)$ distributed inner product over the p-dimensional space $\mathscr{E}$ and Σ is a fixed inner product over $\mathscr{E}$ with rank $q \leq p$. In this situation, π has with probability one a set of r eigenvalues $l_1 > l_2 > \cdots > l_r > 0$ relative to Σ, where $r = \min(q, n)$. If $q < p$, however, the eigenvectors of π relative to Σ are not uniquely defined even up to arbitrary scale factors, so it is more convenient to work with the dual inner products π_d and Σ_d over $\mathscr{F}$. In general Σ_d is a partial inner product defined over a q-dimensional subspace $\mathscr{U}_\Sigma$ of $\mathscr{F}$, while π_d is a random inner product over a random r-dimensional subspace $\mathscr{U}_\pi$ of $\mathscr{U}_\Sigma$. The eigenvalues of π_d relative to Σ_d are $l_1^{-1}, l_2^{-1}, \ldots, l_r^{-1}$ and the

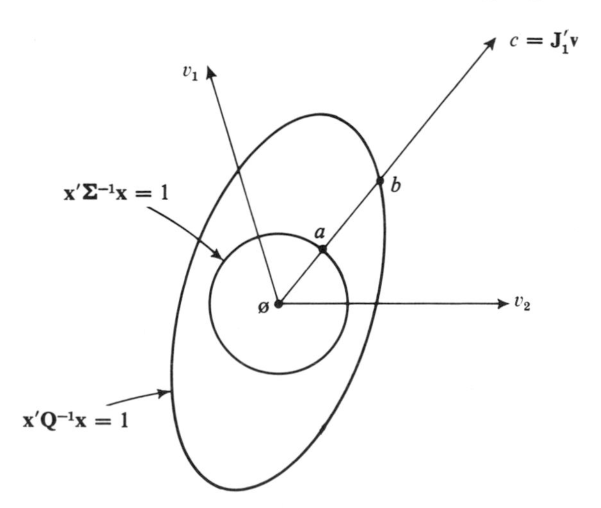

Fig. 13.4.2. Two-dimensional individual-space $\mathscr{F}$ in which $(øc/øb)^2 = \mathbf{J}_1'\mathbf{Q}^{-1}\mathbf{J}_1$ and $(øc/øa)^2 = \mathbf{J}_1'\mathbf{\Sigma}^{-1}\mathbf{J}_1$ so that $(øb/øa)^2 = \mathbf{J}_1'\mathbf{\Sigma}^{-1}\mathbf{J}_1/\mathbf{J}_1'\mathbf{Q}^{-1}\mathbf{J}_1$.

corresponding eigenvectors $z_1, z_2, \ldots, z_r$ are uniquely defined up to scale factors. Suppose that $z_1, z_2, \ldots, z_r$ are defined to be orthonormal relative to Σ_d and chosen at random among the 2^r possible choices for such an orthonormal set with all choices given probability 2^{-r}. Symmetry considerations imply that the conditional distribution of $z_1, z_2, \ldots, z_r$ given $l_1, l_2, \ldots, l_r$ is spherical with respect to Σ_d. It is also clear that $l_1, l_2, \ldots, l_r$ have a distribution uniquely defined by n and q which will be labelled $L(n, q)$. The following theorem is thus immediate, the converse part following because $l_1, l_2, \ldots, l_r$ and $z_1, z_2, \ldots, z_r$ together uniquely determine π and thence uniquely determine the distribution of π.

Theorem 13.4.3. *Suppose that π has the $W(n, \Sigma)$ distribution. Suppose that the eigenvalues $l_1, l_2, \ldots, l_r$, the eigenvectors $z_1, z_2, \ldots, z_r$, and the dimension numbers p, q, and r are defined as above. Then $l_1, l_2, \ldots, l_r$ have the $L(n, q)$ distribution and are distributed independently of $z_1, z_2, \ldots, z_r$ which have the spherical distribution of an orthonormal set relative to Σ_d. Conversely, suppose that $l_1, l_2, \ldots, l_r$ and $z_1, z_2, \ldots, z_r$ have the joint distribution just described and suppose that π_d is defined to be the (partial) inner product specified by declaring $l_1^{1/2}z_1, l_2^{1/2}z_2, \ldots, l_r^{1/2}z_r$ to be orthonormal relative to π_d. Then the dual π of π_d has the $W(n, \Sigma)$ distribution.*

The Wishart family will be generalized in Section 13.7 and corresponding generalizations of the $L(n, q)$ distributions will be given there. In Section 13.8 the probability density functions of several of these distributions will be given, including the $L(n, q)$ family. Unfortunately, however, rather little seems to be known about interesting aspects of the random pattern on the line produced by an $L(n, q)$ distribution. Nor is there any easy method of simulating such random patterns known, other than the long method requiring the simulation of a Wishart matrix followed by an eigenvalue calculation.

13.5 PROPERTIES AND CHARACTERIZATIONS OF THE SPHERICAL DISTRIBUTION OF A SET OF ORTHONORMAL RANDOM OUTCOMES

In the course of the heuristic proof of Lemma 13.3.2, a constructive definition was given for the unique spherical distribution of a set of q orthonormal random outcomes $y_1, y_2, \ldots, y_q$ in an n-dimensional Euclidean space $\mathcal{N}$. The special case $q = 1$ is interesting in its own right, because of its simple geometric interpretation as discussed in Section 12.2, and because it serves as the basis for the constructive definition in the case of general q. The other extreme case $q = n$ is also of special interest, for it embraces all of the others in the sense that any subset consisting of q random outcomes taken from a full set of n spherically distributed orthonormal random outcomes must itself have the unique spherical distribution of an orthonormal set of size q.

In analytic terms, the q orthonormal random outcomes may be represented by a $q \times n$ matrix $\mathbf{G}$ whose rows $\mathbf{G}_1, \mathbf{G}_2, \ldots, \mathbf{G}_q$ provide the coordinates of $y_1, y_2, \ldots, y_q$ relative to an orthonormal basis of $\mathcal{N}$. A method of simulating such a matrix $\mathbf{G}$ was described at the end of Section 13.3.

The main result of the present section is Theorem 13.5.1 which shows how the spherical distribution of a random orthonormal set can be characterized using a set of independently distributed random angles. This theory will be used to demonstrate a basic property of the spherical distribution of an orthonormal random basis, namely that a fixed orthonormal basis viewed from the reference standpoint of a spherically random orthonormal basis itself appears to have the distribution of a spherically random orthonormal basis. Or, analytically, if $\mathbf{G}$ is a random orthogonal matrix representing a spherically distributed orthonormal basis, then $\mathbf{G}'$ has the same distribution as $\mathbf{G}$. Or, in more general mathematical terms, the result states that left and right Haar measures are the same in this situation.

Theorem 13.5.1. *Suppose that $[y_1, y_2, \ldots, y_q]$ is a spherically distributed set of orthonormal random outcomes of the n-dimensional Euclidean space $\mathcal{N}$ while $[u_1, u_2, \ldots, u_n]$ is a fixed orthonormal basis of $\mathcal{N}$. Denote by $\mathcal{N}_{ij}$ for $1 \leq i \leq q$ and $1 \leq j \leq n - i + 1$ the intersection of the subspace spanned by the set of y_{i*} for $i^* \geq i$ and the subspace spanned by the set of u_{j*} for $j^* \geq j$. Correspondingly, denote by z_{ij} the component of y_i in $\mathcal{N}_{ij}$, by v_{ij} the component of u_j in $\mathcal{N}_{ij}$, and by θ_{ij} the angle between z_{ij} and v_{ij}. Then the set of angles θ_{ij} for $1 \leq i \leq q$ and $1 \leq j \leq n - 1 + 1$ uniquely determines the coordinates of $[y_1, y_2, \ldots, y_q]$ relative to $[u_1, u_2, \ldots, u_n]$. The joint distribution of the set of θ_{ij} is specified by asserting that they are independent and that* cot θ_{ij} *has the* $t(0, 1, n - i - j + 1, 0)$ *distribution for $i + j < n + 1$ and $\theta_{ij} = 0$ or π each with probability $\frac{1}{2}$ for $i + j = n + 1$.*

For each i on $1 \leq i \leq n$, the basis consisting of y_h for $h < i$ and v_{ij} for $1 \leq j \leq n - i + 1$ may be described as the basis resulting from the successive orthogonalization of y_h for $h < i$ and u_j for $1 \leq j \leq n - i + 1$. The components of y_i along the members of this orthogonal basis are zero along y_h for $h < i$, $z_{ij} - z_{i\overline{j+1}}$ along v_{ij} for $1 \leq j \leq n - i$, and z_{ij} along v_{ij} for $j = n - i + 1$. It is now easy to see inductively that the θ_{ij} uniquely determine $[y_1, y_2, \ldots, y_q]$. Assume that the θ_{hj} for $h < i$ uniquely determine the y_h for $h < i$. Having this information, the orthogonal basis y_h for $h < i$ and v_{ij} for $1 \leq j \leq n - i + 1$ is determined. The first $i - 1$ components of y_i along the basis are fixed at zero. The component of $y_i = z_{i1}$ along v_{i1} is determined by the angle θ_{i1} between y_i and v_{i1}. Removing this component leaves z_{i2} whose component along v_{i2} is determined by the angle θ_{i2} between z_{i2} and v_{i2}, and so on, until $\theta_{i\overline{n-i+1}} = 0$ or π determines $z_{i\overline{n-i+1}}$ whose length and one-dimensional subspace were already fully determined by the θ_{ij} with $j \leq n - i$. Thus the θ_{ij} together with the θ_{hj} for $h < i$ uniquely determine y_i together with the y_h for $h < i$, thus advancing the induction by one stage. The distribution of the θ_{ij} is easily derived by a similar induction. The conditional distribution of z_{ij} given θ_{hj} for $1 \leq h < i$ and θ_{hk} for $1 \leq k < j$ and $1 \leq h \leq q$ (or, equivalently, given z_{hj} for $1 \leq h < i$ and z_{hk} for $1 \leq k < j$ and $1 \leq h \leq q$) is spherical in the subspace $\mathcal{N}_{ij}$. Thus θ_{ij} is distributed like the angle between a spherically distributed vector in an $(n - i - j + 2)$-dimensional space and a fixed one-dimensional subspace, all conditional on fixed θ_{hj} for $1 \leq h \leq i$ and θ_{hk} for $1 \leq k \leq j$ and $1 \leq h \leq q$. The distribution result given in the theorem follows immediately.

When $q = n$ the two orthonormal bases $[y_1, y_2, \ldots, y_n]$ and $[u_1, u_2, \ldots, u_n]$ of Theorem 13.5.1 enter symmetrically into the definition of the θ_{ij}. Thus the same process used to construct the $n \times n$ orthogonal matrix $\mathbf{G}$ such that $[y_1, y_2, \ldots, y_n] = [u_1, u_2, \ldots, u_n]\mathbf{G}$ may also be applied reversing the roles of the bases to construct $\mathbf{G}'$ such that $[u_1, u_2, \ldots, u_n] = [y_1, y_2, \ldots, y_n]\mathbf{G}'$. The reader may check that this is a nontrivial remark by noting that these processes as defined in the proof of Theorem 13.5.1 are apparently quite different. At the same time the distributions of the θ_{ij} are symmetric in i and j, so that an application of Theorem 13.5.1 with the roles of the bases interchanged yields the following important corollary.

Corollary 13.5.1. *If* $[u_1, u_2, \ldots, u_n]$ *denotes a fixed orthonormal basis and* $[y_1, y_2, \ldots, y_n] = [u_1, u_2, \ldots, u_n]\mathbf{G}$ *denotes a spherically distributed random orthonormal basis in* $\mathcal{N}$, *then* $\mathbf{G}$ *has the same distribution as* $\mathbf{G}'$.

The theory of this section applies to the spherical distribution of a set of vectors in $\mathcal{N}$ having *any* fixed configuration. For, if the vectors are not orthonormal, they may be replaced by a fixed and equivalent set of linear combinations of themselves which are orthonormal. Spherically distributed sets in $\mathcal{N}$ with fixed configuration arise in normal sampling theory as indicated in Section 13.3, and further aspects of their distribution, as related to a pair of independent Wishart matrices, will be discussed in Section 13.7. Spherically distributed orthonormal sets in $\mathcal{F}$ appeared in Theorem 13.4.3 and will reappear in Section 13.7.

13.6 MULTIVARIATE t DISTRIBUTIONS AND RELATED QUANTITIES

Recall the definition of the family of $t(\mu, \Sigma, n)$ distributions given in Section 12.3. The following theorem shows how to characterize any such distribution in terms of a random normal outcome and an independent random Wishart inner product. It will be seen that Hotelling's T^2 statistic is closely related to multivariate t distributions through the characterization of Theorem 13.6.1.

Theorem 13.6.1. *Suppose that* x *is a random outcome with the* $N(\varnothing, \Sigma)$ *distribution over the p-dimensional outcome-space* $\mathcal{F}$, *where* Σ *has rank* $q \leq p$. *Suppose that* π *is a random inner product distributed independently of* x *with the* $W(n, \Sigma)$ *distribution, where* $n \geq q$. *Suppose that* $x \to z$ *under* *the random linear transformation which carries the ellipsoid of* π_d *into the ellipsoid of* Σ_d *by scaling along eigenvectors of* π_d *relative to* Σ_d, *and define*

$$t = \mu + (n - q + 1)^{1/2} z. \tag{13.6.1}$$

Then t *has the* $t(\mu, \Sigma, n - q + 1)$ *distribution.*

Note first that $t - \mu$ and z are spherically distributed about the origin with respect to Σ_d, because the joint distribution of x and π_d which determine z obviously has spherical symmetry. Consequently, one need only check that the squared length of $t - \mu$ relative to Σ_d has the $G(q, n - q + 1, n - q + 1)$ distribution. Now the squared length of z relative to π_d is from the definition of z the same as the squared length of x relative to π_d, and the latter may be expressed by the ratio $(øx/øa)^2/(øb/øa)^2$ as depicted in Fig. 13.4.2 with x replaced by c. Conditionally given x, the denominator $(øb/øa)^2$ is an example of the ratio in Fig. 13.4.2 which has the $\chi^2(n - q + 1, 1)$ distribution. Thus the denominator is independent of the numerator $(øx/øa)^2$ which has the $\chi^2(q, 1)$ distribution, and the squared length of z has the $G(q, n - q + 1, 1)$ distribution. From (13.6.1) the required distribution of the squared length of $t - \mu$ follows.

The coordinate-dependent version of Theorem 13.6.1 will now be given as a corollary which will be directly useful in Chapters 14 and 15. Assume that $q = p$, and suppose that x and π are represented by $\mathbf{X}$ and $\mathbf{Q}$ which are independent with $N(\mathbf{0}, \mathbf{I})$ and $W(n, \mathbf{I})$ distributions. Suppose that $\mathbf{L}$ is a diagonal matrix whose diagonal elements are the eigenvalues of $\mathbf{Q}$ and suppose that $\mathbf{G}$ is an orthogonal matrix whose rows are the eigenvectors of $\mathbf{Q}$, so that $\mathbf{GQG}' = \mathbf{L}$. Then z is represented by $\mathbf{Z} = \mathbf{XG}'\mathbf{L}^{-1/2}\mathbf{G}$ where $\mathbf{L}^{-1/2}$ is a diagonal matrix whose elements are the inverse square roots of the elements of $\mathbf{L}$. Since the conditional distribution of $\mathbf{X}$ given $\mathbf{Q}$ is $N(\mathbf{0}, \mathbf{I})$, the conditional distribution of $\mathbf{T} = \boldsymbol{\mu} + (n - p + 1)^{1/2}\mathbf{Z}$ is $N(\boldsymbol{\mu}, [n - p + 1]\mathbf{Q}^{-1})$ while $\mathbf{T}$ has the $t(\boldsymbol{\mu}, \mathbf{I}, n - p + 1)$ distribution. Expressing this result in terms of a general basis and a general origin gives:

Corollary 13.6.1. *Suppose that the conditional distribution of* $\mathbf{T}$ *given* $\mathbf{Q}$ *is* $N(\boldsymbol{\mu}, [n - p + 1]\mathbf{Q}^{-1})$, *while the marginal distribution of* $\mathbf{Q}$ *is* $W(n, \boldsymbol{\Sigma})$, *where* $\boldsymbol{\Sigma}$ *has full rank* p *and* $n \geq p$. *Then* $\mathbf{T}$ *has the* $t(\boldsymbol{\mu}, \boldsymbol{\Sigma}^{-1}, n - p + 1)$ *marginal distribution.*

It is now appropriate to remark on the two possible definitions of a noncentral multivariate t distribution. First, one could define $t = \mu + s^{-1}x$ as in Section 12.3 except that x would be given the $N(\nu, \Sigma)$ distribution with $\nu \neq ø$. Alternatively, one could assign x in Theorem 13.6.1 the $N(\nu, \Sigma)$ distribution with $\nu \neq ø$ and use (13.6.1) to define t. The results are not the same, except in the case of the one-dimensional noncentral t distributions defined in Section 12.5. Neither definition is specifically used in this book, although the second form seems more likely to appear in normal sampling theory. Under the second form, the norm of z relative to Σ_d has the $G(p, n - p + 1, 1, \tau^2)$ distribution where τ^2 is the norm of ν relative to Σ_d, because the proof of Theorem 13.6.1 remains unchanged except that the numerator $(\phi x/\phi a)^2$ comes to have the $\chi^2(p, 1, \tau^2)$ distribution. In coordinate-dependent terms this result is:

Theorem 13.6.2. *Suppose that* $\mathbf{X}$ *and* $\mathbf{Q}$ *are independent with* $N(\boldsymbol{\nu}, \boldsymbol{\Sigma})$ *and* $W(n, \boldsymbol{\Sigma})$ *distributions where* $\boldsymbol{\Sigma}$ *has full rank* p *and* $n \geq p$. *Then* $\mathbf{X}\mathbf{Q}^{-1}\mathbf{X}'$ *has the* $G(p, n - p + 1, 1, \boldsymbol{\nu}\boldsymbol{\Sigma}^{-1}\boldsymbol{\nu}')$ *distribution.*

A quantity of the form $\mathbf{X}\mathbf{Q}^{-1}\mathbf{X}'$ or some multiple of it is often called a Hotelling's T^2 statistic in honor of Hotelling (1931) who derived the distribution given in Theorem 13.6.2 and pointed out how T^2 could be used for significance testing. Bowker (1960) showed how T^2 could be explicitly represented as a ratio of χ^2 quantities as indicated in Fig. 13.6.1.

A further result on the decomposition on the squared distance T^2 into components in orthogonal subspaces will now be developed. Suppose that $\mathbf{X}$ and $\boldsymbol{\nu}$ are partitioned into

$$\mathbf{X} = [\mathbf{X}_1, \mathbf{X}_2] \qquad \text{and} \qquad \boldsymbol{\nu} = [\boldsymbol{\nu}_1, \boldsymbol{\nu}_2], \tag{13.6.2}$$

corresponding to the partition $p = s + (p - s)$. Suppose that the partition notation of Theorem 13.4.2 is adopted. Then

$$G = \mathbf{X}\mathbf{Q}^{-1}\mathbf{X}' \tag{13.6.3}$$

partitions into

$$G = G_1 + G_{2.1}, \tag{13.6.4}$$

where

$$G_1 = \mathbf{X}_1\mathbf{Q}_{11}^{-1}\mathbf{X}_1' \tag{13.6.5}$$

and

$$G_{2.1} = \mathbf{X}_{2.1}\mathbf{Q}_{22.1}^{-1}\mathbf{X}_{2.1}', \tag{13.6.6}$$

with

$$\mathbf{X}_{2.1} = \mathbf{X}_2 - \mathbf{X}_1\mathbf{H}_{12}. \tag{13.6.7}$$

Similarly,

$$\boldsymbol{\tau}^2 = \boldsymbol{\nu}\boldsymbol{\Sigma}^{-1}\boldsymbol{\nu}' \tag{13.6.8}$$

partitions into

$$\tau^2 = \tau_1^2 + \tau_{2.1}^2, \tag{13.6.9}$$

where

$$\tau_1^2 = \boldsymbol{\nu}_1\boldsymbol{\Sigma}_{11}^{-1}\boldsymbol{\nu}_1' \tag{13.6.10}$$

and

$$\tau_{2.1}^2 = \boldsymbol{\nu}_{2.1}\boldsymbol{\Sigma}_{22.1}\boldsymbol{\nu}_{2.1}', \tag{13.6.11}$$

with

$$\boldsymbol{\nu}_{2.1} = \boldsymbol{\nu}_2 - \boldsymbol{\nu}_1\boldsymbol{\Xi}_{12}. \tag{13.6.12}$$

Theorem 13.6.3. *Suppose that* $\mathbf{X}$ *and* $\mathbf{Q}$ *are independent with* $N(\boldsymbol{\nu}, \boldsymbol{\Sigma})$ *and* $W(n, \boldsymbol{\Sigma})$ *distributions, where* $\boldsymbol{\Sigma}$ *has full rank* p *and* $n \geq p$. *Suppose that the* *notation of* (13.6.2) *through* (13.6.12) *is adopted. Then*

i) $\mathbf{X}_1$ *and* $\mathbf{Q}_{11}$ *are independent with* $N(\boldsymbol{\nu}_1, \boldsymbol{\Sigma}_{11})$ *and* $W(n, \boldsymbol{\Sigma}_{11})$ *distributions,*

ii) *conditional on given* $\mathbf{X}_1$ *and* $\mathbf{Q}_{11}$, $\mathbf{X}_{2.1}$ *and* $\mathbf{Q}_{22.1}$ *are independent with* $N(\boldsymbol{\nu}_{2.1}, [1 + G_1]\boldsymbol{\Sigma}_{22.1})$ *and* $W(n - s, \boldsymbol{\Sigma}_{22.1})$ *distributions,*

iii) G_1 *has the* $G(s, n - s + 1, 1, \tau_1^2)$ *distribution, and*

iv) *conditional on given* G_1, *the distribution of* $G_{2.1}$ *is* $G(p - s, n - p + 1, 1 + G_1, \tau_{2.1}^2/[1 + G_1])$.

Part (i) is an immediate consequence of Theorems 12.4.1 and 13.4.2, and part (i) together with Theorem 13.6.2 gives part (iii). Since $\mathbf{X}$ and $\mathbf{Q}$ are independent, $\mathbf{X}_2$ is independent of any function of $\mathbf{X}_1$ and $\mathbf{Q}$ *after* conditioning on $\mathbf{X}_1$. Further conditioning on $\mathbf{Q}_{11}$ leaves $\mathbf{H}_{12}$ and $\mathbf{Q}_{22.1}$ independent, from Theorem 13.4.2. Thus, given $\mathbf{X}_1$ and $\mathbf{Q}_{11}$, one has $\mathbf{X}_2$, $-\mathbf{X}_1\mathbf{H}_{12}$, and $\mathbf{Q}_{22.1}$ all independent. Since $\mathbf{X}_{2.1} = \mathbf{X}_2 - \mathbf{X}_1\mathbf{H}_{12}$, the conditional independence of $\mathbf{X}_{2.1}$ and $\mathbf{Q}_{22.1}$ is established. The stated distribution of $\mathbf{Q}_{22.1}$ follows from Theorem 13.4.2. This leaves $\mathbf{X}_{2.1}$, which is the sum of two independent normal vectors: $\mathbf{X}_2$ with the $N(\boldsymbol{\nu}_2 + [\mathbf{X}_1 - \boldsymbol{\nu}_1]\boldsymbol{\Xi}_{12}, \boldsymbol{\Sigma}_{22.1})$ distribution from Theorem 12.4.4, and $-\mathbf{X}_1\mathbf{H}_{12}$ with the $N(-\mathbf{X}_1\boldsymbol{\Xi}_{12}, [\mathbf{X}_1\mathbf{C}_{11}'\mathbf{C}_{11}\mathbf{X}_1']\boldsymbol{\Delta}_{22}\boldsymbol{\Delta}_{22}')$ distribution from Theorem 13.4.2. Noting that $\mathbf{X}_1\mathbf{C}_{11}'\mathbf{C}_{11}\mathbf{X}_1' = G_1$ and $\boldsymbol{\Delta}_{22}\boldsymbol{\Delta}_{22}' = \boldsymbol{\Sigma}_{22.1}$, the sum $\mathbf{X}_{2.1} = \mathbf{X}_2 - \mathbf{X}_1\mathbf{H}_{12}$ is seen from Theorem 12.4.1 to have the stated distribution, thus completing the proof of part (ii).

To complete the proof, note that part (iv) follows from Theorem 13.6.2 applied to $\mathbf{X}_{2.1}$ and $\mathbf{Q}_{22.1}$ in place of $\mathbf{X}_1$ and $\mathbf{Q}_{11}$, where the required distribution of $\mathbf{X}_{2.1}$ and $\mathbf{Q}_{22.1}$ is given by part (ii).

13.7 DISTRIBUTIONS AND THEORY RELATED TO GENERALIZED BETA AND *G* DISTRIBUTIONS

The family of one-dimensional beta distributions is generalized here to a family of distributions of a random inner product. Two celebrated families of distributions, one of a set of eigenvalues and one of a quantity often called a Wilks Λ statistic, are closely related to the family of generalized beta distributions. There is also a related family of generalized G distributions with important applications. The theory of this section generalizes in certain ways the theory of both Sections 13.4 and 13.6.

Suppose that π is a random inner product over a p-dimensional quantity-space $\mathscr{E}$, that Σ is a fixed inner product over $\mathscr{E}$ with rank $q \leq p$, and that s and $n - s$ are positive integers. Then π will be said to have the $B(s, n - s, \Sigma)$ distribution if $\mathbf{Q}$ has the $B(s, n - s, \boldsymbol{\Sigma})$ distribution, where $\mathbf{Q}$ and $\boldsymbol{\Sigma}$ are inner product matrices representing π and Σ relative to some fixed basis $\mathbf{V}$ of $\mathscr{E}$. To define the $B(s, n - s, \boldsymbol{\Sigma})$ distribution, suppose that $x_1, x_2, \ldots, x_p$ are spherically distributed random outcomes with a fixed configuration matrix $\mathbf{\Sigma}$ in a Euclidean outcome-space $\mathcal{N}$ of dimension n. Suppose that $\mathbf{Q}$ is the configuration matrix of the orthogonal projections of $x_1, x_2, \ldots, x_p$ into a fixed s-dimensional subspace $\mathcal{U}$ of $\mathcal{N}$. Then $\mathbf{Q}$ will be said to have the $B(s, n - s, \mathbf{\Sigma})$ distribution.

The family of $\beta(s/2, (n - s)/2)$ distributions defined in Section 12.5 may be recovered as special cases of the $B(s, n - s, \mathbf{\Sigma})$ family where $\mathbf{\Sigma} = \mathbf{I}$ and $p = q = 1$. Note that π has the $B(s, n - s, \Sigma)$ distribution if and only if $\Sigma - \pi$ has the $B(n - s, s, \Sigma)$ distribution. Other properties of the generalized beta family go much beyond anything apparent in the one-dimensional case. For example, consider the eigenvalues of π relative to Σ, or equivalently of $\mathbf{Q}$ relative to $\mathbf{\Sigma}$. From the construction of $\mathbf{Q}$ used in defining $B(s, n - s, \mathbf{\Sigma})$, there are q well-defined eigenvalues of $\mathbf{Q}$ with respect to $\mathbf{\Sigma}$ of which $r = \min(q, s)$ are the squared cosines of the canonical angles relating the spherically random q-dimensional subspace spanned by $x_1, x_2, \ldots, x_p$ and the fixed s-dimensional subspace $\mathcal{U}$, while the remaining $q - r$ are necessarily zero. Denote the r largest eigenvalues by $h_1, h_2, \ldots, h_r$ in nondecreasing order. When $q + s \leq n$, these satisfy $1 > h_1 > h_2 > \cdots > h_r > 0$ with probability 1, and their joint distribution will be labeled $H(n, q, s)$. The same set of labels with $q + s \leq n$ is sufficient to cover also the case $q + s > n$, for when $q + s > n$ the random and fixed subspaces intersect in a subspace of dimension $m = |n - q - s|$ with probability 1, so that $h_i = 1$ for $1 \leq i \leq m$ while the remaining h_i have the $H(n - m, q - m, s - m)$ distribution. Two obvious lemmas concerning the $H(n, q, s)$ families of distributions follow. First, from Corollary 13.5.1, the $H(n, q, s)$ distribution is the same as the $H(n, s, q)$ distribution. Second, if $h_1, h_2, \ldots, h_r$ have the $H(n, r, t)$ distribution with $r \leq t$, then

$$1 - h_r, 1 - h_{r-1}, \ldots, 1 - h_1$$

have the $H(n, r, n - t)$ distribution (because they are the nontrivial eigenvalues of $\Sigma - \pi$ relative to Σ).

If $h_1, h_2, \ldots, h_r$ have the $H(n, q, s)$ distribution, then

$$\Lambda = \prod_{i=1}^{r} (1 - h_i) \tag{13.7.1}$$

will be said to have the *Wilks* Λ *distribution* labelled $\Lambda(n, q, s)$. From the properties of the $H(n, q, s)$ family it follows that $\Lambda(n, s, q)$ and $\Lambda(n, q, s)$ are identical distributions. Also, if $h_1, h_2, \ldots, h_r$ have the $H(n, r, t)$ distributions, then $\prod_1^r h_i$ has the $\Lambda(n, r, n - t)$ distribution.

The following theorem gives a characterization in $\mathcal{F}$ of the $B(s, n - s, \Sigma)$ distribution, and may be proved by the reader along the lines of the proof of Theorem 13.4.3. Indeed, the theorem will shortly be recognized as a generalization of Theorem 13.4.3.

Theorem 13.7.1. *Suppose that π has the $B(s, n - s, \Sigma)$ distribution. Suppose that $h_1, h_2, \ldots, h_r$ are the eigenvalues of π relative to Σ while $z_1, z_2, \ldots, z_r$ are the corresponding eigenvectors of π_d relative to Σ_d, chosen from the 2^r possible sets of Σ_d-orthonormal eigenvectors with equal probabilities. Then $h_1, h_2, \ldots, h_r$ have the $H(n, q, s)$ distribution and are distributed independently of $z_1, z_2, \ldots, z_r$ which have the spherical distribution of an orthonormal set with respect to Σ_d. Conversely, suppose that $h_1, h_2, \ldots, h_r$ and $z_1, z_2, \ldots, z_r$ have the joint distribution just described and suppose that π_d is defined to be the (partial) inner product specified by declaring $h_1^{1/2}z_1, h_2^{1/2}z_2, \ldots, h_r^{1/2}z$ to be orthonormal relative to π_d. Then the dual π of π_d has the $B(s, n - s, \Sigma)$ distribution.*

Random matrices with generalized beta distributions, and thence quantities with $H(n, q, s)$ and $\Lambda(n, q, s)$ distributions, appear in normal sampling theory in the context of a pair of independent random inner products having $W(s, \Sigma)$ and $W(n - s, \Sigma)$ distributions. An important property of such a Wishart pair with common Σ is that their sum has the $W(n, \Sigma)$ distribution. This *reproductive property* of the Wishart family is included in the following theorem which generalizes Lemma 12.5.1.

Theorem 13.7.2. *Suppose that π^* and π^{**} are a pair of random inner products over a p-dimensional quantity-space $\mathscr{E}$. Suppose that $\pi = \pi^* + \pi^{**}$, that Σ is an inner product over $\mathscr{E}$ with rank $q \leq p$, and that s and $n - s$ are positive integers. Then the following assertions (A) and (B) imply each other:*

A) π^* and π^{**} are independent with $W(s, \Sigma)$ and $W(n - s, \Sigma)$ distributions, and

B) the conditional distribution of π^* given π is $B(s, n - s, \pi)$ while the marginal distribution of π is $W(n, \Sigma)$.

Under the assumption (*A*), one may regard π^* as the configuration matrix of a set of random outcomes $x_1^*, x_2^*, \ldots, x_p^*$ which represent a random sample of size s from an $N(\varnothing, \Sigma)$ population in an s-dimensional Euclidean space $\mathscr{U}$. Similarly, π^{**} may be viewed as the inner product matrix of $x_1^{**}, x_2^{**}, \ldots, x_p^{**}$ in an $(n - s)$-dimensional space $\mathscr{W}$. It follows that $x_1^* \oplus x_1^{**}, x_2^* \oplus x_2^{**}, \ldots, x_p^* \oplus x_p^{**}$ with inner product matrix $\pi = \pi^* + \pi^{**}$ represent a random sample of size n from an $N(\varnothing, \Sigma)$ population in the n-dimensional space $\mathscr{N} = \mathscr{U} \oplus \mathscr{W}$, and accordingly π has the $W(n, \Sigma)$ distribution. The conditional distribution of π^* given π follows from Theorem 13.3.1 together with the definition of multivariate beta distributions. Thus (*A*) implies (*B*). But (*B*) uniquely determines the joint distribution of π^* and $\pi^{**} = \pi - \pi^*$, which can therefore be none other than that specified by (*A*). Thus (*B*) implies (*A*).

The following theorem indicates how the $\Lambda(n, q, s)$ distributions appear in normal sampling theory. (See also Exercise 13.7.4.)

Theorem 13.7.3. *Suppose that* $\mathbf{Q}^*$ *and* $\mathbf{Q}^{**}$ *are independent random* $p \times p$ *matrices with* $W(s, \mathbf{\Sigma})$ *and* $W(n - s, \mathbf{\Sigma})$ *distributions where* $\mathbf{\Sigma}$ *has rank* $q \leq p$. *Suppose that* $\dot{\mathbf{Q}}^*$, $\dot{\mathbf{Q}}^{**}$, *and* $\dot{\mathbf{\Sigma}}$ *are extracted from* $\mathbf{Q}^*$, $\mathbf{Q}^{**}$, *and* $\mathbf{\Sigma}$ *by using a common subset of* r *rows and columns such that* $\dot{\mathbf{\Sigma}}$ *has rank* r, *where* $r = \min(q, s)$. *Then*

$$\Lambda = \det \dot{\mathbf{Q}}^{**}/\det(\dot{\mathbf{Q}}^* + \dot{\mathbf{Q}}^{**}) \tag{13.7.2}$$

has the $\Lambda(n, s, q)$ *distribution and is independent of* $\dot{\mathbf{Q}}^* + \dot{\mathbf{Q}}^{**}$ *which has the* $W(n, \mathbf{\Sigma})$ *distribution.*

To prove Theorem 13.7.3 one need only recognize the right side of (13.7.2) as having the form of the right side of (13.7.1) where $h_1, h_2, \ldots, h_r$ are the eigenvalues of $\dot{\mathbf{Q}}^*$ relative to $\dot{\mathbf{Q}}^* + \dot{\mathbf{Q}}^{**}$, and the reader may easily check this by re-expressing the right side of (13.7.2) in terms of a basis of eigenvectors.

The distribution of Λ defined in the form (13.7.2) with $q = p$ and $n - s \geq p$ was first investigated by Wilks (1932) who computed the moments of Λ, from which it is easily recognized that Λ has the distribution of a product of independent random values each with a beta distribution. Actual factorizations of Λ into products of such random values will be created from the right side of (13.7.2) by computing numerator and denominator in the usual way by successive orthogonalization, i.e., by setting

$$\Lambda = \frac{\dot{q}_{11}^{**}}{\dot{q}_{11}} \cdot \frac{\dot{q}_{22.1}^{**}}{\dot{q}_{22.1}} \cdot \ldots \cdot \frac{\dot{q}_{rr.12\ldots\overline{r-1}}^{**}}{\dot{q}_{rr.12\ldots\overline{r-1}}}, \tag{13.7.3}$$

where

$$\det \dot{\mathbf{Q}}^{**} = \dot{q}_{11}^{**} \cdot \dot{q}_{22.1}^{**} \cdot \ldots \cdot \dot{q}_{pp.12\ldots\overline{p-1}}^{**}$$

and

$$\det(\dot{\mathbf{Q}}^* + \dot{\mathbf{Q}}^{**}) = \dot{q}_{11} \cdot \dot{q}_{22.1} \cdot \ldots \cdot \dot{q}_{pp.12\ldots\overline{p-1}}.$$

Conditional on fixed $\dot{\mathbf{Q}}^* + \dot{\mathbf{Q}}^{**}$, the first factor in (13.7.3) represents the squared sine of the angle made by a spherically distributed $\dot{x}_1$ in $\mathscr{N}$ with a fixed s-dimensional $\mathscr{U}$, and so has the $\beta((n - s)/2, s/2)$ distribution. Given $\dot{x}_1$, the component of $\dot{x}_2$ orthogonal to $\dot{x}_1$ is spherically distributed in an $(n - 1)$-dimensional subspace of $\mathscr{N}$ and the second factor is the squared cosine of the angle between the component and the $(n - s - 1)$-dimensional subspace orthogonal to $\mathscr{U}$, so that the second factor has the $\beta((n - s - 1)/2, s/2)$ distribution. And so on, so that Λ is represented in (13.7.3) as a product of r independent factors with $\beta((n - s - i + 1)/2, s/2)$ distributions for $i = 1, 2, \ldots, r$.

More generally, suppose that $\mathbf{C}$ is an $r \times p$ matrix defined for each $\mathbf{Q} = \mathbf{Q}^* + \mathbf{Q}^{**}$ such that $\mathbf{CQC}' = \mathbf{I}$. Then $\Lambda = \det \mathbf{T}$ where $\mathbf{T} = \mathbf{CQ}^{**}\mathbf{C}'$; this determinant may be computed by successive orthogonalization to be the product

$$\Lambda = t_{11} t_{22.1} \cdots t_{rr.12\ldots\overline{r-1}}, \tag{13.7.4}$$

where, by an argument similar to that in the preceding paragraph the factors are independent with $\beta((n - s - i + 1)/2, s/2)$ distributions for $i = 1, 2, \ldots, r$.

Suppose that $x_1, x_2, \ldots, x_p$ denote a spherically random set of outcomes in $\mathcal{N}$ with a given configuration matrix $\mathbf{Q}$. Then

$$[y_1, y_2, \ldots, y_r] = [x_1, x_2, \ldots, x_p]\mathbf{C}'$$

denotes a spherically random set of r orthonormal outcomes in $\mathcal{N}$ while $\mathbf{T}$ is the configuration matrix of the components of $y_1, y_2, \ldots, y_r$ orthogonal to the s-dimensional subspace $\mathcal{U}$. Theorem 13.5.1 shows how to factor each of the r factors in (13.7.4) into s factors, all independent with beta distributions. By applying the theorem with q replaced by r and with $\mathcal{U}$ the subspace spanned by $u_1, u_2, \ldots, u_s$, the reader may easily check that

$$t_{ii.12\ldots\overline{i-1}} = \prod_{j=1}^{s} \sin^2 \theta_{ij} \tag{13.7.5}$$

for $1 \leq i \leq r$. The result is the following:

Theorem 13.7.4. *Suppose that $[y_1, y_2, \ldots, y_r]$ is a spherically distributed set of orthonormal random outcomes in the n-dimensional Euclidean space $\mathcal{N}$. Suppose that $\mathcal{U}$ is spanned by fixed orthonormal vectors $u_1, u_2, \ldots, u_s$ in $\mathcal{N}$, and that Λ is the Wilks statistic defined as in* (13.7.1) *using the spherically random orthonormal set $[y_1, y_2, \ldots, y_r]$ and the fixed subspace $\mathcal{U}$ with $r + s \leq n$. Suppose that θ_{ij} is defined as in Theorem* 13.5.1 *applied with $q = r$, for $i = 1, 2, \ldots, r$ and $j = 1, 2, \ldots, s$. Then*

$$\Lambda = \prod_{i=1}^{r} \prod_{j=1}^{s} \sin^2 \theta_{ij}, \tag{13.7.6}$$

where the rs factors are independent and $\sin^2 \theta_{ij}$ *has the* $\beta((n - i - j + 1)/2, 1/2)$ *distribution for $i = 1, 2, \ldots, r$ and $j = 1, 2, \ldots, s$. The r terms in the factorization*

$$\Lambda = \prod_{i=1}^{r} \left[\prod_{j=1}^{s} \sin^2 \theta_{ij} \right] \tag{13.7.7}$$

are independent with $\beta((n - s - i + 1)/2, s/2)$ *distributions for $i = 1, 2, \ldots, r$, while the s terms in the factorization*

$$\Lambda = \prod_{j=1}^{s} \left[\prod_{i=1}^{r} \sin^2 \theta_{ij} \right] \tag{13.7.8}$$

are independent with $\beta((n - r - j + 1)/2, r/2)$ *distributions for* $j = 1, 2, \ldots, s$.

Since Λ is often used for significance testing some practically useful aspects of the distribution will be presented. Consider the $\Lambda(n, r, s)$ distribution with $r \leq s$ and, of course, $r + s \leq n$. The distribution $\Lambda(n, 1, s)$ is simply

$\beta((n - s)/2, s/2)$, while, if Λ has the $\Lambda(n, 2, s)$ distribution, then $\Lambda^{1/2}$ has the $\beta(n - s - 1, s)$ distribution (cf. Exercise 13.7.5). By hard work, one may compute density functions for Λ or $\log \Lambda$, where the latter is a sum of independent random values. Anderson (1958) displays such densities for $r \leq s \leq 4$ while Schatzoff (1964, 1966) followed a similar procedure inside a computer for $r \leq s \leq 10$ and prepared tables of α quantiles of Λ for $\alpha = 0.90$, 0.95, 0.975, 0.990, and 0.995. No manageable closed form for a density with general r has been found.

Various approximate distributions have been suggested for the $\Lambda(n, s, r)$ distributions where n is large. The simplest of these comes from the following lemma: *if b has the $\beta((m - 1)/2, 1/2)$ distribution then the limiting distribution of $-m \log b$ as $m \to \infty$ is $\chi^2(1, 1)$.* To see this suppose that $X_1, X_2, \ldots, X_m$ are independent $N(0, 1)$ random values. Then $(X_1^2 + X_2^2 + \cdots + X_m^2)/m$ has mean 1 and variance $2/m$ and so tends to unity in probability as $m \to \infty$. If $c = X_1^2/[(X_1^2 + \cdots + X_m^2)/m]$, then c/m has the same distribution as $1 - b$, so that $-m \log (1 - c/m)$ has the same distribution as $-m \log b$. Expanding, it is seen that

$$-m \log (1 - c/m) = c + m^{-1}c^2/2 + m^{-2}c^3/3 + \cdots. \qquad (13.7.8)$$

For large m, the ratios among $-m \log (1 - c/m)$, c, and X_1^2 all tend to unity in probability, so that all have the same limiting distribution $\chi^2(1, 1)$ as required. From the lemma it follows that the limiting distribution of $-n \log b_{ij}$ is $\chi^2(1, 1)$ where b_{ij} has the $\beta((n - i - j + 1), 1/2)$ distribution, since the ratio $n/(n - i - j + 2) \to 1$ as $n \to \infty$. Consequently the limiting distribution of $-n \log \Lambda$ where Λ has the $\Lambda(n, r, s)$ distribution is $\chi^2(rs, 1)$, for Λ has the same distribution as $-n \sum_{i=1}^{r} \sum_{j=1}^{s} \log b_{ij}$ with independent b_{ij}.

The expansion (13.7.8) shows that $-m \log b$ has a larger expectation than c. Taking the expected value of the first two terms on the right side, namely $1 + 1/m$, suggests that $-(m - 1) \log b$ may have more nearly a $\chi^2(1, 1)$ distribution than $-m \log b$. A corresponding adjustment for $\Lambda(n, r, s)$ suggests averaging the coefficients $(n - i - j + 1)$ of the $-(n - i - j + 1) \log b_{ij}$ approximation to produce $-[n - (r + s)/2] \log \Lambda$ approximately $\chi^2(rs, 1)$ distributed. Following a slightly deeper approach, Bartlett (1938) suggested approximating the distribution of $-[n - (r + s + 1)/2] \log \Lambda$ by $\chi^2(rs, 1)$. The coefficient

$$k = n - (r + s + 1)/2 \qquad (13.7.9)$$

was used by Rao (1948) for an expansion in terms of power of $1/k$. Denoting by $F_p(x)$ the c.d.f. of the $\chi^2(p, 1)$ distribution Rao worked out his expansion to the point:

$$P(-k \log \Lambda \leq x) = F_{rs}(x) + k^{-2}[\alpha F_{rs+4}(x) - \alpha F_{rs}(x)]$$
$$+ k^{-4}[\beta F_{rs+8}(x) - \alpha^2 F_{rs+4}(x) + (\alpha^2 - \beta)F_{rs}(x)] + \cdots, \qquad (13.7.10)$$

where

$$\alpha = (rs/48)(r^2 + s^2 - 5),$$

and (13.7.11)

$$\beta = \alpha^2/2 + (rs/1920)(3r^4 + 3s^4 + 10r^2s^2 - 50r^2 - 50s^2 + 159).$$

This and similar approximations were also given by Box (1949). Schatzoff (1964, 1966) checks to see when one, two, or three terms of (13.7.10) provide sufficient accuracy for $r \leq s \leq 10$ and $P = 0.900, 0.950, 0.975, 0.990$, and 0.995.

The family of $B(s, n - s, \Sigma)$ distributions has an associated family of $G(s, n - s, \Sigma)$ distributions which generalizes the $G(r, s)$ family of Section 12.5. An economical approach to the G family is through eigenvalues and eigenvectors, by analogy with the beta family property given in Theorem 13.7.1. If $h_1, h_2, \ldots, h_r$ have the $H(n, q, s)$ distribution with $r = \min(q, s)$, then $h_1/(1 - h_1), h_2/(1 - h_2), \ldots, h_r/(1 - h_r)$ will be said to have the $K(n, q, s)$ distribution. If Σ is a rank q inner product over the p-dimensional quantity-space $\mathscr{E}$, if $z_1, z_2, \ldots, z_r$ are spherically distributed and orthonormal with respect to Σ_d in the dual space $\mathscr{F}$, and if $k_1, k_2, \ldots, k_r$ have the $K(n, q, s)$ distribution, then the random rank r inner product π over $\mathscr{E}$ defined by asserting that $k_1^{1/2}z_1, k_2^{1/2}z_2, \ldots, k_r^{1/2}z_r$ are π_d-orthonormal will be said to have the generalized G distribution $G(s, n - s, \Sigma)$.

Although the foregoing definition is valid for $q + s > n$ as well as $q + s \leq n$, only the latter case appears to be of interest in normal sampling theory, and it will henceforth be assumed when discussing $G(s, n - s, \Sigma)$ that $n - s \geq q = \text{rank}\ \Sigma$.

There is a simple and geometrically natural transformation which carries an inner product π with the $B(s, n - s, \Sigma)$ distribution into an inner product $\dot{\pi}$ with the $G(s, n - s, \Sigma)$ distribution, and vice versa. Given π, the principal axes of the ellipsoid of π_d relative to Σ_d are $h_1^{1/2}z_1, h_2^{1/2}z_2, \ldots, h_r^{1/2}z_r$. By scaling along each of these principal axes such that $h_i^{1/2}z_i \to k_i^{1/2}z_i$ with $k_i = h_i/(1 - h_i)$ for $i = 1, 2, \ldots, r$, one obtains from the ellipsoid of π_d the ellipsoid of $\dot{\pi}_d$ where $\dot{\pi}$ has the $G(s, n - s, \Sigma)$ distribution. The reverse operation to determine π from $\dot{\pi}$ is uniquely defined. Thus, it is equivalent to deal with π or with its corresponding $\dot{\pi}$.

Like the B family, the G family appears in normal sampling theory in the context of a pair of independent Wishart inner products. The role of the denominator χ^2 in the generalization of G is played by a dual Wishart distribution, where π will be said to have the $W_d(n, \Sigma)$ distribution if π is characterized exactly as in the second half of Theorem 13.4.3 except that $l_1^{1/2}z_1, l_2^{1/2}z_2, \ldots, l_r^{1/2}z_r$ are replaced by $l_1^{-1/2}z_1, l_2^{-1/2}z_2, \ldots, l_r^{-1/2}z_r$. This definition suggests a natural one-one transformation relating pairs π and $\dot{\pi}$ where π has the $W(n, \Sigma)$ distribution and $\dot{\pi}$ has the $W_d(n, \Sigma)$ distribution. Starting from π, consider the linear transformation in $\mathscr{F}$ which carries the ellipsoid of π_d into the ellipsoid of

Σ_d by scaling along the eigenvectors of π_d relative to Σ_d. This linear transformation carries the ellipsoid of Σ_d into the ellipsoid of $\dot{\pi}_d$ where $\dot{\pi}$ has the $W_d(n, \Sigma)$ distribution as just defined. Starting from $\dot{\pi}$, the process is easily reversed to find π.

The following theorem is analogous to Theorem 13.7.2 using G distributions rather than B distributions. It is fundamental to an understanding of the treatment of Bayesian inference in Section 15.3.

Theorem 13.7.5. *Suppose that π_1 and π_2 are a pair of random inner products over a p-dimensional quantity space $\mathscr{E}$, that Σ is an inner product over $\mathscr{E}$ with rank $q \leq p$, and that s and $n - s$ are positive integers with $n - s \geq q$. Then the following assertions imply each other:*

A) the conditional distribution of π_2 given π_1 is $W(s, \pi_1)$, while the marginal distribution of π_1 is $W_d(n - s, \Sigma)$,

B) the conditional distribution of π_1 given π_2 is $W_d(n, \pi_2 + \Sigma)$, while the marginal distribution of π_2 is $G(s, n - s, \Sigma)$.

Start from (A) and consider the linear transformation which carries the ellipsoid of π_{1d} into the ellipsoid of Σ_d by scaling along their mutual eigenvectors. The ellipsoids of Σ_d and π_{2d} are carried into a pair of ellipsoids of, say, π_d^{**} and π_d^* where π^{**} and π^* are from (A) independent random inner products with $W(n - s, \Sigma)$ and $W(s, \Sigma)$ distributions. From the spherical symmetry of property (A), the principal axes of the ellipsoid of π_{2d} relative to Σ_d are spherically distributed with respect to Σ_d, conditional on any given set of eigenvalues of π_2 relative to Σ. But these eigenvalues are the same as the eigenvalues of π^* relative to π^{**} which from Theorem 13.7.2 have the $K(n, q, s)$ distribution. Thus π_2 has the $G(s, n - s, \Sigma)$ marginal distribution as specified by assertion (B). Next suppose that π_2 is fixed and ask for the conditional distribution of π_1 given π_2. The original assertion (A) is equivalent to the assertion that π^{**} and π^* are independent with $W(n - s, \Sigma)$ and $W(s, \Sigma)$ distributions, and, in these terms, fixing π_2 is equivalent to fixing the eigenvalues of π^* relative to π^{**}. It follows from Theorem 13.7.2 that $\pi^{**} + \pi^*$ has the $W(n, \Sigma)$ distribution given π_2. The eigenvalues of $\pi^* + \pi^{**}$ relative to Σ, are the same as the eigenvalues of Σ_d relative to $(\pi^* + \pi^{**})_d$ which in turn are the same as the eigenvalues of π_{1d} relative to $(\pi_2 + \Sigma)_d$, so that the eigenvalues of π_1 are distributed as indicated in assertion (B). Given these eigenvalues, the conditional distribution of $\pi^* + \pi^{**}$ is spherical with respect to Σ, while given $\pi^* + \pi^{**}$ the conditional distribution of π^* is spherical with respect to $\pi^* + \pi^{**}$. These spherical distributions ensure that π_1 is spherically distributed relative to $\pi_2 + \Sigma$. Thus (A) implies (B) and, since either (A) or (B) uniquely determine the joint distribution of π_1 and π_2, (B) implies (A).

The family of $t(\emptyset, \Sigma, n)$ distributions has a close connection with the family of $G(1, m, \Sigma)$ distributions. The reader may prove the following theorem by checking that the single nonzero eigenvalue of π relative to Σ has the correct distribution.

Theorem 13.7.6. *Suppose that t has the $t(\emptyset, \Sigma, n - q + 1)$ distribution where $q = \text{rank}\ \Sigma$ and $n \geq q$. Suppose that $\dot{\pi}$ is the rank 1 inner product defined by regarding t as a sample of size one with raw sample sum inner product $\dot{\pi}$. Then $\dot{\pi}$ has the $G(1, n, \Sigma)$ distribution. Conversely, if $\dot{\pi}$ has the $G(1, n, \Sigma)$ distribution and if t is chosen with equal probabilities from the two points on the surface of the one-dimensional ellipsoid of $\dot{\pi}_d$, then t has the $t(\emptyset, \Sigma, n)$ distribution.*

In normal sampling theory, a related pair t and $\dot{\pi}$ as in Theorem 13.7.6 would usually appear in the corresponding contexts of Theorem 13.6.1 and Theorem 13.7.5, so that Theorem 13.6.1 is essentially a special case of Theorem 13.7.5 with s replaced by 1 and $n - s$ replaced by n. The role of the single eigenvalue of $\dot{\pi}$ relative to Σ in the special case is played by G in (13.6.4). Recall that any random inner product $\dot{\pi}$ with the $G(1, n, \Sigma)$ distribution has a corresponding random inner product π with the $B(1, n, \Sigma)$ distribution, and that such a π has a related Λ statistic defined as in (13.7.1). The relation between π and $\dot{\pi}$ implies that

$$\Lambda = 1 - h_1 = 1 - k_1(1 + k_1)^{-1} = (1 + k_1)^{-1} = (1 + G)^{-1}, \quad (13.7.12)$$

and the reader may easily check that the distributions assigned to Λ and G are consistent with this relation.

If Q has the ordinary $G(s, n - s, 1)$ distribution, and if $n \to \infty$ while s remains fixed it is clear that the limiting distribution of nQ is $\chi^2(s, 1)$. A similar relation holds for the corresponding $\beta(s/2, (n - s)/2)$ family. It is not surprising, therefore, that a similar relation holds for the generalized G and beta families. The key fact is that if π has the $W(n - s, \Sigma)$ distribution, then in the limit as $n \to \infty$, π/n tends in probability to Σ. Applying Theorem 13.7.2 and related definitions yields the following theorem.

Theorem 13.7.7. *Suppose that π and $\dot{\pi}$ have $B(s, n - s, \Sigma)$ and $G(s, n - s, \Sigma)$ distributions with $n - s \geq q = \text{rank}\ \Sigma$, so that the eigenvalues $h_1, h_2, \ldots, h_r$ of π relative to Σ have the $H(n, q, s)$ distribution, the eigenvalues $k_1, k_2, \ldots, k_r$ of $\dot{\pi}$ relative to Σ have the $K(n, q, s)$ distribution and the Wilks Λ based on π has the $\Lambda(n, q, s)$ distribution. As $n \to \infty$ the limiting distribution of $n\pi$ or of $n\dot{\pi}$ is $W(s, \Sigma)$, the limiting distribution of $nh_1, nh_2, \ldots, nh_r$ or of $nk_1, nk_2, \ldots, nk_r$ is $L(s, r)$, and the limiting distribution of $n^r\Lambda$ is the distribution of the product of r independent random variables with $\chi^2(s - i + 1, 1)$ distributions for $i = 1, 2, \ldots, r$.*

13.8 REMARKS ON PROBABILITY DENSITY FUNCTIONS

Many elegant but sometimes forbidding formulas have been given in books and journals for probability density functions relevant to multivariate normal sampling theory. The reader may wish to consult the books by Anderson

(1958), Kendall and Stuart (1961, 1966), Rao (1965), Roy (1957), and Wilks (1962), and the paper by James (1964), together with the bibliography listed by these authors. A few such distributions appear in the exercises at the end of Section 13.9, but they are not pursued in the text of this book.

The work of A. T. James is unusually rich in mathematical ideas. In his first paper, James (1954) shows essentially how to discuss probability density functions in a way free of coordinate systems using the concept of an exterior differential form. He proceeds to display the exterior differential forms for spherically distributed subspaces and spherically distributed sets of orthonormal vectors. Having these it is but a short step to densities for distributions such as $W(n, \Sigma)$ and $H(n, q, s)$. Later James developed a scheme of zonal polynomials with a matrix argument and expressed many general noncentral probability density functions using power series in zonal polynomials (see James, 1964).

One aim of this chapter has been to show that many basic facts about multivariate normal sampling theory can be understood without recourse to density functions. Beyond these basic facts many complex distributions remain to be understood, and density functions provide one avenue to such understanding. On the whole, however, rather little of practical importance seems to have come from that avenue. For example, the famous density of the $H(n, q, s)$ distribution was simultaneously found by Fisher (1939), Girshick (1939), Hsu (1939), Roy (1939), and Mood (1951). Some limited numerical work has been carried out to find distributions for the largest eigenvalue from the joint density (Foster and Rees, 1957; Foster, 1957, 1958; Heck, 1960) for $r = 2, 3, 4$, but otherwise little seems to have been learned. In time, some blending of computer techniques with understanding of density functions may yield greater practical knowledge of many complicated distributions. Or, it may be that simulation and Monte Carlo techniques will be more productive.

13.9 EXERCISES

13.2.1 Suppose that $\mathbf{X}$ denotes a random sample from an $N(\mathbf{0}, \mathbf{\Sigma})$ population as in Section 13.2, and that the rows of $\mathbf{X}$ are written in a sequence in one line to form a $1 \times np$ random vector $\mathbf{X}^*$. Show that $\mathbf{X}^*$ has the $N(\mathbf{0}, \mathbf{\Sigma}^*)$ distribution and specify the elements of $\mathbf{\Sigma}^*$.

13.2.2 Suppose that $[a_1, a_2, \ldots, a_n]$ in $\mathscr{F}$ represents a random sample of size n from the $N(\varnothing, \Sigma)$ distribution as in (13.2.1). Show that

$$[b_1, b_2, \ldots, b_n] = [a_1, a_2, \ldots, a_n]\mathbf{G}$$

has the same distribution as $[a_1, a_2, \ldots, a_n]$ for any $n \times n$ orthogonal matrix $\mathbf{G}$. Show also that

$$[c_1, c_2, \ldots, c_n] = [\mathsf{A}a_1, \mathsf{A}a_2, \ldots, \mathsf{A}a_n]$$

has the same distribution as $[a_1, a_2, \ldots, a_n]$ for any inner product preserving linear transformation A of $\mathscr{F}$ into itself.

13.3.1 Suppose that $[x_1, x_2, \ldots, x_p]$ is a spherically distributed set of random outcomes in $\mathscr{N}$ with a fixed configuration matrix $\mathbf{Q}$ of rank p. Suppose that

$$[z_1, z_2, \ldots, z_p] = [x_1, x_2, \ldots, x_p]\mathbf{K},$$

where $\mathbf{K}$ is a fixed $p \times p$ matrix of rank p. Characterize the distribution of $z_1, z_2, \ldots, z_p$.

13.3.2 Suppose that $\mathbf{V}$ is a spherically distributed orthonormal basis of a Euclidean space $\mathscr{E}$. Show that the dual basis $\mathbf{v}$ is a spherically distributed orthonormal basis of the dual Euclidean space $\mathscr{F}$.

13.3.3 Suppose that simulated values have been obtained for a random matrix $\mathbf{Q}$ with the $W(n, \mathbf{\Sigma})$ distribution. Describe how to simulate a sample $\mathbf{X}$ from the $N(\mathbf{0}, \mathbf{\Sigma})$ distribution conditional on a fixed $\mathbf{Q} = \mathbf{X}'\mathbf{X}$.

13.4.1 Suppose that $\mathbf{Q}$ has the $W(n, \mathbf{I})$ distribution, where $\mathbf{Q}$ has dimensions $p \times p$. Show that the diagonal elements $q_{11}, q_{22}, \ldots, q_{pp}$ of $\mathbf{Q}$ are independent and each has the $\chi^2(n, 1)$ distribution. Deduce the distribution of tr $\mathbf{Q}$.

13.4.2 Suppose that $\mathbf{R}$ is a $p \times p$ matrix whose (i, j) element r_{ij} is given by $q_{ij}/q_{ii}^{1/2}q_{jj}^{1/2}$ where $\mathbf{Q}$ has the $W(n, \mathbf{I})$ distribution. Show that $\mathbf{R}$ is independent of the diagonal elements of $\mathbf{Q}$. Show that r_{12} and r_{23} are independent but that r_{12}, r_{23}, and r_{13} are not independent. Characterize the distribution of r_{12}.

13.4.3 Suppose that $\mathbf{Q}$ has the $W(n, \mathbf{\Sigma})$ distribution and denote the (i, j) elements of $\mathbf{Q}$ and $\mathbf{\Sigma}$ by q_{ij} and σ_{ij}. Show that

$$E(q_{ij}) = n\sigma_{ij}$$

and

$$\text{cov}\,(q_{ij}, q_{kl}) = n(\sigma_{ik}\sigma_{jl} + \sigma_{il}\sigma_{jk}).$$

13.4.4 Methods for simulating $\mathbf{Q}$ having the $W(n, \Sigma)$ distribution were described in Sections 13.3 and 13.4. Calculate the number of simulated $N(0, 1)$ random values required for each method, assuming that χ^2 random values are simulated by summing the squares of independent $N(0, 1)$ random values. Show that the methods of Section 13.4 require roughly $2/p$ times as many multiplications as do the methods of Section 13.3, when n is large.

13.4.5 Suppose that $\mathbf{Q}$ has the $W(n, \mathbf{\Sigma})$ distribution where $\mathbf{\Sigma}$ has full rank p and $n \geq p$. Suppose that $\mathbf{K}$ is a fixed nonsingular $p \times p$ matrix and that $\mathbf{K} = [\mathbf{K}_1, \mathbf{K}_2]$ where $\mathbf{K}_1$ and $\mathbf{K}_2$ denote the first s and last $p - s$ columns. Show that $[\mathbf{K}_2'\mathbf{Q}^{-1}\mathbf{K}_2]^{-1}$ and $[\mathbf{K}_1'\mathbf{Q}^{-1}\mathbf{K}_1 - \mathbf{K}_1'\mathbf{Q}^{-1}\mathbf{K}_2(\mathbf{K}_2'\mathbf{Q}^{-1}\mathbf{K}_2)^{-1}\mathbf{K}_2'\mathbf{Q}^{-1}\mathbf{K}_1]^{-1}$ are independent with $W(n - s, (\mathbf{K}_2'\mathbf{\Sigma}^{-1}\mathbf{K}_2)^{-1})$ and $W(s, [\mathbf{K}_1'\mathbf{\Sigma}^{-1}\mathbf{K}_1 - \mathbf{K}_1'\mathbf{\Sigma}^{-1}\mathbf{K}_2(\mathbf{K}_2'\mathbf{\Sigma}^{-1}\mathbf{K}_2)^{-1}\mathbf{K}_2'\mathbf{\Sigma}^{-1}\mathbf{K}_1]^{-1})$ distributions.

13.4.6 If P has the $\chi^2(n, 1)$ distribution, then $\log P$ has the $N(\log n, 2/n)$, approximately, for large n. Deduce a corresponding approximation for the distribution of log det $\mathbf{Q}$ where $\mathbf{Q}$ has the $W(n, \mathbf{\Sigma})$ distribution.

13.4.7 Assuming that Σ has rank p, state Theorem 13.4.3 in terms of π, Σ, and E directly, without using dual concepts.

13.4.8 Suppose that $\mathbf{L}$ is an $r \times r$ diagonal matrix whose elements have the $L(n, r)$ distribution. Suppose that $\mathbf{G}$ is an $r \times q$ random matrix defined to be the first r rows of a spherically distributed $q \times q$ orthogonal matrix. Suppose that $\mathbf{\Sigma}$ is a fixed $p \times p$ covariance matrix of rank q and that $\mathbf{\Delta}$ is any fixed $p \times q$ matrix such that $\mathbf{\Sigma} = \mathbf{\Delta\Delta}'$. Show that

$$\mathbf{Q} = \mathbf{\Delta G' L G \Delta'}$$

has the $W(n, \mathbf{\Sigma})$ distribution.

13.4.9 Suppose that $l_1, l_2, \ldots, l_r$ have the $L(n, q)$ distribution. Show that $l_1 + l_2 + \cdots + l_r$ has the $\chi^2(nq, 1)$ distribution.

13.4.10 Show that the $L(n, q)$ and $L(q, n)$ distributions are the same. [*Hint:* use the fact that $\mathbf{XX}'$ and $\mathbf{X'X}$ have the same eigenvalues.]

13.4.11 Suppose that π and τ are the sample raw sum inner products of a pair of samples $a_1, a_2, \ldots, a_n$ and $\nu_1, \nu_2, \ldots, \nu_n$ in $\mathscr{F}$. Suppose that $\nu_1, \nu_2, \ldots, \nu_n$ are fixed while $a_1, a_2, \ldots, a_n$ are independent random outcomes with $N(\nu_i, \Sigma)$ distributions for $i = 1, 2, \ldots, n$. Show that the distribution of π depends only on n, Σ, and τ, and so may be labelled $W(n, \Sigma, \tau)$. The family $W(n, \Sigma, \tau)$ defined in this way may be called the *family of noncentral Wishart distributions.* The reader may supply the obvious coordinate-dependent family $W(n, \mathbf{\Sigma}, \boldsymbol{\tau})$.

13.4.12 Suppose that π_1 and π_2 are independent with $W(n_1, \Sigma, \tau_1)$ and $W(n_2, \Sigma, \tau_2)$ distributions. Show that $\pi_1 + \pi_2$ has the $W(n_1 + n_2, \Sigma, \tau_1 + \tau_2)$ distribution.

13.4.13 Under the assumptions of Theorem 13.4.2, show that $\mathbf{H}_{21}\mathbf{Q}_{11}\mathbf{H}_{12}$ and $\mathbf{Q}_{22.1}$ are independent with $W(s, \mathbf{\Sigma}_{22.1}, \mathbf{\Xi}_{21}\mathbf{Q}_{11}\mathbf{\Xi}_{12})$ and $W(n - s, \mathbf{\Sigma}_{22.1})$ all conditional on given $\mathbf{Q}_{11}$. Deduce the conditional distribution of $\mathbf{Q}_{22}$ given $\mathbf{Q}_{11}$.

13.5.1 Under the assumptions of Theorem 13.5.1, the set of vectors $z_{ij}, z_{\overline{i+1}\,j}, \ldots, z_{\overline{n-j+1}\,j}$ is spherically distributed with fixed configuration in $\mathscr{N}_{ij}$, conditional on given $y_1, y_2, \ldots, y_{i-1}$. Apply Theorem 13.5.1 to this conditional spherical distribution, using positive scale factors to make the random orthogonal basis $z_{ij}, z_{\overline{i+1}\,j}, \ldots, z_{\overline{n-j+1}\,j}$ orthonormal and to make the fixed orthogonal basis $v_{ij}, v_{\overline{ij+1}}, \ldots, v_{\overline{in-i+1}}$ of $\mathscr{N}_{ij}$ orthonormal. Show that a common set of θ_{ij} is used in the new and original applications of the theorem.

13.6.1 Suppose that $l_1, l_2, \ldots, l_q$ have the $L(n, q)$ distribution while $[Z_1, Z_2, \ldots, Z_q]$ independently has the $N(\mathbf{0}, \mathbf{I})$ distribution, where $n \geq q$. Show that

$$Z_1^2/l_1 + Z_2^2/l_2 + \cdots + Z_q^2/l_q$$

has the $G(q, n - q + 1, 1)$ distribution.

13.7.1 Suppose that $\mathbf{Q}$ and $\mathbf{\Sigma}$ are random and fixed inner product matrices of dimensions $p \times p$ where $\mathbf{Q}$ has the $B(m, n - m, \mathbf{\Sigma})$ distribution and $\mathbf{\Sigma}$ has rank p. Assume the standard partition notation of Theorem 13.4.3 where $s \leq \min(p, m)$. Show that $\mathbf{Q}_{11}$ and $\mathbf{Q}_{22.1}$ are independent with $B(m, n - m, \mathbf{\Sigma}_{11})$ and $B(m - s, n - m, \mathbf{\Sigma}_{22.1})$ distributions. How would you characterize the conditional distribution of $\mathbf{H}_{12}$ given $\mathbf{Q}_{11}$?

13.7.2 Describe a procedure for simulating a matrix $\mathbf{Q}$ with the $B(s, n - s, \mathbf{\Sigma})$ distribution for given s, n, and $\mathbf{\Sigma}$.

13.7.3 Show that each of the families $B(s, n - s, \mathbf{\Sigma})$, $H(n, q, s)$, and $\Lambda(n, q, s)$ may be regarded as generalizations of the family $\beta(s/2, (n - s)/2)$.

13.7.4 Suppose that $\mathbf{Q}^*$ and $\mathbf{Q}^{**}$ are independent random $p \times p$ matrices with $W(s, \mathbf{\Sigma})$ and $W(n - s, \mathbf{\Sigma})$ distributions where $\mathbf{\Sigma}$ has rank $q \leq p$. Suppose that $\mathbf{C}$ is an $r \times p$ matrix defined for each $\mathbf{Q} = \mathbf{Q}^* + \mathbf{Q}^{**}$ such that $\mathbf{CQC}' = \mathbf{I}$, where $r = \min(q, s)$. Show that $\det \mathbf{CQ}^{**}\mathbf{C}'$ has the $\Lambda(n, q, s)$ distribution.

13.7.5 Suppose that Λ has the $\Lambda(n, 2, s)$ distribution. Show that $\Lambda^{1/2}$ has the $\beta(n - s - 1, s)$ distribution. [*Hint:* use the fact that Λ has the same distribution as the product of two independent random values with $\beta((n - s)/2, s/2)$ and $\beta((n - s - 1)/2, s/2)$ distributions. It is helpful here to know the basic property $\Gamma(\alpha + \frac{1}{2})\Gamma(\alpha + 1)2^{2\alpha} = \pi^{1/2}\Gamma(2\alpha + 1)$ of the gamma function.]

13.7.6 Suppose that $\mathbf{Q}$ has the $W(n, \mathbf{\Sigma})$ distribution where $\mathbf{\Sigma}$ has full rank p and $n \geq p$. Show that $\mathbf{Q}^{-1}$ has the $W_d(n, \mathbf{\Sigma}^{-1})$ distribution. [*Hint:* if $n < p$, then $\dot{\mathbf{Q}}$ has the $W_d(n, \mathbf{\Sigma}^{-1})$ distribution, where $\dot{\mathbf{Q}}$ is the pseudoinverse of $\mathbf{Q}$ defined in Exercise 3.4.11.]

13.7.7 Suppose that $\mathbf{Q}$ has the $G(s, n - s, \mathbf{\Sigma})$ distribution where $\mathbf{\Sigma}$ has rank q. Show that the rank of $\mathbf{Q}$ is $\min(q, s, n - s)$ with probability 1.

13.7.8 Suppose that $k_1, k_2, \ldots, k_r$ have the $K(n, r, t)$ distribution where $r \leq t$ and $r + t \leq n$. Show that $k_r^{-1}, k_{r-1}^{-1}, \ldots, k_1^{-1}$ have the $K(n, r, n - t)$ distribution.

13.7.9 Suppose that the $G_d(s, n - s, \mathbf{\Sigma})$ distribution is defined exactly as the $G(s, n - s, \Sigma)$ distribution except that the eigenvalues $k_1, k_2, \ldots, k_r$ are replaced by $k_1^{-1}, k_2^{-1}, \ldots, k_r^{-1}$. Show that the $G_d(s, n - s, \Sigma)$ distribution is the same as the $G(n - s, s, \Sigma)$ distribution. Consequently, if $\mathbf{Q}$ has the $G(s, n - s, \mathbf{\Sigma})$ distribution, where $\mathbf{\Sigma}$ has full rank p, $s \geq p$, and $n - s \geq p$, then $\mathbf{Q}^{-1}$ has the $G(n - s, s, \mathbf{\Sigma}^{-1})$ distribution.

13.7.10 Suppose that $\mathbf{Q}$ has the $G(1, n, \mathbf{\Sigma})$ distribution where $n \geq q = \text{rank } \mathbf{\Sigma}$. Show that the single eigenvalue of $\mathbf{Q}$ relative to $\mathbf{\Sigma}$ has the $G(1, n - q + 1, 1)$ distribution.

13.7.11 Suppose that $k_1, k_2, \ldots, k_r$ have the $K(n, r, t)$ distribution with $r \leq t$. Show that $n(k_1 + k_2 + \cdots + k_r)$ has the $\chi^2(rt, 1)$ distribution in the limit as $n \to \infty$.

13.7.12 Suppose that the first m factors in (13.7.4) have product Λ_1 while the remaining factors have product $\Lambda_{2.1}$ where $m \leq r = \min(q, s)$. Show that Λ_1 and $\Lambda_{2.1}$ are independent with $\Lambda(n, m, s)$ and $\Lambda(n - m, q - m, s)$ distributions.

13.7.13 Suppose that $\mathbf{Q}^*$ and $\mathbf{Q}^{**}$ are independent random matrices with $W(s, \mathbf{\Sigma}, \boldsymbol{\tau})$ and $W(n - s, \mathbf{\Sigma})$ distributions, where $\mathbf{\Sigma}$ has full rank p and $\boldsymbol{\tau}$ is a fixed inner product matrix of any rank. Recall the definition of the noncentral Wishart distribution in Exercise 13.4.11. Define $\mathbf{Q}$ and Λ from $\mathbf{Q} = \mathbf{Q}^* + \mathbf{Q}^{**}$ and $\Lambda = \det \mathbf{Q}^{**}/\det \mathbf{Q}$. Show that the distribution of Λ depends only on n, s, p, and $\boldsymbol{\xi}$ where $\boldsymbol{\xi}$ is the $1 \times p$ vector of eigenvalues of $\boldsymbol{\tau}$ relative to $\mathbf{\Sigma}$. The distribution of Λ may be called the *noncentral Wilks Λ distribution* and will be labelled $\Lambda(n, s, p, \boldsymbol{\xi})$.

13.7.14 Generalize the $H(n, s, p)$ family of distributions to the $H(n, s, p, \boldsymbol{\xi})$ family in a manner analogous to the generalization of the $\Lambda(n, s, p)$ family to the $\Lambda(n, s, p, \boldsymbol{\xi})$ family.

13.7.15 Suppose that Λ in Exercise 13.7.13 is factored into $\Lambda_1\Lambda_{2.1}$ as in Exercise 13.7.12. Suppose that $\mathbf{\Sigma}$ and $\boldsymbol{\tau}$ are covariance matrices relative to a basis $\mathbf{V}$ of $\mathscr{E}$ and suppose that $\boldsymbol{\tau}$ assigns zero norm to all variables $\boldsymbol{\Sigma}$-orthogonal to the subspace spanned by $[V_1, V_2, \ldots, V_m]$. Show that Exercise 13.7.12 generalizes so that Λ_1 and $\Lambda_{2.1}$ are independent with $\Lambda(n, m_1, s, \xi_1)$ and $\Lambda(n - m, q - m, s)$ distributions, where ξ_1 is the vector of eigenvalues of $\boldsymbol{\tau}$ relative to $\boldsymbol{\Sigma}$ after restriction to the subspace spanned by $V_1, V_2, \ldots, V_m$.

13.7.16 Show that the relation (13.7.12) may be generalized to a pair of relations of the form

$$\Lambda_1 = (1 + G_1)^{-1} \qquad \text{and} \qquad \Lambda_{2.1} = [1 + G_{2.1}(1 + G_1)^{-1}]^{-1},$$

where $\Lambda = \Lambda_1\Lambda_{2.1}$ is a factorization of the type of Exercise 13.7.15 and $G = G_1 + G_{2.1}$ is a decomposition like (13.6.4).

13.8.1 Any symmetric $p \times p$ matrix $\mathbf{Q}$ whose (i, j) or (j, i) element is denoted by q_{ij} for $1 \leq i \leq j \leq p$ may be represented by the vector of coordinates q_{ij} as a point in a $p(p + 1)/2$-dimensional space $\mathcal{M}$. Suppose that $\mathbf{Q}$ is a positive definite symmetric $p \times p$ matrix.

a) Show that the Jacobian of the transformation $\mathbf{Q} \to \mathrm{SWP}[1]\mathbf{Q}$ is $[q_{11}]^{-p-1}$.

b) Deduce that the Jacobian of the transformation $\mathbf{Q} \to \mathrm{SWP}[1, 2, \ldots, s]\mathbf{Q}$ is $[\det \mathbf{Q}_{11}]^{-p-1}$. In particular, the Jacobian of the transformation $\mathbf{Q} \to \mathbf{Q}^{-1}$ is $[\det \mathbf{Q}]^{-p-1}$.

c) Show that the Jacobian of the transformation $\mathbf{Q} \to \mathbf{AQA}'$ for any nonsingular $p \times p$ matrix $\mathbf{A}$ is $|\det \mathbf{A}|^{p+1}$.

13.8.2 Suppose that $\mathbf{Q}$ is a random symmetric $p \times p$ matrix distributed continuously with respect to Lebesgue measure over the subset of $\mathcal{M}$ such that $\mathbf{Q}$ is positive definite. Suppose that $\mathbf{Q}$ is spherically distributed with respect to $\boldsymbol{\Sigma}$, in the sense that $\mathbf{EQE}'$ has the same distribution as $\mathbf{Q}$ for any fixed matrix $\mathbf{E}$ such that $\mathbf{E\Sigma E}' = \boldsymbol{\Sigma}$. Show that the probability density function of $\mathbf{Q}$ with respect to Lebesgue measure over $\mathcal{M}$ has the form $f(l_1, l_2, \ldots, l_p)$ where $l_1 > l_2 > \cdots > l_p > 0$ denote the eigenvalues of $\mathbf{Q}$ relative to $\boldsymbol{\Sigma}$.

13.8.3 If $\mathbf{Q}$ is distributed as in Exercise 13.8.2 with $\boldsymbol{\Sigma} = \mathbf{I}$, then the probability density function of $l_1, l_2, \ldots, l_p$ is

$$Kf(l_1, l_2, \ldots, l_p) \prod_{i<j} (l_i - l_j)$$

over the region $l_1 > l_2 > \cdots > l_p > 0$, where

$$K^{-1} = \pi^{-p(p+1)/4} \prod_{i=1}^{p} \Gamma((p - i + 1)/2)$$

(Anderson, 1958, Theorem 13.3.1). What modification is required for general $\boldsymbol{\Sigma}$?

13.8.4 Suppose that $\mathbf{Q}$ has the $W(n, \mathbf{I})$ distribution where $\mathbf{Q}$ has dimensions $p \times p$ and $n \geq p$. Show that the probability density function of $\mathbf{Q}$ is given by

$$K[\det \mathbf{Q}]^{(n-p-1)/2} \exp\left(-\tfrac{1}{2} \operatorname{tr} \mathbf{Q}\right)$$

for positive definite symmetric $\mathbf{Q}$, where

$$K^{-1} = 2^{np/2}\pi^{p(p-1)/4} \prod_{i=1}^{p} \Gamma((n - i + 1)/2).$$

Deduce the density when **Q** has the $W(n, \mathbf{\Sigma})$ distribution with $\mathbf{\Sigma}$ of rank p. Deduce also the density of $\mathbf{Q}^{-1}$. A convenient way to approach this problem is to build up by induction, i.e., assuming the result for $p - 1$, use Theorem 13.4.2 to find the density of SWP[1]**Q** and thence for **Q**. See also Wishart (1948), Anderson (1958), and Wilks (1962).

13.8.5 Deduce from Exercises 13.8.3 and 13.8.4 that the probability density function of the $L(n, p)$ distribution for $n \geq p$ is

$$K\left[\prod_{i=1}^{p} l_i\right]^{(n-p-1)/2} \exp\left(-\tfrac{1}{2}\prod_{i=1}^{p} l_i\right)\prod_{i>j}(l_i - l_j)$$

for $l_1 > l_2 > \cdots > l_p > 0$, where

$$K^{-1} = 2^{pn/2}\pi^{-p/2}\prod_{i=1}^{p}[\Gamma((n - i + 1)/2)\Gamma((p - i + 1)/2)].$$

13.8.6 Suppose that **Q** has the $B(s, n - s, \mathbf{\Sigma})$ distribution where **Q** and $\mathbf{\Sigma}$ have dimensions $p \times p$. Then **Q** has a probability density function with respect to uniform measure over $\mathcal{M}$ if and only if $\mathbf{\Sigma}$ has rank p, $s \geq p$, and $n - s \geq p$. (Unless $\mathbf{\Sigma}$ has rank p and $s \geq p$, **Q** is singular with probability 1, and unless $n - s \geq p$, **Q** is restricted to a subset of $\mathcal{M}$ with uniform measure zero on which certain of the eigenvalues of **Q** with respect to $\mathbf{\Sigma}$ are restricted to be unity). Show that, when these conditions hold, **Q** has the density function

$$K[\det \mathbf{\Sigma}]^{n/2}[\det \mathbf{Q}]^{(s-p-1)/2}[\det(\mathbf{\Sigma} - \mathbf{Q})]^{(n-s-p-1)/2}$$

over the region where **Q** is positive definite symmetric, where

$$K^{-1} = \pi^{p(p-1)/4}\prod_{i=1}^{p}[\Gamma((n - s - i + 1)/2)\Gamma((s - i + 1)/1)\Gamma((n - i + 1)/2)^{-1}].$$

Compare with Olkin and Rubin (1964). Deduce that the $H(n, p, s)$ distribution has the density function

$$K\left[\prod_{i=1}^{p} h_i\right]^{(s-p-1)/2}\left[\prod_{i=1}^{p}(1 - h_i)\right]^{(n-s-p-1)/2}$$

over the region $1 > h_1 > h_2 > \cdots > h_p > 0$, where

$$K^{-1} = \pi^{-r/2}\prod_{i=1}^{p}[\Gamma((n - s - i + 1)/2)\Gamma((s - i + 1)/2)$$
$$\Gamma((p - i + 1)/2)/\Gamma((n - i + 1)/2)].$$

These results generalize Exercises 13.8.4 and 13.8.5, and may be derived with some difficulty in the same general way. An alternative approach is to use the result of Exercise 13.8.4 together with Theorem 13.7.2.

13.8.7 From the density of the $H(n, p, s)$ distribution deduce the density of the $K(n, p, s)$ distribution. Working backwards, deduce the density of the $G(s, n - s, \mathbf{\Sigma})$ distribution, where $\mathbf{\Sigma}$ has full rank p, $s \geq p$, and $n - s \geq p$.

CHAPTER 14

SOME SAMPLING DISTRIBUTIONS AND ILLUSTRATIONS OF POSTDICTIVE INFERENCES

14.1 THE SAMPLE MEAN AND SAMPLE COVARIANCE OF A SINGLE SAMPLE

Suppose that $X^{(1)}, X^{(2)}, \ldots, X^{(n)}$ denote a random sample from a one-dimensional $N(\mu, \sigma^2)$ population. In most first courses in mathematical statistics, it is shown that the sample mean $\bar{X} = \sum_1^n X^{(i)}/n$ and the sample variance $s^2 = \sum_1^n (X^{(i)} - \bar{X})^2/(n-1)$ are independent with $N(\mu, \sigma^2/n)$ and $\chi^2(n-1, \sigma^2/(n-1))$ distributions, according to their joint sampling distribution with fixed μ and σ^2. It is then noted that

$$T = \sqrt{n}(\bar{X} - \mu)/s \tag{14.1.1}$$

and

$$Q = s^2/\sigma^2 \tag{14.1.2}$$

have $t(0, 1, n-1)$ and $\chi^2(n-1, (n-1)^{-1})$ distributions, not depending on parameters which are unknown. Such pivotal quantities are then used to define significance tests and confidence procedures which throw light on unknown values of μ and σ. For example if A is any region on the line which has probability $1-\alpha$ according to the $t(0, 1, n-1)$ distribution, then the assertion

$$\sqrt{n}(\bar{X} - \mu)/s \in A \tag{14.1.3}$$

defines for fixed $\bar{X}$ and s a confidence region on the line for values of μ. When the confidence coefficient $1-\alpha$ is close to unity and A is an interval, the confidence intervals (14.1.3) provide a plausible means of excluding unreasonably extreme values of μ from consideration, in the postdictive sense that if μ is more extreme than is allowed by the interval then an improbably extreme value of T must have arisen. A similar collection of confidence statements about σ^2 may be based on (14.1.2).

It may be asked: what becomes of the above theory when the one-dimensional sample $X_1, X_2, \ldots, X_n$ is generalized to a sample $\mathbf{X}^{(1)}, \mathbf{X}^{(2)}, \ldots, \mathbf{X}^{(n)}$ from a p-dimensional $N(\boldsymbol{\mu}, \boldsymbol{\Sigma})$ population? In a nutshell, the answer is that the joint sampling distribution of $\bar{X}$ and s^2 generalizes directly; the multivariate analogue of (14.1.1) exists but is less nice than one might have hoped for; and attempts to generalize (14.1.2) lead to a Pandora's Box whose contents should be used sparingly and with caution, owing to the increased number of parameters.

Theorem 14.1.1. *Suppose that $a_1, a_2, \ldots, a_n$ denote a random sample of individuals from an $N(\mu, \Sigma)$ population whose sample mean m is defined as in* (7.2.1) *and whose sample covariance π is defined as in* (7.2.5). *Then m and π are independent with $N(\mu, \Sigma/n)$ and $W(n-1, \Sigma/(n-1))$ distributions, according to their joint sampling distribution given μ and Σ. Equivalently, if $\mathbf{X}^{(1)}, \mathbf{X}^{(2)}, \ldots, \mathbf{X}^{(n)}$ are independent random $1 \times p$ vectors each with the $N(\boldsymbol{\mu}, \boldsymbol{\Sigma})$ distribution, then*

$$\bar{\mathbf{X}} = \sum_{i=1}^{n} \mathbf{X}^{(i)}/n \tag{14.1.4}$$

and

$$\mathbf{S} = \sum_{i=1}^{n} (\mathbf{X}^{(i)} - \bar{\mathbf{X}})'(\mathbf{X}^{(i)} - \bar{\mathbf{X}})/(n-1) \tag{14.1.5}$$

are independent with $N(\boldsymbol{\mu}, \boldsymbol{\Sigma}/n)$ and $W(n-1, \boldsymbol{\Sigma}/(n-1))$ distributions.

The theorem is an immediate consequence of the theory of Section 13.2 applied to the sample $\mathbf{X}^{(1)} - \boldsymbol{\mu}, \mathbf{X}^{(2)} - \boldsymbol{\mu}, \ldots, \mathbf{X}^{(n)} - \boldsymbol{\mu}$ drawn randomly from the $N(\mathbf{0}, \boldsymbol{\Sigma})$ population. If $\mathbf{u} = [u_1, u_2, \ldots, u_n]'$ denotes an orthonormal basis of $\mathcal{N}$ such that $u_1 = n^{-1/2}(N_1 + N_2 + \cdots + N_n)$, and if $\mathbf{Z}^{(1)}, \mathbf{Z}^{(2)}, \ldots, \mathbf{Z}^{(n)}$ represent the sample $\mathbf{X}^{(1)} - \boldsymbol{\mu}, \mathbf{X}^{(2)} - \boldsymbol{\mu}, \ldots, \mathbf{X}^{(n)} - \boldsymbol{\mu}$ relative to $\mathbf{u}$ rather than $\mathbf{N}$, then the $\mathbf{Z}^{(i)}$ are independent and each has the $N(\mathbf{0}, \boldsymbol{\Sigma})$ distribution. But it is easily checked, as in Section 7.4, that

$$\sqrt{n}(\bar{\mathbf{X}} - \boldsymbol{\mu}) = \mathbf{Z}^{(1)} \tag{14.1.6}$$

and

$$(n-1)\mathbf{S} = \sum_{i=2}^{n} \mathbf{Z}^{(i)\prime}\mathbf{Z}^{(i)}. \tag{14.1.7}$$

Thus $\bar{\mathbf{X}}$ and $\mathbf{S}$ are independent because they depend on disjoint subsets of a set of independent random quantities, namely $\mathbf{Z}^{(1)}, \mathbf{Z}^{(2)}, \mathbf{Z}^{(3)}, \ldots, \mathbf{Z}^{(n)}$. They have the stated distributions directly from (14.1.6) and (14.1.7). Note especially that $\boldsymbol{\mu}$ does not appear in the expressions for $\mathbf{Z}^{(2)}, \mathbf{Z}^{(3)}, \ldots, \mathbf{Z}^{(n)}$ in terms of $\mathbf{X}^{(1)} - \boldsymbol{\mu}, \mathbf{X}^{(2)} - \boldsymbol{\mu}, \ldots, \mathbf{X}^{(n)} - \boldsymbol{\mu}$ because of the special choice of u_1.

Consider next how to generalize (14.1.1) in correspondence with the generalization of the univariate sample $X^{(1)}, X^{(2)}, \ldots, X^{(n)}$ to a p-variate sample $\mathbf{X}^{(1)}, \mathbf{X}^{(2)}, \ldots, \mathbf{X}^{(n)}$. One may of course apply (14.1.1) to each of the p variables

$V_1, V_2, \ldots, V_p$ to define corresponding $T_1, T_2, \ldots, T_p$. It would be nice if $T_1, T_2, \ldots, T_p$ had a multivariate t distribution, for then the individual confidence procedures about each μ_i based on T_i could be recognized as members of a large class such that a member of the class would be determined by a region in the outcome-space of a single t distributed random outcome. This does not happen, as may be checked by showing that $\alpha_1 T_1 + \alpha_2 T_2$ does not have a one-dimensional t distribution. Correspondingly, the application of (14.1.1) to $\alpha_1 V_1 + \alpha_2 V_2 + \cdots + \alpha_p V_p$ leads to T which yields confidence statements about $\alpha_1 \mu_1 + \alpha_2 \mu_2 + \cdots + \alpha_p \mu_p$, but this T is not $\alpha_1 T_1 + \alpha_2 T_2 + \cdots + \alpha_p T_p$. One is left therefore with a nonunified theory of confidence statements about single components of $\boldsymbol{\mu}$.

Another approach is to apply Theorem 13.6.1 with $\sqrt{n}(\bar{\mathbf{X}} - \boldsymbol{\mu})$ defining x and $(n-1)\mathbf{S}$ defining π. This leads to a random vector t with the $t(\varnothing, \Sigma, n-p)$ distribution, but the only part of t usable for tests or confidence statements is its random norm with respect to Σ_d, whose square

$$G = n(\bar{\mathbf{X}} - \boldsymbol{\mu})\mathbf{S}^{-1}(\bar{\mathbf{X}} - \boldsymbol{\mu})'/(n-1) \tag{14.1.8}$$

has according to Theorem 13.6.2 the $G(p, n-p, 1)$ distribution. G has an essential property required for tests or confidence statements about $\boldsymbol{\mu}$, namely, that it depends on $\bar{\mathbf{X}}$, $\mathbf{S}$, and $\boldsymbol{\mu}$ only. The direction of t, on the other hand, depends on $\boldsymbol{\Sigma}$ and remains unknown even given $\boldsymbol{\mu}$ unless $\boldsymbol{\Sigma}$ is specified up to an unknown scale factor. Consequently tests and confidence statements about $\boldsymbol{\mu}$ based on t cannot in general be made selective on the direction of t. In particular, t cannot be used for confidence statements about individual components of $\boldsymbol{\mu}$, as described in the preceding paragraph.

While unsuccessful in the aim of producing a directly useful random outcome with a t distribution, the second attempt to generalize (14.1.1) has turned up Hotelling's T^2 statistic in the form (14.1.8). If $G(p, n-p, 1)_{[1-\alpha]}$ denotes the $1-\alpha$ quantile of the $G(p, n-p, 1)$ distribution, then (14.1.8) yields the confidence region

$$(\boldsymbol{\mu} - \bar{\mathbf{X}})\mathbf{S}^{-1}(\boldsymbol{\mu} - \bar{\mathbf{X}})' \leq (1 - 1/n)G(p, n-p, 1)_{[1-\alpha]} \tag{14.1.9}$$

with confidence coefficient $1-\alpha$. Note that this region is an ellipsoid found by rescaling each radius of the sample mean-centered concentration ellipsoid by a common factor.

The applicability of G or Hotelling's T^2 is wider than may be apparent at first. Note that G is squared Euclidean distance and so is free of the choice of basis in the variable-space $\mathscr{E}$ to which it is applied. This suggests considering the family of G statistics defined for each subspace $\mathscr{U}$ of $\mathscr{E}$. Thus, for each $\mathscr{U}$, confidence ellipsoids may be constructed for the population mean vector of the variables in $\mathscr{U}$. In particular, if T in (14.1.1) is applied to a variable $\alpha_1 V_1 + \alpha_2 V_2 + \cdots + \alpha_p V_p$, then tests or confidence intervals based on T^2 are examples of the use of G applied to a one-dimensional subspace.

Theorem 13.6.2 shows that the generalization of (14.1.8) to

$$G = n(n-1)^{-1}(\bar{\mathbf{X}} - \boldsymbol{\nu})\mathbf{S}^{-1}(\bar{\mathbf{X}} - \boldsymbol{\nu})' \tag{14.1.10}$$

has the $G(p, n-p, 1, (\boldsymbol{\mu} - \boldsymbol{\nu})\boldsymbol{\Sigma}^{-1}(\boldsymbol{\mu} - \boldsymbol{\nu})')$ distribution. Consequently one may use G statistics over $\mathscr{E}$ in the following ways:

i) To test the null hypothesis that $\boldsymbol{\mu} = \boldsymbol{\mu}_0$ for some given $\boldsymbol{\mu}_0$. To do this, set $\boldsymbol{\nu} = \boldsymbol{\mu}_0$ in (14.1.10) and reject the null hypothesis if G is too large in relation to its $G(p, n-p, 1)$ null distribution.

ii) To compute the power functions of the test defined in (i) for any values of $\boldsymbol{\mu}$ and $\boldsymbol{\Sigma}$. The non-null distribution of G is $G(p, n-p, 1, (\boldsymbol{\mu} - \boldsymbol{\mu}_0)\boldsymbol{\Sigma}^{-1}(\boldsymbol{\mu} - \boldsymbol{\mu}_0)')$.

iii) To assign confidence limits to the values of $(\boldsymbol{\mu} - \boldsymbol{\mu}_0)\boldsymbol{\Sigma}^{-1}(\boldsymbol{\mu} - \boldsymbol{\mu}_0)'$ for any prespecified $\boldsymbol{\mu}_0$. For example a confidence region with confidence coefficient $1 - \alpha$ is defined by including those $(\boldsymbol{\mu} - \boldsymbol{\mu}_0)\boldsymbol{\Sigma}^{-1}(\boldsymbol{\mu} - \boldsymbol{\mu}_0)'$ for which

$$G(p, n-p, 1, (\boldsymbol{\mu} - \boldsymbol{\mu}_0)\Sigma^{-1}(\boldsymbol{\mu} - \boldsymbol{\mu}_0)')_{[1-\alpha]} \geq G$$

where G is defined by (14.1.10) with $\boldsymbol{\nu} = \boldsymbol{\mu}_0$. This procedure has the disturbing property of including all values of the parameter if $G \leq G(p, n-p, 1)_{[1-\alpha]}$.

iv) To determine a confidence region like (14.1.9) for $\boldsymbol{\mu}$.

Any of the theory of the preceding paragraph may be applied with a subspace $\mathscr{U}$ in place of $\mathscr{E}$. From Theorem 13.6.3, one may define G_1 in relation to a subspace $\mathscr{U}$ and subsequently apply an *independent* $G_{2.1}$ in relation to a complementary subspace $\mathscr{V}$. To do this, choose $V_1, V_2, \ldots, V_s$ to span $\mathscr{U}$ and $V_{s+1}, V_{s+2}, \ldots, V_p$ to span $\mathscr{V}$. Applying Theorem 13.6.3 with $\mathbf{X} = \sqrt{n}(\bar{\mathbf{X}} - \boldsymbol{\nu})$ and $\mathbf{Q} = (n-1)\mathbf{S}$ as in (14.1.10), one finds

$$\mathbf{X}_{2.1} = \sqrt{n}[(\bar{\mathbf{X}}_2 - \boldsymbol{\nu}_2) - (\bar{\mathbf{X}}_1 - \boldsymbol{\nu}_1)\mathbf{H}_{12}] \tag{14.1.11}$$

and

$$\boldsymbol{\nu}_{2.1} = \sqrt{n}[(\boldsymbol{\mu}_2 - \boldsymbol{\nu}_2) - (\boldsymbol{\mu}_1 - \boldsymbol{\nu}_1)\boldsymbol{\Xi}_{12}]. \tag{14.1.12}$$

$G_{2.1}$ may be used in the four ways described above for G: (i) to test whether $\boldsymbol{\mu}_2 - \boldsymbol{\mu}_1\boldsymbol{\Xi}_{12}$ has a specified value, (ii) to evaluate the power of this test, (iii) to put confidence limits on $\boldsymbol{\nu}_{2.1}\boldsymbol{\Sigma}_{22.1}^{-1}\boldsymbol{\nu}_{2.1}'$, and (iv) to put confidence limits on $\boldsymbol{\mu}_2 - \boldsymbol{\mu}_1\boldsymbol{\Xi}_{12}$. The partition need not be restricted to two parts, for Theorem 13.6.3 may be applied repeatedly to create parts up to p in number. It should be remembered that any part consisting of one variable only leads to a T as in (14.1.1), i.e., it is not necessary to restrict attention to the square of T.

The partition theory is elegant but suffers from the defect that $\boldsymbol{\mu}_2 - \boldsymbol{\mu}_1\boldsymbol{\Xi}_{12}$, about which it provides inferences, is not in general a directly interesting set of components of $\boldsymbol{\mu}$ because it involves an unknown $\boldsymbol{\Xi}_{12}$. The exception occurs when $\boldsymbol{\mu}_1$ is known to have a fixed value, which may be taken after translation to be $\mathbf{0}$. In this case $G_{2.1}$ provides inferences directly about $\boldsymbol{\mu}_2$. It is interesting to compare the sampling distributions of $\bar{\mathbf{X}}_2$ and $\bar{\mathbf{X}}_2 - \bar{\mathbf{X}}_1\mathbf{H}_{12}$. The first is of course $N(\boldsymbol{\mu}_2, \boldsymbol{\Sigma}_{22}/n)$. Assuming $\boldsymbol{\mu}_1 = \mathbf{0}$, the second is $N(\boldsymbol{\mu}_2, (1 + G_1)\boldsymbol{\Sigma}_{22.1}/n)$ conditional on given $\bar{\mathbf{X}}_1$ and $\mathbf{S}_{11}$. It is not obvious which of these estimators is preferable, for the decrease in variances from the use of $\boldsymbol{\Sigma}_{22.1}$ rather than $\boldsymbol{\Sigma}_{22}$ is counterbalanced by the increase due to the factor $(1 + G_1)$. But the second estimator is generally preferable, first because the factor $1 + G_1$ (which is observed) is usually close to unity, and second because postdictive inferences based on conditional distributions are widely considered to have greater validity than those based on marginal distributions which involve averages taken over quantities whose values are in fact known. The exceptional case occurs when $\boldsymbol{\Sigma}_{12}$ is known to be close to $\mathbf{0}$, for then $\mathbf{X}_2$ is nearly independent of G_1 and its conditional distribution given G_1 is nearly the same as its unconditional distribution.

The natural way to compute G and its related quantities may be described beginning from formula (7.5.4). If $\bar{\mathbf{X}}$ is replaced by $\bar{\mathbf{X}} - \boldsymbol{\nu}$ in SWP$[p + 1]\mathbf{Q}_{(+)}$ and if SWP$[1, 2, \ldots, p]$ is applied, then the $(p + 1, p + 1)$ element of the result is $-(1 + G)/n$ where G is defined by (14.1.10). More generally, if SWP$[1, 2, \ldots, p]$ is replaced by SWP$[1, 2, \ldots, s]$, the resulting $(p + 1, p + 1)$ element is $-(1 + G_1)/n$ while the $(s + 1, p + 1), (s + 2, p + 1), \ldots, (p, p + 1)$ elements provide $n^{-1/2}\mathbf{X}_{2.1}$ as defined in (14.1.11).

Example 8.1. The data of Example 8.1 will be used to give a simple numerical illustration of the single sample application of Hotelling's T^2. In this example there is some reason to think *a priori* that $\mu_1 + 2\mu_2 - \mu_3$ is close to zero. The main point of the following analysis is to show how inferences about μ_1 and μ_2 are affected by an *a priori* decision to regard $\mu_1 + 2\mu_2 - \mu_3$ as zero or nonzero.

A convenient point of departure is the matrix SWP$[4]\mathbf{Q}_{(+)}$ which gives the sample mean vector and the sample corrected sum inner product matrix for V_1, V_2, V_3. Premultiplying by

$$\begin{bmatrix} 1 & 0 & 0 & 0 \\ 0 & 1 & 0 & 0 \\ 1 & 2 & -1 & 0 \\ 0 & 0 & 0 & 1 \end{bmatrix}$$

and postmultiplying by its transpose gives the analogous matrix in terms of the variables V_1, V_2 and $W_3 = V_1 + 2V_2 - V_3$, namely

$$\begin{bmatrix} 0.003017 & -0.000379 & 0.000749 & 0.7634 \\ -0.000379 & 0.000719 & 0.000033 & 0.6277 \\ 0.000749 & 0.000033 & 0.002014 & 0.0041 \\ 0.7634 & 0.6207 & 0.0041 & -0.08333 \end{bmatrix}.$$

If the population mean of W_3 is denoted by ν_3, then (14.1.1) applied to W_3 is

$$\sqrt{12}(0.0041 - \nu_3)/(0.002014/11)^{1/2}.$$

From tables of the $t(0, 1, 11)$ distribution, $\Pr(|T| \leq 2.201) = 0.95$, so that a confidence interval for ν_3 with confidence coefficient 0.95 is $|\nu_3 - 0.0041| \leq 0.0087$ or

$$-0.0046 \leq \nu_3 \leq 0.0128.$$

Such a conclusion does not contradict the hypothesis that $\nu_3 = 0$, nor does it offer reassurance that $\nu_3 = 0$.

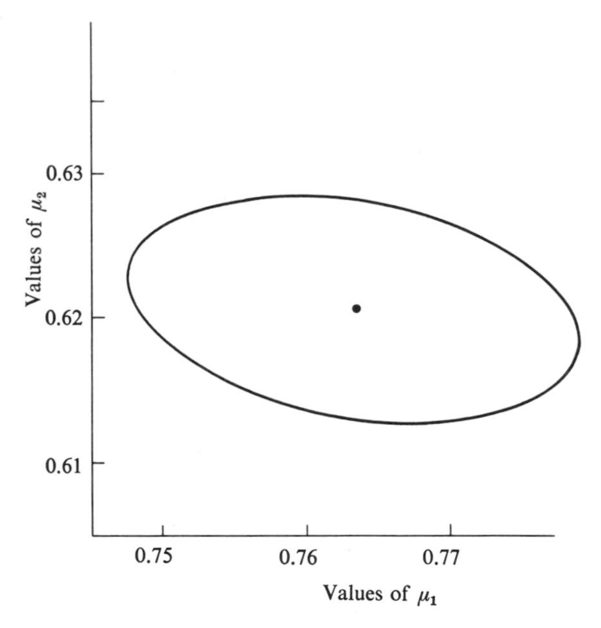

Fig. 14.1.1. The confidence ellipse for $[\mu_1, \mu_2]$ based on the data on V_1 and V_2 alone from Example 8.1.

If no assumption is made concerning ν_3, then the natural choice of a confidence ellipse for $[\mu_1, \mu_2]$ is made by applying (14.1.9) to V_1 and V_2. The ellipse is defined by

$$[\mu_1 - 0.7634, \mu_2 - 0.6207]\begin{bmatrix} 0.003017 & -0.000379 \\ -0.000379 & 0.000719 \end{bmatrix}^{-1}\begin{bmatrix} \mu_1 - 0.7634 \\ \mu_2 - 0.6207 \end{bmatrix} \leq G(2, 10, \tfrac{1}{12})_{[0.95]} = (0.288)^2,$$

and is sketched in Fig. 14.1.1.

On the other hand, if the assumption $\nu_3 = 0$ is accepted, then the natural choice of a confidence ellipse for $[\mu_1, \mu_2]$ is found by applying $G_{2.1}$ with W_3 in the role of $V_1, V_2, \ldots, V_s$ and V_1, V_2 in the role of $V_{s+1}, V_{s+2}, \ldots, V_p$. The first step here is to apply SWP[3] to the above matrix SWP[4]$\mathbf{Q}_{(+)}$ for V_1, V_2, W_3. The result is

$$\begin{bmatrix} 0.002739 & -0.000391 & 0.3719 & 0.7619 \\ -0.000391 & 0.000714 & 0.0164 & 0.6206 \\ 0.3719 & 0.0164 & -496.5 & 2.04 \\ 0.7619 & 0.6206 & 2.04 & -0.0917 \end{bmatrix}.$$

Note that the (4, 4) element here is $-0.0833 - 0.0084 = -0.0833(1 + G_1)$, where G_1 refers to W_3 alone. Thence $G_1 = 0.101$. The associated confidence ellipse for (μ_1, μ_2) is

$$[\mu_1 - 0.7619, \mu_2 - 0.6206]\begin{bmatrix} 0.002739 & -0.000391 \\ 0.000391 & 0.000714 \end{bmatrix}^{-1}\begin{bmatrix} \mu_1 - 0.7619 \\ \mu_2 - 0.6206 \end{bmatrix}$$
$$\leq G(2, 9, 1.101/12)_{[0.95]} = (0.294)^2.$$

To see the effect on the latter ellipse of the assumption $\nu_3 = 0$, consider what ellipse would correspond to a general known value of ν_3. The (3, 4) or (4, 3) elements of SWP[4]$\mathbf{Q}_{(+)}$ above would be corrected by subtracting ν_3, and the last column of SWP[3] applied to this corrected matrix would be

$$\begin{bmatrix} 0.7634 - 0.3719(0.0041 - \nu_3) \\ 0.6207 - 0.0164(0.0041 - \nu_3) \\ (0.0041 - \nu_3)/0.002014 \\ -0.08333 - (0.0041 - \nu_3)^2/0.002014 \end{bmatrix}.$$

Taking $\nu_3 = -0.0046$ and 0.0128, which are the ends of the confidence interval quoted above, the numerical values of these last columns are:

$$\begin{bmatrix} 0.7602 \\ 0.6188 \\ 4.32 \\ -0.0833 \times 1.451 \end{bmatrix} \quad \text{and} \quad \begin{bmatrix} 0.7662 \\ 0.6226 \\ -4.32 \\ -0.0833 \times 1.451 \end{bmatrix}.$$

The result is that the radii of the ellipse would be scaled up by a factor of $(1.451/1.101)^{1/2} - 1.09$, while the means would be shifted by $[-0.0017, -0.0018]$ and $[0.0043, 0.0020]$.

The reader should sketch the three ellipses corresponding to $\nu_3 = 0, -0.0046$, and 0.0128. The case $\nu_3 = 0$ produces a result not substantially different from the ellipse of Fig. 14.1.1, the reasons being *(a)* that the sample mean of W_3 differs little from zero and *(b)* that W_3 exhibits fairly small correlation with V_1 and V_2. The ellipses corresponding to $\nu_3 = -0.0046$ and 0.0128 show more substantial shifts. It follows that the procedure involving W_3 is fairly sensitive to unknowns, specifically to the unknown value of the population mean of W_3. On the other hand the use of the original ellipse as shown in Fig. 14.1.1

is compromised in the eyes of some because it is based on an unconditional procedure which ignores the fact that the sample values on W_3 are fixed by observation. Such is the dilemma of real world inference by postdictive methods.

Any theory of statistical inference, including the postdictive theory of this chapter, meets severe challenges when the joint estimation of a large number of parameters is desired. For example, if many confidence statements are made about components of a 1×100 mean vector $\boldsymbol{\mu}$, how much trust can be put in any one of them? On the other hand, if one grand 100-dimensional ellipsoid is used to provide a confidence region for $\boldsymbol{\mu}$, how can one report or make use of the result? These questions are not taken up in detail here, but see Exercise 14.1.1 and Section 15.3.

Turning now to the estimation of a covariance inner product, note first that there are $p(p + 1)/2$ functionally independent quantities so that the problem of many parameters is likely to be much more acute for covariance estimation than for mean estimation. Indeed, certain paradoxes which are touched upon in Section 15.3 make the author feel extremely wary about treading too far in this area. Another difference between covariance estimation and mean estimation has nothing to do with numbers of parameters. It is simply that the standard approach to the former does not incorporate the "studentization" feature of the standard approach to the latter, i.e., $\mathbf{S}$ is used to estimate certain aspects of the sampling distribution of $\bar{\mathbf{X}}$, but no widely established approach to the partial estimation of the sampling distribution of $\mathbf{S}$ exists. Confidence procedures for covariance estimation are moreover much more sensitive to the failure of the assumption of normality than are confidence procedures for mean estimation.

The various characterizations of Wishart distributions given in Section 13.4 lead to a large collection of potential quantities from which one may construct tests and confidence intervals concerning different aspects of $\boldsymbol{\Sigma}$. Many of these procedures are very difficult to visualize, and only a few rather direct examples mostly concerning correlation and regression coefficients are given in this book. Some preliminary remarks are made here, preceding the main discussion in Section 14.2.

The marginal distributions of the individual elements of $\mathbf{S}$ are easily characterized. Applying (14.1.2) directly to each diagonal element of $\mathbf{S}$, it is seen that

$$Q_i = (n - 1)s_{ii}/\sigma_{ii} \tag{14.1.13}$$

has the $\chi^2(n - 1, 1)$ distribution for $i = 1, 2, \ldots, p$. In general only the marginal distributions of the Q_i are known, since their joint distribution depends on an unknown population correlation matrix. Tests and confidence procedures about each individual σ_{ii} may be based on Q_i in the familiar one-dimensional way, but the mutual dependence of the Q_i must be remembered.

The situation with the covariances s_{ij} for $i \neq j$ is less pleasant. Note that

$$U_{ij} = [s_{ij}/s_{jj} - \sigma_{ij}/\sigma_{jj}][(\sigma_{ii} - \sigma_{ij}^2/\sigma_{jj})/(n-1)s_{jj}]^{-1/2} \qquad (14.1.14)$$

is independent of Q_j and has an $N(0, 1)$ distribution, according to Theorem 13.4.2. It follows that

$$s_{ij} = \sigma_{ij}[Q_j/(n-1)] + [(\sigma_{ii}\sigma_{jj} - \sigma_{ij}^2)/(n-1)]^{1/2}U_{ij}[Q_j/(n-1)]^{1/2} \qquad (14.1.15)$$

which provides a convenient representation of s_{ij} and thence a characterization of its distribution. The distribution of s_{ij} is seen to depend on σ_{ij} and $\sigma_{ii}\sigma_{jj}$. Consequently, from s_{ij} alone, tests and confidence statements for σ_{ij} alone are not available, and it is a plausible conjecture that no exact confidence statements about σ_{ij} exist. For large n, the second term in (14.1.15) becomes unimportant while the distribution of the first term converges to σ_{ij}. Formula (14.1.15) continues to hold when $i = j$, and so includes (14.1.13) as a special case. Note also that (14.1.15) may be applied to any pair of linear combinations of $V_1, V_2, \ldots, V_p$. The mean and variance of the sampling distribution of s_{ij} are given by

$$E(s_{ij}) = \sigma_{ij} \qquad (14.1.16)$$

and

$$\operatorname{var}(s_{ij}) = 2\sigma_{ij}^2/n, \qquad (14.1.17)$$

as follows easily from (14.1.15). More generally, cf. Exercise 13.4.3,

$$\operatorname{cov}(s_{ij}, s_{kl}) = (\sigma_{ik}\sigma_{jl} + \sigma_{il}\sigma_{jk})/n. \qquad (14.1.18)$$

For large n, the joint sampling distribution of the s_{ij} is approximately normal with moments given by (14.1.16), (14.1.17), and (14.1.18).

Theorem 13.4.2 asserts that the sampling distribution of $\mathbf{S}_{22.1}$ is $W(n-s, \mathbf{\Sigma}_{22.1}/(n-1))$, which suggests that

$$\hat{\mathbf{S}}_{22.1} = (n-1)\mathbf{S}_{22.1}/(n-s) = \mathbf{T}_{22.1}/(n-s) \qquad (14.1.19)$$

is a more appropriate estimator for $\mathbf{\Sigma}_{22.1}$ than is $\mathbf{S}_{22.1}$, especially if the fraction $(n-1)/(n-s)$ is noticeably greater than unity. For $\hat{\mathbf{S}}_{22.1}$ has the $W(n-s, \mathbf{\Sigma}_{22.1}/(n-s))$ distribution and therefore is comparable in scale to $\mathbf{S}$ itself, which has the $W(n-1, \mathbf{\Sigma}/(n-1))$ distribution. It may be argued heuristically that no correction factor would be necessary if the ordinary sample covariance matrix of $\mathbf{V}_2 - \mathbf{\Xi}_{21}\mathbf{V}_1$, i.e., $\mathbf{S}_{22} - \mathbf{\Xi}_{21}\mathbf{S}_{12} - \mathbf{S}_{21}\mathbf{\Xi}_{12} + \mathbf{\Xi}_{21}\mathbf{S}_{11}\mathbf{\Xi}_{12}$, could be used. But $\mathbf{S}_{22.1} = \mathbf{S}_{22} - \mathbf{H}_{21}\mathbf{S}_{12} - \mathbf{S}_{21}\mathbf{H}_{12} + \mathbf{H}_{21}\mathbf{S}_{11}\mathbf{H}_{12}$, and the effect of replacing $\mathbf{\Xi}_{12}$ by $\mathbf{H}_{12}$ is to reduce all the diagonal elements, because $\mathbf{V}_2 - \mathbf{H}_{21}\mathbf{V}_1$ has smaller *sample* variances than $\mathbf{V}_2 - \mathbf{\Xi}_{21}\mathbf{V}_1$. Thus it is clear that some inflationary factor is desirable. The sampling theory approach to inference suggests the factor $(n-1)/(n-s)$. See Section 15.3 for a Bayesian answer to this question.

14.2 SAMPLING DISTRIBUTIONS AND POSTDICTIVE INFERENCE PROCEDURES FOR REGRESSION AND CORRELATION ANALYSES

The emphasis here is on the analyses considered in Chapter 8, with some extensions to the analyses of Chapter 9. Consider first the linear prediction scheme for V_p in terms of $V_1, V_2, \ldots, V_{p-1}$ based on a single sample of size n. The notation of Section 8.2 will be used. Thus

$$\mathbf{T} = \begin{bmatrix} \mathbf{T}_{11} & \mathbf{T}_{12} \\ \mathbf{T}_{21} & t_{pp} \end{bmatrix} \tag{14.2.1}$$

denotes the sample corrected sum inner product matrix, with the rows and columns partitioned into $p = (p - 1) + 1$, while

$$\text{SWP}[1, 2, \ldots, p - 1]\mathbf{T} = \begin{bmatrix} -\mathbf{T}_{11}^{-1} & \mathbf{w}' \\ \mathbf{w} & t_{pp.12\ldots\overline{p-1}} \end{bmatrix}, \tag{14.2.2}$$

where $\mathbf{w} = [w_1, w_2, \ldots, w_{p-1}]$ is the vector of regression coefficients and $t_{pp.12\ldots\overline{p-1}}$ is the residual sum of squares after fitting the best linear predictor.

Assuming a random sample of size n from an $N(\boldsymbol{\mu}, \boldsymbol{\Sigma})$ population, $\mathbf{T} = (n - 1)\mathbf{S}$ has the $W(n - 1, \boldsymbol{\Sigma})$ sampling distribution and the sampling distributions of the parts of (14.2.2) follow from Theorem 13.4.2. Specifically, if one writes

$$\text{SWP}[1, 2, \ldots, p - 1]\boldsymbol{\Sigma} = \begin{bmatrix} -\boldsymbol{\Sigma}_{11}^{-1} & \boldsymbol{\omega}' \\ \boldsymbol{\omega} & \sigma_{pp.12\ldots\overline{p-1}} \end{bmatrix}, \tag{14.2.3}$$

then the vector of sample regression coefficients $\mathbf{w}$ has the $N(\boldsymbol{\omega}, \sigma_{pp.12\ldots\overline{p-1}}\mathbf{T}_{11}^{-1})$ distribution and is independent of $t_{pp.12\ldots\overline{p-1}}$ which has the $\chi^2(n - p, \sigma_{pp.12\ldots\overline{p-1}})$ distribution, all conditional on given $\mathbf{T}_{11}$. It follows that $\mathbf{w}$ is a plausible estimate of $\boldsymbol{\omega}$. Recall that $t_{pp.12\ldots\overline{p-1}}/(n - p)$ has already been suggested as an estimate of $\sigma_{pp.12\ldots\overline{p-1}}$ (cf. 14.1.19).

There are two multivariate t distributions associated with $\mathbf{w}$. First, from Corollary 13.6.1 it follows that the marginal distribution of $\mathbf{w}$ is

$$t(\boldsymbol{\omega}, \sigma_{pp.12\ldots\overline{p-1}}\boldsymbol{\Sigma}_{11}^{-1}/(n - p), n - p).$$

This is not useful for inferences about $\boldsymbol{\omega}$ except in the rare circumstance that $\sigma_{pp.12\ldots\overline{p-1}}\boldsymbol{\Sigma}_{11}^{-1}$ is known. The other way to achieve a t distribution is through the vector

$$(\mathbf{w} - \boldsymbol{\omega})[t_{pp.12\ldots\overline{p-1}}/(n - p)]^{-1/2}$$

which, from the original definition of the t family of distributions, has the $t(\mathbf{0}, \mathbf{S}_{11}^{-1}/(n - 1), n - p)$ distribution conditional on given $\mathbf{S}_{11}$. In principle, any region in a $(p - 1)$-dimensional outcome-space has some probability $1 - \alpha$ under the $t(\mathbf{0}, \mathbf{S}_{11}^{-1}/(n - 1), n - p)$ distribution, and such a region leads to a confidence region for $\boldsymbol{\omega}$ with confidence $1 - \alpha$. In particular,

$(w_i - \omega_i)[t_{pp.12...\overline{p-1}}/(n-p)]^{-1/2}[s^{ii}/(n-1)]^{-1/2}$ has the $t(0, 1, n-p)$ distribution, where s^{ii} is the (i, i) element of $\mathbf{S}_{11}^{-1}$, so that

$$w_i - [s^{ii}t_{pp.12...\overline{p-1}}/(n-1)(n-p)]^{1/2}t(0, 1, n-p)_{[1-2\alpha]}$$
$$\leq \omega_i \leq w_i + [s^{ii}t_{pp.12...\overline{p-1}}/(n-1)(n-p)]^{1/2}t(0, 1, n-p)_{[1-2\alpha]} \quad (14.2.5)$$

is a confidence interval for ω_i with confidence coefficient $1 - \alpha$. More generally, a confidence interval of this kind may be given for any linear combination of $\omega_1, \omega_2, \ldots, \omega_{p-1}$. At the other extreme, a confidence ellipsoid for $\omega_1, \omega_2, \ldots, \omega_{p-1}$ jointly is easily defined using the norm of the t outcome (14.2.4), namely the ellipsoid defined by

$$(\mathbf{w} - \boldsymbol{\omega})\mathbf{S}_{11}(\mathbf{w} - \boldsymbol{\omega})' \leq [t_{pp.12...\overline{p-1}}/(n-1)(n-p)]G(p-1, n-p, 1)_{[1-\alpha]}. \quad (14.2.6)$$

More generally, such an ellipsoid could be defined for any set of linear combinations of $\omega_1, \omega_2, \ldots, \omega_{p-1}$.

Next consider the partition of the first $p - 1$ variables into $s + (p - s - 1)$, so that (14.2.1) takes the form

$$\mathbf{T} = \begin{bmatrix} \mathbf{T}_{11} & \mathbf{T}_{12} & \mathbf{T}_{13} \\ \mathbf{T}_{21} & \mathbf{T}_{22} & \mathbf{T}_{23} \\ \mathbf{T}_{31} & \mathbf{T}_{32} & t_{pp} \end{bmatrix}. \quad (14.2.7)$$

The first s elements of the last row of SWP$[1, 2, \ldots, s]\mathbf{T}$ provide the sample regression coefficients $w_{p1(12...s)}, w_{p2(12...s)}, \ldots, w_{ps(12...s)}$, and the foregoing theory applies directly to these, simply replacing $V_1, V_2, \ldots, V_p$ by $V_1, V_2, \ldots, V_s, V_p$. Given $\mathbf{T}_{11}$, the lower right $(p - s) \times (p - s)$ part of SWP$[1, 2, \ldots, s]\mathbf{T}$ is independent of $w_{p1(12...s)}, \ldots, w_{ps(12...s)}$ and like $\mathbf{T}_{11}$ has a Wishart distribution. Applying the SWP operation to the first $(p - s - 1)$ indices of the latter Wishart matrix determines in the usual way the partial regression coefficients $w_{p\overline{s+1}(\overline{s+1}\,\overline{s+2}...\overline{p-1}).12...s}, \ldots, w_{p\overline{p-1}(\overline{s+1}\,\overline{s+2}...\overline{p-1}).12...s}$ whose sampling distribution given $\mathbf{T}_{11}$ is therefore of the same general form as the above sampling distribution of $\boldsymbol{\omega}$. Of course, these partial regression coefficients are just the last $p - s - 1$ clements of $\mathbf{w}$. The reader may easily check that the last $p - s - 1$ elements of (14.2.4) coincide with the result of applying (14.2.4) to the lower right $(p - s) \times (p - s)$ part of SWP$[1, 2, \ldots, s]\mathbf{T}$, so that confidence statements about $w_{p\overline{s+1}(12...\overline{p-1})}, \ldots, w_{p\overline{p-1}(12...\overline{p-1})}$ given by this paragraph or by the preceding paragraph are the same. The main point of this paragraph is to remark that, given $\mathbf{T}_{11}$, the random values providing these confidence statements are independent of those yielding confidence statements about $w_{p1(12...s)}, w_{p2(12...s)}, w_{ps(12...s)}$.

If the best linear predictor is written in the form $wV_0 + \mathbf{wV}$, then $w = \bar{X}_p - \mathbf{w}\bar{\mathbf{X}}_1'$. Given $\bar{\mathbf{X}}_1$ and $\mathbf{S}_{11}$, the terms $\bar{X}_p$ and $-\mathbf{w}\bar{\mathbf{X}}_1'$ are conditionally independent with

$$N(\mu_p - \boldsymbol{\omega}(\bar{\mathbf{X}}_1 - \boldsymbol{\mu}_1)', \sigma_{pp.12...\overline{p-1}}/n)$$

and

$$N(-\boldsymbol{\omega}\bar{\mathbf{X}}_1', \sigma_{pp.12...\overline{p-1}}\bar{\mathbf{X}}_1\mathbf{T}_{11}^{-1}\bar{\mathbf{X}}_1')$$

distributions, so that w is conditionally distributed with the

$$N(\omega, \sigma_{pp.12...\overline{p-1}}[1/n + \bar{\mathbf{X}}_1\mathbf{T}_{11}^{-1}\bar{\mathbf{X}}_1'])$$

distribution where $\omega = \mu_p - \boldsymbol{\omega}\bar{\mathbf{X}}_1'$. Note that the term in square brackets is the negative of the $(p + 1, p + 1)$ element of (8.2.8), and that w is the $(p, p + 1)$ element of the same matrix. The reader may easily supply the indicated confidence regions for ω.

Suppose now that $\mathbf{X}^*$ together with $\mathbf{X}^{(1)}, \mathbf{X}^{(2)}, \ldots, \mathbf{X}^{(n)}$ defines a sample of size $n + 1$ from the $N(\boldsymbol{\mu}, \boldsymbol{\Sigma})$ population. Suppose that the best linear predictor defined by the sample of size n is applied to $\mathbf{X}^*$, where $\mathbf{X}^*$ is regarded as a subsequent observation. The $1 \times p$ vector $\mathbf{X}^*$ may be partitioned into $[\mathbf{X}_1^*, X_p^*]$ and the predicted value for X_p^* is

$$\hat{X}_p = \bar{X}_p + \mathbf{w}(\mathbf{X}_1^* - \bar{\mathbf{X}}_1)'. \tag{14.2.8}$$

What is the sampling distribution of the prediction error $X_p^* - \hat{X}_p^*$? This is easily found, conditional on fixed $\bar{\mathbf{X}}_1, \mathbf{X}_1^*$, and $\mathbf{S}_{11}$. Indeed, the three components X_p^*, $-\bar{X}_p$, and $\mathbf{w}(\mathbf{X}_1^* - \bar{\mathbf{X}}_1)'$ are conditionally independent with distributions $N(\mu_p + \boldsymbol{\omega}(\bar{\mathbf{X}}_1^* - \boldsymbol{\mu}_1)', \sigma_{pp.12...\overline{p-1}})$, $N(-\mu_p - \boldsymbol{\omega}(\bar{\mathbf{X}}_1 - \boldsymbol{\mu}_1)', \sigma_{pp.12...\overline{p-1}}/n)$ and $N(-\boldsymbol{\omega}(\mathbf{X}_1^* - \bar{\mathbf{X}}_1)', \sigma_{pp.12...p-1}(\mathbf{X}_1^* - \bar{\mathbf{X}}_1)\mathbf{T}_{11}^{-1}(\mathbf{X}_1^* - \bar{\mathbf{X}}_1)')$, so that $X_p^* - \hat{X}_p^*$ is conditionally $N(0, \sigma_{pp.12...\overline{p-1}}[(n + 1)/n + (\mathbf{X}^* - \bar{\mathbf{X}}_1)\mathbf{T}_{11}^{-1}(\mathbf{X}_1^* - \bar{\mathbf{X}}_1)'])$ distributed, given $\mathbf{T}_{11}, \mathbf{X}_1^*$, and $\bar{\mathbf{X}}_1$. Note that the term

$$[n/(n + 1)](\mathbf{X}_1^* - \bar{\mathbf{X}}_1)\mathbf{T}_{11}^{-1}(\mathbf{X}_1^* - \bar{\mathbf{X}}_1)'$$

has marginally the $G(p - 1, n - p + 1, 1)$ distribution. Confidence statements about X_p^* having observed $\mathbf{X}_1^*$, $\bar{\mathbf{X}}$, and $\mathbf{S}$ may be based on the obvious fact that $(X_p^* - \hat{X}_p^*)/t_{pp.12...\overline{p-1}}$ has a one-dimensional t distribution with a known scale factor, conditional on given $\mathbf{X}_1^*$, $\bar{\mathbf{X}}_1$, and $\mathbf{S}_{11}$.

Example 8.1. The matrix SWP[1, 2, 4]$\mathbf{Q}_{(+)}$ contains much of the information concerning the ordinary multiple regression analysis of V_3 on V_1 and V_2. Specifically

$$[w_1, w_2] = [0.7280, 1.8109],$$
$$w = 0.3208,$$
$$t_{33.12} = 0.001803,$$
$$\tfrac{1}{12} + \bar{\mathbf{X}}_1\mathbf{T}_{11}^{-1}\mathbf{T}_1' = 958.092.$$

Confidence limits for ω may be based on

$$T = (w - \omega)/[(t_{33.12}/9)(\tfrac{1}{12} + \bar{\mathbf{X}}_1\mathbf{T}_{11}^{-1}\bar{\mathbf{X}}_1')]^{1/2},$$

which has the $t(0, 1, 9)$ distribution. Since $\Pr(|T| \leq 2.262) = 0.95$, one finds the 0.95 level confidence interval

$$-0.6706 \leq \omega \leq 1.312.$$

These limits do not contradict the hypothesis $\omega = 0$, but they are so wide as to be of little value. The conditional distribution of $[w_1, w_2]$ given $\bar{\mathbf{X}}_1$ and $\mathbf{T}_{11}$ is

$$N\left([\omega_1, \omega_2], \sigma_{33.12}\begin{bmatrix} 354.984 & 187.059 \\ 187.059 & 1489.280 \end{bmatrix}\right).$$

Confidence limits for ω_1 at level 0.95 are $0.7280 \pm 2.262[(0.001803/9)(354.984)]^{1/2}$ or

$$0.124 \leq \omega_1 \leq 1.332,$$

and similarly for ω_2 the confidence limits are

$$0.575 \leq \omega_2 \leq 3.047.$$

Again, these limits do not contradict $\omega_1 = 1$ and $\omega_2 = 2$, but they are seen to be very wide. The expression (14.2.6) leads to the confidence ellipse at level 0.95 expressible as

$$\begin{bmatrix} \omega_1 - 0.7280 \\ \omega_2 - 1.8109 \end{bmatrix}' \begin{bmatrix} 354.984 & 187.059 \\ 187.059 & 1489.280 \end{bmatrix}^{-1} \begin{bmatrix} \omega_1 - 0.7280 \\ \omega_2 - 1.8109 \end{bmatrix}$$

$$\leq \frac{0.001803}{9} G(2, 9, 1)_{[0.95]} = \frac{0.001803}{9} \cdot \frac{9}{2} \cdot G(2, 9, \tfrac{9}{2})_{[0.95]}$$

$$= \frac{0.001803}{2} \times 4.2569 = 0.003837.$$

The ellipse is shown in Fig. 14.2.1.

If it may be assumed *a priori* that $\omega = 0$, then the reduced linear predictor analysis becomes appropriate. The relevant output matrix becomes $\mathrm{SWP}[1, 2]\mathbf{Q}_{(+)}$. The reader may easily check that the appropriate sampling distribution for $[w_1^*, w_2^*]$ is

$$N\left([\omega_1, \omega_2], \sigma_{33.12}\begin{bmatrix} 198.575 & -244.158 \\ -244.158 & 300.419 \end{bmatrix}\right),$$

while $q_{33.12}$ independently has the $\chi^2(10, \sigma_{33.11})$ distribution, all conditional on given $\mathbf{Q}_{11}$. Now $[w_1^*, w_2^*] = [0.8577, 2.1682]$ and $q_{33.12} = 0.001910$. Confidence limits for ω_1 are $0.8577 \pm 2.228(0.001910/10 \times 198.575)^{1/2}$ or

$$0.424 \leq \omega_1 \leq 1.292$$

and analogous 0.95 level confidence limits for ω_2 are

$$1.635 \leq \omega_2 \leq 2.702.$$

A confidence ellipse at level 0.95 is given by

$$\begin{bmatrix} \omega_1 - 0.8577 \\ \omega_2 - 2.1682 \end{bmatrix}' \begin{bmatrix} 198.575 & -244.158 \\ -244.158 & 300.419 \end{bmatrix}^{-1} \begin{bmatrix} \omega_1 - 0.8577 \\ \omega_2 - 2.1682 \end{bmatrix} \le \frac{0.001910}{10} G(2, 10, 1)_{[0.95]} = 0.003918.$$

This ellipse is also shown in Fig. 14.2.1.

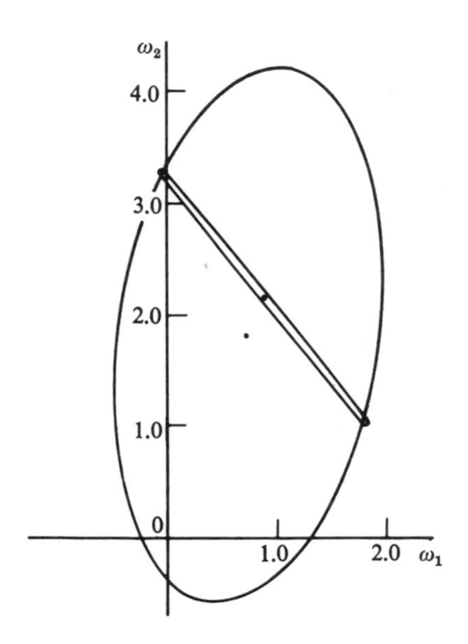

Fig. 14.2.1. Confidence ellipses for regression coefficients from ordinary multiple regression analysis (large ellipse) and from reduced multiple regression analysis (thin ellipse).

The assumption $\omega = 0$ brings a substantial reduction in the spread of the sampling distribution of error in estimating ω_1, ω_2, especially in one direction. It is fairly clear, however, that the data offer little support for the assumption. A formal test of the hypothesis $\omega = 0$ may be based on the same T quantity used for confidence intervals about ω; specifically, one computes

$$T = \frac{0.3208 - 0.0000}{(0.001803/9 \times 958.095)^{1/2}} = 0.732$$

and asks if the value of T lies too far out in the tail of the $t(0, 1, 9)$ distribution, which it clearly does not. Equivalently, one may look at $T^2 = 0.536$ and place it on the $G(1, 9, 9)$ distribution. This G statistic may be computed a different way as

$$\begin{aligned} T^2 &= \frac{(q_{33.12} - t_{33.12})}{t_{33.12}} \times 9 \\ &= \frac{0.001910 - 0.001803}{0.001803} \times 9 \\ &= 0.534, \end{aligned}$$

differing from 0.536 due to rounding error. Assuming the null hypothesis $\omega = 0$, it is easily checked that $q_{33.12} - t_{33.12}$ and $t_{33.12}$ are independent with $\chi^2(1, \sigma_{33.12})$ and $\chi^2(9, \sigma_{33.12})$ distributions conditional on $\bar{\mathbf{X}}_1$ and $\mathbf{T}_{11}$, so that the null distribution of T^2 is directly verified from the second representation. The reader may wish to devise equivalent forms for tests of the null hypothesis that $\boldsymbol{\omega}$ is a specific vector.

In general it is very difficult to make a meaningful assessment of population covariation on the basis of so small a sample. The wide limits on ω_1 and ω_2 are symptoms of this. Another example is given by the confidence intervals on $\sigma_{33.12}$. Depending on the strength of *a priori* assumptions about ω, ω_1, ω_2 one may treat 0.001803 as arising from $\chi^2(9, \sigma_{33.12})$, 0.001910 as arising from $\chi^2(10, \sigma_{33.12})$, and 0.002226 as arising from $\chi^2(11, \sigma_{33.12})$. Using the 0.025 and 0.975 quantiles of these distributions, the corresponding 0.95 level confidence intervals are

$$\begin{aligned} 0.000095 &< \sigma_{33.12} < 0.000668 \\ 0.000093 &< \sigma_{33.12} < 0.000588 \\ 0.000102 &< \sigma_{33.12} < 0.000583. \end{aligned}$$

Example 8.2. According to Cochran, the matrix $\mathbf{T}$ was computed on 72 degrees of freedom, and assuming normality it may be regarded as a realization of a random matrix with a $W(72, \boldsymbol{\Sigma})$ distribution for an unknown 6×6 matrix $\boldsymbol{\Sigma}$. The stepwise inclusion of $V_1, V_2, \ldots, V_5$ in this order makes it possible to assign confidence intervals in order to $\omega_{61}, \omega_{62(12)}, \omega_{63(123)}, \omega_{65(12345)}$, but these are rarely an interesting sequence of quantities. One may however wish to test the sequence of null hypotheses that these regression coefficients are zero. There are three equivalent ways to write each such null hypothesis: for example,

$$\omega_{63(123)} = 0 \qquad \text{or} \qquad \sigma_{66.12} = \sigma_{66.123} \qquad \text{or} \qquad \rho_{63.12} = 0.$$

Correspondingly, there are three equivalent ways to write a test statistic having the $F(1, 69)$ distribution under the null hypothesis, namely

$$\frac{w^2_{63(123)}}{t_{66.123}/69 \cdot 1/t_{33.12}} = \frac{t_{66.12} - t_{66.123}}{t_{66.123}/69} = \frac{r^2_{63.12}}{1 - r^2_{63.12}}.$$

The middle form is the easiest to compute. The following table gives the F statistics for the five tests together with their corresponding observed quantiles.

Null hypothesis	F statistic	Observed quantile
$\omega_{61} = 0$	6.71	0.98
$\omega_{62(12)} = 0$	0.97	0.66
$\omega_{63(123)} = 0$	11.59	0.99
$\omega_{64(1234)} = 0$	0.41	0.35
$\omega_{65(12345)} = 0$	6.64	0.98

There is no evidence that V_2 and V_4 contribute anything here. The evidence for V_1 and V_5 is weak, and for V_3 is quite strong.

The independence of the statistics just considered under their respective null hypotheses offers some assurance that a single random fluctuation is not coloring several conclusions. The absence of such assurance makes it difficult to judge the complete array in Table 8.3.1 by means of tests and confidence statements. Nor should one be too impressed by the above table of F statistics, for the data are nearly indifferent between V_2, V_3, V_5 or V_1, V_3, V_5 as sets of predictors.

Example 8.3. It may be asked here: why is the sum of squared residuals inflated by a factor of nearly 12 when the residuals are computed from the prediction equation based on the remaining 11 individuals? Normal sampling theory assigns $t_{77.12...6}$ the $\chi^2(6, \sigma_{77.12...6})$ distribution while a sum of squares of 12 residuals from the true prediction equation would have a $\chi^2(12, \sigma_{77.12...6})$ distribution. A factor of 2 comes from this source. Also, when a prediction equation is applied to an independent individual, the prediction error is inflated on the average by the errors in the regression coefficients in the prediction equation. In fact, the error variance includes the factor $1 + G$, where G would have a $G(6, 5, 1)$ distribution in the present context. The expected value of this G is $6/(5 - 3) = 2$, so the factor $1 + G$ may be regarded as roughly 3. Thus, a factor of $2 \times 3 = 6$ might have been expected for the ratio of sums of squares in question. The source of the remaining factor of 2 remains unclear. Perhaps it comes from a sampling fluctuation in $\mathbf{Z}$ values, or perhaps it is an indication of the inadequacy of normality assumptions to represent the situation.

Attention is now turned toward characterizing the sampling distribution of a sample correlation coefficient. Suppose that r_{ij} and ρ_{ij} denote, respectively, the sample and population correlation coefficients between V_i and V_j based on a sample of size n from a p-variate normal population. Only the marginal distribution of a single r_{ij} is treated here, and this in turn involves only the bivariate sample on V_i and V_j alone. Expressions for the density function of the sampling distribution of r_{ij} given ρ_{ij} were first given by Fisher (1915). Extensive tables of the distribution of r_{ij} given ρ_{ij} were given by David (1938) and partly reproduced by Pearson and Hartley (1958). These sources also give charts from which confidence intervals for r_{ij} given ρ_{ij} may be read.

Here, the equivalent but more convenient forms

$$d_{ij} = r_{ij}(1 - r_{ij}^2)^{-1/2} = s_{ij}(s_{ii}s_{jj} - s_{ij}^2)^{-1/2},$$

and

$$\delta_{ij} = \rho_{ij}(1 - \rho_{ij}^2)^{-1/2} = \sigma_{ij}(\sigma_{ii}\sigma_{jj} - \sigma_{ij}^2)^{-1/2} \tag{14.2.9}$$

will be used. From (14.1.15) it follows that

$$d_{ij} = (\delta_{ij}Q_j^{1/2} + U_{ij})Q_{i.j}^{-1/2}, \tag{14.2.10}$$

where Q_j, U_{ij}, and $Q_{i.j}$ are defined by (14.1.13), (14.1.14), and

$$Q_{i.j} = (n - 1)(s_{ii} - s_{ij}^2/s_{jj})^{1/2}/(\sigma_{ii} - \sigma_{ij}^2/\sigma_{jj})^{1/2}. \tag{14.2.11}$$

Since Q_j, U_{ij}, and $Q_{i.j}$ are independently distributed with $\chi^2(n - 1, 1)$, $N(0, 1)$, and $\chi^2(n - 2, 1)$ sampling distributions, the expression (14.2.10) gives a convenient characterization of the distribution of d_{ij} in terms of quantities with a simple distribution, and incidentally confirms that the distribution of d_{ij} depends only on δ_{ij}. When $\delta_{ij} = 0$, the sampling distribution of $\sqrt{n - 2}\, d_{ij}$ is clearly $t(0, 1, n - 2)$, but when $\delta_{ij} \neq 0$ the computation of a tail area from (14.2.10) requires a numerical triple integration. One of these integrations may be removed by expressing

$$d_{ij} = G_{ij}^{1/2}[(\delta_{ij} + Z_{ij}/\sqrt{n - 1})/(1 + Z_{ij}^2/(n - 1))^{1/2}], \tag{14.2.12}$$

where

$$Z_{ij} = \sqrt{n - 1}\, U_{ij}Q_j^{-1/2},$$
$$G_{ij} = Q_{ij}/Q_{i.j}, \quad \text{and} \quad Q_{ij} = Q_j + U_{ij}^2. \tag{14.2.13}$$

Note that Q_{ij} and Z_{ij} are independent with $\chi^2(n, 1)$ and $t(0, 1, n - 1)$ distributions (cf. Lemma 12.5.4) and are independent of $Q_{i.j}$. Thus G_{ij} and Z_{ij} are independent with $G(n, n - 2, 1)$ and $t(0, 1, n - 2)$ distributions, so that (14.2.12) expresses d_{ij} as a product of two independent factors of which only one depends on δ_{ij}.

As $n \to \infty$ with δ_{ij} fixed, it is easily verified, for example from (14.2.10), that

$$\sqrt{n}\,(d_{ij} - \delta_{ij})/(1 + \delta_{ij}^2)^{1/2} \tag{14.2.14}$$

has in the limit an $N(0, 1)$ distribution. Fisher (1958) uses the equivalent result that

$$\sqrt{n - 3}\left[\log\frac{1 + r_{ij}}{1 - r_{ij}} - \log\frac{1 + \rho_{ij}}{1 - \rho_{ij}}\right] \tag{14.2.15}$$

has a limiting $N(0, 1)$ distribution. For sufficiently large n, one may therefore assign an $N(0, 1)$ distribution to either (14.2.14) or (14.2.15), and invert the expressions to determine confidence limits for the unknown parameter values. It is also of interest to consider the slightly different asymptotic theory under which $\sqrt{n}\,\delta_{ij} \to \gamma_{ij}$ as $n \to \infty$. Again, from (14.2.10) it is easily checked that

$$n(d_{ij} - \delta_{ij}) \tag{14.2.16}$$

has a limiting $N(0, 1)$ distribution. Note that, if $d_{ij}^2 \ll 1$, then the confidence limits derived from the approximations suggested by (14.2.14) or (14.2.16) are virtually the same.

Kendall and Stuart (1961) discuss the distribution of the simple correlation coefficient, including approaches omitted here.

The absolute value $|r_{ij}|$ is the simplest example of a multiple correlation coefficient whose general form is $r_{p(12\ldots\overline{p-1})}$ as introduced in Chapter 8. For simplicity, denote $r_{p(12\ldots\overline{p-1})}$ by r and the population analogue $\rho_{p(12\ldots\overline{p-1})}$ by ρ, and denote $r(1 - r^2)^{-1/2}$ by d and $\rho(1 - \rho^2)^{-1/2}$ by δ. In this paragraph, unlike the preceding paragraphs, the quantities r, ρ, d, and δ are nonnegative. From (14.2.2) it follows that

$$d^2 = \mathbf{w}\mathbf{T}_{11}\mathbf{w}'/t_{pp.12\ldots\overline{p-1}} \tag{14.2.17}$$

and has the $G(p - 1, n - p, 1, \boldsymbol{\omega}\mathbf{T}_{11}\boldsymbol{\omega}'/\rho_{pp.12\ldots\overline{p-1}})$ distribution given $\mathbf{T}_{11}$, while the marginal distribution of the noncentrality parameter is $\chi^2(n - 1, \delta^2)$. When δ is zero, the distribution of d^2 is simply $G(p - 1, n - p, 1)$. The general case was first penetrated by Fisher (1928) who gave several expressions for the density function of the sampling distribution of r given ρ. (See also Exercise 14.2.4.) Remarkably little work has been carried out on this distribution, and no tables appear to be available.

From (14.2.17) the mean of the sampling distribution of d^2 is

$$E(d^2) = \frac{(p - 1) + (n - 1)\delta^2}{n - p - 2}, \tag{14.2.18}$$

so that

$$\hat{\delta}^2 = \frac{(n - p - 2)d^2 - (p - 1)}{(n - 1)} \tag{14.2.19}$$

has zero bias, in the sampling theory sense, when regarded as estimate of δ^2.

As $n \to \infty$ with fixed δ, it may be checked that $\sqrt{n}\,(d^2 - \delta^2)/2\delta$ has a limiting $N(0, 1)$ distribution, while, if $n\delta^2 \to \tau^2$, the limiting distribution of $(n - p)\,d^2$ is $\chi^2(p - 1, 1, \tau^2)$.

Example 8.4. The null distribution appropriate for judging any one of the simple correlation coefficients r_{ij} exhibited on p. 173 for $i = 1, 2$ and $j = 5, 10, 15, 19$ may be described as follows. Under the hypothesis of sampling from a normal population with $\rho_{ij} = 0$ and sample size $n = 264$, the distribution of r_{ij} is symmetric about zero and r_{ij}^2 has the $\beta(\frac{1}{2}, \frac{262}{2})$ distribution, or $r_{ij}^2/(1 - r_{ij}^2)$ has the $G(1, 262, 1)$ distribution. It follows that the $(1 - \alpha)$ quantile $r_{[1-\alpha]}$ of the relevant distribution is related by

$$r_{[1-\alpha]}^2/(1 - r_{[1-\alpha]}^2) = G_{[1-2\alpha]}$$

for $\alpha \geq \frac{1}{2}$ to the $(1 - 2\alpha)$ quantile of the $G(1, 262, 1)$ distribution. For n large, the $G(1, n, 1)$ distribution is close to the $\chi^2(1, 1/n)$ distribution. Starting therefore from the 0.90 and 0.98 quantiles 2.7055 and 5.4118 of the $\chi^2(1, 1)$ distribution, one can solve back to find roughly that $r_{[0.95]} = 0.10$ and $r_{[0.99]} = 0.14$. The 8 observed correlation coefficients all lie in 0.01 tails in either a positive or negative direction.

The observed correlation coefficient $r_{12} = 0.594$ may be used to put confidence limits on ρ_{12}. Interpolating visually from the charts of David (1938) or Pearson and Hartley (1958) for $n = 200$ and $n = 400$, one finds the 0.95 level confidence interval

$$0.52 < \rho_{12} < 0.66.$$

Using Fisher's transformation, the corresponding approximation is given by

$$\left| \log \frac{1.594}{0.406} - \log \frac{1 + \rho_{12}}{1 - \rho_{12}} \right| \leq 1.9600\sqrt{\frac{1}{261}}$$

which leads to

$$0.553 < \rho_{12} < 0.631.$$

Using the normal approximation for d, one finds

$$|0.594/(1 - 0.594^2)^{1/2} - \rho_{12}/(1 - \rho_{12}^2)^{1/2}| \leq 1.9600\{[1 + \rho_{12}^2/(1 - \rho_{12}^2)]/263\}^{1/2}$$

which leads to

$$0.513 < \rho < 0.669.$$

The latter approximation agrees more closely with the charts.

Finally, consider the observed squared multiple correlation coefficient $r_{34(12)}^2 = 0.0477$. The corresponding $F(2, 261)$ statistic has the value

$$\tfrac{261}{2}(0.0477)(1 - 0.0477)^{-1} = 6.54$$

which is well beyond the 0.995 quantile of its sampling distribution under the hypothesis $\rho_{34(12)}^2 = 0$. To assess the deviation of $\rho_{34(12)}^2$ from zero, one may use the approximation that $261(0.0477)(1 - 0.0477)^{-1}$ was drawn from a $\chi^2(2, 263, \rho_{34(12)}^2/(1 - \rho_{34(12)}^2))$ distribution. Interpolating in the tables of Owen (1962) pp. 172–180, one finds

$$0.018 < \rho_{34(12)}^2 < 0.102,$$

rejecting at level 0.025 in each tail. The unbiased estimate from (14.2.18) is $\hat{\delta}^2_{34(12)} = 0.0417$ which corresponds to

$$\hat{\rho}^2_{34(12)} = 0.0400.$$

Consider next the situation described in Section 9.2, leading to canonical correlation analysis and related analyses as illustrated in Example 9.1. Denote the sample mean-corrected inner product matrix by $\mathbf{T}$ as in (9.2.7). $\mathbf{T}$ has the $W(n-1, \mathbf{\Sigma})$ sampling distribution under sampling from an $N(\boldsymbol{\mu}, \mathbf{\Sigma})$ population, and Theorem 13.4.2 specifies the distribution of the various parts of

$$\text{SWP}[1, 2, \ldots, s]\mathbf{T} = \begin{bmatrix} -\mathbf{T}_{11}^{-1} & \mathbf{H}_{12} \\ \mathbf{H}_{21} & \mathbf{T}_{22.1} \end{bmatrix}. \tag{14.2.20}$$

The sample canonical coefficients relating $V_1, V_2, \ldots, V_s$ with $V_{s+1}, V_{s+2}, \ldots, V_p$ are denoted by $r_1, r_2, \ldots, r_t$ where $t = \min(s, p-s)$.

As with the special case $s = p - 1$ discussed above, it may be convenient sometimes to use $d_1, d_2, \ldots, d_t$ where $d_i = r_i(1 - r_i^2)^{-1/2}$. From the theory of Section 9.2 it follows that $d_1, d_2, \ldots, d_t$ are the eigenvalues of $\mathbf{H}_{21}\mathbf{T}_{11}\mathbf{H}_{12}$ relative to $\mathbf{T}_{22.1}$. These two inner product matrices define a decomposition of $\mathbf{T}_{22}$ into two pieces, which are independent with $W(s, \mathbf{\Sigma}_{22.1}, \mathbf{\Xi}_{21}\mathbf{T}_{11}\mathbf{\Xi}_{12})$ and $W(n-s, \mathbf{\Sigma}_{22.1})$ distributions, given $\mathbf{T}_{11}$ (cf. Exercise 13.4.13). The distribution of $1 - r_t^2, 1 - r_{t-1}^2, \ldots, 1 - r_1^2$ given $\mathbf{T}_{11}$ is the $H(n-1, p, s, \boldsymbol{\xi})$ distribution where $\boldsymbol{\xi}$ is the vector of eigenvalues of $\mathbf{\Xi}_{21}\mathbf{T}_{11}\mathbf{\Xi}_{12}$ relative to $\mathbf{\Sigma}_{22.1}$ (cf. Exercise 13.7.13). Averaging this distribution over the $W(n-1, \mathbf{\Sigma}_{11})$ distribution of $\mathbf{T}_{11}$ gives the marginal distribution of $1 - r_t^2, 1 - r_{t-1}^2, \ldots, 1 - r_1^2$ which is seen therefore to depend only on $n-1, p, s$ and the eigenvalues of $\mathbf{\Xi}_{21}\mathbf{\Sigma}_{11}\mathbf{\Xi}_{12}$ relative to $\mathbf{\Sigma}_{22.1}$. These eigenvalues are the population values $\delta_1, \delta_2, \ldots, \delta_t$ of $d_1, d_2, \ldots, d_t$, and so are equivalent to the population canonical correlation coefficients $\rho_1, \rho_2, \ldots, \rho_t$. Reasoning of this kind can be used to derive expressions for the probability density function of the sample canonical correlation coefficients given $n-1, p, s$ and $\rho_1, \rho_2, \ldots, \rho_t$, in terms of series expansions in zonal polynomials (Constantine, 1964; James, 1964).

The exact distribution of $1 - r_t^2, 1 - r_{t-1}^2, \ldots, 1 - r_1^2$ is the relatively simple $H(n-1, p, s)$ distribution when $\mathbf{\Sigma}_{12} = \mathbf{0}$, i.e., when the population canonical correlation coefficients are all zero. The associated

$$\Lambda = \prod_{i=1}^{t} (1 - r_i^2) \tag{14.2.21}$$

has the $\Lambda(n-1, p, s)$ distribution which was discussed at length in Section 13.7. Note that (14.2.21) is a direct example of (13.7.1) and the distribution of Λ may be viewed as a consequence of the fact that canonical correlation coefficients are cosines of canonical angles between a pair of independent spherically distributed random subspaces in an $(n-1)$-dimensional Euclidean space. The condition $\mathbf{\Sigma}_{12} = \mathbf{0}$ may be adopted as a null hypothesis and the statistic Λ may be used to test the null hypothesis, the idea being that a value of Λ improbably far below unity indicates the presence of correlation between the two sets of variables. Other tests are possible; this one derives weak justification from being a likelihood ratio test (cf. Exercise 15.2) and has a tractable null distribution theory. Still, it is rarely possible to consider plausible *a priori* the null hypothesis $\mathbf{\Sigma}_{12} = \mathbf{0}$ and a deeper look at a set of data can be achieved by some factorization of Λ of the kind indicated in Theorem 13.5.2.

Consideration of the joint distribution of $\mathbf{H}_{21}\mathbf{T}_{11}\mathbf{H}_{12}$ and $\mathbf{T}_{22.1}$ as described above shows that the limiting distribution of $-n \log \Lambda$ as $n \to \infty$ while $n(\delta_1^2 + \delta_2^2 + \cdots + \delta_t^2)$ or $n(\rho_1^2 + \rho_2^2 + \cdots + \rho_t^2) \to \tau^2$ is $\chi^2(qs, 1, \tau^2)$. Beyond the scope of this discussion, the limiting form of the probability density function of $r_1, r_2, \ldots, r_t$ from large samples was derived by Hsu (1941) for the very general situation where the population values $\rho_1, \rho_2, \ldots, \rho_t$ are equal in sets. A more practical form of asymptotic theory was developed by Lawley (1959) and Chambers (1966, 1967) who gave moment expansions which make possible normal approximations past the zeroth order. Thus

$$E(r_i) = \rho_i + \frac{1}{n}\frac{1-\rho_i^2}{2\rho_i}\left[(p-2-\rho_i^2) + 2(1-p_i^2)\sum_{j\neq i}\frac{\rho_j^2}{\rho_i^2-\rho_j^2}\right] + \frac{1}{n^2}[\cdots] + \cdots \tag{14.2.22}$$

while

$$\operatorname{var}(r_i) = \frac{1}{n}[(1-\rho_i^2)^2] + \frac{1}{n^2}[\cdots] + \cdots \tag{14.2.23}$$

and

$$\operatorname{cov}(r_i, r_j) = \frac{1}{n}\left[\frac{2\rho_i\rho_j(1-\rho_i^2)(1-\rho_j^2)}{\rho_i^2-\rho_j^2}\right] + \frac{1}{n^2}[\cdots] + \cdots. \tag{14.2.24}$$

No attempt will be made here to derive these results concerning the first and second moments of the sampling distribution. The formulas assume that $\rho_i^2 \neq \rho_j^2$ for $i \neq j$. Little is known about how accurate an associated normal approximation to the sampling distribution might be for given values of p, s, n, and the ρ_i. Moreover, like most sampling distributions in complex situations they are difficult to use in practice because they depend on many unknown parameters. The light cast by these sampling distributions on sample-population relations while filtered in several ways is nevertheless the best currently available.

Example 9.1. The Wilks Λ statistic (14.2.21) computed from Table 9.1.1 is 0.0193. Using the Bartlett approximation, $-[220 - (16 + 31 + 1)/2] \log 0.0193 = 724$ may be viewed as having arisen from a $\chi^2(476, 1, 220(\delta_1^2 + \cdots + \delta_{16}^2))$

distribution, where this may be a very rough approximation since its accuracy in the relevant regions has not been investigated. A highly significant Λ is indicated under the null hypothesis $\mathbf{\Sigma}_{12} = \mathbf{0}$, and equating 724 with the mean of the approximate sampling distribution suggests the estimate 1.13 for $\delta_1^2 + \cdots + \delta_{16}^2$. This compares with $d_1^2 + d_2^2 + \cdots + d_{16}^2 = 4.96$ which surely has a large upward bias. Even 1.13 appears large, however, relative to the picture given by Table 9.1.3.

Two further examples of Wilks Λ statistics were computed from Table 9.1.5, namely 0.3901 corresponding to the five principal variables vs. five principal variables analysis and 0.5551 corresponding to the two principal variables vs. two principal variables analysis. Assuming a random sample from a normal population and assuming $\mathbf{\Sigma}_{12} = \mathbf{0}$, these have $\Lambda(220, 5, 5)$ and $\Lambda(220, 2, 2)$ null distributions because of their relations to a pair of independent spherically random subspaces. This is not quite a trivial remark, because the principal variables are themselves functions of the sample data. But the principal variables are functions of the corrected sample sum inner product which is distributed independently of the spherically distributed random subspace governing Λ (cf. Theorem 13.3.1). When $\mathbf{\Sigma}_{12} \neq \mathbf{0}$, Theorem 13.3.1 no longer applies and the distribution theory for the Λ's of this paragraph is less clear. Still it is natural to compute their corresponding Bartlett χ^2 approximations:

Table 14.2.1

	n, q, s	$-[n - (q + s + 1)/2] \log \Lambda$	χ^2 degrees of freedom
0.5551	220, 2, 2	128.	4
0.3901	220, 5, 5	202.	25
0.0193	220, 16, 31	724.	496

Compared to null χ^2 distributions, each value is highly significant. The differences $202.0 - 128.0 = 74.0$ and $724.0 - 202.0 = 522.0$ are likewise highly significant relative to $\chi^2(21, 1)$ and $\chi^2(471, 1)$. The excesses over degrees of freedom of the values 128.0, 74.0, and 522.0 are $128.0 - 4.0 = 124.0$, $74.0 - 21.0 = 53.0$, and $522.0 - 471.0 = 51.0$ which are indications of the noncentrality in the associated χ^2 quantities. These indications show a rapid decline in noncentrality per degree of freedom, an observation which bears out the hypothesis that the earlier principal variables tend to carry greater predictive power.

As remarked above, there is often considerably more to be learned from a factorization of Λ than from Λ alone. The double factorization defined in Theorem 13.7.4 will now be illustrated in the case of $\Lambda = 0.3901$ relating the two sets of five principal variables. Since the two sets of principal variables are uncorrelated within themselves, their 10×10 correlation matrix $\mathbf{R}$ is completely defined by the 5×5 matrix of correlation coefficients given in Table 9.1.4. The factorization was computed as follows from $\mathbf{R}$:

i) Define

$$\mathbf{R}_1 = \mathbf{R}, \quad \mathbf{R}_2 = \mathrm{SWP}[1]\mathbf{R}_1, \quad \mathbf{R}_3 = \mathrm{SWP}[2]\mathbf{R}_2, \ldots, \mathbf{R}_5 = \mathrm{SWP}[4]\mathbf{R}_4.$$

For $i = 1, 2, \ldots, 5$ compute

$$[a_{i1}, a_{i2}, \ldots, a_{i6}],$$

where a_{ij} is the (i, i) element of $\mathrm{SWP}[6, \ldots, 5 + j]\mathbf{R}_i$.

ii) For $i = 1, 2, \ldots, 5$ compute

$$[b_{i1}, b_{i2}, \ldots, b_{i5}],$$

where $b_{ij} = a_{i\overline{j+1}}/a_{ij}$. These b_{ij} are the factors $\sin^2 \theta_{ij}$ in (13.7.6). The reasoning here is that a_{ij} is the squared length of z_{ij} as defined in Theorem 13.5.1 and that passage from z_{ij} to $z_{i\overline{j+1}}$ removes from z_{ij} the component along v_{ij}, leaving the component $z_{i\overline{j+1}}$ whose squared length is the fraction $\sin^2 \theta_{ij}$ of the original squared length of z_{ij}.

iii) Compute $c_{ij} = -(220 - i - j + 1) \log b_{ij}$ and $\sqrt{c_{ij}}$ for $i = 1, 2, \ldots, 5$ and $j = 1, 2, \ldots, 5$. Note that c_{ij} has an approximate $\chi^2(1, 1)$ distribution under the null distribution corresponding to independence of the two sets of variables. The associated distribution of $\sqrt{c_{ij}}$ is often called "half-normal" since it is the positive half of an $N(0, 1)$ distribution scaled up to have total probability unity. The final output is shown below:

Table 14.2.2

$\sqrt{c_{ij}}$		Smith principal variables				
		1	2	3	4	5
Cattell principal variables	1	3.40	2.68	0.63	0.26	2.13
	2	4.60	9.46	1.68	1.18	1.56
	3	2.24	0.37	2.57	1.99	0.19
	4	0.67	0.96	0.61	2.70	0.18
	5	0.08	0.52	1.15	5.56	1.95

The numbers in Table 14.2.2 were ordered and the 25 ordered values were divided by the 0.02, 0.06, 0.10, ..., 0.94, 0.98 quantiles of the half normal distribution. Plotting as in Fig. 14.2.2 shows that an excess over the null value of unity appears through the whole range of values. The leftmost points are

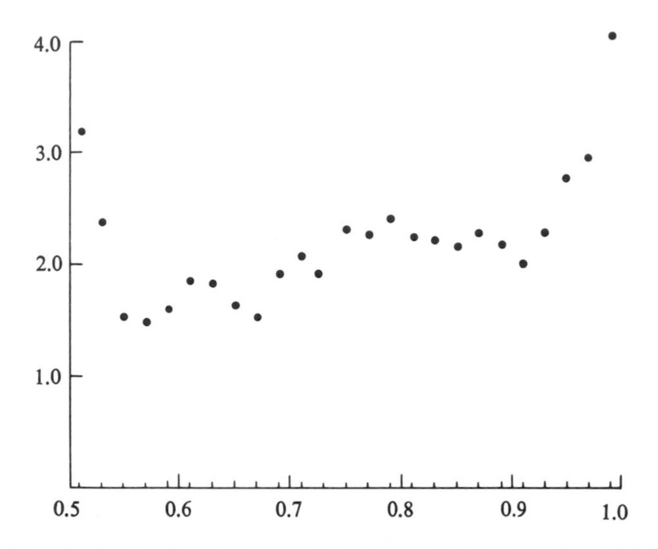

Fig. 14.2.2. The half normal plot associated with Table 14.2.2.

relatively unstable since they come from ratios with small denominators. The increase in the last three of the rightmost points is more likely to represent a meaningful increase over the average of the remaining points. The sum of squares of the 25 elements of Table 14.2.2 is 201.0 which is comparable to the 202.0 in Table 14.2.1. The two numbers represent two ways to define for a finite sample a quantity which is uniquely defined only in the limit as $n \to \infty$.

14.3 SAMPLING DISTRIBUTIONS AND POSTDICTIVE INFERENCE PROCEDURES IN THE ANALYSIS OF TWO OR MORE SAMPLES

Suppose that $\mathbf{X}^{(l)}$ denotes a random sample of size n_l from the normal population $N(\boldsymbol{\mu}^{(l)}, \boldsymbol{\Sigma}^{(l)})$ for $l = 1, 2, \ldots, k$. Then the various matrices (10.1.1) through (10.1.4) have sampling distributions as given directly by k applications of single sample theory. Assuming that $\boldsymbol{\Sigma}^{(1)} = \boldsymbol{\Sigma}^{(2)} = \cdots = \boldsymbol{\Sigma}^{(k)} = \boldsymbol{\Sigma}$, the sampling distribution of $\mathbf{T}_W$ in (10.1.11) follows from the reproductive property of the family of Wishart distributions (Theorem 13.6.1), i.e., $\mathbf{T}_W$ has the $W(n - k, \boldsymbol{\Sigma})$ distribution. More generally, by regarding the pooled samples as p vectors in $\mathcal{N}$ in the usual way, it is easily seen that $\mathbf{T}_A$ and $\mathbf{T}_W$ are independent, $\mathbf{T}_W$ has the central Wishart distribution just given, and $\mathbf{T}_A$ has the noncentral Wishart distribution $W(k - 1, \boldsymbol{\Sigma}, \boldsymbol{\tau})$ as defined in Exercise 13.4.11, where

$$\boldsymbol{\tau} = \sum_{l=1}^{k} n_l(\boldsymbol{\mu}^{(l)} - \boldsymbol{\mu})'(\boldsymbol{\mu}^{(l)} - \boldsymbol{\mu}) \tag{14.3.1}$$

and

$$\boldsymbol{\mu} = \sum_{l=1}^{k} n_l \boldsymbol{\mu}^{(l)} \Big/ \sum_{l=1}^{k} n^{(l)}. \tag{14.3.2}$$

It should be kept in mind that the relative simplicity of the distribution of $\mathbf{T}_W$ requires both the assumption of equal population covariances and the special weighting (10.1.14) of sample covariance matrices. On the other hand, any weighting $c_1\bar{\mathbf{X}}^{(1)} + c_2\bar{\mathbf{X}}^{(2)} + \cdots + c_k\bar{\mathbf{X}}^{(k)}$ of the sample mean has the $N(c_1\boldsymbol{\mu}^{(1)} + c_2\boldsymbol{\mu}^{(2)} + \cdots + c_k\boldsymbol{\mu}^{(k)},\ c_1^2\boldsymbol{\Sigma}^{(1)}/n_1 + c_2^2\boldsymbol{\Sigma}^{(2)}/n_2 + \cdots + c_k^2\boldsymbol{\Sigma}^{(k)}/n_k)$ distribution, from Theorem 12.4.1, for any choices of the $\boldsymbol{\mu}^{(l)}$ and $\boldsymbol{\Sigma}^{(l)}$.

The distance and best linear discriminator concepts of Section 10.2 provide methods for analyzing a mean difference vector $\bar{\mathbf{X}}^{(1)} - \bar{\mathbf{X}}^{(2)}$ in relation to an inner product π defined over variable-space. Related sampling distributions are determined from the sampling distributions of the basic statistics $\bar{\mathbf{X}}^{(1)} - \bar{\mathbf{X}}^{(2)}$, $\mathbf{T}^{(1)}$, and $\mathbf{T}^{(2)}$ which are independent with $N(\boldsymbol{\mu}^{(1)} - \boldsymbol{\mu}^{(2)}, \boldsymbol{\Sigma}^{(1)}/n_1 + \boldsymbol{\Sigma}^{(2)}/n_2)$, $W(n_1 - 1, \boldsymbol{\Sigma}^{(1)})$, and $W(n_2 - 1, \boldsymbol{\Sigma}^{(2)})$ distributions.

If π does not depend on the sample data and may be regarded as fixed for sampling distribution purposes, then D^2 as defined in (10.2.1) has a distribution of the general type specified in Exercise 12.3.3 with $q = p$. The special case $\Sigma^{(1)} = \Sigma^{(2)} = \pi$ is of theoretical interest since the sampling distribution of

$$\frac{n_1 n_2}{n_1 + n_2} D^2 \quad \text{is} \quad \chi^2\left(p, 1, \frac{n_1 n_2}{n_1 + n_2} \Delta^2\right), \tag{14.3.3}$$

where Δ^2 is the population squared distance defined using $\boldsymbol{\mu}^{(1)}$ and $\boldsymbol{\mu}^{(2)}$ in place of $\bar{\mathbf{X}}^{(1)}$ and $\bar{\mathbf{X}}^{(2)}$.

If π is a sample based inner product, the distribution of D^2 becomes more complicated, and the only easily accessible case arises when $\boldsymbol{\Sigma}^{(1)} = \boldsymbol{\Sigma}^{(2)}$ and $\mathbf{S}_W$ rather than $\boldsymbol{\Sigma}$ is used for π to define distance. Theorem 13.6.2 becomes applicable with $[n_1 n_2/(n_1 + n_2)]^{1/2}(\mathbf{X}^{(1)} - \mathbf{X}^{(2)})$ in the role of $\mathbf{X}$, and $\mathbf{T}_W$ in the role of $\mathbf{Q}$, from which it follows that the sampling distribution of

$$\frac{n_1 n_2}{n_1 + n_2} D^2 \quad \text{is} \quad G\left(p, n - 2, n - 2, \frac{n_1 n_2}{n_1 + n_2} \Delta^2\right), \tag{14.3.4}$$

where

$$\Delta^2 = (\boldsymbol{\mu}^{(1)} - \boldsymbol{\mu}^{(2)})\boldsymbol{\Sigma}^{-1}(\boldsymbol{\mu}^{(1)} - \boldsymbol{\mu}^{(2)})'. \tag{14.3.5}$$

More generally, Theorem 13.6.3 becomes applicable and distribution theory associated with a decomposition of D^2 is easily specified. In effect, the inference procedures about $\boldsymbol{\mu}$ based on the decomposition of G (cf. Section 14.1) extend directly to analogous procedures about $\boldsymbol{\mu}^{(1)} - \boldsymbol{\mu}^{(2)}$, provided of course that $\boldsymbol{\Sigma}^{(1)} = \boldsymbol{\Sigma}^{(2)}$ may be assumed roughly valid. Another application of the decomposition of D^2 makes it possible to define a confidence region for a best linear discriminator. Specifically, consider a basis of variable-space whose first element is the population best linear discriminator $\boldsymbol{\alpha}\mathbf{V}$, and apply Theorem 13.6.3 with $s = 1$. In terms of the new basis, the analogue of $\boldsymbol{\nu}_{2.1}$ is $\mathbf{0}$ (cf. Theorem 10.2). It follows that

$$(G - G_1)/(1 + G_1) \tag{14.3.6}$$

has the central $G(p-1, n-p-1, 1)$ distribution, where

$$G = \frac{n_1 n_2}{n_1 + n_2} (\bar{\mathbf{X}}^{(1)} - \bar{\mathbf{X}}^{(2)}) \mathbf{T}_W^{-1} (\bar{\mathbf{X}}^{(1)} - \bar{\mathbf{X}}^{(2)})' \tag{14.3.7}$$

and

$$G_1 = \frac{n_1 n_2}{n_1 + n_2} \frac{[\boldsymbol{\alpha}(\bar{\mathbf{X}}^{(1)} - \bar{\mathbf{X}}^{(2)})']^2}{\boldsymbol{\alpha}\mathbf{T}_W\boldsymbol{\alpha}'} . \tag{14.3.8}$$

In principle, therefore, the quantity (14.3.6) can be used as a pivotal quantity from which confidence regions for $\boldsymbol{\alpha}$ may be deduced. It is quite possible, however, that a confidence region based on the pivotal quantity (14.3.6) shall include the whole of $\mathscr{E}$. Some users of confidence methods are disturbed by finding all-inclusive or empty confidence regions with a confidence level strictly between 0 and 1. The phenomenon should therefore be taken as a reminder of the logic underlying confidence regions. Specifically, a 0.95 level confidence region is *not* a region associated with a degree of belief of 0.95, for such an interpretation is definitely not compatible with an all-inclusive or empty region. A 0.95 level confidence region is simply a region of value-sets of unknowns which are not rejected at the 0.05 level by certain significance tests. It is quite possible that $G_{2.1}$ or (14.3.6) should not be significantly large for any $\boldsymbol{\alpha}$ and therefore that every $\boldsymbol{\alpha}$ should be included in the confidence region. In statistical practice it is usual to avoid confidence procedures whose postdictive interpretation is clearly invalid predictively, and for this reason the above confidence procedures, or their generalizations to k sample situations, are not recommended.

It is also of interest to investigate the sampling distribution of sample best linear discriminators, and a brief sketch will now be given. To ask for the sampling distribution of a sample best linear discriminator is to ask for the distribution of a random direction in variable-space $\mathscr{E}$, for a best linear discriminator is determined only up to an indeterminate scale factor. Two parallel cases will be considered, corresponding to (14.3.3) and (14.3.4). In the first case, the relevant population information is supplied by the population mean difference $\delta = \mu^{(1)} - \mu^{(2)}$ and by the common population covariance Σ which plays the role of π. Together, δ and Σ determine the population best linear discriminator direction in $\mathscr{E}$ while $d = m^{(1)} - m^{(2)}$ and Σ determine in the same way the sample best linear discriminator direction in $\mathscr{E}$. Denote by V_{pop} and V_{obs} a pair of vectors in $\mathscr{E}$ lying along these directions, and denote by θ the random angle between them, angles being taken in the sense of Σ. Symmetry implies that the sampling distribution of the direction of V_{obs} is uniquely determined by the sampling distribution of θ alone. For, using Σ as the inner product over $\mathscr{E}$, the component of V_{obs} orthogonal to V_{pop} is spherically distributed in the $(p-1)$-dimensional subspace orthogonal to V_{pop}, conditional on any given θ and therefore independently of θ. Now θ is also the angle between δ and d in $\mathscr{F}$

relative to the inner product Σ_d so that the sampling distribution of

$$\cot^2 \theta \quad \text{is} \quad G\left(1, p-1, 1, \frac{n_1 n_2}{n_1 + n_2} \Delta^2\right), \tag{14.3.9}$$

which thereby characterizes the distribution of the sample best linear discriminator. In the second case, which is of more practical interest, $\mathbf{S}_W$ is used to define the sample best linear discriminator on the assumption that $\mathbf{\Sigma}^{(1)} = \mathbf{\Sigma}^{(2)} = \mathbf{\Sigma}$. As above, the distribution is uniquely determined by the distribution of θ alone. Unfortunately, the distribution of θ is not simple and it is not pursued here. The formula (14.3.9) holds approximately in the second case when samples are large enough that $\mathbf{S}_W$ is an accurate approximation to $\mathbf{\Sigma}$.

Turning back to k samples, the data may be reduced in analysis of variance fashion to $\mathbf{T}_A$ and $\mathbf{T}_W$ whose distribution is specified in the first paragraph of this section. Many criteria could be used to assess the relative sizes of "among group" and "within group" variation; usually these would be functions of the eigenvalues of $\mathbf{T}_A$ relative to $\mathbf{T}_W$. The Wilks criterion

$$\Lambda = \frac{\det \mathbf{T}_W}{\det (\mathbf{T}_A + \mathbf{T}_W)} \tag{14.3.10}$$

is stressed in this book. Under the hypothesis of samples from normal populations with the same $\boldsymbol{\mu}$ and the same $\mathbf{\Sigma}$, the sampling distribution of (14.3.10) is $\Lambda(n-1, p, k-1)$, from Theorem 13.7.3. The general distribution allowing for different $\boldsymbol{\mu}^{(l)}$ but common $\mathbf{\Sigma}$ is of the form specified in Exercise 13.7.13.

Formula (13.7.3), or, more generally, (13.7.4) shows how to factor Λ in such a way that variables are brought into the analysis one at a time in a specified order. In the case of (13.7.3) the original variables are used, while in the case of (13.7.4) any basis of variables may be used. Such decompositions are illustrated in Example 10.2, where $k = 2$ and the equivalent quantity D^2 is used, and in Example 11.2.

Example 10.1. Using the vector of sample mean differences, together with the diagonal elements of $\mathbf{S}_W$ and $t(0, 1, 438)_{[0.975]} = 1.965$, confidence statements may be attached to the population mean differences:

$$\begin{aligned}
\mu_1^{(1)} - \mu_1^{(2)} &= 2.24 \pm 1.24 \\
\mu_2^{(1)} - \mu_2^{(2)} &= -2.94 \pm 1.68 \\
\mu_3^{(1)} - \mu_3^{(2)} &= -0.49 \pm 1.68 \\
\mu_4^{(1)} - \mu_4^{(2)} &= 2.13 \pm 1.36 \\
\mu_5^{(1)} - \mu_5^{(2)} &= -1.68 \pm 1.24 \\
\mu_6^{(1)} - \mu_6^{(2)} &= -0.24 \pm 2.05.
\end{aligned}$$

Assuming random samples from normal populations both with the same covariance matrix, each statement has confidence coefficient 0.95. Of course, the random intervals of which these confidence intervals are realized values are not independently distributed. It is possible to write down a confidence ellipsoid for all six means (which would actually lie in the five-dimensional subspace of $\mathscr{F}$ where the six coordinates have zero sum) with confidence coefficient 0.95. The ranges of $\mu_1, \mu_2, \ldots, \mu_6$ allowed by this ellipsoid are

$$\begin{aligned}
\mu_1^{(1)} - \mu_1^{(2)} &= 2.24 \pm 1.89 \\
\mu_2^{(1)} - \mu_2^{(2)} &= -2.94 \pm 2.55 \\
\mu_3^{(1)} - \mu_3^{(2)} &= -0.49 \pm 2.56 \\
\mu_4^{(1)} - \mu_4^{(2)} &= 2.13 \pm 2.07 \\
\mu_5^{(1)} - \mu_5^{(2)} &= -1.68 \pm 1.88 \\
\mu_6^{(1)} - \mu_6^{(2)} &= -0.24 \pm 3.12
\end{aligned}$$

found as from the above intervals replacing $t(0, 1, 438)_{[0.975]}$ by $[4F(5, 434)_{[0.95]}]^{1/2} = 2.99$. These statements hold *simultaneously* with confidence *exceeding* 0.95.

The observed value $D^2 = 0.318$ may be regarded as drawn from the $G(5, 434, 434 \times 440/204 \times 236, 204 \times 236\Delta^2/440)$ distribution, again assuming normal populations with a common covariance matrix $\mathbf{\Sigma}$, where Δ is the population distance between means defined by $\mathbf{\Sigma}$. Under the null hypothesis $\Delta = 0$, $\frac{1}{5} \times 204 \times 236D^2/440 = 6.96$ comes from the $F(5, 434)$ distribution and is quite far out in the tail of this distribution, indicating strongly that the null hypothesis is false (but not saying anything in itself about what is true). For general Δ, $204 \times 236D^2/440 = 34.8$ comes very nearly from a $\chi^2(51, 204 \times 236\Delta^2/440)$ distribution, and equating means leads to the estimate

$$\hat{\Delta}^2 = 0.272$$

which offers considerable bias-correction to the naive value $D^2 = 0.318$.

The sample covariances are not strikingly different to the eye, and are probably not enough different to invalidate the above use of $\mathbf{S}_W$ on the assumption of common population $\mathbf{\Sigma}$. It is possible to judge the ratios $(øs_1/øs_2)^2$, K_1, and K_2 against their null distributions assuming a common $\mathbf{\Sigma}$. The required theory was given by Dempster (1964) where a pair of statistics were shown to be independent with $G(n_1 - 1, n_2 - 1, 1)$ and $G(p - 1, n_1 + n_2 - 2p, 1)$ distributions under the null hypothesis of samples from normal populations with common covariances. Specifically, the statistics are

$$C_3 = [(n_1 - 1)/(n_2 - 1)][øs_1/øs_2]^2$$

and

$$C_4 = H([øs_1/øs^{(1)}]^2 - 1, [øs_2/øs^{(2)}]^2 - 1, \sin^2\theta, \cos^2\theta),$$

where $H(x, y, p, q)$ denotes the weighted harmonic mean $(p + q)/(px^{-1} + qy^{-1})$ and θ is an angle satisfying $C_3 = \cot^2\theta$.

The present data yield $[øs_1/øs_2]^2 = 1.325$ to be placed on the $F(203, 205)$ null distribution. Roughly this means that $\log 1.325 = 0.281$ should be placed on the $N(0, 2[203^{-1} + 235^{-1}])$ distribution which puts 0.281 at 2.09 standard deviations from the mean. This indicates borderline significance between the 0.05 and 0.01 levels. Likewise $[430/5]C_4 = [0.466 \times 0.072^{-1} + 0.534 \times 0.048^{-1}]^{-1} \times [430/5] = 4.9$ which is highly significant on the $F(5, 430)$ distribution. The data are saying that the samples are sufficiently large for small differences in population covariance matrices to be detected. No formal theory for measuring these differences is given here. Also it should be remembered that tests of the kind described in this paragraph have no studentization factor in them and are sensitive to failures of normality assumptions.

Example 10.2. The earlier discussion of these data in Chapter 10 provided three analyses showing different ways to look at successive contributions to D^2. The theory of Section 14.3 shows how to judge these D^2 contributions from the viewpoint of significance testing.

The computational details of finding the successive test statistics need only be given for the first of the three decompositions, since the other two are similar. To achieve the first decomposition, the operations SWP[11, 10], SWP[1], SWP[2], . . . , SWP[9] were successively applied, yielding a sequence of matrices whose (10, 10) elements are 0.2262, 0.2267, 0.5940, . . . , 3.1399. The successive differences in these values after multiplication by 17 are shown in Chapter 10 as the successive contributions to D^2. Successive applications of Theorem 13.6.3 suggest that one should look at the fractional increases at each stage, namely (0.2267 – 0.2262)/0.2262, (0.5490 – 0.2267)/0.2267, . . . , (3.1399 – 2.1080)/ 2.1080 which are realizations of random quantities which are independent with $G(1, 17, 1)$, $G(1, 16, 1)$, . . . , $G(1, 9, 1)$ distributions under an appropriate sequence of null hypotheses. For example, the null hypotheses going with the third test is that the first three variables have no more power to discriminate between the two populations than have the first two variables.

The sequence of test statistics computed as indicated may also be computed for the alternative decomposition based on principal variables or on polynomial fitting. The three sequences are reproduced as shown at top of next page.

A double star indicates a significance level below 1%, a single star indicates a level between 5% and 1%, while no star indicates a failure to achieve significance at these conventional levels. The picture provided by these tests is quite different from that given by a direct look at the D^2 contributions. In the successive time analysis, only the contributions from times 2, 3, and 4 are indicated to be beyond reasonable limits of sampling variation. Similarly, the first two principal components are clear contributors, while the fourth and sixth are borderline cases. The orthogonal polynomial analysis comes out the cleanest of the three (even too clean?), indicating that the differences between treated and control means appear to be quite well explained in terms of a cubic curve.

Null distribution	Analysis of $V_1, V_2, \ldots, V_9$	Analysis of $U_1, U_2 \ldots, U_9$	Analysis of $V_1, W_2, \ldots, W_9$
$F(1, 17)$	0.037	24.5**	0.037
$F(1, 16)$	22.8**	17.0**	42.1**
$F(1, 15)$	7.40*	1.91	17.2**
$F(1, 14)$	8.38*	4.72*	11.3**
$F(1, 13)$	2.20	1.68	0.26
$F(1, 12)$	0.08	5.22*	0.48
$F(1, 11)$	0.64	0.07	0.87
$F(1, 10)$	2.92	0.11	0.43
$F(1, 9)$	4.40	1.00	1.00

It should be stressed that the later contributions to D^2 have substantial sampling variation associated with them, and can therefore appear to be quite large while being consistent with very small underlying population values. With small samples, a correcting device such as the above sequence of significance tests is a practical necessity.

The sets of variables $V_1, V_2, \ldots, V_9$ and $V_1, W_2, \ldots, W_9$ were not chosen on the basis of sample data, while the set $V_1, V_2, \ldots, V_9$ was so chosen. The successive tests in the case of $U_1, U_2, \ldots, U_9$ have a corresponding weakness, namely that the successive test statistics are independent with the stated distributions only if the two sample mean vectors are identical in all their components. This stringent null hypothesis can be successively weakened in the case of prechosen sets of variables. For example, 2.20 in the first column is a value drawn from the $F(1, 13)$ distribution and is independent of the preceding test statistics provided only that the two population means coincide for $V_5 - w_1V_1 - w_2V_2 - w_3V_3 - w_4V_4$, where w_1, w_2, w_3, w_4 are regression coefficients computed from the common population covariance inner product.

Example 10.3. The various eigenvalues in Example 10.3 measure different aspects of the separation of the six racial groups. For example, the first eigenvalue 2.4184 represents

$$(\text{Male mean} - \text{Female mean})^2/(\tfrac{1}{151} + \tfrac{1}{125})$$

taken on the sample best linear discriminator associated with *sex*, where the discriminator is scaled to have unit norm on the pooled within sample sum inner product. It follows that the *sample* mean difference on the *sample* discriminator scaled to have pooled within *sample* variance unity is

$$[270 \times 2.4184 \times (\tfrac{1}{151} + \tfrac{1}{125})]^{1/2} = 3.09.$$

Two of the many questions which could be asked about such an eigenvalue will be essayed here. First, one may ask whether the apparent difference 3.09 is consistent with an assumption of zero sex differences in the populations. Second, one may ask for a correction to the estimate 3.09 which will take account of the upward bias expected from the selection of a variable with the greatest apparent sex difference. These questions will be answered not only for the sex eigenvalue 2.4184, but also for the race after sex eigenvalues 2.6015, 0.7714, for the interaction eigenvalues 0.1570, 0.0671, and for the six group-differences eigenvalues 2.9037, 2.2021, 0.7476, 0.1017, 0.0605.

Each of these eigenvalue sets is the set of nonzero eigenvalues of a $\mathbf{T}_A$ matrix relative to a common $\mathbf{T}_W$ matrix. Assuming samples from normal populations with common $\mathbf{\Sigma}$, each $\mathbf{T}_A$ is independent of $\mathbf{T}_W$, $\mathbf{T}_A$ has a $W(\ldots, \mathbf{\Sigma}, \ldots)$ distribution, and $\mathbf{T}_W$ has a $W(270, \mathbf{\Sigma})$ distribution. In the case of the sex discriminator, $\mathbf{T}_A$ has the

$$W(1, \mathbf{\Sigma}, \boldsymbol{\tau})$$

distribution, where $\boldsymbol{\tau}$ denotes the same function as $\mathbf{T}_A$ except that sample means are replaced by population means. If follows that the eigenvalue 2.4184 may be regarded as having arisen from a $G(21, 250, 1, \lambda)$ distribution where λ is the nonzero eigenvalue of $\boldsymbol{\tau}$ relative to $\mathbf{\Sigma}$. Under the null hypothesis $\boldsymbol{\tau} = \mathbf{0}$ or $\lambda = 0$, $2.4184 \times \frac{250}{21}$ may be placed on the $F(21, 250)$ distribution, and lies in the extreme tail of the distribution rendering very implausible the null hypothesis $\lambda = 0$. In the case of the other sets of eigenvalues, one may define the Λ statistics

$$\Lambda = \frac{1}{1 + 2.6015} \frac{1}{1 + 0.7714} = 0.1567$$

for the race after sex differences,

$$\Lambda = \frac{1}{1 + 0.1570} \cdot \frac{1}{1 + 0.0671} = 0.8100$$

for the interaction differences, and

$$\Lambda = \frac{1}{1 + 2.9037} \cdot \frac{1}{1 + 2.2021} \cdot \cdots \cdot \frac{1}{1 + 0.0605} = 0.0392$$

for all differences among the six groups. Under the corresponding null hypotheses of zero population differences, these Λ statistics came from $\Lambda(2, 21, 272)$, $\Lambda(2, 21, 272)$, and $\Lambda(5, 21, 275)$ distributions. The reader may check that the first and third of these Λ values are both highly significant. But the second is of more interest in relation to the null distribution. Recall that, if Λ has the $\Lambda(2, 21, 275)$ distribution, then $(1 - \Lambda^{1/2})/\Lambda^{1/2}$ has the $G(42, 500)$ distribution, so that $[(1 - 0.8100^{1/2})/0.8100^{1/2}][500/42] = 1.32$ should be placed on the $F(42, 500)$ distribution. The value 1.32 falls just short of the 0.95 quantile, suggesting that some small but not definitely established interaction effects are present in the populations. Recall that these interactions effects are variables whose race differences change sign when passing from males to females, and such effects are *a priori* implausible.

Having established the significance of three of the four sets of differences tested, it is sensible to go back to estimate these effects. A value like 2.4184 arising from the $G(21, 250, 1, \lambda)$ distribution may be regarded as having a bias component on the average of $21/248 = 0.085$ which is the mean of the $G(21, 250, 1, 0)$ distribution. A possible bias correction of 2.418 is therefore 0.085 reducing the estimate of the corresponding population quantity to 2.333. This indicates a population mean sex difference of

$$[270 \times 2.333 \times (\tfrac{1}{151} + \tfrac{1}{125})^{1/2}] = 3.03,$$

rather than the 3.10 suggested by the original eigenvalue. It may be noted in passing that a χ^2 approximation to

$$-\log \Lambda = \log (1 + 2.4184)$$

is clearly not valid with these data, because such approximations as discussed in Section 13.7 rely on $\log (1 + x) \approx x$ which is certainly not true in this case.

A bias correction for the sum of the two race-after-sex eigenvalues is roughly $2 \times 21/248 = 0.169$, reducing 3.373 to 3.204, and similarly for the sum of the five eigenvalues for all group differences a correction is $4 \times 21/248 = 0.423$, reducing 6.020 to 5.597. The bias-corrected residual estimate for the sum of the two population interactions eigenvalues is $5.597 - 2.333 - 3.204 = 0.060$.

The improvements which covariates permit in the estimation of population mean differences may be analyzed mathematically in terms of sampling distributions of estimators. Other mathematical analyses would be possible, based, for example, on the ideas of Bayesian inference, but these other analyses are not pursued here. Theorem 13.6.3 provides the required theory, and the theorem is applied in a way parallel to (14.1.11) and (14.1.12), the difference being that the first s variables are called covariates and the means $\boldsymbol{\mu}_2$ and $\boldsymbol{\mu}_1$ are replaced by mean differences $\boldsymbol{\mu}_2^{(i)} - \boldsymbol{\mu}_2^{(j)}$ and $\boldsymbol{\mu}_1^{(i)} - \boldsymbol{\mu}_1^{(j)}$. Randomized experimentation makes it possible to assume that $\boldsymbol{\mu}_1^{(i)} - \boldsymbol{\mu}_1^{(j)} = \mathbf{0}$, which in turn assures that the sampling distribution of $\bar{\mathbf{X}}_2^{(i)} - \bar{\mathbf{X}}_2^{(j)} - (\bar{\mathbf{X}}_1^{(i)} - \bar{\mathbf{X}}_1^{(j)})\mathbf{H}_{12}$ is centered about $\boldsymbol{\mu}_2^{(i)} - \boldsymbol{\mu}_2^{(j)}$. To be more precise, consider the model where $\bar{\mathbf{X}}^{(1)}, \bar{\mathbf{X}}^{(2)}, \ldots, \bar{\mathbf{X}}^{(k)}$ and $\mathbf{T}_W$ are independent with $N(\boldsymbol{\mu}^{(1)}, \boldsymbol{\Sigma}/n_1), N(\boldsymbol{\mu}^{(2)}, \boldsymbol{\Sigma}/n_2), \ldots, N(\boldsymbol{\mu}^{(k)}, \boldsymbol{\Sigma}/n_k)$, and $W(n - k, \boldsymbol{\Sigma})$ distributions. Using the standard partition notation, and applying Theorem 13.6.1 with $\mathbf{X} = (\bar{\mathbf{X}}^{(i)} - \bar{\mathbf{X}}^{(j)})/(1/n_i + 1/n_j)^{1/2}$ and $\mathbf{Q} = \mathbf{T}$, one finds

$$\mathbf{X}_{2.1} = [(\bar{\mathbf{X}}_2^{(i)} - \bar{\mathbf{X}}_2^{(j)}) - (\boldsymbol{\mu}_2^{(i)} - \boldsymbol{\mu}_2^{(j)}) - (\bar{\mathbf{X}}_1^{(i)} - \bar{\mathbf{X}}_1^{(j)})\mathbf{H}_{12}]/(1/n_i + 1/n_j)^{1/2} \tag{14.3.11}$$

and

$$\boldsymbol{\nu}_{2.1} = (\boldsymbol{\mu}_2^{(i)} - \boldsymbol{\mu}_2^{(j)})/(1/n_i + 1/n_j)^{1/2}, \tag{14.3.12}$$

where it is assumed that $\boldsymbol{\mu}_1^{(i)} - \boldsymbol{\mu}_1^{(j)} = \mathbf{0}$. It follows that the conditional distribution of $\bar{\mathbf{X}}_2^{(i)} - \bar{\mathbf{X}}_2^{(j)} - (\bar{\mathbf{X}}_1^{(i)} - \bar{\mathbf{X}}_1^{(j)})\mathbf{H}_{12}$ given $\bar{\mathbf{X}}_1^{(l)}$ for $l = 1, 2, \ldots, k$ and $\mathbf{T}_{11W}$ is $N(\boldsymbol{\mu}_2^{(i)} - \boldsymbol{\mu}_2^{(j)}, (1/n_i + 1/n_j)(1 + G_1)\boldsymbol{\Sigma}_{22.1})$, where

$$G_1 = (\bar{\mathbf{X}}_1^{(i)} - \bar{\mathbf{X}}_1^{(j)})\mathbf{T}_{11W}^{-1}(\bar{\mathbf{X}}_1^{(i)} - \bar{\mathbf{X}}_1^{(j)})'/(1/n_1 + 1/n_2). \tag{14.3.13}$$

The reader may compare the original estimator $\bar{\mathbf{X}}_2^{(i)} - \bar{\mathbf{X}}_2^{(j)}$ with the adjusted estimator $\bar{\mathbf{X}}_2^{(i)} - \bar{\mathbf{X}}_2^{(j)}$ by finding and following the parallel discussion in Section 14.1.

Note that the Hotelling T^2 statistic (14.3.13) has the $G(s, n - k - s + 1, 1)$ distribution under the hypothesis $\boldsymbol{\mu}_1^{(i)} - \boldsymbol{\mu}_1^{(j)} = \mathbf{0}$ and provides a test of this hypothesis, in effect a test of the adequacy of randomization. Note also that $\mathbf{T}_{22.1W}$ may be used to estimate $\boldsymbol{\Sigma}_{22.1}$ in (14.3.12) and is independent of (14.3.11) so may be used along with (14.3.11) to construct T^2 type inferences. More generally, with k samples, a Wilks Λ statistic Λ_1 may be computed from the covariates and compared against the $\Lambda(n - k, s, k - 1)$ distribution to test the null hypothesis $\boldsymbol{\mu}_1^{(1)} = \boldsymbol{\mu}_1^{(2)} = \cdots = \boldsymbol{\mu}_1^{(k)}$. The quantity Λ computed from the covariates and response variables together may be factored into $\Lambda = \Lambda_1\Lambda_{2.1}$, and $\Lambda_{2.1}$ may be compared against the $\Lambda(n - k - s, p - s, k - 1)$ distribution to test the null hypothesis $\boldsymbol{\mu}_2^{(1)} = \boldsymbol{\mu}_2^{(2)} = \cdots = \boldsymbol{\mu}_2^{(k)}$. Even without the assumption $\boldsymbol{\mu}_1^{(1)} = \boldsymbol{\mu}_1^{(2)} = \cdots = \boldsymbol{\mu}_1^{(k)}$, $\Lambda_{2.1}$ is distributed independently of Λ_1 and has the above null distribution provided that the residual vectors $\boldsymbol{\mu}_2^{(l)} - \boldsymbol{\mu}_1^{(l)}\boldsymbol{\Xi}_{12}$ are equal for $l = 1, 2, \ldots, k$. But $\Lambda_{2.1}$ is not appropriate for testing the null hypothesis of common $\boldsymbol{\mu}_2^{(l)}$ unless the hypothesis of common $\boldsymbol{\mu}_1^{(l)}$ is accepted *a priori*.

See Exercises 14.3.2, 14.3.3, 14.3.4, and 14.3.5 for numerical examples involving covariates.

14.4 EXERCISES

14.1.1 Consider the following two ways, each associated with the level 0.95, to assign an interval of values to $\boldsymbol{\alpha\mu}'$ where $\boldsymbol{\alpha}$ is a fixed $1 \times p$ vector and $\boldsymbol{\mu}$ is an unknown population mean vector of a sampled normal population. First, remove equal tail areas 0.025 from each tail of the distribution of (14.1.1) applied to the single variable $\boldsymbol{\alpha}\mathbf{V}$. Second, define the 0.95 level confidence ellipsoid based on (14.1.10) and find the interval of $\boldsymbol{\alpha}\mathbf{V}$ values allowed by this ellipsoid. The ratio of the lengths of this interval is an *inflation* factor which protects one against picking $\boldsymbol{\alpha}$ values on the basis of the data. Prepare a table of these inflation factors for $p = 1, 2, 5, 10, 20, 50, 100$ assuming n large, using tables of the central χ^2 distributions.

14.2.1 Derive the sampling distribution theory analogous to that given in Section 14.2 for the model in which the constant term w in the population best linear predictor may be assumed *a priori* to be zero.

14.2.2 What is the origin of R. A. Fisher's suggestion that the sampling distribution of $\log(1 + r)/(1 - r)$ is approximately $N(\log(1 + \rho)/(1 - \rho), 1/(n - 3))$?

14.2.3 Use (14.2.12) to write an expression for the density of the sampling distribution of d_{ij} which involves a single definite integral.

14.2.4 Suppose that $G_r(x)$ denotes the cumulative distribution function of the $G(p - 1 + r, n - p, 1)$ distribution. Show that the cumulative distribution function of d^2 in (14.2.16), conditional on given $\mathbf{T}_{11}$, is expressible as the Poisson mixture

$$\sum_{r=0}^{\infty} G_r(x) \frac{\lambda^r}{r!} e^{-\lambda},$$

where $\lambda = \frac{1}{2}\boldsymbol{\omega}\mathbf{T}_{11}\boldsymbol{\omega}'/\sigma_{pp.12...\overline{p-1}}$. Deduce that the marginal cumulative distribution function of d^2 may be expressed as the negative binomial mixture

$$\sum_{r=0}^{\infty} G_r(x) \frac{\Gamma((n - 1)/2 + r)}{\Gamma((n - 1)/2)r!} q^{(n-1)/2} p^r,$$

where $p = 1 - q = \delta^2/(1 + \delta^2) = \rho^2$. [*Hint*: follow Exercises 12.5.10, 12.5.11, and 12.5.12.]

14.2.5 Use formulas (14.2.21), (14.2.22), and (14.2.23) to compute approximate bias corrections and approximate sampling variances for the sample canonical correlation coefficients shown in Table 9.1.5. Are the results plausible? How far would you trust these formulas?

14.3.1 Carry out the sequence of tests indicated in the last paragraph of Example 10.4 of Section 10.6 and verify the results claimed in that paragraph.

14.3.2 Using the data of Example 11.1, carry out a test of the null hypothesis $\boldsymbol{\mu}_1^{(1)} = \boldsymbol{\mu}_1^{(2)}$ based on the statistic (14.3.12). Assuming $\boldsymbol{\mu}_1^{(1)} = \boldsymbol{\mu}_1^{(2)}$, carry out a test of the null hypothesis $\boldsymbol{\mu}_2^{(1)} = \boldsymbol{\mu}_2^{(2)}$ using the appropriate version of $G_{2.1}$ as defined in Theorem 13.6.3. Is the combined $G = G_1 + G_{2.1}$ significant for the test $\boldsymbol{\mu}^{(1)} = \boldsymbol{\mu}^{(2)}$? How would you compare the sensitivity of the tests based on G and $G_{2.1}$ for the null hypothesis $\boldsymbol{\mu}_2^{(1)} = \boldsymbol{\mu}_2^{(2)}$?

14.3.3 The three values 2.6834, 2.0696, and 2.1531 were proposed as point estimates of the population mean differences on the response variable V in Example 11.1. What are the sampling distributions of the associated estimators? Show that associated 95% confidence intervals based on $t(0, 1, 106)_{[0.975]} = 1.9826$ and $t(0, 1, 105)_{[0.975]} = 1.9828$ are (0.227, 5.139), (0.376, 3.764), and (0.454, 3.852).

14.3.4 Check the significance tests which were described in Example 11.2 of Chapter 11.

14.3.5 Compute a set of confidence limits for the elements of $\overline{\mathbf{X}}_2^{(1)}$ in Example 11.3. First, choose the limits so that each corresponds to a confidence level 0.95. Second, define a confidence ellipsoid for all six means with overall confidence 0.95 and deduce the limits on individual means implied by the confidence ellipsoid.

14.3.6 Three sets of point estimates for μ_2 were computed in Example 11.3, namely

$$[-1.32, 10.26, -6.60, -3.87, 10.85, -9.32]$$
$$[-3.00, 10.72, -6.56, -3.10, 9.27, -7.35]$$
$$[-2.09, 10.91, -6.54, -3.73, 9.89, -8.45].$$

Specify sampling distributions for the estimators which gave rise to these estimated values. Provide estimates for the unknown covariance matrices in these sampling distributions. Compare the accuracies of the three sets of estimators.

CHAPTER 15

THE ROLE OF CONTEMPORARY THEORIES OF STATISTICAL INFERENCE

15.1 LIKELIHOOD

If $\mathbf{X}^{(1)}, \mathbf{X}^{(2)}, \ldots, \mathbf{X}^{(n)}$ denote a random sample of size n from an $N(\boldsymbol{\mu}, \boldsymbol{\Sigma})$ population where $\boldsymbol{\Sigma}$ has full rank p, then

$$L(\boldsymbol{\mu}, \boldsymbol{\Sigma}; \mathbf{X}^{(1)}, \mathbf{X}^{(2)}, \ldots, \mathbf{X}^{(n)})$$
$$= (2\pi)^{-pm/2}(\det \boldsymbol{\Sigma})^{-n/2} \exp\left(-\tfrac{1}{2}\sum_{i=1}^{n}(\mathbf{X}^{(i)} - \boldsymbol{\mu})\boldsymbol{\Sigma}^{-1}(\mathbf{X}^{(i)} - \boldsymbol{\mu})'\right) \qquad (15.1.1)$$

is called the *likelihood of* $\boldsymbol{\mu}$ *and* $\boldsymbol{\Sigma}$ *given the sample* $\mathbf{X}^{(1)}, \mathbf{X}^{(2)}, \ldots, \mathbf{X}^{(n)}$. Regarded as a function of $\mathbf{X}^{(1)}, \mathbf{X}^{(2)}, \ldots, \mathbf{X}^{(n)}$ for fixed $\boldsymbol{\mu}$ and $\boldsymbol{\Sigma}$, the likelihood is simply the probability density function of the sampling distribution of $\mathbf{X}^{(1)}, \mathbf{X}^{(2)}, \ldots, \mathbf{X}^{(n)}$. The purpose of the term likelihood is to stress the reverse interpretation as a function of unknown $\boldsymbol{\mu}$ and $\boldsymbol{\Sigma}$ to be considered after the sample observations become fixed. This reverse emphasis is plainly visible in the original definition of the general concept given by Fisher (1922):

> Likelihood. The likelihood that any parameter (or set of parameters) should have any assigned value (or set of values) is proportional to the probability that if this were so, the totality of observations should be that observed.

Likelihood functions were implicit in mathematical statistics long before Fisher coined the term, mainly due to their role in what is now called Bayesian inference. The Bayesian statistician starts from a probability distribution representing the uncertainty of his knowledge of the values of all relevant quantities, and after observing the values of a subset of these quantities he alters his probability distributions over the remaining unknown set of values by conditioning on the observations. In the present situation the relevant quantities are $\mathbf{X}^{(1)}, \mathbf{X}^{(2)}, \ldots, \mathbf{X}^{(n)}$, $\boldsymbol{\mu}$, and $\boldsymbol{\Sigma}$, whose distribution is specified by defining two distributions, namely the conditional distribution of $\mathbf{X}^{(1)}, \mathbf{X}^{(2)}, \ldots, \mathbf{X}^{(n)}$ given $\boldsymbol{\mu}$ and $\boldsymbol{\Sigma}$ and the marginal (often called *prior*) distribution of $\boldsymbol{\mu}$ and $\boldsymbol{\Sigma}$.

Consequently, the initial probability density function of $\mathbf{X}^{(1)}, \mathbf{X}^{(2)}, \ldots, \mathbf{X}^{(n)}$, $\boldsymbol{\mu}, \boldsymbol{\Sigma}$ has the form

$$h(\mathbf{X}^{(1)}, \mathbf{X}^{(2)}, \ldots, \mathbf{X}^{(n)}, \boldsymbol{\mu}, \boldsymbol{\Sigma}) = L(\boldsymbol{\mu}, \boldsymbol{\Sigma}; \mathbf{X}^{(1)}, \mathbf{X}^{(2)}, \ldots, \mathbf{X}^{(n)}) f(\boldsymbol{\mu}, \boldsymbol{\Sigma}), \quad (15.1.2)$$

where $f(\boldsymbol{\mu}, \boldsymbol{\Sigma})$ is the density of the prior distribution of $\boldsymbol{\mu}$ and $\boldsymbol{\Sigma}$. The density of the conditional or posterior distribution of $\boldsymbol{\mu}$ and $\boldsymbol{\Sigma}$ given $\mathbf{X}^{(1)}, \mathbf{X}^{(2)}, \ldots, \mathbf{X}^{(n)}$ is

$$K(\mathbf{X}^{(1)}, \mathbf{X}^{(2)}, \ldots, \mathbf{X}^{(n)}) h(\mathbf{X}^{(1)}, \mathbf{X}^{(2)}, \ldots, \mathbf{X}^{(n)}, \boldsymbol{\mu}, \boldsymbol{\Sigma}), \quad (15.1.3)$$

where $K(\mathbf{X}^{(1)}, \mathbf{X}^{(2)}, \ldots, \mathbf{X}^{(n)})$ is a normalizing constant given $\mathbf{X}^{(1)}, \mathbf{X}^{(2)}, \ldots, \mathbf{X}^{(n)}$. The reason for this paragraph is to remark that an instance of Bayesian inference may be described in terms of the following program: (*i*) compute the likelihood $L(\boldsymbol{\mu}, \boldsymbol{\Sigma}; \mathbf{X}^{(1)}, \mathbf{X}^{(2)}, \ldots, \mathbf{X}^{(n)})$ as a function of $\boldsymbol{\mu}$ and $\boldsymbol{\Sigma}$ with $\mathbf{X}^{(1)}, \mathbf{X}^{(2)}, \ldots, \mathbf{X}^{(n)}$ *fixed at their observed values*, (ii) multiply the likelihood of $\boldsymbol{\mu}$ and $\boldsymbol{\Sigma}$ by the prior density $f(\boldsymbol{\mu}, \boldsymbol{\Sigma})$, (*iii*) compute the normalizing constant K, and (*iv*) compute any desired probabilities or expectations from the density of the posterior distribution. Note especially that $\mathbf{X}^{(1)}, \mathbf{X}^{(2)}, \ldots, \mathbf{X}^{(n)}$ enter the analysis only through the likelihood $L(\boldsymbol{\mu}, \boldsymbol{\Sigma}; \mathbf{X}^{(1)}, \mathbf{X}^{(2)}, \ldots, \mathbf{X}^{(n)})$. A form of Bayesian analysis is developed and discussed in Section 15.3.

The basic idea behind Fisher's introduction of likelihood was that the likelihood function should be regarded as containing all of the information in a set of data even when the absence of a well-established prior distribution rendered Bayesian analysis untenable. In his wide-ranging contributions to statistical inference, Fisher generally tried to conform to this idea. Other writers such as Barnard (1949) and Birnbaum (1962) have also argued for the fundamental importance of likelihood in non-Bayesian terms. Unfortunately, the reasoning behind the direct interpretation of a likelihood function alone has not been fully explicated and remains somewhat obscure to most statisticians. For example, suppose that a sample $\mathbf{X}^{(1)}, \mathbf{X}^{(2)}, \ldots, \mathbf{X}^{(n)}$ is observed and denote by L_1 and L_2 the values of (15.1.1) corresponding to $\boldsymbol{\mu}_1, \boldsymbol{\Sigma}_1$ and $\boldsymbol{\mu}_2, \boldsymbol{\Sigma}_2$ which define two possible underlying normal populations. Usually, the likelihood function is regarded as defined only up to an undetermined multiplier, so that the likelihood ratio L_1/L_2 provides the hard information in L_1 and L_2. An actual value such as $L_1/L_2 = 99.0$ means that the actual observations $\mathbf{X}^{(1)}, \mathbf{X}^{(2)}, \ldots, \mathbf{X}^{(n)}$ would have been regarded *before sampling* as 99.0 times more probable under $\boldsymbol{\mu}_1, \boldsymbol{\Sigma}_1$ as under $\boldsymbol{\mu}_2, \boldsymbol{\Sigma}_2$, had anyone thought before observing $\mathbf{X}^{(1)}, \mathbf{X}^{(2)}, \ldots, \mathbf{X}^{(n)}$ to make such a comparison. After sampling, one may therefore make the judgment that $\boldsymbol{\mu}_2, \boldsymbol{\Sigma}_2$ is implausible relative to $\boldsymbol{\mu}_1, \boldsymbol{\Sigma}_1$ in the *postdictive* sense that acceptance of $\boldsymbol{\mu}_2, \boldsymbol{\Sigma}_2$ over $\boldsymbol{\mu}_1, \boldsymbol{\Sigma}_1$ implies acceptance of the fact that a relatively improbable sample must have been drawn. This reasoning is already tortuous enough, but a complete interpretation of the likelihood function must be based on the consideration of many such pairs, generally selected after $\mathbf{X}^{(1)}, \mathbf{X}^{(2)}, \ldots, \mathbf{X}^{(n)}$ are known. It is difficult to know what trust may be put in any single postdictive judgment extracted from such a complex. Moreover, if interest focuses on a single quantity, perhaps the first element of $\boldsymbol{\mu}$, direct contemplation of the likelihood function is not much help since a likelihood function is rarely determined even roughly by the values of a single quantity. Supporters of an approach to data via the direct interpretation of a likelihood usually find themselves pushed to a procedure of integrating over the outcome-spaces of nuisance parameters, much as a Bayesian would do (cf. Barnard, Winsten, and Jenkins, 1962). It is also possible to modify the likelihood function by integrating over subspaces of the outcome-space of observations, in effect getting the likelihood function determined by a reduced amount of sample information (cf. James, 1966).

But even without direct interpretation, likelihood plays important technical roles in non-Bayesian theories of statistical inference. Perhaps the most important of these roles is in maximum likelihood estimation whose application to multivariate normal sampling theory will be sketched shortly. First, however, it may be useful to have a geometric understanding of the likelihood function produced by a sample from a normal population.

The likelihood (15.1.1) will be seen to depend on $\mathbf{X}^{(1)}, \mathbf{X}^{(2)}, \ldots, \mathbf{X}^{(n)}$ only through the sample first and second moments, which are represented here by $\bar{\mathbf{X}}$ and $\mathbf{T}$ in the notation of Chapter 7. Beyond this, the likelihood will be seen to depend on the distance from $\bar{\mathbf{X}}$ to $\boldsymbol{\mu}$ in terms of the inner products defined by $\boldsymbol{\Sigma}$ and on the eigenvalues of $\mathbf{T}$ relative to $\boldsymbol{\Sigma}$. The exponent in (15.1.1) may be written

$$-\tfrac{1}{2}\sum_{i=1}^{n}(\mathbf{X}^{(i)} - \boldsymbol{\mu})\boldsymbol{\Sigma}^{-1}(\mathbf{X}^{(i)} - \boldsymbol{\mu})' = -\tfrac{1}{2}A_1 - \tfrac{1}{2}A_2, \tag{15.1.4}$$

where

$$A_1 = n(\bar{\mathbf{X}} - \boldsymbol{\mu})\boldsymbol{\Sigma}^{-1}(\bar{\mathbf{X}} - \boldsymbol{\mu})' \tag{15.1.5}$$

and

$$A_2 = \sum_{i=1}^{n}(\mathbf{X}^{(i)} - \bar{\mathbf{X}})\boldsymbol{\Sigma}^{-1}(\mathbf{X}^{(i)} - \bar{\mathbf{X}})'. \tag{15.1.6}$$

A_1 depends on the sample data through $\bar{\mathbf{X}}$ only, while A_2 depends only on $\mathbf{T}$ and $\boldsymbol{\Sigma}$. To check the latter statement, regard $\boldsymbol{\Sigma}$ as a covariance matrix relative to the basis $\mathbf{V}$ of variable-space $\mathscr{E}$ and define $\mathbf{U} = \boldsymbol{\Gamma}\mathbf{V}$ to be any basis with orthonormal covariance. Then

$$\begin{aligned} A_2 &= \sum_{i=1}^{n}[(\mathbf{X}^{(i)} - \bar{\mathbf{X}})\boldsymbol{\Gamma}'][(\mathbf{X}^{(i)} - \bar{\mathbf{X}})\boldsymbol{\Gamma}']' \\ &= \operatorname{tr}\sum_{i=1}^{n}[(\mathbf{X}^{(i)} - \bar{\mathbf{X}})\boldsymbol{\Gamma}']'[(\mathbf{X}^{(i)} - \bar{\mathbf{X}})\boldsymbol{\Gamma}'] \\ &= \operatorname{tr}\boldsymbol{\Gamma}\mathbf{T}\boldsymbol{\Gamma}'. \end{aligned} \tag{15.1.7}$$

When $\mathbf{U}$ is specially chosen to be a basis of eigenvectors of $\mathbf{T}$ relative to $\boldsymbol{\Sigma}$, the last formula becomes

$$A_2 = \sum_{i=1}^{p} l_i, \tag{15.1.8}$$

where $l_1, l_2, \ldots, l_p$ denote the eigenvalues of **T** relative to **Σ**.

If **T** has rank p, then

$$L(\boldsymbol{\mu}, \boldsymbol{\Sigma}, \mathbf{X}^{(1)}, \mathbf{X}^{(2)}, \ldots, \mathbf{X}^{(n)} = B_1 B_2 B_3, \tag{15.1.9}$$

where

$$B_1 = (2\pi)^{-pm/2} (\det \mathbf{T})^{-n/2} \tag{15.1.10}$$

$$B_2 = \exp(-\tfrac{1}{2}A_1), \tag{15.1.11}$$

and

$$B_2 = (\det \mathbf{T}/\det \boldsymbol{\Sigma})^{n/2} \exp(-\tfrac{1}{2}A_2) = \prod_{i=1}^{p} [l_i^{n/2} \exp(-\tfrac{1}{2}l_i)]. \tag{15.1.12}$$

Since B_1 does not depend on $\boldsymbol{\mu}$ or $\boldsymbol{\Sigma}$, it may be ignored as part of an undetermined scale factor. The factor B_2 depends in a simple way on the distance from the sample mean to the population mean where distance is determined by the population covariance. The third factor is a simple function of the eigenvalues of the sample covariance relative to the population covariance.

Suppose now that **T** has rank $r < p$. Since **Σ** is assumed to have full rank p, the condition $r < p$ occurs with probability 1 if and only if $n - 1 = r < p$. The factorization

$$\det \boldsymbol{\Sigma} = (\det \boldsymbol{\Sigma}/\det \mathbf{T}) \det \mathbf{T} \tag{15.1.13}$$

is basic to (15.1.9), but is no longer defined when $r < p$ because $\det \mathbf{T} = 0$. In general, **T** defines a concentration ellipsoid in an r-dimensional subspace of $\mathscr{F}$. The concentration ellipsoid of **Σ** intersects this subspace in an ellipsoid whose principal axes relative to the **T**-ellipsoid have relative squared lengths $l_1, l_2, \ldots, l_r$ which are the nonzero eigenvalues of **T** relative to **Σ**. A natural generalization of (15.1.13) is

$$\det \boldsymbol{\Sigma} = \left(\prod_{i=1}^{r} l_i\right)(l_0), \tag{15.1.14}$$

where $l_0 = \det \mathbf{T}$ if $r = p$, but l_0 depends on both **T** and **Σ** if $r < p$. In the corresponding generalization of (15.1.9), B_2 remains as in (15.1.11) while (15.1.10) and (15.1.12) are replaced by

$$B_1 = (2\pi)^{-pn/2}(l_0)^{-n/2} \tag{15.1.15}$$

and

$$B_3 = \prod_{i=1}^{r} [l_i^{n/2} \exp(-\tfrac{1}{2}l_i)]. \tag{15.1.16}$$

Note especially that when $r < p$, B_1 depends on **Σ** and so is an essential part of the likelihood.

The maximum likelihood *estimates* $\hat{\boldsymbol{\mu}}$ and $\hat{\boldsymbol{\Sigma}}$ for $\boldsymbol{\mu}$ and **Σ** based on a given set of data $\mathbf{X}^{(1)}, \mathbf{X}^{(2)}, \ldots, \mathbf{X}^{(n)}$ are defined to be those sets of values $\boldsymbol{\mu}$ and **Σ** which maximize (15.1.1). Assume first that $\mathbf{T}$ has rank p. The factor B_1 in (15.1.10) is fixed given $\mathbf{X}^{(1)}, \mathbf{X}^{(2)}, \ldots, \mathbf{X}^{(n)}$. The factor B_2 in (15.1.11) is maximized uniformly over values of $\mathbf{\Sigma}$ by the choice $\boldsymbol{\mu} = \bar{\mathbf{X}}$. Finally, the factors in the second line of (15.1.12) are simultaneously maximized by making $l_1 = l_2 = \cdots = l_p = n$, which is equivalent to the choice $\mathbf{\Sigma} = \mathbf{T}/n$. Thus the maximum likelihood estimates are given by

$$\hat{\boldsymbol{\mu}} = \bar{\mathbf{X}} \quad \text{and} \quad \hat{\mathbf{\Sigma}} = \frac{1}{n}\mathbf{T}. \tag{15.1.17}$$

Note that

$$\hat{\mathbf{\Sigma}} = (1 - 1/n)\mathbf{S}, \tag{15.1.18}$$

where $\mathbf{S}$ is the sample covariance matrix. When $\mathbf{T}$ has rank $r < p$, the factors B_2 and B_3 are bounded above, but the factor B_1 defined in (15.1.15) may range freely from zero to infinity. Geometrically speaking, one need only squeeze the concentration ellipsoid of $\mathbf{\Sigma}$ arbitrarily flat into the subspace determined by the concentration ellipsoid of $\mathbf{T}$ in order to make the likelihood arbitrarily large. Thus the maximum likelihood estimates $\hat{\boldsymbol{\mu}}$ and $\hat{\mathbf{\Sigma}}$ are not defined when $r < p$, which is to say when the sample size n is less than $p + 1$.

The maximum likelihood *estimators* $\hat{\boldsymbol{\mu}}$ and $\hat{\mathbf{\Sigma}}$ are defined to be those functions of the observable quantities $\mathbf{X}^{(1)}, \mathbf{X}^{(2)}, \ldots, \mathbf{X}^{(n)}$ whose values are the maximum likelihood estimates. If $\mathbf{X}^{(1)}, \mathbf{X}^{(2)}, \ldots, \mathbf{X}^{(n)}$ are regarded as random quantities which are independent with $N(\boldsymbol{\mu}, \mathbf{\Sigma})$ sampling distributions, where fixed values of $\boldsymbol{\mu}$ and $\mathbf{\Sigma}$ are contemplated, then $\hat{\boldsymbol{\mu}}$ and $\hat{\mathbf{\Sigma}}$ are independent with $N(\boldsymbol{\mu}, \mathbf{\Sigma}/n)$ and $W(n - 1, (1 - 1/n)\mathbf{\Sigma})$ distributions. The general theory of maximum likelihood estimators asserts that $\hat{\boldsymbol{\mu}}$ and $\hat{\mathbf{\Sigma}}$ should have approximately a $(p + p(p + 1)/2)$-dimensional normal sampling distribution in large samples. This result may be verified directly in the present situation because $\sqrt{n}(\bar{\mathbf{X}} - \boldsymbol{\mu})$ has exactly an $N(\mathbf{0}, \mathbf{\Sigma})$ distribution while the $p(p + 1)/2$ distinct elements of $\sqrt{n}(\hat{\mathbf{\Sigma}} - \mathbf{\Sigma})$ have a limiting normal distribution with means of zero and covariances implied by (14.1.8). The latter result follows from the reproductive property of Wishart distributions together with the central limit theorem in a multivariate form. The asymptotic optimality properties of maximum likelihood estimators will be discussed briefly in Section 15.2.

The idea of maximizing likelihood was carried over to the choice of tests of significance by Neyman and Pearson (1928) with their concept of a *likelihood ratio test*. Suppose it is asked whether or not an observed random sample from a normal population appears concordant with the null hypothesis $\boldsymbol{\mu} = \boldsymbol{\mu}_0$ where nothing is specified about $\mathbf{\Sigma}$. The *likelihood ratio test criterion* for this situation is defined to be

$$\lambda = \frac{\sup_{\mathbf{\Sigma}} L(\boldsymbol{\mu}_0, \mathbf{\Sigma}; \mathbf{X}^{(1)}, \mathbf{X}^{(2)}, \ldots, \mathbf{X}^{(n)})}{\sup_{\boldsymbol{\mu}, \mathbf{\Sigma}} L(\boldsymbol{\mu}, \mathbf{\Sigma}; \mathbf{X}^{(1)}, \mathbf{X}^{(2)}, \ldots, \mathbf{X}^{(n)})}. \tag{15.1.19}$$

In general, a likelihood ratio criterion is the ratio of the maximum of the likelihood over the parameters values inside the null hypothesis to the maximum of the likelihood over the full range of the parameters both in and out of the null hypothesis. The idea is to construct a measure which will be sensitive to parameter sets "far" from the null hypothesis while being little affected by the "composite" character of the null hypothesis. The former requirement is met because λ should be less than but close to unity if the data agree with $\boldsymbol{\mu} = \mathbf{0}$ while the denominator of (15.1.19) should be much greater than the numerator if the data indicate a value of $\boldsymbol{\mu}$ far from $\mathbf{0}$. The latter requirement, namely that the unknown character of $\boldsymbol{\Sigma}$ should not unduly interfere with the judgment, is effectively met by estimating $\boldsymbol{\Sigma}$ via the method of maximum likelihood.

The reader may check that (15.1.19) works out to give

$$\lambda = (1 + G)^{-n/2}, \tag{15.1.20}$$

where

$$G = n(\bar{\mathbf{X}} - \boldsymbol{\mu}_0)\mathbf{T}^{-1}(\bar{\mathbf{X}} - \boldsymbol{\mu}_0)'. \tag{15.1.21}$$

A significance test which rejects the null hypothesis when λ is too small is logically equivalent to a significance test which rejects when G is too large. Since G is one version of the Hotelling's T^2 statistic, the likelihood ratio test is equivalent to the test discussed in Section 14.1.

The likelihood ratio principle was applied to multivariate normal sampling in a pathbreaking work of Wilks (1932). The Λ statistic used in Section 14.2 for canonical correlation analysis and in Section 14.3 for multiple discriminant analysis actually had its origin in the likelihood ratio principle. See Anderson (1958) for an extensive set of examples of likelihood ratio criteria in multivariate normal sampling situations. See also Exercises 15.1.5, 15.1.6, and 15.1.7.

A sequence of likelihood ratio statistics based on samples of sizes n_0, $n_0 + 1, n_0 + 2, \ldots$ has limiting distribution theory closely related to that of the associated maximum likelihood estimators. Thus $(-n/2) \log \lambda$ has a limiting $\chi^2(p, 1)$ distribution under the null hypothesis, a fact which the reader may easily check. Under the general hypothesis, a noncentral χ^2 limiting distribution obtains provided that $\sqrt{n}(\boldsymbol{\mu} - \boldsymbol{\mu}_0) \to \boldsymbol{\tau}$ as $n \to \infty$. In the general case, the degrees of freedom p is replaced by the number of parameters fixed under the null hypothesis. This type of distribution theory was first given by Wilks (1938) for general families of distributions. Further work on distributions associated with classes of likelihood ratio criteria may be found in Box (1949) and Lawley (1958). Optimum properties of likelihood ratio tests, also of course in large samples, will be discussed briefly in Section 15.2.

To summarize, the likelihood function of $\boldsymbol{\mu}$ and $\boldsymbol{\Sigma}$ may be described in simple geometric terms. The direct interpretation of such a likelihood function of $p + p(p + 1)/2$ quantities is difficult, but likelihood plays important roles in both Bayesian and sampling theory approaches to inference.

15.2 JUSTIFICATIONS BASED ON SAMPLING DISTRIBUTIONS

Many sample-based quantities have been given featured roles in this book. Sample means, sample covariances, and many functions of these are obvious estimators for corresponding population quantities. Other quantities such as Wilks Λ statistics are intended to measure deviations from certain null hypotheses. Throughout Chapter 14 these quantities were considered in the light of postdictive reasoning which interprets observed values in relation to their associated sampling distributions. Sampling distributions are also used to make judgments, in advance of observations, about the choice of quantities (estimators or test criteria) to be fed into the postdictive reasoning process. For example, in Example 9.2 of Section 14.2 and in Example 10.3 of Section 14.3, certain bias-corrected estimates were suggested on the grounds that the sampling distributions of their errors of estimation were more nearly centered about zero than the sampling distributions of the original errors of estimation. Mathematical statisticians have constructed many theories of optimal or desirable choices of quantities. Section 15.2 is devoted to a brief survey of what some of these theories imply for the normal sampling situation.

The work of R. A. Fisher (1922, 1925) was set apart from earlier work of a similar kind by his recognition that the likelihood function possessed certain optimal or desirable *sampling distribution* properties. Witness his theory of the large sample *efficiency* of maximum likelihood estimators. Fisher's theorems and proofs of efficiency were rather imprecise; indeed, the production of good mathematical theorems along this line is still a live research topic among mathematical statisticians (Le Cam, 1953, 1958; Bahadur, 1964; Wolfowitz, 1965; Rao, 1962, 1965). Only a rough statement will be given here. Suppose that $\boldsymbol{\theta}$ denotes a $1 \times m$ vector of parameters, where, in sampling a general p-variate normal family, $\boldsymbol{\theta}$ consists of $p + p(p+1)/2$ elements determining $\boldsymbol{\mu}$ and $\boldsymbol{\Sigma}$. Suppose that $R(\boldsymbol{\theta})$ denotes an ellipsoid centered at $\boldsymbol{\theta}$ defined for each point in the space of parameter values. Suppose that $\hat{\boldsymbol{\theta}}_n$ denotes an estimator for $\boldsymbol{\theta}$ based on a sample of size n, defined for $n = n_0, n_0 + 1, n_0 + 2, \ldots$, and suppose that the sampling distribution of $\sqrt{n}(\hat{\boldsymbol{\theta}}_n - \boldsymbol{\theta})$ converges to the $N(\mathbf{0}, \mathbf{I}(\boldsymbol{\theta})^{-1})$ distribution, uniformly in $\boldsymbol{\theta}$, where $\mathbf{I}(\boldsymbol{\theta})$ denotes Fisher's information matrix and $N(\mathbf{0}, \mathbf{I}(\boldsymbol{\theta})^{-1})$ is the limiting distribution associated with a maximum likelihood estimator $\hat{\boldsymbol{\theta}}_n$ or with any asymptotically equivalent estimator. Then, under certain "regularity conditions,"

$$\lim_{n\to\infty} \Pr\left(\sqrt{n}(\hat{\boldsymbol{\theta}}_n - \boldsymbol{\theta}) + \boldsymbol{\theta} \in R(\boldsymbol{\theta})\right) \geq \lim_{n\to\infty} \Pr\left(\sqrt{n}(\hat{\hat{\boldsymbol{\theta}}}_n - \boldsymbol{\theta}) + \boldsymbol{\theta} \in R(\boldsymbol{\theta})\right) \quad (15.2.1)$$

for any other sequence of estimators $\hat{\hat{\boldsymbol{\theta}}}_n$, and for all $\boldsymbol{\theta}$ excepting a set of Lebesgue measure zero. In simpler terms, the sampling distribution given $\boldsymbol{\theta}$ of the maximum likelihood estimator $\hat{\boldsymbol{\theta}}$ clusters with maximum "closeness" around $\boldsymbol{\theta}$, in the limit as $n \to \infty$. The maximum likelihood estimators (15.1.17) possess an asymptotic optimality property of this kind.

The same type of asymptotic theory leads to justifications for likelihood ratio test procedures. The nature of these justifications may be seen by considering a simple example. Suppose that $\mathbf{X}$ has the $N(\boldsymbol{\mu}, \mathbf{I})$ distribution over a p-dimensional outcome-space $\mathscr{F}$, and consider the null hypothesis $\boldsymbol{\mu} = \mathbf{0}$. In the formulation of Neyman and Pearson, a test of the null hypothesis $\boldsymbol{\mu} = \mathbf{0}$ based on the data $\mathbf{X}$ is defined by a region $R \subset \mathscr{F}$ which is regarded as a region of $\mathbf{X}$ values for which the hypothesis is to be rejected. The *size* of the test, namely $\Pr(\mathbf{X} \in R \mid \boldsymbol{\mu} = \mathbf{0})$, is fixed at a conventional level like 0.05 or 0.01. The principle of test construction is to maximize the power of the test for a given size. But the power is a function $P(\boldsymbol{\mu}) = \Pr(\mathbf{X} \in R(\boldsymbol{\mu}))$, and the same test will not maximize the power for all $\boldsymbol{\mu}$. A popular test which is also the likelihood ratio test for the simple example under consideration rejects the null hypothesis if $\mathbf{XX}'$ is too large, or in the formal Neyman-Pearson language, rejects at size α, if $\mathbf{XX}' \geq \chi^2(p, 1)_{[1-\alpha]}$. Such a χ^2 test does have optimal properties, but of a quite devious kind. For example, the test has maximum average power over the surface of the sphere $\boldsymbol{\mu\mu}' = c$ where the average is taken with respect to the uniform distribution over the surface of the sphere. Or, it has maximum power against all $\boldsymbol{\mu}$ but only within the restricted class of tests whose rejection regions are invariant under rotations leaving the $N(\mathbf{0}, \mathbf{I})$ distribution invariant. These devious justifications could rarely be compelling in their relation to the real world, but they do contribute to the mathematical niceness of χ^2 tests. This mathematical niceness is surely the large factor in their widespread use. Now the asymptotic situation with likelihood ratio tests in general is just like that of the simple example, and the nature of the justification (accepting large sample approximations) is exactly the same. In other words, many of the commonly used significance tests described in this book possess in large samples a mathematically nice but practically uncompelling property of balanced optimality.

The asymptotic optimality properties outlined above have the important weakness of depending on theorems which say nothing about a specific sample size n, but only about infinite n. In fact, the asymptotic normal and χ^2 approximations suggested by the theorems need not begin to be reasonable until n is unreasonably large, for example $n = 10^{10}$. In practice, however, the approximations often do tend to stabilize for modest values of n and the optimality properties presumably become nearly operative at the same time. It is important to recognize that many sequences of estimators will have the same limiting distribution properties as maximum likelihood estimators and thereby have the same asymptotic optimality properties. Such estimators were called BAN (best asymptotically normal) by Neyman (1949). Asymptotically equivalent variants of likelihood ratio test criteria are also possible, and indeed are often more easily found than the likelihood ratio criteria themselves. For example, if $\boldsymbol{\theta} = [\boldsymbol{\theta}_1, \boldsymbol{\theta}_2]$ denotes a set of parameters and $\hat{\boldsymbol{\theta}} = [\hat{\boldsymbol{\theta}}_1, \hat{\boldsymbol{\theta}}_2]$ denotes maximum likelihood estimators based on a sample of size n, then the test criterion

$$n(\hat{\boldsymbol{\theta}}_1 - \boldsymbol{\theta}_{10})\mathbf{I}^{11}(\hat{\boldsymbol{\theta}})^{-1}(\hat{\boldsymbol{\theta}}_1 - \boldsymbol{\theta}_{10})'$$

has the $\chi^2(m, 1)$ distribution under the null hypothesis $\boldsymbol{\theta}_1 = \boldsymbol{\theta}_{10}$ where m is the number of elements of $\boldsymbol{\theta}$ and $\mathbf{I}^{11}(\boldsymbol{\theta})$ is the covariance matrix of the limiting normal sampling distribution of $\sqrt{n}(\hat{\boldsymbol{\theta}}_1 - \boldsymbol{\theta}_1)$ given $\boldsymbol{\theta}$. In fact, under a wide range of interesting cases, the difference between $n(\hat{\boldsymbol{\theta}}_1 - \boldsymbol{\theta}_{10})\mathbf{I}^{11}(\hat{\boldsymbol{\theta}})^{-1}(\hat{\boldsymbol{\theta}}_1 - \boldsymbol{\theta}_{10})'$ and $(-n/2) \log \lambda$ could be shown to tend to zero in probability. Tests based on $\sqrt{n}(\hat{\boldsymbol{\theta}}_1 - \boldsymbol{\theta})$ are often computationally simpler than likelihood ratio tests because they require the solution of one rather than two maximization problems.

The discussion now turns to theories applicable for a given fixed sample size n, as opposed to theorems applicable only in the limit as $n \to \infty$. The sample mean vector $\bar{\mathbf{X}}$ and the sample covariance matrix $\mathbf{S}$ determined by a random sample $\mathbf{X}^{(1)}, \mathbf{X}^{(2)}, \ldots, \mathbf{X}^{(n)}$ from an $N(\boldsymbol{\mu}, \boldsymbol{\Sigma})$ distribution possess the property of *sufficiency* relative to the unknowns $\boldsymbol{\mu}$ and $\boldsymbol{\Sigma}$. Sufficiency may be defined in terms of the likelihood function; specifically, a set of quantities is said to be sufficient for a set of parameters if the values of the sufficient set of quantities uniquely determine the likelihood function specified by any complete set of observations. The term sufficiency is due to R. A. Fisher (1922) who recognized the basic sampling distribution property of sufficiency, namely that the conditional distribution of an entire set of observable quantities given the values of a sufficient set of quantities is free of dependence on the (unknown) values of the parameters in question. Most textbooks in the sampling theory tradition use the latter property as the definition of sufficiency, but prove under stated conditions a theorem which implies the equivalence of the two definitions. For example, see Rao (1965). Either definition may easily be verified in the case of the sufficiency of $\bar{\mathbf{X}}$ and $\mathbf{S}$. First, it follows from (15.1.9) that $\bar{\mathbf{X}}$ and $\mathbf{S}$ completely determine the likelihood function. Second, the conditional distribution of $\mathbf{X}^{(1)}, \mathbf{X}^{(2)}, \ldots, \mathbf{X}^{(n)}$ given $\bar{\mathbf{X}}$ and $\mathbf{S}$ follows easily from the representation used in Section 14.1 to characterize the sampling distribution of $\bar{\mathbf{X}}$ and $\mathbf{S}$. Recall that $\bar{\mathbf{X}}$ is equivalent to the component of the sample in one direction in $\mathscr{N}$, while $(n - 1)\mathbf{S}$ is equivalent to the configuration matrix of the components in the $(n - 1)$-dimensional orthogonal complement. Given $\bar{\mathbf{X}}$ and $\mathbf{S}$, the orientation in the $(n - 1)$-dimensional subspace is spherically distributed and therefore distributed in a way free of $\boldsymbol{\mu}$ and $\boldsymbol{\Sigma}$ as was required to be shown.

In itself, sufficiency does not justify the use of $\bar{\mathbf{X}}$ and $\mathbf{S}$ to estimate $\boldsymbol{\mu}$ and $\boldsymbol{\Sigma}$, respectively. The principle of sufficiency asserts only that no information is lost by throwing away $\mathbf{X}^{(1)}, \mathbf{X}^{(2)}, \ldots, \mathbf{X}^{(n)}$ if $\bar{\mathbf{X}}$ and $\mathbf{S}$ *or any equivalent set of quantities* is retained. But there are further theories closely tied to sufficiency which may be used to justify specific techniques. Prominent among these is the Rao-Blackwell theory of minimum variance unbiased estimators, which asserts that an unbiased estimator of some parameter which depends only on a *complete* sufficient set of quantities has minimum variance among all unbiased estimators of that parameter. Again, see Rao (1965) for further details. Now $\bar{\mathbf{X}}$ and $\mathbf{S}$ are unbiased estimators for $\boldsymbol{\mu}$ and $\boldsymbol{\Sigma}$ in the ordinary sampling distribution sense, and the Rao-Blackwell theory can be used to justify $\bar{\mathbf{X}}$ and $\mathbf{S}$ as minimum variance unbiased estimators. Sufficiency also plays important technical roles in the theory of hypothesis testing (Lehmann, 1959).

The theory of minimum variance unbiased estimation is artificially restricted in the sense that unbiasedness is required in the theory largely to make it work. An aim more fundamental than to minimize variance among unbiased estimators is to minimize expected squared error among all estimators. In such a broadened class of estimators it is easily shown that $\bar{\mathbf{X}}$ is not *admissible* as an estimator for $\boldsymbol{\mu}$ in a natural expected squared error sense, i.e., there exists an estimator $\hat{\boldsymbol{\mu}}$ such that $E([\hat{\boldsymbol{\mu}} - \boldsymbol{\mu}][\hat{\boldsymbol{\mu}} - \boldsymbol{\mu}]' \mid \mu) \leq E([\bar{\mathbf{X}} - \boldsymbol{\mu}][\bar{\mathbf{X}} - \boldsymbol{\mu}]' \mid \boldsymbol{\mu})$ for all values of $\boldsymbol{\mu}$ with strict inequality holding for some $\boldsymbol{\mu}$ values (cf. James and Stein, 1961 and Stein, 1962). A similar inadmissibility property holds for variance estimation (Stein, 1964) and presumably for the estimation of a covariance matrix as well. On the other hand, the admissible estimators proposed by Stein do not satisfy invariance properties which seem natural to many mathematical statisticians. Nor is the criterion of expected squared error universally acceptable. It is interesting to note that many standard multivariate significance tests are admissible in the sense that no tests with uniformly greater power for a given size may be found. See Kiefer (1966), Kiefer and Schwartz (1965), and Schwartz (1966, 1967). The requirement of fixed size of a test plays a mathematical role analogous to that of unbiasedness in estimation; such side conditions render admissibility possible.

Admissibility considerations applied to the choice of estimators, or to the choice of decision procedures in general, lead logically under wide conditions to *Bayes rules*, i.e., procedures with minimum risk under the posterior distribution associated with some prior distribution. This basic result of Wald (1950) suggests that the search for optimum procedures based on sampling theory considerations leads only back to the Bayesian fold. The author believes that the elegant and sophisticated theories of justification by sampling theory are overextended and will gradually lose their importance as better forms of predictive inference become available.

15.3 PREDICTIVE INFERENCE

As described in Section 1.4, the aim of predictive inference is to assign probability distributions over the outcome-space of a set of unobserved quantities (parameters) whose unknown values determine the population or populations under study. These distributions depend on the sample observations and they are meant for interpretation in a forward-looking or predictive way in the sense that they reflect residual uncertainty about the parameter values *after* the sample observations are taken into account. The classical approach here, usually called *Bayesian inference*, originated in the posthumous note of Bayes (1763) and was widely extended and popularized by Laplace from roughly 1780 onwards. Many writers beginning with Laplace apparently confused the notions of sampling distribution of an error of estimation and a Bayes posterior distribution of an error of estimation, and thus conferred the predictive content deserved by the latter on inferences actually based on the former. Fisher (1930, 1956) was the first to proclaim that in fact such a conferral is legitimate, if protected by certain safeguards, and he called the "valid" predictive inferences achieved in this way *fiducial inferences*. Fisher's safeguards were not free from ambiguity, with the result that different fiducial inferences seemed to compete in the same circumstances. Such inconsistencies are on prominent display in the case of multivariate normal sampling (cf. Mauldon (1955), Dempster (1963)). Most observers have regarded the fiducial argument as essentially dead (cf. Dempster (1964)). But the writer sees much hope in a loosened form of Bayesian inference which easily encompasses arguments like that of Fisher (cf. Dempster (1966, 1967a, 1967b, 1968)). The mathematical computations posed by these newer methods in the area of sampling multivariate normal populations have not been solved at the time of writing, so that the exposition here is limited to a form of Bayesian inference. The methods to be described may differ in some rather surprising ways from the postdictive inferences illustrated in Chapter 14. In conclusion, an attempt will be made to assess the implications of the divergence of predictive and postdictive inferences.

In Bayesian inference, one must start from an *initial* or *prior* distribution reflecting the state of uncertainty about unknown parameter values *before* the sample data are observed. If the sampling distribution of the observable quantities given the parameter values is regarded as a *conditional* distribution of the observables given the parameter values, while the prior distribution of the parameters is regarded as a marginal distribution, the combination provides a joint probability distribution of parameters and observables representing uncertainty *before* any observations are made. The Bayesian argument proceeds by conditioning this joint distribution on fixed values of the observable quantities, thus leading to a conditional distribution or *Bayes posterior* distribution of the parameters given the observed data.

To illustrate the Bayesian argument suppose that $\mathbf{X}^{(1)}, \mathbf{X}^{(2)}, \ldots, \mathbf{X}^{(n)}$ denote a random sample from an $N(\boldsymbol{\mu}, \boldsymbol{\Sigma})$ population where $\boldsymbol{\mu}$ and $\boldsymbol{\Sigma}$ are unknown. In principle, any prior distribution for $\boldsymbol{\mu}$ and $\boldsymbol{\Sigma}$ could be assigned and a posterior distribution computed. For reasons of mathematical convenience a quite restricted class of prior distributions will be considered: *suppose that the distribution of*

$$\boldsymbol{\Sigma}^{-1} \quad \textit{is} \quad W(c, \boldsymbol{\Lambda}^{-1}), \tag{15.3.1}$$

and that conditional on fixed $\boldsymbol{\Sigma}$ *the distribution of*

$$\boldsymbol{\mu} \quad \textit{is} \quad N(\mathbf{a}, b^2\boldsymbol{\Sigma}), \tag{15.3.2}$$

where $\boldsymbol{\Lambda}$ *is a* $p \times p$ *positive definite symmetric matrix,* c *is an integer satisfying* $c \geq p$, $\mathbf{a}$ *is* a $1 \times p$ *vector, and* b^2 *is a real number satisfying* $b^2 > 0$. The user of this restricted Bayesian theory must agree to represent his initial uncertainty as in (15.3.1) and (15.3.2), meaning that he must settle on fixed and known values of $\mathbf{\Lambda}$, c, $\mathbf{a}$, and b^2. Perhaps the most arbitrary feature of the above prior distribution is the precisely specified $\mathbf{\Lambda}$ with the requirement that *both* $\boldsymbol{\mu} - \mathbf{a}$ and $\mathbf{\Sigma}$ are essentially spherically distributed with respect to the *same* inner product determined by $\mathbf{\Lambda}$. Of course, as with any other application of a mathematical model, one need not feel totally committed to the veracity of the theory (whatever that means!) in order to gain useful insights from it. And it is common practice to consider a range of Bayesian analyses applied to a single set of data, in order to hedge against uncertainties in the model.

The mathematical niceness of (15.3.1) and (15.3.2) is due to the relative simplicity of the family of prior distributions together with the fact that the posterior distributions belong to the same family. Specifically, the posterior distribution of $\boldsymbol{\mu}$ and $\mathbf{\Sigma}$ given the sample $\mathbf{X}^{(1)}, \mathbf{X}^{(2)}, \ldots, \mathbf{X}^{(n)}$ is given by (15.3.1) and (15.3.2) with $\mathbf{\Lambda}$, c, $\mathbf{a}$, and b^2 replaced by $\mathbf{\Lambda}^*$, c^*, $\mathbf{a}^*$, and b^{*2} where

$$\mathbf{\Lambda}^* = \mathbf{\Lambda} + \mathbf{T} + (\bar{\mathbf{X}} - \mathbf{a})'(\bar{\mathbf{X}} - \mathbf{a})/(1/n + b^2), \tag{15.3.3}$$

$$c^* = c + n, \tag{15.3.4}$$

$$\mathbf{a}^* = (\mathbf{a}/n + b^2\bar{\mathbf{X}})/(1/n + b^2), \tag{15.3.5}$$

and

$$b^{*2} = (b^2/n)/(1/n + b^2). \tag{15.3.6}$$

The result will be stated as a theorem and proved formally from the theory of Chapter 13.

Theorem 15.3.1. *Suppose that* $\mathbf{X}^{(1)}, \mathbf{X}^{(2)}, \ldots, \mathbf{X}^{(n)}$ *are independently distributed each with the* $N(\boldsymbol{\mu}, \mathbf{\Sigma})$ *distribution, conditionally given* $\boldsymbol{\mu}$ *and* $\mathbf{\Sigma}$. *Suppose that the marginal distribution of* $\boldsymbol{\mu}$ *and* $\mathbf{\Sigma}$ *is specified by* (15.3.1) *and* (15.3.2). *Then the conditional distribution of* $\boldsymbol{\mu}$ *and* $\mathbf{\Sigma}$ *given* $\mathbf{X}^{(1)}, \mathbf{X}^{(2)}, \ldots, \mathbf{X}^{(n)}$ *is defined by the substitution of* $\mathbf{\Lambda}^*$, c^*, $\mathbf{a}^*$, *and* b^* *for* $\mathbf{\Lambda}$, c, $\mathbf{a}$, *and* b *in* (15.3.1) *and* (15.3.2), *where* $\mathbf{\Lambda}^*$, c^*, $\mathbf{a}^*$, *and* b *are defined by* (15.3.3) *through* (15.3.6), *and* $\bar{\mathbf{X}}$ *and* $\mathbf{T}$ *are defined by* (7.2.11) *and* (7.2.16).

Note first that because the conditional distribution of $\mathbf{X}^{(1)}, \mathbf{X}^{(2)}, \ldots, \mathbf{X}^{(n)}$ given the sufficient statistics $\bar{\mathbf{X}}$ and $\mathbf{T}$ as well as given $\boldsymbol{\mu}$ and $\mathbf{\Sigma}$ does not depend on $\boldsymbol{\mu}$ and $\mathbf{\Sigma}$, the conditional distribution of $\boldsymbol{\mu}$ and $\mathbf{\Sigma}$ given $\mathbf{X}^{(1)}, \mathbf{X}^{(2)}, \ldots, \mathbf{X}^{(n)}$ is the same as the conditional distribution of $\boldsymbol{\mu}$ and $\mathbf{\Sigma}$ given $\bar{\mathbf{X}}$ and $\mathbf{T}$. One need therefore find only the latter. The joint distribution of $\bar{\mathbf{X}}$, $\mathbf{T}$, $\boldsymbol{\mu}$, and $\mathbf{\Sigma}$ is specified by the conditional distribution of $\bar{\mathbf{X}}$ and $\mathbf{T}$ given $\boldsymbol{\mu}$ and $\mathbf{\Sigma}$ (as in (14.1.4) and (14.1.5)) together with the marginal distribution of $\boldsymbol{\mu}$ and $\mathbf{\Sigma}$ (as in (15.3.1) and (15.3.2)). A more convenient form of this joint distribution may be achieved in two stages. First it is easily checked that, given $\mathbf{\Sigma}$, the random matrices $\bar{\mathbf{X}} - \boldsymbol{\mu}$, $\boldsymbol{\mu} - \mathbf{a}$, and $\mathbf{T}$ are independent with $N(\mathbf{0}, \mathbf{\Sigma}/n)$, $N(\mathbf{0}, b^2\mathbf{\Sigma})$, and $W(n - 1, \mathbf{\Sigma})$ distributions. Secondly the reader may check (cf. Exercise 15.3.1) that, given

$\boldsymbol{\Sigma}$, the random matrices $\bar{\mathbf{X}} - \mathbf{a}$, $\boldsymbol{\mu} - (\mathbf{a}/n + b^2\bar{\mathbf{X}})/(1/n + b^2)$, and $\mathbf{T}$ are independent with $N(\mathbf{0}, (1/n + b^2)\boldsymbol{\Sigma})$, $N(\mathbf{0}, [(b^2/n)/(1/n + b^2)]\boldsymbol{\Sigma})$, and $W(n - 1, \boldsymbol{\Sigma})$ distributions. The latter form is important because to fix the sample is to fix the first and third of $\bar{\mathbf{X}} - \mathbf{a}$, $\boldsymbol{\mu} - (\mathbf{a}/n + b^2\bar{\mathbf{X}})/(1/n + b^2)$, and $\mathbf{T}$ but not the second. It follows that the conditional distribution of $\boldsymbol{\mu} - (\mathbf{a}/n + b^2\bar{\mathbf{X}})/(1/n + b^2)$ given $\bar{\mathbf{X}}$, $\mathbf{T}$, and $\boldsymbol{\Sigma}$ is still $N(\mathbf{0}, [(b^2/n)/(1/n + b^2)]\boldsymbol{\Sigma})$; i.e., the posterior distribution of $\boldsymbol{\mu}$ given $\boldsymbol{\Sigma}$ is given by (15.3.2) with $\mathbf{a}$ and b replaced by $\mathbf{a}^*$ and b^*, as was required to be shown. It remains only to check the conditional distribution of $\boldsymbol{\Sigma}$ given $\bar{\mathbf{X}}$ and $\mathbf{T}$, or, equivalently, given $\bar{\mathbf{X}} - \mathbf{a}$ and $\mathbf{T}$. Since the conditional distribution of $\bar{\mathbf{X}} - \mathbf{a}$ given $(\bar{\mathbf{X}} - \mathbf{a})'(\bar{\mathbf{X}} - \mathbf{a})$ does not depend on $\boldsymbol{\Sigma}$, (i.e., each of the two possible choices $\pm(\bar{\mathbf{X}} - \mathbf{a})$ are equally probable as indicated by Theorem 13.7.6) one need find only the conditional distribution of $\boldsymbol{\Sigma}$ given $(\bar{\mathbf{X}} - \mathbf{a})'(\bar{\mathbf{X}} - \mathbf{a})$ and $\mathbf{T}$. Two applications of Theorem 13.7.5 give the desired result. First, taking coordinate-dependent forms of π_2, π_1, and Σ to be $\mathbf{T}$, $\boldsymbol{\Sigma}$, and $\boldsymbol{\Lambda}$ and replacing s and $n - s$ by $n - 1$ and c, one finds that the conditions (A) of Theorem 13.7.5 are satisfied and thence from condition (B) that the conditional distribution of $\boldsymbol{\Sigma}^{-1}$ given $\mathbf{T}$ is $W(n - 1 + c, (\boldsymbol{\Lambda} + \mathbf{T})^{-1})$. The second application incorporates $(\bar{\mathbf{X}} - \mathbf{a})'(\bar{\mathbf{X}} - \mathbf{a})$ in a similar fashion, to complete the proof of Theorem 15.3.1.

The type of Bayesian analysis illustrated by Theorem 15.3.1 is sometimes called *conjugate* Bayesian analysis, because the specified family of prior distributions coincides with the resulting family of posterior distributions. See Raiffa and Schlaifer (1961) and Pratt, Raiffa, and Schlaifer (1966) for further examples of conjugate Bayesian analysis. If one understands how to compute interesting probabilities and expected values from a general prior distribution in the conjugate family, one can immediately do the same for the posterior distribution given by the analysis. In this connection, note that the marginal distribution of $\boldsymbol{\mu}$ implied by (15.3.1) and (15.3.2) is

$$t(\mathbf{a}, b^2\boldsymbol{\Lambda}/(c - p + 1), c - p + 1), \qquad (15.3.7)$$

as follows from Corollary 13.6.2 with the roles of $\mathbf{Q}$, $\boldsymbol{\Sigma}$, n, and $\boldsymbol{\mu}$ played by $[(c - p + 1)/b^2]\boldsymbol{\Sigma}^{-1}$, $[(c - p + 1)/b^2]\boldsymbol{\Lambda}^{-1}$, c, and $\mathbf{a}$. The posterior distribution of $\boldsymbol{\mu}$ is therefore the same as (15.3.7) except that $\boldsymbol{\Lambda}$, c, $\mathbf{a}$, and b are replaced by $\boldsymbol{\Lambda}^*$, c^*, $\mathbf{a}^*$, and b^*. Since any one-dimensional marginal distribution from a multivariate t distribution is a one-dimensional t distribution, it is easy to compute posterior probabilities of events determined by single components of $\boldsymbol{\mu}$ using only tables of the central one-dimensional t distributions.

Some special features of the posterior distribution of $\boldsymbol{\Sigma}$ will now be exposed to view. In advance of observation, each of $\boldsymbol{\Lambda}/c$, $\mathbf{T}/(n - 1)$, and $(\bar{\mathbf{X}} - \mathbf{a})'(\bar{\mathbf{X}} - \mathbf{a})/(1/n + b^2)$ could be regarded as estimating $\boldsymbol{\Sigma}$ on c, $n - 1$, and 1 degree of freedom, respectively. It would not be surprising therefore if $\boldsymbol{\Lambda}^*$ in (15.3.3) should turn out to be approximately $(n + c)\mathbf{S}$ where $\mathbf{S} = \mathbf{T}/(n - 1)$. Indeed, if large discrepancies appeared among $\boldsymbol{\Lambda}/c$, $\mathbf{S}$, and

$(\bar{\mathbf{X}} - \mathbf{a})'(\bar{\mathbf{X}} - \mathbf{a})/(1/n + b^2)$ there could be grounds for postdictive surprise and doubt that the assumed probability distributions could be valid. If $\mathbf{\Lambda}^*$ is approximately $(n + c)\mathbf{S}$, then the posterior distribution of $\mathbf{\Sigma}^{-1}$ is approximately $W(n + c, \mathbf{S}^{-1}/(n + c))$. Correspondingly, the posterior distribution of the quantity

$$s_{pp.12\ldots\overline{p-1}}/\sigma_{pp.12\ldots\overline{p-1}} = \sigma^{pp}/s^{pp} \tag{15.3.8}$$

is approximately $\chi^2(n + c, (n + c)^{-1})$, where σ^{pp} and s^{pp} denote the (p, p) elements of $\mathbf{\Sigma}^{-1}$ and $\mathbf{S}^{-1}$, respectively.

Now the sampling distribution of the ratio (15.3.8) is $\chi^2(n - p + 1, (n - 1)^{-1})$ as was in fact used in Section 14.2 as a justification for altering the estimator

$$s_{pp.12\ldots\overline{p-1}} \quad \text{to} \quad [(n - 1)/(n - p + 1)]s_{pp.12\ldots\overline{p-1}}. \tag{15.3.9}$$

A striking feature of the posterior distribution of the same ratio is that it appears to deny the need for a correction of the form (15.3.9). Thus, if p amounts to a substantial fraction of n, a non-trivial difference is likely to appear between a standard Bayesian inference and a standard postdictive inference. A similar remark is made in Dempster (1963).

Since the logic of postdictive inference is inherently weak, the author regards the divergence of the logically more satisfying Bayesian inferences from the postdictive inferences as a warning not to take the postdictive arguments too seriously, especially insofar as they refer to estimation of deeply buried aspects of $\mathbf{\Sigma}$. On the other hand, it cannot be pretended that the stereotyped form of prior distribution used here to illustrate the Bayesian argument is very often realistic, nor that many scientists could be persuaded to build such precise forms of prior information into statistical analyses. Until more flexible forms of predictive inference are better developed, it seems likely that wary applications of postdictive arguments will be the most widely used and useful tools of statistical inference.

15.4 EXERCISES

15.1.1 Consider data providing samples from k normal populations with different mean vectors $\boldsymbol{\mu}^{(1)}, \boldsymbol{\mu}^{(2)}, \ldots, \boldsymbol{\mu}^{(k)}$ but a common covariance matrix $\mathbf{\Sigma}$. The likelihood function $L(\boldsymbol{\mu}^{(1)}, \boldsymbol{\mu}^{(2)}, \ldots, \boldsymbol{\mu}^{(k)}, \mathbf{\Sigma}; \ldots)$ defined by these k samples is the product of the k single sample likelihood functions. Generalize the factorization (15.1.19) and thence show that the likelihood function is determined solely by the k sample means $\bar{\mathbf{X}}^{(1)}, \bar{\mathbf{X}}^{(2)}, \ldots, \bar{\mathbf{X}}^{(k)}$ and the pooled within sample sum inner product matrix $\mathbf{T}_W$.

15.1.2 For the situation described in Exercise 15.1.1, show that the maximum likelihood estimators for $\boldsymbol{\mu}^{(1)}, \boldsymbol{\mu}^{(2)}, \ldots, \boldsymbol{\mu}^{(k)}$ and $\mathbf{\Sigma}$ are $\bar{\mathbf{X}}^{(1)}, \bar{\mathbf{X}}^{(2)}, \ldots, \bar{\mathbf{X}}^{(k)}$ and $\mathbf{T}_W/n$, in the notation of Section 10.1, when $n - k \geq p$.

15.1.3 Suppose that a sample is given from an $N(\boldsymbol{\mu}, \boldsymbol{\Sigma})$ population where it is known *a priori* that the components of $\boldsymbol{\mu}$ are all equal. Describe how one might compute maximum likelihood estimates in this situation.

15.1.4 Verify that the alleged maximum likelihood estimators in Example 11.3 are in fact maximum likelihood estimators (cf. Anderson, 1957).

15.1.5 In Section 14.1 a statistic $G_{2.1}$ was proposed for testing the null hypothesis that a certain $\boldsymbol{\mu}_2 - \boldsymbol{\mu}_1\boldsymbol{\Xi}_{12}$ has a specified value. Show that the test based on $G_{2.1}$ is equivalent to a likelihood ratio test.

15.1.6 A Wilks Λ statistic was proposed in Section 14.1 for testing a null hypothesis that a set of population canonical correlation coefficients are all zero. Show that this test is equivalent to a likelihood ratio test.

15.1.7 Suppose that k samples are drawn from $N(\boldsymbol{\mu}^{(1)}, \boldsymbol{\Sigma}), N(\boldsymbol{\mu}^{(2)}, \boldsymbol{\Sigma}), \ldots, N(\boldsymbol{\mu}^{(k)}, \boldsymbol{\Sigma})$ populations. Compute the likelihood ratio test criterion for the null hypothesis $\boldsymbol{\mu}^{(1)} = \boldsymbol{\mu}^{(2)} = \cdots = \boldsymbol{\mu}^{(k)}$ and check that it is equivalent to the criterion

$$\Lambda = \frac{\det \mathbf{T}_W}{\det (\mathbf{T}_A + \mathbf{T}_W)}$$

in terms of the notation of Section 10.1.

15.2.1 For the situation described in Exercise 15.1.1 verify that the statistics $\bar{\mathbf{X}}^{(1)}, \bar{\mathbf{X}}^{(2)}, \ldots, \bar{\mathbf{X}}^{(k)}$ and $\mathbf{T}_W$ are sufficient under both of the definitions considered in Section 15.2.

15.3.1 Suppose that the distribution of

$$\begin{bmatrix} \mathbf{X} - \boldsymbol{\mu} \\ \boldsymbol{\mu} - \mathbf{a} \end{bmatrix} \quad \text{is} \quad N\left(\begin{bmatrix} \mathbf{0} \\ \mathbf{0} \end{bmatrix}, \begin{bmatrix} (1/n)\boldsymbol{\Sigma} & \mathbf{0} \\ \mathbf{0} & b^2\boldsymbol{\Sigma} \end{bmatrix}\right).$$

Show that the distribution of

$$\begin{bmatrix} \bar{\mathbf{X}} - \mathbf{a} \\ \boldsymbol{\mu} - \mathbf{a} \end{bmatrix} \quad \text{is} \quad N\left(\begin{bmatrix} \mathbf{0} \\ \mathbf{0} \end{bmatrix}, \begin{bmatrix} (1/n + b^2)\boldsymbol{\Sigma} & b^2\boldsymbol{\Sigma} \\ b^2\boldsymbol{\Sigma} & b^2\boldsymbol{\Sigma} \end{bmatrix}\right),$$

and thence that the distribution of

$$\begin{bmatrix} \bar{\mathbf{X}} - \mathbf{a} \\ (\boldsymbol{\mu} - \mathbf{a}) - [b^2/(1/n + b^2)](\bar{\mathbf{X}} - \mathbf{a}) \end{bmatrix}$$

is

$$N\left(\begin{bmatrix} \mathbf{0} \\ \mathbf{0} \end{bmatrix}, \begin{bmatrix} (1/n + b^2)\boldsymbol{\Sigma} & \mathbf{0} \\ \mathbf{0} & [(b^2/n)/(1/n + b^2)]\boldsymbol{\Sigma} \end{bmatrix}\right).$$

15.3.2 Suppose that two independent samples of sizes n_1 and n_2 are obtained from the same $N(\boldsymbol{\mu}, \boldsymbol{\Sigma})$ population. Show that the posterior distribution obtained by treating the two samples as a single combined sample is the same as the posterior distribution obtained by using the posterior distribution from the first sample as a prior distribution for the Bayesian analysis of the second sample, according to the conjugate Bayesian analysis of Section 15.3.

15.3.3 Write out the posterior version of (15.3.7). Write out also an expression for the interval of values of $\boldsymbol{\alpha\mu}'$ formed by removing 0.025 from each tail of the posterior distribution of $\boldsymbol{\alpha\mu}'$.

15.3.4 Show that $n[b^{*2}/(c^* - p + 1)]\boldsymbol{\Lambda}^*$ tends in probability to $\boldsymbol{\Sigma}$ as $n \to \infty$, according to the sequence of sampling distributions of $\mathbf{T}$ with fixed $\boldsymbol{\Sigma}$. What is the implication of this for large sample Bayesian inferences about $\boldsymbol{\mu}$?

15.3.5 Describe the posterior distribution of $\boldsymbol{\Sigma}_{22.1}$ according to the Bayesian analysis of Section 15.3. What does this imply about estimation of $\boldsymbol{\Sigma}_{22.1}$?

15.3.6 Suppose that $\boldsymbol{\Sigma}$ is known and may therefore be taken to be $\mathbf{I}$. A limiting form of the Bayesian analysis of Section 15.3 may be applied where c is large and $\boldsymbol{\Lambda} = \mathbf{I}/c$. What is the posterior distribution of $\boldsymbol{\mu\mu}'$? Compare the posterior distribution of $\boldsymbol{\mu\mu}' - \bar{\mathbf{X}}\bar{\mathbf{X}}'$ with the sampling distribution of $\boldsymbol{\mu\mu}' - \bar{\mathbf{X}}\bar{\mathbf{X}}'$, for a range of plausible examples, to see how predictive and postdictive inferences about $\boldsymbol{\mu\mu}'$ may differ (cf. Stein, 1959).

BIBLIOGRAPHY

ACTON, F. S. (1959). *Analysis of Straight Line Data*. Wiley, New York.

AITKEN, A. C. (1958). *Determinants and Matrices* (9th edition). Interscience, New York.

ALLPORT, G. W., P. E. VERNON, and G. LINDZEY (1960). *Study of Values* and *Manual for the Study of Values*. Houghton-Mifflin, Boston.

ANDERSON, T. W. (1957). "Maximum likelihood estimates for a multivariate normal distribution when some observations are missing," *J. Am. Stat. Assoc.* **52,** 200–203.

ANDERSON, T. W. (1958). *An Introduction to Multivariate Statistical Analysis*. Wiley, New York.

ANDERSON, T. W., S. DAS GUPTA, and G. P. H. STYAN (1969). *A Bibliography of Multivariate Statistical Analysis*. To be published by Oliver and Boyd.

BAHADUR, R. R. (1964). "On Fisher's bound for asymptotic variances," *Ann. Math. Stat.* **35,** 1545–1552.

BARNARD, G. A. (1949). "Statistical inference," *J. Roy. Stat. Soc., Series B.* **11,** 115–139.

BARNARD, G. A., G. M. JENKINS, and C. B. WINSTEN (1962). "Likelihood inference and time series," *J. Roy. Stat. Soc., Series A.* **125,** 321–352.

BARTLETT, M. S. (1933). "On the theory of statistical regression," *Proc. Roy. Soc. Edinburgh.* **53,** 260–283.

BARTLETT, M. S. (1938). "Further aspects of the theory of multiple regression," *Proc. Cam. Phil. Soc.* **34,** 33–40.

BARTLETT, M. S. (1947). "Multivariate analysis," *J. Roy. Stat. Soc., Supp.* **9,** 176–197.

BAYES, T. (1763). "Essay towards solving a problem in the doctrine of chances," *Phil. Tran. Roy. Soc. London.* **53,** 370–418. Reprinted in *Biometrika.* **45** (1958), 296–315.

BEATON, A. E. (1964). *The Use of Special Matrix Operators in Statistical Calculus*. Ed.D thesis, Harvard University. Reprinted as Educational Testing Service Research Bulletin 64–51. Princeton, N.J.

BIRKHOFF, G. and S. MACLANE (1965). *A Survey of Modern Algebra* (3rd edition). Macmillan, New York.

BIRNBAUM, A. (1962). "On the foundations of statistical inference," *J. Am. Stat. Assoc.* **57,** 269–326.

BOWKER, A. H. (1960). "A representation of Hotelling's T^2 and Anderson's classification statistic," *Cont. Prob. Stat.* (*Essays in honor of Harold Hotelling*). Edited by I. Olkin, Stanford University Press.

BOX, G. E. P. (1949). "A general distribution theory for a class of likelihood criteria," *Biometrika*. **36**, 317–346.

CATTELL, R. B., D. R. SAUNDERS, and G. STICE (1957). *Handbook for the Sixteen Personality Factor Questionnaire*. Institute for Personality and Ability Testing. Champaign, Illinois.

CATTELL, R. B. (1965). "Factor analysis: an introduction to essentials. I. The purpose and underlying models. II. The role of factor analysis in research," *Biometrics*. **21**, 190–215, 405–435.

CHAMBERS, J. M. (1966). *Some Methods of Asymptotic Approximation in Multivariate Statistical Analysis*. Ph.D thesis, Department of Statistics, Harvard University.

CHAMBERS, J. M. (1967). "On methods of asymptotic approximation for multivariate distributions," *Biometrika*. **54**, 367–384.

COCHRAN, W. G. (1938). "The omission or addition of an independent variate in multiple linear regression," *J. Roy. Stat. Soc., Supp.* **5**, 171–176.

COCHRAN, W. G. (1964). "Comparison of two methods for handling covariates," *Ann. Inst. Stat. Math.* **16**, 43–53.

COCHRAN, W. G. and C. I. BLISS (1948). "Discriminant functions with covariance," *Ann. Math. Stat.* **19**, 151–176.

CONSTANTINE, A. G. (1963). "Some noncentral distribution problems in multivariate analysis," *Ann. Math. Stat.* **34**, 1270–1285.

COOLEY, W. W. and P. R. LOHNES. (1962). *Multivariate Procedures for the Behavorial Sciences*. Wiley, New York.

COXETER, H. S. M. (1961). *Introduction to Geometry*. Wiley, New York.

CRAMÉR, H. (1946). *Mathematical Methods of Statistics* (especially Chapters 21, 22, 23, 24, 29, 36, 37). Princeton University Press, Princeton, N.J.

DAVID, F. N. (1938). *Tables of the Correlation Coefficient*. Camb.idge University Press.

DEMPSTER, A. P. (1958). "A high-dimensional two sample significance test," *Ann. Math. Stat.* **29**, 995–1010.

DEMPSTER, A. P. (1960). "A significance test for the separation of two highly multivariate small samples," *Biometrics*. **16**, 41–50.

DEMPSTER, A. P. (1963a). "Multivariate theory for general stepwise methods," *Ann. Math. Stat.* **34**, 873–883.

DEMPSTER, A. P. (1963b). "Stepwise multivariate analysis of variance based on principal variables," *Biometrics*. **19**, 478–490.

DEMPSTER, A. P. (1963c). "Further examples of inconsistencies in the fiducial argument," *Ann. Math. Stat.* **34**, 884–891.

DEMPSTER, A. P. (1964a). "On the difficulties inherent in Fisher's fiducial argument," *J. Am. Stat. Assoc.* **59**, 56–66.

DEMPSTER, A. P. (1964b). "Tests for the equality of two covariance matrices in relation to a best linear discriminator analysis," *Ann. Math. Stat.* **35**, 190–199.

DEMPSTER, A. P. (1966). "New approaches for reasoning towards posterior distributions based on sample data," *Ann. Math. Stat.* **37**, 355–374.

DEMPSTER, A. P. (1967a). "Upper and lower probabilities induced by a multivalued mapping," *Ann. Math. Stat.* **38**, 325–339.

DEMPSTER, A. P. (1967b). "Upper and lower probability inferences based on a sample from a finite univariate population," *Biometrika*. **54**, 515–528.

DEMPSTER, A. P. (1968). "A generalization of Bayesian inference," to appear in the *J. Roy. Stat. Soc., Series B.* **29**.

DEUTSCH, R. (1965). *Estimation Theory*. Prentice-Hall, Englewood Cliffs, N.J.

DRAPER, N. and H. SMITH (1966). *Applied Regression Analysis*. Wiley, New York.

DUNNETT, C. W. and M. SOBEL (1954). "A bivariate generalization of Student's *t*-distribution with tables for certain special cases," *Biometrika*. **41**, 153–169.

DUNNETT, C. W. and M. SOBEL (1955). "Approximations to the probability integrals and certain percentage points of a multivariate analogue of Student's *t*-distribution," *Biometrika*. **42**, 258–260.

DWYER, P. (1951). *Linear Computations*. Wiley, New York.

EDWARDS, A. L. (1959). *Manual for Edwards Personal Preference Schedule*. The Psychological Corporation, New York.

EISENHART, C. (1963). "The background and evolution of the method of least squares," paper presented to the 34th session of the International Statistical Institute, Ottawa.

FADDEEVA, V. N. (1959). *Computational Methods of Linear Algebra* (translated by Curtis D. Benster). Dover, New York.

FISHER, R. A. (1915). "Frequency distribution of the values of the correlation coefficient in samples from an indefinitely large population," *Biometrika*. **10**, 507–521.

FISHER, R. A. (1922). "On the mathematical foundations of theoretical statistics," *Phil. Trans. Roy. Soc. London, Series A*. **222**, 309–368. Reprinted in Fisher (1950).

FISHER, R. A. (1925). "Theory of statistical estimation," *Proc. Cam. Phil. Soc.* **22**, 700–725. Reprinted in Fisher (1950).

FISHER, R. A. (1928). "The general sampling distribution of the multiple correlation coefficient," *Proc. Roy. Soc. London, Series A*. **121**, 654–673.

FISHER, R. A. (1930). "Inverse probability," *Proc. Cam. Phil. Soc.* **26**, 528–535. Reprinted in Fisher (1950).

FISHER, R. A. (1936). "The use of multiple measurements in taxonomic problems," *Ann. Eugen.* **7**, 179–188. Reprinted in Fisher (1950).

FISHER, R. A. (1938). "The statistical utilization of multiple measurements," *Ann. Eugen.* **8**, 376–386. Reprinted in Fisher (1950).

FISHER, R. A. (1939). "The sampling distribution of some statistics obtained from non-linear equations," *Ann. Eugen.* **9**, 238–249.

FISHER, R. A. (1950). *Contributions to Mathematical Statistics*. Wiley, New York.

FISHER, R. A. (1958a). *Statistical Methods and Scientific Induction* (2nd edition). Hafner, New York.

FISHER, R. A. (1958b). *Statistical Methods for Research Workers* (13th edition). Hafner, New York.

FISHER, R. A. (1966). *Design of Experiments* (8th edition). Hafner, New York.

FISHER, R. A. and F. YATES (1963). *Statistical Tables for Biological, Agricultural and Medical Research* (6th edition). Oliver and Boyd, London.

FOSTER, F. G. (1957, 1958). "Upper percentage points of the generalized beta distribution, II and III," *Biometrika*. **44**, 441–453 and **45**, 492–503.

FOSTER, F. G. and D. H. REES (1957). "Upper percentage points of the generalized beta distribution, I," *Biometrika*. **44**, 237–247.

FRANCIS, J. G. F. (1961, 1962). "The QR transformation, I and II," *Computer Journal*, **4**, 265–271 and 332–345.

FRISCH, R. (1929). "Correlation and scatter in statistical variables," *Nord. Stat. Tid.* **8**, 36–102.

GALTON, F. (1886). "Regression towards mediocrity in hereditary stature," *J. Anthro. Inst.* **15**, 246–263.

GANTMACHER, F. R. (1959). *The Theory of Matrices*, Vols. 1 and 2. Chelsea, New York.

GAUSS, C. F. (1809). *Theoria Motus Corporum Coelestium.* Hamburg. English translation by Charles Henry Davis (1857).

GAUSS, C. F. (1811). "Disquisitiones de elementis ellipticis Pallidis," Gottingen. Reprinted in *Werke* **6**, 1–24.

GIRSHICK, M. A. (1939). "On the sampling theory of roots of determinantal equations," *Ann. Math. Stat.* **10**, 203–224.

HALMOS, P. R. (1958). *Finite-Dimensional Vector Spaces* (2nd edition). Van Nostrand, Princeton, N.J.

HECK, D. L. (1960). "Charts of some upper percentage points of the distribution of the largest characteristic root," *Ann. Math. Stat.* **31**, 625–642.

HORST, P. (1963). *Matrix Algebra for Social Scientists.* Holt, Rinehart, and Winston, New York.

HOTELLING, H. (1931). "The generalization of Student's ratio," *Ann. Math. Stat.* **2**, 360–378.

HOTELLING, H. (1933). "Analysis of a complex of statistical variables into principal components," *J. Educ. Psych.* **24**, 417–441, 498–520.

HOTELLING, H. (1935). "The most predictable criterion," *J. Educ. Psych.* **26**, 139–142.

HOTELLING, H. (1936). "Simplified calculation of principal components," *Psychometrika.* **1**, 27–35.

HOUSEHOLDER, A. S. (1958). "Unitary triangularization of a nonsymmetric matrix," *J. Assoc. Comp. Mach.* **5**, 339–342.

HOUSEHOLDER, A. S. (1964). *The Theory of Matrices in Numerical Analysis.* Blaisdell, New York.

HOWELLS, W. W. (1966). "The Jomon population of Japan. A study by discriminant analysis of Japanese and Ainu crania," *Papers of the Peabody Museum* (*Harvard University*). **57**, 1, 1–43.

HSU, P. L. (1939). "On the distribution of roots of certain determinantal equations," *Ann. Eugen.* **9**, 250–258.

HSU, P. L. (1941). "On the limiting distribution of the canonical correlations," *Biometrika.* **33**, 38–45.

JACOBI, C. G. J. (1846). "Über ein leichtes Verfahren die in der Theorie der Säculärstöringen verkommender Gleichen numerisch aufzulösen," *Crelle's Journal.* **30**, 51–94.

JAMES, A. T. (1954). "Normal multivariate analysis and the orthogonal group," *Ann. Math. Stat.* **25**, 40–75.

JAMES, A. T. (1964). "Distributions of matrix variates and latent roots derived from normal samples," *Ann. Math. Stat.* **35**, 475–501.

JAMES, A. T. (1966). "Inference on latent roots by calculation of hypergeometric functions of matrix argument," *Multivariate Analysis* (edited by P. R. Krishnaiah). Academic Press, New York, 209–235.

JAMES, W. and C. STEIN (1961). "Estimation with quadratic loss," *Fourth Berkeley Symposium on Mathematical Statistics and Probability.* **1,** 361–379.

KENDALL, M. G. (1957). *A Course in Multivariate Analysis.* Griffin's Statistical Monographs and Courses, Hafner, New York.

KENDALL, M. G. and A. STUART (1961). *The Advanced Theory of Statistics,* Vol. 2 (especially Chapters 26, 27, 28, 29). Hafner, New York.

KENDALL, M. G. and A. STUART (1966). *The Advanced Theory of Statistics,* Vol. 3 (especially Chapters 35, 36, 37, 41, 42, 43, 44). Hafner, New York.

KIEFER, J. (1966). "Multivariate optimality results," *Multivariate Analysis* (edited by P. R. Krishnaiah). Academic Press, New York, pp. 255–274.

KIEFER, J. and R. SCHWARTZ (1965). "Admissible Bayes character of T^2-, R^2-, and other fully invariant tests for classical multivariate normal problems," *Ann. Math. Stat.* **36,** 747–770.

KRISHNAIAH, P. R. (ed.) (1966). *Multivariate Analysis Proceedings of an International Symposium held in Dayton, Ohio, June 14–19, 1965.* Academic Press, New York.

LAWLEY, D. N. (1956). "A general method for approximating to the distribution of likelihood ratio criteria," *Biometrika.* **43,** 295–303.

LAWLEY, D. N. (1959). "Tests of significance in canonical analysis," *Biometrika.* **46,** 59–66.

LAWLEY, D. N. and A. E. MAXWELL (1963). *Factor Analysis as a Statistical Method.* Butterworths, London.

LECAM, L. (1953). "On some asymptotic properties of maximum likelihood estimates and related Bayes estimates," *Univ. Calif. Pub. Stat.* **1,** 277–330.

LECAM, L. (1958). "Les propriétés asymptotiques des solutions de Bayes," *Pub. l'Inst. Stat. l'Univ. Paris.* **7,** fasciscule 3–4, 17–35.

LEGENDRE, A. M. (1806). *Nouvelles Méthodes pour la détermination des orbites des comètes.* Paris.

LEHMANN, E. L. (1959). *Testing Statistical Hypotheses.* Wiley, New York.

LUKACS, E. (1956). "Characterization of populations by properties of suitable statistics," *Proc. Third Berkeley Symp. Math. Stat. Prob.* **2,** 195–214. University of California.

MACDUFFEE, C. C. (1943). *Vectors and Matrices.* Mathematical Association of America.

MAHALANOBIS, P. C. (1936). "On the generalized distance in statistics," *Proc. Nat. Inst. Sci. India.* **12,** 49–55.

MAULDON, J. G. (1955). "Pivotal quantities for Wishart's and related distributions, and a paradox in fiducial theory," *J. Roy. Stat. Soc., Series B.* **17,** 79–90.

MCNEMAR, Q. (1962). *Psychological Statistics* (3rd edition). Wiley, New York.

MILLER, R. G. (1961). *An Application of Multiple Discriminant Analysis to the Probabilistic Prediction of Meteorological Conditions Affecting Operational Decisions.* Ph.D Thesis, Department of Statistics, Harvard University.

MILLER, R. G. (1962). *Statistical Prediction by Discriminant Analysis.* American Meteorological Society, Boston.

MOOD, A. M. (1951). "On the distribution of the characteristic roots of normal second-moment matrices," *Ann. Math. Stat.* **22,** 266–273.

MORRISON, D. F. (1967). *Multivariate Statistical Methods.* McGraw-Hill, New York.

MOSTELLER, C. F. and J. W. TUKEY (1968). "Data analysis, including statistics," *Handbook of Social Psychology* (edited by G. Lindzey and E. Aronson). Addison-Wesley, Reading, Mass.

NACHBIN, L. (1965). *The Haar Integral.* Van Nostrand, Princeton, N.J.

NEYMAN, J. (1949). "Contribution to the theory of the χ^2 test," *Proc. Berkeley Symp. Math. Stat. Prob.* 239–273.

NEYMAN, J. and E. S. PEARSON (1928). "On the use and interpretation of certain test criteria for purposes of statistical inference," *Biometrika.* **20A,** 175–240, 263–294.

OLKIN, I. and H. RUBIN (1964). "Multivariate beta distributions and independence properties of the Wishart distribution," *Ann. Math. Stat.* **35,** 261–269.

OWEN, D. B. (1962). *Handbook of Statistical Tables.* Addison-Wesley, Reading, Mass.

PEARSON, E. S. and H. O. HARTLEY (1966). *Biometrika Tables for Statisticians* (3rd edition). Cambridge University Press.

PEARSON, E. S. (1967). "Studies in the history of probability and statistics. XVII. Some reflections on the continuity in the development of mathematical statistics, 1885–1920," *Biometrika.* **54,** 341–356.

PEARSON, KARL (1896). "Mathematical contributions to the theory of evolution. III. Regression, heredity and panmixia," *Phil. Trans. Roy. Soc. London, Series A.* **187,** 253–318.

PLACKETT, R. L. (1960). *Principles of Regression Analysis.* Clarendon Press, Oxford.

POTTHOFF, R. F. and S. N. ROY (1964). "A generalized multivariate analysis of variance model useful especially for growth curve problems," *Biometrika.* **51,** 313–326.

PRATT, J. W., H. RAIFFA, and R. SCHLAIFER (1965). *Introduction to Statistical Decision Theory.* McGraw-Hill, New York.

RAIFFA, H. and R. SCHLAIFER (1961). *Applied Statistical Decision Theory.* Harvard Business School, Cambridge, Mass.

RALSTON, A. and H. S. WILF (eds.) (1960). *Mathematical Methods for Digital Computers.* Wiley, New York.

RAND CORPORATION (1955). *A Million Random Digits with 100,000 Normal Deviates.* Free Press, Glencoe, Illinois.

RAO, C. R. (1948). "Tests of significance in multivariate analysis," *Biometrika.* **35,** 58–79.

RAO, C. R. (1952). *Advanced Statistical Methods in Biometric Research.* Wiley, New York.

RAO, C. R. (1962). "Efficient estimates and optimum inference procedures in large samples," *J. Roy. Stat. Soc., Series B.* **24,** 46–72.

RAO, C. R. (1965a). *Linear Statistical Inference and its Applications* (especially Chapters 1, 3, 4, 8). Wiley, New York.

RAO, C. R. (1965b). "The theory of least squares when the parameters are stochastic and its application to the analysis of growth curves," *Biometrika.* **52,** 447–458.

ROY, S. N. (1939). "*p*-statistics or some generalizations in analysis of variance appropriate to multivariate problems," *Sankhya.* **4,** 381–396.

ROY, S. N. (1957). *Some Aspects of Multivariate Analysis.* Wiley, New York.

SCHATZOFF, M. (1964). *Exact Distributions of Wilks's likelihood Ratio Criterion and Comparisons with Competitive Tests.* Ph.D. Thesis, Department of Statistics, Harvard University.

SCHATZOFF, M. (1966). "Exact distributions of Wilks's likelihood ratio criterion," *Biometrika*. **53,** 347–358.

SCHEFFÉ, H. (1959). *The Analysis of Variance*. Wiley, New York.

SCHWARTZ, R. (1966). "Fully invariant proper Bayes tests," *Multivariate Analysis* (edited by P. R. Krishnaiah). Academic Press, New York, 275–284.

SCHWARTZ, R. (1967). "Admissible tests in multivariate analysis of variance," *Ann. Math. Stat.* **38,** 698–710.

SEAL, H. (1964). *Multivariate Statistical Analysis for Biologists*. Wiley, New York.

SEAL, H. L. (1967). "Studies in the history of probability and statistics. XV. The historical development of the Gauss linear model," *Biometrika*. **54,** 1–24.

SEARLE, S. R. (1966). *Matrix Algebra for the Biological Sciences, including Applications in Statistics*. Wiley, New York.

SOMMERVILLE, D. M. Y. (1958). *An Introduction to the Geometry of N Dimensions*. Dover, New York.

STEIN, C. (1959). "An example of wide discrepancy between fiducial and confidence intervals," *Ann. Math. Stat.* **30,** 877–880.

STEIN, C. (1962). "Confidence sets for the mean of a multivariate normal distribution," *J. Roy. Stat. Soc., Series B*. **24,** 265–296.

STEIN, C. (1964). "Inadmissibility of the usual estimator for the variance of a normal distribution with unknown mean," *Ann. Inst. Stat. Math.* **16,** 155–160.

TAGIURI, R. (1965). "Value orientations and the relationship of managers and scientists," *Admin. Sci. Quart.* **10,** 39–51.

VARGA, R. S. (1962). *Matrix Iterative Analysis*. Prentice-Hall, Englewood Cliffs, N.J.

WALD. A. (1950). *Statistical Decision Functions*. Wiley, New York.

WALKER, H. M. (1931). *Studies in the History of Statistical Method*. Williams and Wilkins, Baltimore.

WILKINSON, J. H. (1963). *Rounding Errors in Algebraic Processes*. Prentice-Hall, Englewood Cliffs, N.J.

WILKINSON, J. H. (1965). *The Algebraic Eigenvalue Problem*. Clarendon Press, Oxford.

WILKS, S. S. (1932). "Certain generalizations in the analysis of variance," *Biometrika*. **24,** 471–494.

WILKS, S. S. (1938). "The large-sample distribution of the likelihood ratio for testing composite hypotheses," *Ann. Math. Stat.* **9,** 60–62.

WILKS, S. S. (1962). *Mathematical Statistics* (especially Chapters 10, 18). Wiley, New York.

WILLIAMS, E. J. (1959). *Regression Analysis*. Wiley, New York.

WILLIAMS, R. J. *et al.* (1950). "Biochemical individuality. V. Explorations with respect to the metabolic patterns of compulsive drinkers," *Arch. Biochem.* **29,** 27–4.

WISHART, J. (1928). "The generalized product moment distribution in samples from a normal multivariate population," *Biometrika*. **20A,** 32–52.

WISHART, J. (1948). "Proofs of the distribution law of the second order moment statistics," *Biometrika*. **9,** 55–57.

WITTENBORN, J. R., A. P. DEMPSTER, H. MAURER, and M. PLANTE (1964). "Pretreatment individual differences as potential predictors of response to pharmacology," *J. Nerv. Ment. Dis.* **139,** 186–194.

WOLFOWITZ, J. (1965). "Asymptotic efficiency of the maximum likelihood estimator," *Theory Prob. Applic.* **10,** 247–260.

INDEX

ABCDE 698